DIGITAL COMPUTER PROGRAMS FOR PHYSICAL CHEMISTRY

VOLUME II

DIGITAL COMPUTER PROGRAMS FOR PHYSICAL CHEMISTRY

VOLUME II

AUTOPLOTTER, EXPANSION, SELF-JUDGMENT, SPECTRAL, POLARIZATION, CONDUCTANCE, KINETIC, AND SPECIAL ITERATIVE PROGRAMS

PAUL A. D. de MAINE

Department of Chemistry
University of California at Santa Barbara

ALGOL 60 TRANSLATION OF FORTRAN AND
FOR-TO-GO PROGRAMS BY

ROBERT D. SEAWRIGHT

THE MACMILLAN COMPANY, NEW YORK

COLLIER-MACMILLAN LIMITED, LONDON

First Printing

Preliminary edition, entitled *Digital Computer Programs for Physical Chemistry*, Volume II, © copyright 1963 by Paul A. D. de Maine and R. D. Seawright. Appendix *C* © copyright 1962, 1963, previously published as Appendix *H* in *Digital Computer Programs for Physical Chemistry*, Volume I.

Library of Congress catalogue card number: 63–15053

THE MACMILLAN COMPANY, NEW YORK
COLLIER-MACMILLAN CANADA, LTD.
TORONTO, ONTARIO

PRINTED IN THE UNITED STATES OF AMERICA

TO OUR MOTHERS
and
OUR WIVES

1314856

PREFACE

In the preceding volume, *Digital Computer Programs for Physical Chemistry*, Volume I (New York: The Macmillan Co., 1963), a computer method was given for testing data compatibility with equations (or mathematical models) to within preselected limits of experimental error (self-judgment, spectral, conductance, viscosity, cryoscopic, thermodynamic, and solvent-shift programs). From May, 1962, to September, 1963, members of the group at the University of Mississippi used this scheme to process all their experimental information, and in so doing have amply demonstrated the exceptional versatility and advantages of the new method. Exact analysis of experimental data has shown that many laws of conductance, spectra, viscosity, and solvent shift have very limited application. It appears that workers in the experimental sciences frequently use mathematical functions which are insensitive to small variations in the measured quantities. Also, the failures to correct for small density-volume changes and to consider the limits of experimental error often lead to conclusions with little scientific merit. Our experiences have shown that quantitative physical data processed by ordinary methods are of strictly limited value.

In this volume there are FORTRAN and FOR-TO-GO programs for testing data compatibility with conductance, polarization, spectral, and multi-equilibria equations, and FOR-TO-GO programs for communicating with the IBM 836 Autoplotter.

The *autoplotter programs*, written in FOR-TO-GO 3-62, have been specifically designed to convert input information for FORTRAN Programs 1-4, 9-15, 22-29, 301-304, 309-315, 322-329, and 410-415 to visual form. Graphic representations of the input information are especially useful for reports and for selecting the input commands which activate the semiautomatic *reject–restore mechanism*.

In FORTRAN Programs 25-29 and 325-329, both the number of data

vii

points and the dimension of the equation to be processed can be easily changed. Additional optional commands for these programs greatly increase their versatility without destroying their compatibility with related programs in both volumes. FORTRAN Programs 410–415 are special, almost fully automatic, forms of Programs 310–315 in the preceding volume. The *expansion programs* (9, 22–25, 309, 322–325), *self-judgment programs* (26 or 326), and the *mathematical French curve program* (27 or 327) can be used to generate the functional form for any distribution of data points. Program 32 (Chapter IX), which supersedes Program 16 in the preceding volume, has instructions for testing data compatibility with recent conductance equations.

All FORTRAN and FOR-TO-GO programs have been thoroughly tested with *raw data* or, for the more complicated programs, with information generated by the *test programs* in Appendix A. Specific instructions for introducing activity coefficients into the FORTRAN programs are given in each chapter.

The *Maximum Permitted Errors* in the parameters of an equation, which are computed after application of the *Self-Judgment Principle*, have been redefined in Appendix E. The changes to be made in certain FORTRAN programs in both volumes are given. At the end of Appendix E there are discussed the special requirements of the iterative programs (10–15, 310–315 and 410–415). For those workers who are prepared to sacrifice the special advantages of the extremely sensitive Crout reduction method for the relatively insensitive Cramer's method, Appendix D will be of special interest. A detailed example of the use of the New Method appears in Appendix C.

I am especially indebted to George G. Clement for his help in working out the basic autoplotter program and for a copy of his FORTRAN program for solving simultaneous equations by the Crout reduction method. His program has been incorporated in the variable dimension programs (25–29, 325–329). I am also indebted to David E. Ross who frequently repaired the equipment at the University of Mississippi outside office hours. The helpfulness of Richard D. Ross is also appreciated.

Special thanks are due my wife for correcting the manuscript and proofs, and Mrs. Camelia Thompson for typing the manuscript. Mrs. Sheila Jurinski typed many of the FORTRAN and FOR-TO-GO programs in this volume.

These additional computer programs resulted directly from experimental research supported in part by funds from both the Petroleum Research Fund, administered by the American Chemical Society, and the United States Air Force under Grant No. AF-AFOSR 62–19. The author is deeply indebted to Dr. Karl Dittmer and Dr. Amos G. Horney for their support and encouragement.

PAUL A. D. DE MAINE

CONTENTS

Computer Facilities Required (FOR-TO-GO Programs)*

Program Number	Call Word	Number of Cards	MT, min
501	AEEEE	580	2.0 to 4.0
502	BEEEE	473	1.5 to 2.0
503	CEEEE	438	1.5
504	DEEEE	485	1.5 to 10.0
505	EEEEE	40	0.5

* The figures given above refer to the IBM 1620 with card input-output and 60K storage at the University of Mississippi. MT is the machine time (in minutes) required to transform input information for Programs 501 to 504 to input for the IBM 836 autoplotter. For Program 505, MT is the time required to process one deck of information. All programs are written in IBM 3–62 FOR-TO-GO.

Program Number	Call Word	ML	Storage Object	Storage Data	MT min	Special Instructions
1	AAAAA	1016	22478	2840	5.5	J = 1
2	BAAAA	1338	29283	3800	9.5	J = 1
3	CAAAA	1751	40267	4800	10.0	J = 1
4	DAAAA	2265	47343	5990	13.0	J = 1
5	EAAAA	1142	32746	4650	0.5–0.6	
6	FAAAA	777	17078	4130	0.5	
7	GAAAA	922	20095	4500	0.6	
8	HAAAA	663	15575	2880	0.5	
9	IAAAA	1414	30487	4730	6.0	J = 1; M6 = 1
10	JAAAA	1750	37015	8210	8.0	J = 1; M6 = 1
11	KAAAA	1740	36899	7560	13.0	J = 1; M6 = 1; A†
12	LAAAA	1870	40271	9460	50	J = 4; M6 = 1
13	MAAAA	1921	41231	9530	182	J = 4; M6 = 1; B†
14	NAAAA	1856	39215	12220	1560	J = 4; M6 = 5; M88 = 5; A†
15	OAAAA	2040	43590	14380	4200	J = 4; M6 = 5; M88 = 5; B†
16	PAAAA	805	21896	3760	0.5	
17	QAAAA	1700	36099	7600	0.5–1.0	
18	RAAAA	1155	25331	5400	1.0–1.5	
19	SAAAA	1250	27267	6200	0.5–0.6	QQ1 = QQ2 = 1.0
20	TAAAA	926	21579	4850	1.0	
21	UAAAA	847	20107	4150	0.5	
22	VAAAA	1583	≈ 30,000		17.0	J = 3; M6 = 1
23	WAAAA	1977	≈ 42,000		21.0	J = 3; M6 = 1
24	XAAAA	2446	≈ 59,500		25.0	J = 3; M6 = 1
25	YAAAA					
26	ZAAAA		Storage, MT, and ML are determined by the number of data points and the dimension of the equation processed.			
27	ABAAA					
28	BBAAA					
29*	CBAAA					
30	DBAAA	931	≈ 40,000		0.5	
31	EBAAA	1664	≈ 40,000		0.5	
32	FBAAA		Storage, MT, and ML are determined by the number of data points and the dimension of the equation.			
33	GBAAA					
34	HBAAA	351	≈ 56,000		20.0	M6 = 20; M4 = 12

* Feeder program 37 (*call word* KBAAA) is described in Chapter VI. Programs 22–37, 106–107, 322–329, and 410–415 are given in this volume. All other programs are given in *Digital Computer Programs for Physical Chemistry*, vol. I (Macmillan, 1963). All figures refer to the IBM 1620 with card input-output and 60K storage at the University of Mississippi. ML is the number of machine language cards without the error trace. MT is the machine time (in minutes) measured from the beginning of the *data read in* operation to the end of the last *punch out* operation. All programs were written in IBM 4–1–61 FORTRAN without FORMAT.

† A denotes QQ1 = QQ2 = 1.0. B denotes QQ1 = QQ2 = 2.0; QQ3 = QQ4 = 1.0.

Program Number	Call Word	ML	Storage		MT min	Special Instructions
			Object	Data		
35	IBAAA	657	≈ 35,000		1.0	M6 = 1
36	JBAAA	891	≈ 35,000		1.0	M6 = 1
101	ABBBB	359	9624	1310	0.3	
102	BBBBB	402	10511	1770	0.5	
103	CBBBB	442	11338	2240	0.6	
104	DBBBB	484	12166	2710	0.8	
105	EBBBB	1404	31103	6470	5.0–65	
106	FBBBB	631	≈ 30,000		0.25	
107	GBBBB	1051	≈ 45,000		0.50	
201	ACCCC	292	8455	710	0.25	
202	BCCCC	370	9807	2130	0.25	
301	AAAAS	1010	22478	2840	5.5.	J = 1
302	BAAAS	1340	29283	3800	9.5	J = 1
303	CAAAS	1750	40267	4800	10.0	J = 1
304	DAAAS	2265	47343	5990	13.0	J = 1
309	IAAAS	1410	30487	4730	6.0	J = 1; M6 = 1
310	JAAAS	1750	37015	8210	8.0	J = 1; M6 = 1
311	KAAAS	1740	36899	7560	13.0	J = 1; M6 = 1; A†
312	LAAAS	1870	40271	9460	50	J = 4; M6 = 1
313	MAAAS	1920	41231	9530	182	J = 4; M6 = 1; B†
314	NAAAS	1860	39215	12220	1560	J = 4; M6 = 5; M88 = 5; A†
315	OAAAS	2040	43590	14380	4200	J = 4; M6 = 5; M88 = 5; B†
322	VAAAS	1605	≈ 30,000		17.0	J = 3; M6 = 1
323	WAAAS	1998	≈ 40,000		21.0	J = 3; M6 = 1
324	XAAAS	2445	≈ 59,500		25.0	J = 3; M6 = 1
325	YAAAS		Storage, MT, and ML are deter-			
326	ZAAAS		mined by the number of data			
327	ABAAS		points and the dimension of the			
328	BBAAS		equation processed.			
329	CBAAS					
410	JAASS	1835	≈ 45,000		8.0	J = 1; M6 = 1
411	KAASS	1825	≈ 44,000		13.0	J = 1; M6 = 1; A†
412	LAASS	1970	≈ 50,000		50	J = 4; M6 = 1
413	MAASS	2000	≈ 51,000		182	J = 4; M6 = 1; B†
414	NAASS	1980	≈ 53,000		1560	J = 4; M6 = 5; M88 = 5; A†
415	OAASS	2200	≈ 58,000		4200	J = 4; M6 = 5; M88 = 5; B†

* Feeder program 37 (*call word* KBAAA) is described in Chapter VI. Programs 22–37, 106–107, 322–329, and 410–415 are given in this volume. All other programs are given in *Digital Computer Programs for Physical Chemistry*, vol. I (Macmillan, 1963). All figures refer to the IBM 1620 with card input-output and 60K storage at the University of Mississippi. ML is the number of machine language cards without the error trace. MT is the machine time (in minutes) measured from the beginning of the *data read in* operation to the end of the last *punch out* operation. All programs were written in IBM 4–1–61 FORTRAN without FORMAT.

† A denotes QQ1 = QQ2 = 1.0. B denotes QQ1 = QQ2 = 2.0; QQ3 = QQ4 = 1.0.

SYMBOLS

If the same symbol appears more than once in the same program it is subscripted thus: VOL1, VOL2, VOL3, and VOL4 or VOL11, VOL12, VOL21, VOL22.

In Programs 22–36, 322–329, and 501–505, matrix representations (i.e., Y(I,J)) are frequently used in place of the one-dimensional arrays used in Programs 1–21, 101–107, 201, 202, 301–304, 309–315, and 410–415 and defined here. Definitions of the matrix elements are given in the input and output formats for each program. Symbols used only in special programs are listed only in the subject arrangement.

ALPHABETIC ARRANGEMENT

AI1	Absorbancy index of first component	DEN, DENS	Density (grams/cc)
AIA	Absorbancy index of A	DENM	Measured density
AIB	Absorbancy index of B	DESL	Maximum permitted error in the slope
AIC	Absorbancy index of the complex	DEVSL	Maximum permitted error in the parameter SL
AIAX, AIBX, AICX	Concentration-independent part of the absorbancy indices for A, B and the complex	DEV, DEVF	Maximum permitted deviation (input)
		DEV	Actual error (output)
B, BB	Intercept, or mean maximum permitted error (Program 505)	DEAIC, DEVAI	Maximum error in the absorbancy index
		DEVB	Maximum error in the intercept
C	Concentration (moles/liter) or mole fraction	DEVEQ	Maximum error in the equilibrium constant
CS	Concentration (moles/liter) of solvent	DEVX	Actual error in X
CM	Molar conductance	DEVY	Actual error in Y
COMP	Component used		
		EQ	Equilibrium constant
D, DE	Dielectric constant	EQF	Final value for the equilibrium constant

EQO	Arbitrarily selected value for EQ	J or JC	The cycle number (output)
		JD	The maximum-dimensioned equation to be solved with Programs 25–28, 325–328
F	Change in Gibbs free energy (kcal/mole)		
FC	Freezing-point suppression constant (°C/mole/100 grams)	JI	The actual number of sets of conjugate data, in multiples of four, to be read in programs 25–29, 32, 33, 325–329, 501. *Note:* JI ≤ JQ
FEEDP	Feeder program number		
FM	Mole fraction		
FT	Flow time	JJ	Output command for programs 5–7 or the actual dimensions of the equation to be solved with Programs 25–29, 325–329. *Note:* JJ ≤ JD
FUNX	Weighting function for X		
FUNY	Weighting function for Y		
FUNB } FNSL	Correction functions for B and SL1 if FUNX and FUNY are used		
		JQ	The maximum number of sets of conjugate data which can be read in Programs 25–29, 32, 33, 325–329, 501
G	Number of sets of conjugate data after applications of fail-safe procedure		
		JR	Equals (JD + 1). It is the maximum number of columns in the principal matrix of the Crout reduction method
G1	Number of sets of conjugate information entering the self-judgment cycle (Programs 10–15, 25–29, 310–315, 325–329, 410–415) or remaining after the cycle (Programs 1–4, 9, 301–304, 309, 22–24, 322–324)		
		K	Input command defining the form in which the maximum permitted deviations (DEV and DEVF) are to be entered
G2	Number of sets of conjugate information remaining after application of the self-judgment principle (Programs 10–15, 25–29, 310–315, 325–329, 410–415)	KA	Input command designating which sets of conjugate data are to be ignored until the restore mechanism is invoked. In Programs 25–29, 325–329, KA can also designate which sets are to be removed from memory
G3	Number of sets of conjugate information actually used to calculate SQRM in Programs 10–15, 310–315, 410–415, or standard deviation in programs 25–29, 325–329		
		KB } KC KD } KE KF	Input commands designating which sets of conjugate information are to be ignored until the reject-restore mechanism is applied
H	Change in enthalpy (kcal/mole)		
HO	Temperature-independent part of the change in enthalpy (kcal/mole)		
		L	Input command defining mode of calculation
INSTR	Instrument used	LL	Input command for Programs 17 and 202
II	Input command for Programs 5, 6, 7		
		M	Input command defining concentration units
J or JC	Number of cycles before error analysis (Programs 1–4, 9, 22–28, 301–304, 309, 322–328), or before invoking the self-judgment principle (10–15, 29, 310–315, 329, 410–415) (input)	M4	The number of the wavelengths processed or the number of wavelengths per block of data (Program 34)
		M6	The number of wavelengths to be processed or the number of blocks of data (Program 34)

M88	The number which designates the value for QQ processed in Programs 14, 15, 314, 315, 414, and 415	SQRM	Square-root-mean-square deviation
		ST	Surface tension (dynes/cm)
		SV	Specific viscosity coefficient
OA	Absorbance	T	Temperature (°C or °A) or time (Program 33)
OAC	Absorbance of the complex		
OAM	Measured absorbance		
OPER	Operator of instrument	VC	Viscosity coefficient of the solution (cps)
P	Volume or molar polarization	VCS	Viscosity coefficient of the pure solvent (cps)
PA ⎫ PB ⎭	Polarization of A and B (concentration-independent part)		
		VOL	Volume (cc)
PP	Increment used to calculate concentrations	W	Weight (grams)
		WAC	The lowest fraction of the observable which can be used in iterative procedures
PPQQ	Increment of QQ		
PS	Polarization of solvent (concentration-independent part)	WACT	The lowest temperature increment that can be used in cryoscopic calculations
QQ	Association constant (i.e., $QQ1 \cdot A \rightleftarrows C$)	WAVEL	Wavelength of measurements or WAVEL designates the mode of calculating the polarization
R	Mean value of parameter (Program 505)		
RI	Refractive index	WL	The lowest reliable value for the observable
RLM	Measured limit of reliability or reproducibility	WM	Molecular weight
		WMS	Molecular weight of the solvent
RUN	The number of the experiment		
S	Change in entropy (eu)	WU	The highest reliable value for the observable
SDEV	Standard deviation		
SC	Specific conductivity		
SSC	Specific conductivity of the pure solvent	X	Variable
		X–ER	Maximum permitted error in X where "–" is a number denoting each ordinate
SHIFT	Wavelength or frequency shift		
SL	Slope or intercept (25–29, 322–329)		
SMV	Salt molar viscosity	Y	Ordinate
SOLVT	Solvent used	YER	Maximum permitted error in Y

SUBJECT ARRANGEMENT

Symbols Common to Most Programs

C	Concentration (moles/liter) or mole fraction	INSTR	Instrument used
		K	Input command defining the form in which the maximum permitted deviation (DEV or DEVF) is entered
DEV ⎫ DEVF ⎬ DEVFT ⎭	Maximum permitted deviation (input)		
		KA, KB ⎫ KC, KD ⎬ KE, KF ⎭	Input commands which activate the reject-restore mechanism
FEEDP	Feeder program number		
FM	Mole fraction		
G	Number of sets of conjugate data after application of the fail-safe procedure	L	Input commands designating mode of calculation of ordinates

M	Input command defining the concentration units used	WL WLT }	Lowest reliable value for the observable
OPER	Operator of instrument	WU WUT }	Highest reliable value for the observable
RLM RLMT }	Measured limit of reliability or reproducibility		
RUN	The number of the experiment	X	Variable
SOLVT	Solvent used	X–ER	Maximum permitted error in X where "–" is a number denoting each ordinate
T TEMP }	Temperature (°C or °A)		
WAVEL	Wavelength or frequency of measurement or input command (Program 30)	Y	Ordinate
		YER	Maximum permitted error in Y

Autoplotter Programs*

AM	Amount of margin	NQR	Number of FORTRAN program for which data are to be autoplotted
BC	Black crosses		
BD	Black dots		
F3	Straight-line fill	RC	Red crosses
F4	Second degree curve fill	RD	Red dots
H	Height of paper	W	Width of paper
NF	No fill	WM	Equals W–200·0
NLS	Input command for autoplotter		

* *Dimensions* (AM, H, W, WM) are in hundredths of inches.

Expansion Programs

AI1	Absorbancy index of first component		information actually used in calculating EQ and AIC or SL and DEVSL (25, 325)
AIA	Absorbancy index of A		
AIB	Absorbancy index of B	G3	Equals (G2 + 1·0) (25, 325)
AIC	Absorbancy index of the complex		
		J or JC	Number of cycles to be completed before doing error analysis (input)
B or BB	Intercept		
		J or JC	Cycle number (output)
DEV	Maximum permitted deviation in the observable (input)	JD	Maximum dimensioned equation that will be solved with Programs 25 and 325
DEV	Actual error in the observable (output)	JI	The actual number of sets of conjugate data to be processed with Program 25 or 325
DEVAI	Maximum permitted error in AIC		
DEVEQ	Maximum permitted error in EQ	JJ	The actual dimension of the equation to be solved with Programs 25 and 325
DEVSL	Maximum permitted error in SL		
		JQ	The maximum number of sets of conjugate data that can be processed with Program 25 or 325
G1	Number of sets of conjugate information actually used to calculate EQ or SL (9, 22–24, 309, 322–324)		
G1	Number of sets of conjugate information entering the self-judgment cycle (25, 325)	M4	The number designating the wavelength for which data are being processed
G2	Number of sets of conjugate	M6	The number of wavelengths for which data are to be processed

OAM	Measured absorbance (Programs 9, 22–24, 309, 322–324)		
			for the designated observable
		SQRMS	The standard deviation in accepted values for the designated observable
SL	Parameter		
SQRM	The square-root-mean-square deviation in accepted values	Y(I, JJ)	Measured absorbance (Program 25, 325)

Self-Judgment Programs with Variable Dimensions

DEV	Actual error in the designated variable (output)	JD	The maximum-dimensioned equation that can be solved with this program
DEVSL	Maximum permitted error in the parameter SL	JI	Number of sets of conjugate data actually to be processed
G1	Number of sets of conjugate information entering the self-judgment cycle	JJ	Actual dimension of the equation to be solved
G2	Number of sets of conjugate information remaining at the end of the cycle	JQ	The maximum number of sets of conjugate data that can be processed
		JR	Equals $(JD + 1)$
JC	Number of cycles to be completed before doing error analyses (input)	SL	Parameter (slope and intercept)
JC	Cycle number (output)	SQRMS	Standard deviation in accepted values for the designated variable

Mathematical French Curve Program

Symbols used in Programs 27 and 327 are identical with those for the preceding section, except for the additional quantities defined below.

FR	First variable	QQ1 ⎱	Indexes for arbitrary
L ⎰	Input commands	QQ2 ⎰	function
M ⎰	to select function	Y(I,JJ)	Second variable

Job's Method Equations

Symbols used in Programs 28 and 328 are identical with those for the self-judgment programs with variable dimensions, except for the following additional quantities defined below.

C1	Concentration of first component	RAM	Ratio of C1 to C2 at point of inflection
C2	Concentration of second component	RAMER	Maximum permitted error in RAM
M	Defines index of expansion	RLM(2)	Defines curvature
QQ	Index of expansion	WAC(2)	Dimension of expansion
		Y(I,JJ)	Measured absorbance

Twin Equilibria

Symbols used in Programs 29 and 329 are identical with those used in Programs 26 and 326 except for the additional quantities defined below.

AIA ⎱		AIAER, ⎱	
AC1, ⎰	Symbols defining the	AC1ER ⎰	Maximum permitted errors in
AC2, ⎰	absorbancy indices	AC2ER, ⎰	AIA, AC1, etc.
AIB ⎰		AIBER ⎰	

C1 C2	Concentrations before equilibrium		M OAM	Designates equation set Measured absorbance
DEEQ1 DEEQ2	Maximum permitted errors in EQX(J,1) and EQX(J,2)		RLM(1) RLM(2)	Arbitrary value for EQX(J,1) Arbitrary value for EQX(J,2)
EQX(J,1) EQX(J,2)	First formation constant Second formation constant		WAC(1) WAC(2)	Instrument reliability factors for C1 or C2

Molar Polarization Equations

A1, A2 A3, A4 B1, B2 B3, B4	Coefficients for the concentration-dependent part of the polarization of A and B		PA PB PS	Concentration independent parts of the polarization of A, B, and S
C CS	Concentration (moles/liter) Concentration of solvent		QQ	Association constant $(QQ1 \cdot A \rightleftarrows C)$
DE	Dielectric constant or refractive index		S1, S2 S3, S4	Coefficients for the concentration dependent part of the polarization of the solvent
DEN	Density of solutions (grams/cc)			
EQO	Arbitrarily selected value for the equilibrium constant		VOL	Volume of solution at room temperature
J	Number of cycles before application of the self-judgment principle (input and output)		WACRR	The fractional part of the equilibrium constant which determines the number of cycles in the special iterative programs (Chapter XI)
NQR	Spectrophotometric program for which the input information is to be generated		WAVEL	Input command defining PA, PB, and PS

Resolution of Spectra

In addition to the symbols used in the parent programs for the mean and the mean maximum permitted errors of the absorbancy indices for the complex, there occur the following.

EQ	Mean value for the equilibrium constant		PROGN	Number of program for which data are to be processed
EQER	Mean maximum permitted error in EQ			

Conductance Equations

In addition to the symbols defined in Programs 26 and 326 the following are used

AONS BONS	Onsager coefficients		SSC	Specific conductivity of the solvent
DE	Dielectric constant of solvent		T	Temperature ($^{\circ}$A)
SC	Specific conductivity of the solution		VIS	Viscosity coefficient of the solvent

QQ	Onsager q term	WAC	All SC less than WAC*SSC are not reliable and discarded
QQ1	Association constant or dimension, (i.e. $SC = SL1*C**QQ1 + B$)		

Kinetic Equations

C(I,J)	Concentration	LEQ2(J,I)	Expansions used in rate equation
CE(I,J)	Concentration expression	LEX1(I)	Number of concentrations in concentration term
CER(I,J)	Maximum permitted error in CE(I,J)	LEX2(J,I)	Concentrations in concentration term
		LL(I)	Type of expansion
		NC	Number of concentrations
		NEX	Number of expansions
DEVC (I,J)		NEQ	Number of rate equations
DEVFC(J)	Maximum permitted deviations		
DEVFT		QI(I)	Expansion index
DEVT(I)		QQ(J)	Order of reaction with respect to Jth concentration
DEVX(I)	Maximum permitted error in X	SL(J)	Expansion coefficient
DEVSL	Maximum permitted error in SL	T(I)	Time
JJ(I)	Dimension of expansion	X(1)	Select function of T(I)
LEQ1(I)	Dimension of rate equation	ZAP	Dummy

Special Iterative Programs

A1, A2 A3, A4	Coefficients for the concentration-dependent part of AIA	EQ	Equilibrium constant
		EQF	Final value for EQ
AIA	Absorbancy index of A	EQO	Arbitrarily selected value for EQ
AIB	Absorbancy index of B		
AIC	Absorbancy index of C	G1	Number of sets of conjugate information entering the self-judgment cycle
AIAX AIBX AIC1X AIC2X	Concentration-independent parts of the absorbancy indices for A, B, C1 and C2		
		G2	Number of sets of conjugate information used to calculate EQ
B1, B2 B3, B4	Coefficients for the concentration-dependent part of AIB	G3	The number of sets of conjugate information used to calculate SQRM
CA1, CA2 CA3, CA4	Coefficients for the concentration-dependent part of AIC1	J	The maximum number of cycles to be completed before application of the self-judgment principle (input)
CB1, CB2 CB3, CB4	Coefficients for the concentration-dependent part of AIC2	J	Cycle number (output)
DEVAI	Maximum permitted error in AIC	M4	The number designating the wavelength for which data are being processed
DEVEQ	Maximum permitted error in EQ	M6	The number of wavelengths for which data are to be processed
DEVX	Actual error in X	M88	The number designating the value for QQ processed
DEVY	Actual error in Y		

OAM	Measured absorbance		SDEV	Standard deviation
			SQRM	Square-root-mean-square
PP	Increment used to calculate			deviation in values for
	concentrations			the designated ordinate
PPQQ	Increment of QQ			
			WAC	The lowest fraction of the
				designated observable that
QQ	Association constant (i.e.,			can be used in iterative
	$QQ1 \cdot A \leftrightarrows C$)			methods
QQ – L	Lower and upper scan limits on		WACRR	The fractional part of the
	the values of the unknown			equilibrium constant which
	QQ, where "–" is a number			determines the total
	denoting each limit			number of cycles

Special Techniques

Program 505

Except for the following, symbols have been defined in the section, "Resolution of Spectra."

B	Mean maximum permitted		R	Mean value for the parameter
	error in R			Y(I)
G	The number of values averaged		X1(I)	Integral values selected as
				outlined in Chapter XII
			X1ER(I)	Equals zero
J	The number of cycles to be			
	completed before doing the		Y(I)	The Ith value of the parameter
	error analysis in program			to be averaged
	301, if used		YER(I)	The maximum permitted error
				in Y(I)

Program 34

BLOCK	Identification		OAM	Rearranged measured
				absorbance (output)
C1	Concentration of first			
	component		M6	Number of blocks of data (i.e.,
C2	Concentration of second			at constant temperature and
	component			with C1 constant)
			M4	Number of wavelengths per
OAM	Measured absorbance (input)			block

Program 35

Except for the following, the symbols used in Program 35 have been defined in the section "Expansion Programs." The second nonvariable subscript refers to the data deck at either the first or second temperatures.

A	Equals zero (dummy value)		Y(I,J)	The Ith value for the measured
				absorbance at the Jth
JJ	Number of cycles to be			wavelength at second
	completed before doing			temperature (input)
	the error analysis on			
	Program 301 (output)			
			Y(I,J)	The Ith value of the measured
X1(I,M4)	Integral value for the ordinate			absorbance at the Jth wave-
	selected as described in			length for the first temper-
	Chapter XII (output)			ature (input)

Y(I,M4)   The Ith ratio of the measured   YER(I, M4) Maximum permitted error in
          absorbance (second temper-   Y(I, M4)
          ature/first temperature) at
          the M4th wavelength
          (output)

Program 36

All symbols have been defined for Programs 10, 310, and 410. Output of Program 36 is compatible with Program 303 (*call word* CAAAS).

NUMERICAL CODES

Code	Significance
5555.0	When DEVF = 5555.0 appears in the output format, the *maximum permitted deviation* for the indicated observable was entered in the form DEV.
88888888.0	If *code* = 88888888.0, *code* is both printed and punched and the calculation is terminated. The data are not compatible with the equation but they are described by an equation of lower dimension.*
99999999.0	If *code* = 99999999.0, *code* is both printed and punched and the calculation is terminated. This means that for an N-dimensional equation there are fewer than $N + 2$ acceptable sets of conjugate information.

* In programs with the Crout reduction method incorporated, *code* = 88888888.0 means that all sets of conjugate information have been rejected.

DIGITAL COMPUTER PROGRAMS FOR PHYSICAL CHEMISTRY

VOLUME II

INTRODUCTION

THE NEW METHOD

If a competent experimentalist asserts that his data are reliable to within stated limits of error we infer that *nearly all* his items of information can be reproduced within the stated limits if his work is repeated under precisely the same conditions and if the instruments and techniques used are equally reliable. Thus the concept of a *limit of reliability* for each observation is natural and is accepted by national agencies such as the United States Bureau of Standards.

In the *statistical method* of curve-fitting, the *limit of reliability* of the raw data is not considered. Rather this method seeks to find the *error* in the data themselves without reference to the conditions or reliability of the instruments and techniques employed. Thus, with a change in the mathematical form of an equation to increase or decrease the variance or spread, virtually any hypothesis can be *proved* or *disproved* with precisely the same information. This serious fault, which is not generally recognized, results solely from the failure to consider the *limits of reliability* as an intrinsic part of the experimental information.

The *new method* for processing numerical experimental information which is described in this volume and in the preceding volume[1] uses the *limits of reliability* as an intrinsic part of the data. There are provisions in all computer programs for entering these *limits of reliability* either as a fractional part or as an individual quantity for each observation. The worker can arbitrarily select the *limits of reliability,* or he can determine them accurately in separate calibration experiments. In the calculation of ordinates for the equations to be tested, these *limits of reliability* are used to compute the *maximum permitted error* for each value of each ordinate. The values of the ordinates and the associated error zones (defined by the maximum permitted errors) together define the compatibility of the raw data with the equation to be tested.

[1] P. A. D. de Maine and R. D. Seawright, *Digital Computer Programs for Physical Chemistry*, Vol. I (New York: The Macmillan Co., 1963).

The *self-judgment principle* serves to reject values of the ordinates which are farther from the median curve than the *maximum permitted error*. Only *accepted* ordinate values and the associated *maximum permitted errors* are used to compute the parameters and their associated *maximum permitted errors*. Thus the results are irrevokably linked to the *limits of reliability*. The weaknesses of the *statistical method* do not exist, and direct comparison of different equations is possible.

The additional freedom which results from preselection of *limits of reliability* permits the solution of some quite intractable problems, and in this regard attention should be directed to the material in Chapters IV, VI, VII, and X.

An actual example which uses the new method is given in Appendix C. The terms and principles peculiar to the method are fully discussed in Volume I. References to published papers and theses in which the new techniques are used will be found throughout this volume. Both volumes assume that the reader has a full knowledge of physical chemistry. A detailed knowledge of computers or of their languages is neither assumed nor required. The minimal information required for use of the FORTRAN programs with an IBM 1620 computer and IBM 4–1–61 FORTRAN WITHOUT FORMAT COMPILER is given in Appendix C. In Appendix D the FORTRAN version of *Cramer's Method* for solving linear equations is given. Instructions are also given for replacing the *Crout reduction method* in the *self-judgment programs* with variable dimensions. The extreme sensitivity of the *Crout reduction method* may not be desired by some workers.

Given in this volume are details of the computer facilities required to process data with each of the 71 FORTRAN and five FOR-TO-GO programs.

All FORTRAN and FOR-TO-GO programs are compatible with any IBM 1620 60K computer with card input–output. Many of the smaller programs can be used with a 20K or 40K capacity IBM 1620. The four *autoplotter* programs have been designed specifically for use with the IBM 1620 autoplotter system. Information generated by this system is compatible with the IBM 836 *autoplotter*. Slightly modified versions of all FORTRAN and FOR-TO-GO programs can be used with most digital computers with storage capacity greater than 60K digits. If compilers are not available, the FORTRAN or FOR-TO-GO programs or their ALGOL 60 equivalents can be easily translated into a language compatible with the computer.

Although the ten FORTRAN programs with variable dimension (25–29, 325–329) can be tailored for use with 20K to 80K storage computers by changes in two commands (JI and JJ), they are intended for use with larger computers. For these programs the storage capacity of the computer will determine the maximum dimension equation and the number of data points which can be handled.

COMPARISON OF STATISTICAL AND NEW METHODS

The use of conventional statistical methods in processing experimental data is justified only if a sufficiently large number of equally weighted data points is considered. Applications by different workers of these cumbersome mathematical techniques to different truncated sets of information, which describe the same phenomenon, often yield ambiguous results. Frequently, experimental conditions prevent equal weighting of values and limit the number of data points. Other weaknesses inherent in applications of statistical methods are as follows:

1. Rules for discarding wrong data points are by no means decided. In some cases the retention or rejection of even a single point can significantly alter an analysis.

2. Conventional statistical methods of curve-fitting have a limited usefulness even when all the data points are considered "equally reliable," as terminal points are frequently not symmetrical about the origin and are therefore not "equally weighted." If the functional form of the distribution is unknown, conventional statistical curve-fitting techniques will yield at best an equation of questionable reliability because deviations are averaged. On the other hand, the new method is especially useful for deducing exact equations which describe any distribution of data points (see Chapters II, III, IV, V, and VI).

3. Although the experimentalist usually evaluates his data with consideration of the error limits of his measuring devices, conventional statistical methods are often applied without consideration of the reliability of individual items of data. Instead, deviations in data are averaged over the entire set of values, and the limits of experimental error, which determine the validity of the analysis, are ignored.

4. There exists no precise, unambiguous method for comparing results obtained by statistical analyses of two different sets of data describing the same phenomenon. At best one can say only that these results are in good agreement or that the agreement is poor. Such general statements, even if supported by numerical values for the variance, standard deviation, and other statistical quantities, foster the growth of mutually incompatible theories in physical chemistry.

With the *new method* experimental data can be tested for compatibility with any number of alternate equations (or theories) to within preselected limits of experimental error. The development of the *self-judgment principle*,[2] the concept of *error zones*, whose limits are determined by the *instrument reliability factors*, and *error analyses* provide a practical alternate method for processing new experimental data. This

[2] P. A. D. de Maine and R. D. Seawright, *Ind. Eng. Chem.*, **55**, No. 4, (1963), 29.

new method does not suffer from the weaknesses inherent in conventional treatments. The preselected limits of experimental error determine the *maximum permitted error* in each value of each parameter. The results obtained by different workers can be precisely compared.

To illustrate the advantages consider twenty points (y, x) which have been collected to test data compatibility with the equation: $y = mx + c$. Any meaningful analysis must give specific answers to the following questions..

(a) Are these data described by the equation: $y = mx + c$?

(b) If these data are compatible with the equation, what are the values for the parameters m and c?

(c) What are the precise limits of reliability for the values of m and c?

Conventional statistical methods yield definite answers to the second question, but the answers to the first and third questions are not precise.

The *new method* requires, in addition to the data points, an estimate of the actual error limit in each point. This requirement is met by giving for each observable the *instrument reliability factors* which are used to calculate for each y and each x the *maximum permitted errors* which in turn define the *error zone*. All data lying outside the *error zone* are discarded and the remaining G1 values are used to calculate the parameters m and c and their associated *maximum permitted errors*. Definite answers to each of the three questions are obtained in the following form.

(a) Of the original twenty data points, G1 are compatible with the equation $y = mx + c$, to within the preselected limits of error, defined by the *instrument reliability factors*.

(b) The values for m and c, calculated with the accepted data points (G1), are given.

(c) The *maximum permitted errors* determined by the dimensions of the *error zone* for the G1 accepted data points are given for both parameters.

Direct comparison of different values obtained for each parameter is possible. For example, if two values $(C'$ and $C'')$ for a particular parameter and their *maximum permitted errors* $(\Delta C'$ and $\Delta C'')$ do not overlap, at least one value is wrong. An example of inconsistent values is $C' = 1.000$, $\Delta C' = 0.001$, and $C'' = 1.020$, $\Delta C'' = 0.018$. The lower *mean maximum permitted error* does not make the first value the more accurate.

During the past year members of the group at the University of Mississippi have used the *new method* extensively to process spectral, conductance, viscosity, cryoscopic, dielectric constant, and thermodynamic data. The exceptional versatility of the *new method* has been amply demonstrated.

Other recent developments of additional computer techniques and their application to areas of physical chemistry are also discussed in this book. The *autoplotter* (Chapter I) and *expansion* (Chapter II) programs are especially useful for processing experimental data for the physical sciences. The *method of limiting intercepts* and the *mathematical French curve technique* permit an easy reduction of any distribution of data points to exact functional forms.

CHAPTER I

AUTOPLOTTER PROGRAMS

With the recent development of high-speed autoplotters there is a rapid method for converting numerical data to graphical form by means of a computer. Autoplots can be used with a planimeter for calculating the areas under curves, or they may be included in reports to illustrate results. We have found that an autoplotter is necessary for adequate and economic processing of experimental data. Autoplots facilitate the rapid selection of the input commands which activate the semiautomatic *reject–restore mechanism,* frequently enable the operator to detect data incompatibility, and thus save computer time.

The four FOR-TO-GO programs in this chapter have been specifically designed to process input information for FORTRAN programs, with the *self-judgment principle* incorporated, by use of the IBM 836 autoplotter (see *input commands* for Programs 501 to 504). The FOR-TO-GO program (henceforth called the *autoplotter program*) to be used for processing input information for each FORTRAN program is given in Table 1. *Autoplotter Programs* 501, 502, 503, and 504 have been tested with information generated by *Test Programs* 101 to 107 (see Appendix A in this volume and in the preceding volume).

In all *autoplotter programs* the *fail–safe procedure* is applied first. Input commands which activate the semiautomatic *reject–restore mechanism* are then executed. However, the *self-judgment principle* and the *normalization* and *transposition mechanisms* are inoperative. Input commands exclusively associated with the four *autoplotter programs* will be discussed later.

THE AUTOPLOTTER SYSTEM

No attempt will be made to describe here the programming rules followed in writing the rather difficult FORGO or FOR-TO-GO program

Table 1*

Relationship Between Autoplotter and FORTRAN Programs

FORTRAN *Program Numbers*	Autoplotter Programs		
	Number	*Call Word*	*Pages for Input Commands*
1–4, 26, 301–304, 326	501	AEEEE	8–9
9, 22–25, 27, 309, 322–325, 327	502	BEEEE	8–9, 9–11
10, 11, 14, 28, 29, 310, 311, 314, 328, 329, 410 411, 414	503	CEEEE	8–9, 11–12
12, 13, 15, 312, 313, 315, 412, 413, 415	504	DEEEE	8–9, 12–14

* Input information for the indicated FORTRAN programs can be used in assembling the *data deck* for processing with the associated *autoplotter program* in step 1 of the IBM 1620 autoplotter system. The composition of the *data decks* is described under input format for Programs 501–504.

for the IBM 1620 *autoplotter system*. Readers who desire to write their own programs or to change the programs in this chapter are advised to study pamphlet E, *Programming Rules: 1620 Autoplotter System*, which is distributed by IBM.

In any *autoplotter system*, numerical information is first rescaled in fixed-point form (step 1) and then the fixed-point information is translated (step 2) for compatibility with the autoplotter. In step 3 the translated information is converted to graphical form by the autoplotter. A computer is used only in steps 1 and 2. In the IBM 1620 *autoplotter system* the information generated on punched cards in step 1 is used as input information for step 2. The procedure for using the IBM system is now given. The *data deck* includes the input information for the FORTRAN program.

Step 1: (a) Assemble the FOR-TO-GO *deck* thus: FOR-TO-GO 3–62A *deck* plus *autoplotter program* (501, 502, 503, or 504) plus FOR-TO-GO 3–62B *deck* plus *data deck*. The composition of the *data deck* is described in the section on input format for Programs 501–504.

(b) The *parity* and I/O *program switches* on the console of the IBM 1620 60K computer are turned *on*. All other switches should be *off*. The memory is cleared in the normal way.

(c) Load the FOR-TO-GO *deck*.

Step 2: (a) Assemble the *autoplotter deck* thus: *autoplotter deck* 7/3/62 plus *output information* from *step* 1.

(b) Turn all switches on the computer console *off*, and then zero the memory in the normal way.

(c) Load the *autoplotter deck*. The *start switch* on the console must be pushed when the computer stops after reading the *autoplotter deck*.

Step 3: The *output information* generated in *step* 2 is loaded onto the IBM 836 *autoplotter*. To avoid unnecessary noise the *print switch* should be *off*.

Computer times required to process data through *steps* 1 and 2 seldom exceed two minutes. With the more complicated FORTRAN programs, several hours are required to completely process the same information. In some special cases erroneous data points, not considered in selecting the input commands which activate the semiautomatic *reject-restore mechanism*, may lead to an erroneous analysis (see *statistical bias* in Volume I). The use of an *autoplotter system* to detect wrong data points is an important part of the *new method*.

INPUT COMMANDS FOR PROGRAMS 501–504

The *data deck* used in *step* 1 consists of the input information for the FORTRAN program preceded by one (Program 501) or two (Programs 502–504) cards with the following information.

Card for Programs 502, 503, and 504: This card contains only the one item, NQR, which is the number of the FORTRAN program (expressed as a fixed-point number) whose input information is to be processed.

Card for Programs 501, 502, 503, and 504: This card contains either five (502, 503, and 504) or six (501) items of information. The first five items, designated by the symbols W, H, AM, WM, and NLS, are entered for all *autoplotter programs*. The sixth item of information, JI, is entered only for Program 501.

The first four items determine the size of the autoplot in hundredths of inches thus:

W	The width of the paper for each autoplot
H	The height of the autoplotter paper which is normally the distance between the sprockets on the typewriter roller
AM	The amount of margin, or the distance of each of the two axes from the nearest edge of the paper
WM	A quantity equal to W − AM which determines the number of scale increments on both axes
NLS	A fixed-point number which determines for each autoplot the number of curves, their color, and their mode
JI	The number of data points, which must be a multiple of four. The maximum value for JI is twenty

The relationship between each of the two coordinates (y and x) and the raw data is determined by L (defined for each FORTRAN program), NLS, and NQR. The input commands for each *autoplotter program* are given in Table 2. *Color* and *Fill* codes used throughout this text are given in Table 2. NC and NP are the number of curves and the number of autoplots, respectively, obtained from a single set of input information.

Table 2

Color and Fill Codes used in the Input Commands for Autoplotter Programs 501 to 504

Fill Code

NF	Points are plotted without fill-in
F3	Points are connected by straight lines
F4	Points are connected by second-order curves

Color Code

BC	Black crosses	BD	Black dots
RC	Red crosses	RD	Red dots

Instructions for correcting wrong input commands have been included in all four *autoplotter programs*. The corrections made are obvious on the autoplot generated.

The *input commands* L and M6, which appear in discussions of the *input commands* for Programs 502, 503, and 504, have been defined for the associated FORTRAN programs. Specimen autoplots are given later in this chapter.

INPUT COMMANDS FOR PROGRAM 501

Autoplots of input information for FORTRAN Programs 1–4, 26, 301–304, and 326 can be obtained with FOR-TO-GO Program 501. The value entered for NLS determines the number of curves, their color and mode on each autoplot, and the number of autoplots obtained with each set of input information. Y(I), X1(I), X2(I), X3(I), and X4(I) are the values of the designated ordinates for the Ith data point. YER(I) is the *maximum permitted error* for Y(I). (See Table 3.)

INPUT COMMANDS FOR PROGRAM 502

Autoplotter program 502 can be used to process input information for FORTRAN Programs 9, 22–25, 27, 309, 322–325, and 327. The NLS value determines the number of curves, their color, and their mode on each autoplot. Values for NLS and NQR together determine the choice

Table 3

Input Commands for Program 501

NLS	Vertical Axis	Horizontal Axis	Fill	NC	NP
1	Y(I)(BC)	X1(I)	NF	1	1
2	Y(I)(BC)	X1(I)	F3	1	1
3	X1(I)(BC);X2(I)(RC)	Y(I)	F4	2	1
4	X1(I)(BC);X2(I)(RC);X3(I)(BD)	Y(I)	F4	3	1
5	X1(I)(BC);X2(I)(RC);X3(I)(BD);X4(I)(RD)	Y(I)	F4	4	1
6	(Y(I)+YER(I))(RC);Y(I)(BC);(Y(I)−YER(I))(RC)	X1(I)	F3	3	1
7	(Y(I)+YER(I))(RC);Y(I)(BC);(Y(I)−YER(I))(RC)	X1(I)	F3	3	2
	(Y(I)+YER(I))(RC);Y(I)(BC);(Y(I)−YER(I))(RC)	X2(I)	F3	3	
8	(Y(I)+YER(I))(RC);Y(I)(BC);(Y(I)−YER(I))(RC)	X1(I)	F3	3	
	(Y(I)+YER(I))(RC);Y(I)(BC);Y((I)−YER(I))(RC)	X2(I)	F3	3	3
	(Y(I)+YER(I))(RC);Y(I)(BC);(Y(I)−YER(I))(RC)	X3(I)	F3	3	
9	(Y(I)+YER(I))(RC);Y(I)(BC);(Y(I)−YER(I))(RC)	X1(I)	F3	3	
	(Y(I)+YER(I))(RC);Y(I)(BC);(Y(I)−YER(I))(RC)	X2(I)	F3	3	4
	(Y(I)+YER(I))(RC);Y(I)(BC);(Y(I)−YER(I))(RC)	X3(I)	F3	3	
	(Y(I)+YER(I))(RC);Y(I)(BC);(Y(I)−YER(I))(RC)	X4(I)	F3	3	

of axes, and L defines the relation between the ordinates and the raw data. The number of autoplots obtained from a single set of input information is determined by the values for NLS, NQR, and M6. L and M6 are input commands defined for each FORTRAN program.

Input commands for *Autoplotter Program 502* can be conveniently selected from Tables 4 and 5. Y(I), X1(I), X2(I), X3(I), and X4(I) are the values for the designated ordinates calculated from the Ith set of conjugate data. The mode of calculation is defined by the value for L. YER(I) is the *maximum permitted error* for Y(I). The meanings of BC, RC, BD, RD, FILL, NC, and NP have been given.

Table 4

Input Commands for Program 502 with NQR = 9 or 309*

NLS	Vertical Axis	Horizontal Axis	Fill	NC	NP
1	Y(I)(BC)	X1(I)	NF	1	M6
2	Y(I)(BC)	X1(I)	F3	1	M6
3	Y_1(I)(BC);Y_2(I)(RC)	X1(I)	F3	2	M6/2
4	Y_1(I)(BC);Y_2(I)(RC);Y_3(I)(BD)	X1(I)	F3	3	M6/3
5	Y_1(I)(BC);Y_2(I)(RC);Y_3(I)(BD);Y_4(I)(RD)	X1(I)	F3	4	M6/4
6	(Y(I)+YER(I))(RC);Y(I)(BC);(Y(I)−YER(I))(RC)	X1(I)	F3	3	M6

* Y_1(I), Y_2(I), Y_3(I), and Y_4(I) are the values for Y(I) calculated with data for the first, second, third, and fourth wavelengths in each autoplot. M6 is the total number of wavelengths for which data are to be processed.

The *expansion programs* (9, 22–25, 27, 309, 322–325, 327) can be used to expand sets of data points (Y(I), X1(I)) thus:

$$Y(I) = B + S_1 X1(I) + S_2(X1(I))^2 + S_3(X1(I))^3 + S_4(X1(I))^4 + \cdots$$

The dimension of the *expansion program* used to solve for the constants, B, S_1, $S_2 \cdots$, will determine the dimension of the expansion (see Chapters II and IV).

In *Autoplotter Program* 502 (*call word* BEEEE), the dimension of the FORTRAN (*expansion*) program is ignored and X1(I), X2(I)($= (X1(I))^2$), X3(I)($= (X1(I))^3$), and X4(I)($= (X1(I))^4$) are calculated. For the *expansion programs* with *variable dimensions* (25 and 325), concentration terms with X1(I) raised to a power higher than four are not calculated. With the *mathematical French curve programs* (27 and 327) the values for X1(I) are not exponentiated. Input commands for NLS with NQR = 22–25, 27, 322–325, 327 are given in Table 5.

Table 5

Input Commands for Program 502 when NQR = 22–25, 27, 322–325, 327

NLS	Vertical Axis	Horizontal Axis	Fill	NC	NP
1	Y(I)(BC)	X1(I)	NF	1	M6
2	Y(I)(BC)	X1(I)	F3	1	M6
3	X1(I)(BC);X2(I)(RC)	Y(I)	F4	2	M6
4	X1(I)(BC);X2(I)(RC);X3(I)(BD)	Y(I)	F4	3	M6
5	X1(I)(BC);X2(I)(RC);X3(I)(BD);X4(I)(RD)	Y(I)	F4	4	M6
6	(Y(I)+YER(I))(RC);Y(I)(BC);(Y(I)−YER(I))(RC)	X1(I)	F3	3	M6

INPUT COMMANDS FOR PROGRAM 503

Input information for FORTRAN Programs 10, 11, 14, 28, 29, 310, 311, 314, 328, 329, 410, 411, and 414 can be converted to autoplots with Program 503. The number of curves, their color, and their mode on each autoplot are determined by the value for NLS. The relationships between raw data and the ordinates (Y(I), X1(I)) are defined by the value entered for NQR.

In all the FORTRAN programs except 28 and 328 the formation constant (K) and molar absorbancy index of the complex, C, for the reversible reaction

$$n_1 A + n_2 B \overset{K}{\rightleftarrows} C$$

are calculated by an iterative method. Information required by the computer for all FORTRAN programs includes the following.

(a) The concentrations or mole fractions of A (C1(I)) and B (C2(I)) before the reaction occurs.

(b) The molar absorbancy indices for A (AIA(I)), and for B (AIB(I)), determined in separate experiments. AIA(I) and AIB(I) need not be independent of the concentrations of A and B.

(c) The measured absorbance (OAM(I)) at a fixed wavelength and temperature for solutions containing initial concentrations of A and B equal to C1(I) and C2(I) respectively.

In FORTRAN Programs 10, 11, 14, 29, 310, 311, 314, 329, 410, 411, and 414, n_2 can be zero.

In *Autoplotter Program* 503 the ordinates are calculated from the *raw data* as follows.

For All Programs:
$$Y(I) = (OAM(I) - AIA(I) * C1(I) - AIB(I) * C2(I))/C1(I)$$
For Programs 10, 11, 14, 29, 310, 311, 314, 329, 410, 411, and 414:
$$X1(I) = C1(I) \qquad \text{(if } n_2 = 0)$$
or
$$X1(I) = C2(I) \qquad \text{(if } n_2 \neq 0)$$
For Programs 28 and 328:
$$X1(I) = C1(I)/C2(I)$$

YER(I), the *maximum permitted error* for each Y(I), is calculated from the instrument reliability factors for the two observables (OAM(I) and C1(I) or C2(I)) in the normal way.

In Table 6, $Y_1(I)$, $Y_2(I)$, $Y_3(I)$, and $Y_4(I)$ are the values for Y(I) calculated with data for the first, second, third, and fourth wavelengths used in the autoplot. The symbols BC, RC, BD, RD, *Fill*, NC, and NP have been defined.

Table 6

Input Commands for Program 503 with NQR = 10, 11, 14, 28, 29, 310, 311, 314, 328, 329, 410, 411, and 414

NLS	Vertical Axis	Horizontal Axis	Fill	NC	NP
1	Y(I)(BC)	X1(I)	NF	1	M6
2	Y(I)(BC)	X1(I)	F3	1	M6
3	Y_1(I)(BC);Y_2(I)(RC)	X1(I)	F4	2	M6/2
4	Y_1(I)(BC);Y_2(I)(RC);Y_3(I)(BD)	X1(I)	F4	3	M6/3
5	Y_1(I)(BC);Y_2(I)(RC);Y_3(I)(BD);Y_4(I)(RD)	X1(I)	F4	4	M6/4
6	(Y(I)+YER(I))(RC);Y(I)(BC);(Y(I)−YER(I))(RC)	X1(I)	F3	3	M6

INPUT COMMANDS FOR PROGRAM 504

With *Autoplotter Program* 504 input information for FORTRAN Programs 12, 13, 15, 312, 313, 315, 412, 413, and 415 can be processed for the IBM 836 autoplotter. The NLS value determines the number of curves, their color, their mode, and the choice of axes on each autoplot. M6 and NLS together determine the maximum number of autoplots that can be obtained from any one set of input information. The value for NQR determines the method used for calculating the concentrations of complexes, C_1 and C_2, from the formation constants, K_1 and K_2.

With FORTRAN Programs 12, 13, 15, 312, 313, 315, 412, 413, and 415 the formation constant, K_3, and the absorbancy index for C_3 in the simultaneous reversible reactions:

$$n_1 A \overset{K_1}{\rightleftharpoons} C_1$$

$$n_2 B \overset{K_2}{\rightleftharpoons} C_2$$

$$n_3 A + n_4 B \overset{K_3}{\rightleftharpoons} C_3$$

are calculated by iterative methods. The information required by the computer includes the following.

(a) The concentrations of A (C1(I)), and B (C2(I)), before any reactions have occurred.

(b) AIA(I), AIB(I), AIC1(I), and AIC2(I), the molar absorbancy indices for A, B, C_1, and C_2, respectively, calculated from data for solutions containing A or B. These absorbancy indices need not be concentration independent.

(c) The measured absorbancies, (OAM(I)), for solutions containing both A and B at a fixed temperature and wavelength.

In Program 504 (*call word* DEEEE), after the *fail–safe procedure* and the *input commands* for the *reject–restore mechanism* are executed, the concentrations C4(I) and C5(I), of the complexes C_1 and C_2 respectively, are calculated with the assumption that K_3 is zero. For NQR = 12 or 312, C4(I) and C5(I) are computed by a direct method. For NQR = 13, 15, 313, or 315 a much slower iterative method is used to calculate the concentrations of C_1 and C_2.

The ordinates for all values of NQR are calculated as follows.

$$Y(I) = (OAM(I) - AA - BB)/C1(I)$$

and

$$X1(I) = C2(I)$$

Here

$$AA = AIA(I) * C6(I) + AIB(I) * C7(I)$$
$$C6(I) = C1(I) - QQ1 * C4(I)$$
$$C7(I) = C2(I) - QQ2 * C5(I)$$
$$QQ1 = n_1, \quad QQ2 = n_2$$
$$BB = AIC1(I) * C4(I) + AIC2(I) * C5(I)$$

The values for YER(I), the *maximum permitted error* for Y(I), are calculated in the normal way from the *instrument reliability factors* for OAM(I) and C2(I).

Input commands for the *Autoplotter Program* 504 are given in Table 7. The meanings of the symbols BC, RC, BD, RD, FILL, NC, and NP have been given. $Y_1(I)$, $Y_2(I)$, $Y_3(I)$, and $Y_4(I)$ again designate values for the ordinate calculated from data for the first, second, third, and fourth wavelengths used in the autoplot. M6 is the number of wavelengths for which data are to be processed.

Table 7

Input Commands for Program 504 with NQR = 12, 13, 15, 312, 313, 315, 412, 413, and 415

NLS	*Vertical Axis*	*Horizontal Axis*	*Fill*	NC	NP
1	Y(I)(BC)	X1(I)	NF	1	M6
2	Y(I)(BC)	X1(I)	F3	1	M6
3	$Y_1(I)(BC);Y_2(I)(RC)$	X1(I)	F4	2	M6/2
4	$Y_1(I)(BC);Y_2(I)(RC);Y_3(I)(BD)$	X1(I)	F4	3	M6/3
5	$Y_1(I)(BC);Y_2(I)(RC);Y_3(I)(BD);Y_4(I)(RD)$	X1(I)	F4	4	M6/4
6	$(Y(I)+YER(I))(RC);Y(I)(BC);(Y(I)-YER(I))(RC)$	X1(I)	F3	3	M6

INPUT FORMAT FOR AUTOPLOTTER PROGRAMS 501, 502, 503, AND 504

In this section a *read* statement signifies that the designated input commands for the *Autoplotter Program* must be entered on a single card at the indicated location.

The composition of the *data deck* for *Program* 501 is

READ,W,H,AM,WM,NLS,JI

Input information for FORTRAN Programs 1–4, 26, 301–304, 326

Input information for FORTRAN Programs 1–4, 26, 301–304, 326

   etc.

There is no limit to the number of sets of input information in a *data deck*.

Autoplotter Programs 502, 503, and 504 have *data decks* identical in form. Input information for the FORTRAN programs with variable dimensions (25, 27–29, 325, 327–329) can be converted to autoplots with these FOR-TO-GO programs only if there are twenty data points. In each *data deck* each NQR can have any of the values associated with each *autoplotter program* (see Tables 4 through 7). The schematic composition of each *data deck* is:

READ,W,H,AM,WM,NLS
READ,NQR
Input information for FORTRAN Program NQR
READ,NQR
Input information for FORTRAN Program NQR
READ,NQR
Input information for FORTRAN Program NQR
      etc.

There is no limit to the number of sets of input information in a *data deck*.

AUTOPLOTS FOR PROGRAMS 501 THROUGH 504

Typical autoplots obtained with the IBM 1620 *autoplotter system* using *Autoplotter Programs* 501–504 (Figures 1–12) are shown on the next 13 pages. In the caption for each of the thirteen autoplots there are described other autoplots that can be obtained with the programs. The information in parentheses on each autoplot is not given by the IBM 836 *autoplotter*. The *color code* was described earlier in Table 2.

LIST OF SAMPLE AUTOPLOTS

NQR designates the FORTRAN program whose input information yielded the indicated autoplot for the value of NLS. OPN denotes the FORTRAN programs whose input information would yield very similar autoplots with the same NLS value. Details are given in the legend to each autoplot.

Autoplot	Page	Autoplotter Program	NLS	NQR	OPN
I	16	501	1	—	
II	17	501	2	—	
III	18	501	3	—	1–4, 26, 301–304, 326
IV	19	501	6	—	
V(a)	20	501	7	—	
(b)	21	501	7	—	
VI	22	502	1	309	9, 22–25, 27, 309, 322–325, 327
VII	23	502	2	309	9, 22–25, 27, 309, 322–325, 327
VIII	24	502	5	309	9, 309
IX	25	502	6	309	9, 22–25, 27, 309, 322–325, 327
X	26	502	5	324	22–25, 27, 322–325, 327
XI	27	503	5	410	10, 11, 14, 28, 29, 310, 311, 314, 328, 329, 410, 411, 414
XII	28	504	5	412	12, 13, 15, 312, 313, 315, 412, 413, 415

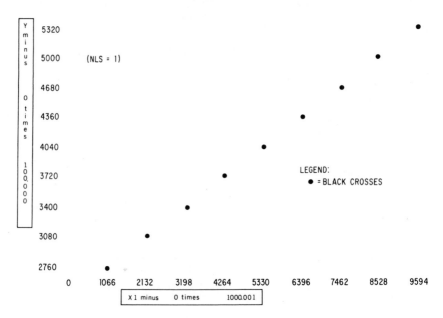

AUTOPLOT I

PROGRAM 302.0 L1 RUN 1.0 TEMP 20.0
OPERATOR   1. INSTRUMENT 12 WAVEL 3500.0
9.0 POINTS ARE RETAINED OUT OF 20.0

FIGURE 1. *Autoplot* I: Input information for Program 302 (*call word* BAAAS) was processed with the IBM 1620 *autoplotter system, Autoplotter Program* 501 (*call word* AEEEE), and the IBM 836 autoplotter to yield *autoplot* I. *Autoplotter input commands* (entered on a single card) were $W = 1125.0$; $H = 1130.0$; $AM = 200.0$; $WM = 925.0$; $NLS = 1$; $JI = 20$. *Reject–restore commands* in the input information for FORTRAN Program 302 were $KA = 0$; $KB = 1$; $KC = 11$; $KD = 0$. The final label on *autoplot* I indicates that only the last nine of the original twenty data points were plotted *without fill* (NF). Except for the program number in the label, identical autoplots were obtained with input information for Programs 1–4, 26, 301–304, and 326. The value of JI, the number of data points as a multiple of four, does not determine the color, dimensions, or mode of the autoplot. For Programs 1–4 and 301–304, $JI = 20$.

AUTOPLOT II

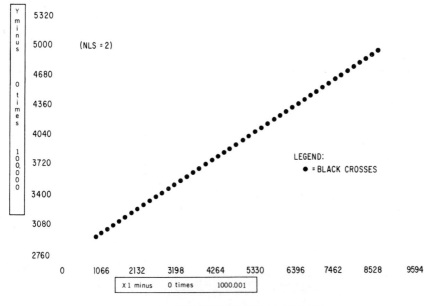

PROGRAM 302.0 L 1 RUN 1.0 TEMP 20.0
OPERATOR   I. INSTRUMENT I2 WAVEL 3500.0
9. 0 POINTS ARE RETAINED OUT OF 20.0

FIGURE 2. *Autoplot* II: This autoplot was obtained by processing input information for FORTRAN Program 302 (*call word* BAAAS) with the IBM 1620 *autoplotter system* and the IBM autoplotter. *Autoplotter Program* 501 (*call word* AEEEE) was used in the first stage of the IBM 1620 autoplotter system. *Autoplotter input commands* (entered on a single card) were W = 1125.0; H = 1150.0; AM = 200.0; WM = 925.0; NLS = 2; JI = 20. *Reject–restore commands* in the input information for Program 302 were KA = 0; KB = 1; KC = 11; KD = 0. The final label on *autoplot* I indicates that the last nine of the original twenty data points were plotted with *fill* (F3). Except for the program number in the label, identical autoplots were obtained with input information for Programs 1–4, 26, 301–304, and 326. Except for FORTRAN Programs 26 and 326, JI = 20. The values of L, RUN, TEMP, and OPERATOR are defined for the *feeder program* for Program 302.

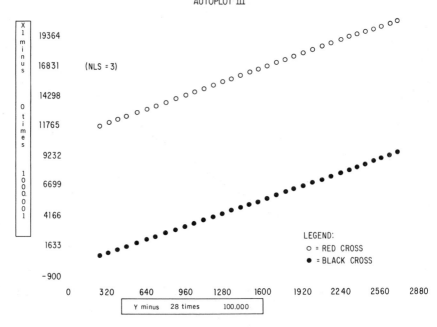

FIGURE 3. *Autoplot* III: The information used to obtain *autoplot* III is described in the legend to *autoplot* II except that here NLS = 3. Black crosses denote X1(I) values, and red crosses denote X2(I) values on the vertical axis. Except for the program number in the label, identical autoplots were obtained with input information for Programs 2–4, and 302–304, and for Programs 26 and 326 if JJ is greater than two. The autoplots for NLS = 4 with input information for Programs 3, 4, 303, and 304, and for Programs 26 and 326 if JJ is greater than three, have an additional curve (black dots) for X3(I) on the vertical axis. With NLS = 5 and input information for Program 4 or 304 and Program 26 or 326 if JJ is greater than four, a fourth curve (red dots) denotes X4(I) on the vertical axis. JJ denotes the dimension of the equation being tested.

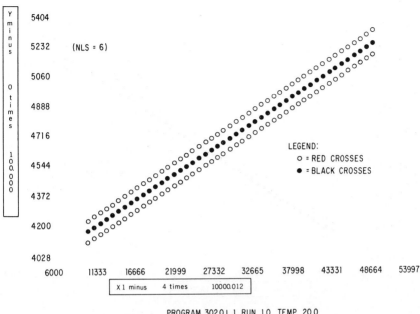

FIGURE 4. *Autoplot* IV: The information used to obtain *autoplot* IV is described in the legend to *autoplot* II, except that here NLS = 6. The red crosses denote the *maximum permitted errors* in the values of Y(I), which are denoted by black crosses. Except for the program number in the label, identical autoplots were obtained with input information for Programs 1–4, 26, 301–304, and 326.

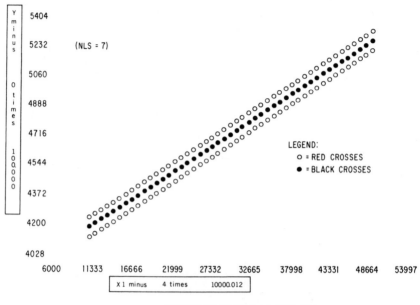

AUTOPLOT V(a)

PROGRAM 302.0 L1 RUN 1.0 TEMP 20.0
OPERATOR 1. INSTRUMENT 12 WAVEL 3500.0
5.0 POINTS ARE RETAINED OUT OF 20.0

FIGURE 5(a). *Autoplot* V(a): *Autoplots* V(a) and V(b) were obtained from the information described in the legend to *Autoplot* II except that here NLS = 7. The red crosses define the *maximum permitted errors* in values for Y(I), which are denoted by black crosses. The number of autoplots obtained with NLS = 7, 8, and 9 is determined by the FORTRAN program number (see *input commands* for Program 501). With NLS = 7 and input information for FORTRAN Programs 2–4 or 302–304, and 26 or 326 if JJ is greater than two, two autoplots nearly identical to *autoplots* V(a) and V(b) are obtained.

AUTOPLOT V (b)

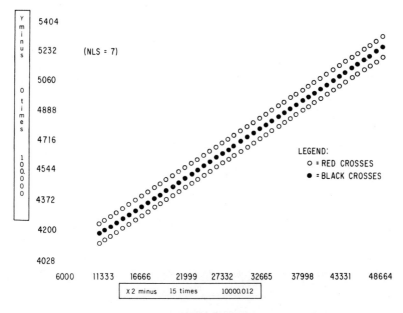

PROGRAM 302.0 L 1 RUN 1.0 TEMP 20.0
OPERATOR 1. INSTRUMENT 12 WAVEL 3500.0
5.0 POINTS ARE RETAINED OUT OF 20.0

FIGURE 5(b). *Autoplot* V(b): This is the second plot obtained with NLS = 7 and input information for Program 302 (*call word* BAAAS). The red crosses define the *maximum permitted errors* in the Y(I) values, which are denoted by black crosses. With NLS = 8 and input information for Program 3, 4, 303, or 304 or for Program 26 or 326 if JJ is greater than three, three similar autoplots are obtained. If input information for Program 4 or 304, or for Program 26 or 326 if JJ is greater than four, is processed with NLS = 9, four similar autoplots are obtained.

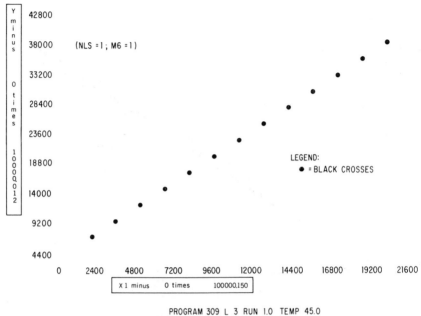

AUTOPLOT VI

PROGRAM 309 L 3 RUN 1.0 TEMP 45.0
WAVELENGTH IS 1 OPERATOR   1.
19.0 POINTS ARE RETAINED OUT OF 20.0

FIGURE 6. *Autoplot* VI: This autoplot was obtained from input information for FORTRAN Program 309 (*call word* IAAAS) with the use of the IBM 1620 autoplotter system, *Autoplotter Program* 502 (*call word* BEEEE), and the IBM 836 autoplotter. *Autoplotter input commands* were: Card one: W = 1125.0, H = 1150.0; AM = 200.0; WM = 925.0; NLS = 1. Card two: NQR = 309. Only the actual data points appear on the autoplot. L defines the relationship between the ordinates and the raw data (see *input commands* for Program 9, Volume I). "WAVELENGTH IS 1" indicates that absorbancies measured at the first wavelength have been used in the calculation of Y. *Reject–restore commands* in the input information for Program 309 were KA = -1, KB = 0, KC = 0, and KD = 0. The final label on the autoplot indicates that one of the original twenty *sets of conjugate data* was rejected when the *fail–safe procedure* was applied. Similar autoplots are obtained for each wavelength at which data are processed with input information for FORTRAN Programs 9, 22–24, 309, or 322–324 and Programs 25, 27, 325, or 327, if JI = 20.

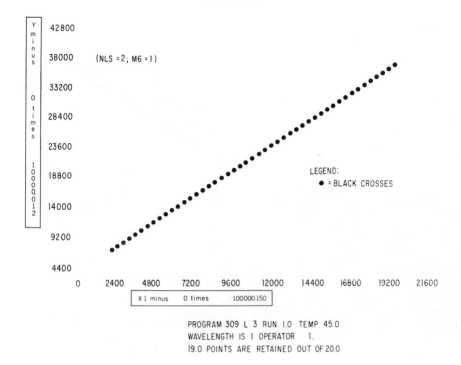

FIGURE 7. *Autoplot* VII: The information used to obtain *autoplot* VII is described in the legend to *autoplot* VI except that NLS = 2. Except for the wavelength number in the label, identical autoplots were obtained for each wavelength at which data were processed. Similar autoplots are obtained with input information for FORTRAN Programs 9, 22–24, 309, or 322–324 and Programs 25, 27, 325, or 327, if JI = 20.

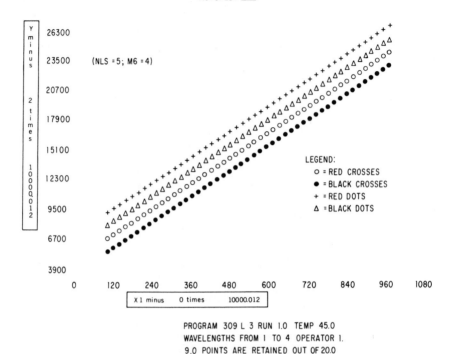

AUTOPLOT VIII

(NLS = 5; M6 = 4)

LEGEND:
O = RED CROSSES
● = BLACK CROSSES
+ = RED DOTS
△ = BLACK DOTS

X 1 minus   0 times   10000.012

PROGRAM 309 L 3 RUN 1.0 TEMP 45.0
WAVELENGTHS FROM 1 TO 4 OPERATOR 1.
9.0 POINTS ARE RETAINED OUT OF 20.0

FIGURE 8. *Autoplot* VIII: This autoplot was obtained from information described in the legend to *autoplot* VI except that M6, the number of wavelengths at which data were processed, was set equal to four and NLS = 5. Black crosses, red crosses, black dots, and red dots denote the first, second, third and fourth wavelengths respectively. Similar autoplots are obtained for each set of four wavelengths (see *input commands* for Program 502). If M6 = 11 and NLS = 5, three autoplots are obtained. Two will have four curves, and the third will have three curves. If NLS = 4 the same data will yield four autoplots, three with three curves and one with two curves. For NLS = 3, six autoplots, five with two curves and one with a single curve, will be obtained. Except for the program and wavelength numbers in the labels, identical autoplots were obtained with input information for Programs 9 and 309.

AUTOPLOT IX

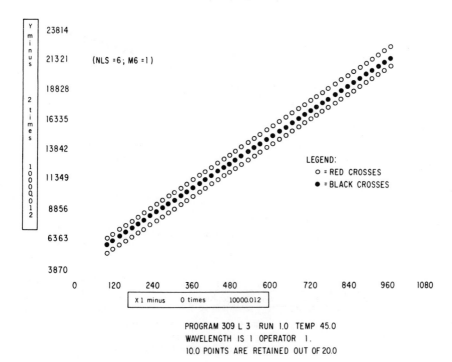

PROGRAM 309 L 3   RUN 1.0   TEMP 45.0
WAVELENGTH IS 1 OPERATOR 1.
10.0 POINTS ARE RETAINED OUT OF 20.0

FIGURE 9. *Autoplot* IX: The information used to obtain *autoplot* IX with the use of the IBM 1620 autoplotter system, *Autoplotter Program* 502 (*call word* BEEEE) and the IBM 836 *autoplotter* is described in the legend to *autoplot* VI except that here NLS = 6. The red crosses define the *maximum permitted errors* for the values of Y(I), which are denoted by black crosses. One autoplot is obtained for each wavelength for which data are processed. Similar autoplots were obtained with input information for FORTRAN Programs 9, 22–24, 309, or 322–324 and Programs 25, 27, 325, or 327, if JI = 20.

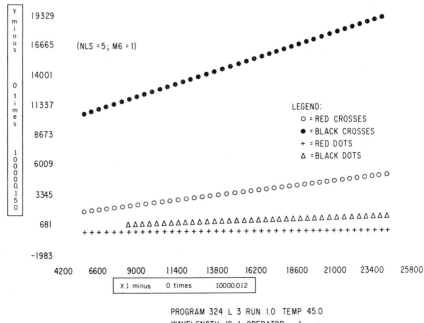

FIGURE 10. *Autoplot* X: This autoplot was obtained from input information for FORTRAN Program 324 (*call word* XAAAS) using the IBM 1620 *autoplotter system, Autoplotter Program* 502 (*call word* BEEEE) and the IBM 836 autoplotter. *Autoplotter input commands* are described in the legend to *autoplot* VIII except that here NQR = 324. M6, the number of wavelengths at which data were processed, was set equal to one. Black crosses, red crosses, black dots, and red dots denote X1(I), X2(I), X3(I), and X4(I) values on the vertical axis. If C(I) is the concentration of the first component, for a *homogeneous expansion,* or the second component, for a *heterogeneous expansion,* then: $X1(I) = C1(I)$; $X2(I) = (C(I))^2$; $X3(I) = (C(I))^3$, and $X4(I) = (C(I))^4$. Similar autoplots were obtained for each wavelength at which data were processed with input information for Programs 22–24 or 322–324 and Programs 25 and 325, if JI = 20. For NLS = 3 single autoplots are obtained with two curves for each wavelength. If NLS = 4 the autoplots have three curves (see *input commands* for Program 502).

AUTOPLOTTER PROGRAMS

27

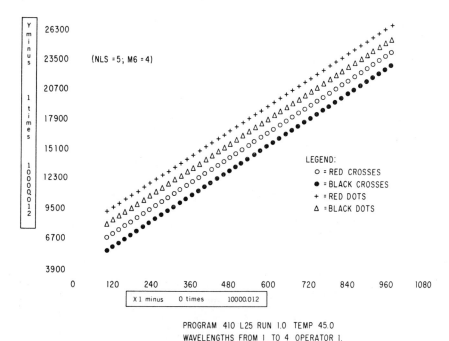

PROGRAM 410 L25 RUN 1.0 TEMP 45.0
WAVELENGTHS FROM 1 TO 4 OPERATOR 1.
10.0 POINTS ARE RETAINED OUT OF 20.0

FIGURE 11. *Autoplot* XI: Input information for FORTRAN Program 410 (*call word* JAASS), processed with the IBM 1620 *autoplotter system*, *Autoplotter Program* 503 (*call word* CEEEE) and the IBM 836 *autoplotter*, yielded *autoplot* XI. *Autoplotter input commands* are given in the legend to *autoplot* VIII except that here NQR = 410. M6 was set equal to four. Black crosses, red crosses, black dots, and red dots denote the first, second, third and fourth wavelengths respectively. Similar autoplots were obtained with input information for FORTRAN Programs 10, 11, 14, 28, 29, 310, 311, 314, 328, 329, 410, 411, and 414. For the *variable dimension programs* (28, 29, 328, and 329), JI must equal 20. With NLS equal to 3 and 4, there are a maximum of two and three curves respectively on each autoplot.

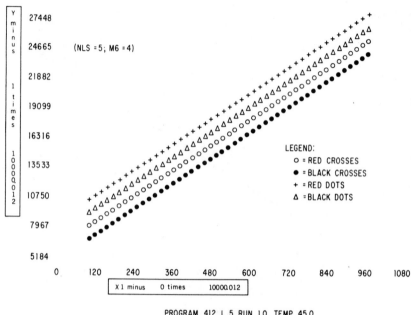

PROGRAM 412 L 5 RUN 1.0 TEMP 45.0
WAVELENGTHS FROM 1 TO 4 OPERATOR 1.
10.0 POINTS ARE RETAINED OUT OF 20.0

FIGURE 12. *Autoplot* XII: Input information for Program 412 (*call word* LAASS) was processed with the IBM 1620 autoplotter system, *Autoplotter Program* 504 (*call word* DEEEE) and the IBM 836 autoplotter to yield *autoplot* XII. *Autoplotter input commands* are described in the legend to *autoplot* VIII except that here NQR = 412. M6, the number of wavelengths at which data were processed, was set equal to four. Black crosses, red crosses, black dots, and red dots denote the first, second, third, and fourth wavelengths respectively. With NLS equal to 3 and 4 the maximum number of curves on each autoplot would be two and three respectively. Similar autoplots were obtained with input information for FORTRAN Programs 12, 13, 15, 312, 313, 315, 412, 413, and 415.

AUTOPLOTTER PROGRAM NUMBER 501

CALL WORD AEEEE

```
C  C   AUTOPLOTTERPROGRAM NUMBER 501(CALL WORD AEEEE)
300    FORMAT (I5,I5,I5,I5,I5,I5,I5,I5)
301    FORMAT (8HPROGRAM ,F5.1,4H  L ,I2,6H  RUN ,F4.1,7H  TEMP ,F4.1)
302    FORMAT (9HOPERATOR ,F9.0,13H INSTRUMENT ,I4,8H  WAVEL ,F6.1)
303    FORMAT (F4.1,28H POINTS ARE RETAINED OUT OF ,F4.1)
304    FORMAT (8HYMINUS ,I6,7HTIMES ,F12.3)
305    FORMAT (1HX,I1,7H MINUS ,I6,7H TIMES ,F12.3)
       DIMENSION Y(20,10),NY(20,6)
       READ,W,H,AM,WM,NLS,JI
       Q99=NLS
1      READ,PROGN,FEEDP
       NLS=Q99
       Y5M=0.0
       Y5N=0.0
       Y6M=0.0
       Y6N=0.0
       Y7M=0.0
       Y7N=0.0
       NPR=PROGN
       IF(NPR-100)2,2,3
3      NPR=NPR-300
2      IF(NPR-26)281,282,1
282    READ,KA,KB,KC,KD,KE,KF
       READ,JJ
       GO TO 283
281    READ,KA,KB,KC,KD
283    READ,J
       IF(NPR-4)284,284,280
280    NPR=4
284    DO 267 I=1,20
       DO 266 J=1,10
266    Y(I,J)=0.0
267    CONTINUE
       GO TO(256,257,258,259),NPR
256    IF(NLS-7)259,261,261
261    NLS=6
       GO TO 259
257    IF(NLS-8)259,262,262
262    NLS=7
       GO TO 259
258    IF(NLS-9)259,263,263
263    NLS=8
259    IF(NLS-9)264,264,265
265    NLS=9
264    READ,K,L,M
       READ,D1,D2,D3,D4
       READ,D1,D2,D3,D4
       GO TO (252,253,254,255),NPR
255    READ,D1,D2,D3,D4
254    READ,D1,D2,D3,D4
253    READ,D1,D2,D3,D4
252    NPR=2*NPR+2
       DO 4 I=1,JI,4
       DO 5 J=1,NPR
5      READ,Y(I,J),Y(I+1,J),Y(I+2,J),Y(I+3,J)
4      CONTINUE
       NPR=(NPR-2)/2
       KQ=KA+2
       IF(KQ-8)285,285,274
```

```
274     KQ=KQ-8
        IF(KQ-8)285,285,279
279     KQ=KQ-8
285     GO TO (6,7,8,9,10,275,276,277),KQ
277     DO 278 I=KD,KE
278     Y(I,1)=0.0
7       DO 11 I=KB,KC
11      Y(I,1)=0.0
        GO TO 6
276     Y(KF,1)=0.0
275     Y(KE,1)=0.0
10      Y(KD,1)=0.0
9       Y(KC,1)=0.0
8       Y(KB,1)=0.0
6       READ,G
        G1=20.0
        READ,OPER,INSTR
        READ,RUN,TEMP,WAVEL
        DO 12 I=1,20
        IF(Y(I,1))12,13,12
13      G1=G1-1.0
        DO 14 J=2,10
14      Y(I,J)=0.0
12      CONTINUE
        GO TO (15,15,16,17,18,19,19,19,19),NLS
15      DO 20 I=1,20
        Y(I,2)=Y(I,1)
20      Y(I,1)=Y(I,3)
        NQ=3
        GO TO 32
16      IF(NPR-1)1,22,21
22      NLS=2
        GO TO 15
21      DO 23 I=1,20
        Y(I,2)=Y(I,3)
23      Y(I,3)=Y(I,5)
        NQ=4
        GO TO 32
17      IF(NPR-2)24,24,25
24      NLS=3
        GO TO 16
25      DO 26 I=1,20
        Y(I,2)=Y(I,3)
        Y(I,3)=Y(I,5)
26      Y(I,4)=Y(I,7)
        NQ=5
        GO TO 32
18      IF(NPR-3)27,27,28
27      NLS=4
        GO TO 17
28      DO 29 I=1,20
        Y(I,2)=Y(I,3)
        Y(I,3)=Y(I,5)
        Y(I,4)=Y(I,7)
29      Y(I,5)=Y(I,9)
        NQ=6
32      DO 30 I=1,20
        DO 31 J=NQ,10
31      Y(I,J)=0.0
30      CONTINUE
        GO TO 35
19      DO 33 I=1,20
```

```
        Y(I,8)=Y(I,9)
        Y(I,6)=Y(I,5)
        Y(I,5)=Y(I,3)
        Y(I,3)=Y(I,1)+Y(I,2)
        Y(I,4)=Y(I,1)-Y(I,2)
        Y(I,2)=Y(I,1)
        Y(I,1)=Y(I,5)
        Y(I,5)=Y(I,6)
        Y(I,6)=Y(I,7)
33      Y(I,7)=Y(I,8)
        NQ=0
        GO TO (69,70,71,72),NPR
72      NQ=NQ+1
71      NQ=NQ+1
70      NQ=NQ+1
69      NQ=NQ+5
        GO TO 32
35      DO 36 I=1,20
        IF(Y(I,1))37,36,37
37      Y1M=Y(I,1)
        Y1N=Y(I,1)
        Y2M=Y(I,2)
        Y2N=Y(I,2)
        GO TO (36,38,39,40),NPR
40      Y7M=Y(I,7)
        Y7N=Y(I,7)
39      Y6M=Y(I,6)
        Y6N=Y(I,6)
38      Y5M=Y(I,5)
        Y5N=Y(I,5)
        GO TO 42
36      CONTINUE
42      DO 41 I=1,20
        IF(Y(I,1))425,41,425
425     IF(Y1M-Y(I,1))44,43,43
44      Y1M=Y(I,1)
43      IF(Y1N-Y(I,1))46,46,45
45      Y1N=Y(I,1)
46      MM=4
        IF(NLS-5)67,68,67
68      MM=5
67      DO 47 J=2,MM
        IF(Y(I,J))48,47,48
48      IF(Y2M-Y(I,J))49,50,50
49      Y2M=Y(I,J)
50      IF(Y2N-Y(I,J))47,47,51
51      Y2N=Y(I,J)
47      CONTINUE
41      CONTINUE
        IF(NLS-7)66,73,56
73      DO 52 I=1,20
        IF(Y(I,1))426,52,426
426     IF(Y5M-Y(I,5))53,54,54
53      Y5M=Y(I,5)
54      IF(Y5N-Y(I,5))52,52,55
55      Y5N=Y(I,5)
52      CONTINUE
        GO TO 66
56      IF(NLS-8)73,57,62
57      DO 58 I=1,20
        IF(Y(I,1))427,58,427
427     IF(Y6M-Y(I,6))59,60,60
```

```
59        Y6M=Y(I,6)
60        IF(Y6N-Y(I,6))58,58,61
61        Y6N=Y(I,6)
58        CONTINUE
          GO TO 73
62        DO 63 I=1,20
          IF(Y(I,1))428,63,428
428       IF(Y7M-Y(I,7))64,65,65
64        Y7M=Y(I,7)
65        IF(Y7N-Y(I,7))63,63,74
74        Y7N=Y(I,7)
63        CONTINUE
          GO TO 57
66        CONTINUE
          PD1=(Y1M-Y1N)*0.1
          Y1M=Y1M+PD1
          Y1N=Y1N-PD1
          PD2=(Y2M-Y2N)*0.1
          Y2M=Y2M+PD2
          Y2N=Y2N-PD2
          PD5=0.0
          PD6=0.0
          PD7=0.0
          IF(NLS-7)104,101,101
101       PD5=(Y5M-Y5N)*0.1
          Y5M=Y5M+PD5
          Y5N=Y5N-PD5
          IF(NLS-8)104,102,102
102       PD6=(Y6M-Y6N)*0.1
          Y6M=Y6M+PD6
          Y6N=Y6N-PD6
          IF(NLS-9)104,103,103
103       PD7=(Y7M-Y7N)*0.1
          Y7M=Y7M+PD7
          Y7N=Y7N-PD7
104       WA=W-AM
          N=WA/100.0
          WA=N*100
          HA=H-AM
          N=HA/100.0
          HA=N*100
          A=0.0
          B=0.0
          C=0.0
          D=0.0
          P1=100.0*(Y1M-Y1N)/WA
          IF(NLS-8)107,106,105
105       P7=100.0*(Y7M-Y7N)/WA
106       P6=100.0*(Y6M-Y6N)/WA
107       IF(NLS-7)109,108,108
108       P5=100.0*(Y5M-Y5N)/WA
109       DO 110 I=1,20
          PY=I
          IF(A)1,129,130
129       Q1=SQR(P1*P1)
          Q2=SQR(Y1N*Y1N)
          NQ2=Q2
          N1X=0
          O1=0.0
          O=O1
          YN=0.0
130       IF(NLS-8)113,112,111
```

```
111     IF(D)1,131,112
131     Q3=SQR(P7*P7)
        Q4=SQR(Y7N*Y7N)
        NQ4=Q4
        N7X=0
        07=0.0
112     IF(C)1,132,113
132     Q5=SQR(P6*P6)
        Q6=SQR(Y6N*Y6N)
        NQ6=Q6
        N6X=0
        06=0.0
113     IF(NLS-7)115,114,114
114     IF(B)1,221,115
221     Q7=SQR(P5*P5)
        Q8=SQR(Y5N*Y5N)
        NQ8=Q8
        N5X=0
        05=0.0
115     N9=0
        IF(NLS-6)273,273,272
272     NQ=NLS-6
        GO TO (269,270,271),NQ
269     N9=N9+1
270     N9=N9+1
271     N9=N9+1
273     IF(A)1,133,117
133     DO 116 J=1,10000
        IF(NQ2-J)117,118,116
118     NN1=J
        01=J
        0=01
        Q2=Q2-01
        YN=Y1N
        GO TO 117
116     CONTINUE
117     IF(N9-1)128,222,122
222     IF(D)1,134,122
134     DO 119 J=1,10000
        IF(NQ4-J)122,120,119
120     NN7=J
        07=J
        Q4=Q4-07
        GO TO 121
119     CONTINUE
122     IF(N9-2)121,121,125
121     IF(C)1,135,125
135     DO 123 J=1,10000
        IF(NQ6-J)125,124,123
124     NN6=J
        06=J
        Q6=Q6-06
        GO TO 125
123     CONTINUE
125     IF(B)1,136,128
136     DO 126 J=1,10000
        IF(NQ8-J)128,127,126
127     NN5=J
        05=J
        Q8=Q8-05
        GO TO 128
126     CONTINUE
```

```
128     N10=0
        N13=1
        N11=NLS-5
146     IF(A)1,137,138
138     IF(N9-1)163,139,141
139     IF(D)1,140,141
140     Q1=Q3
        Q2=Q4
        O=O7
        YN=Y7N
        N13=4
        GO TO 137
141     IF(N9-2)142,142,144
142     IF(C)1,143,144
143     Q1=Q5
        Q2=Q6
        O=O6
        YN=Y6N
        N13=3
        GO TO 137
144     IF(B)1,145,163
145     Q1=Q7
        Q2=Q8
        O=O5
        YN=Y5N
        N13=2
137     N10=N10+1
        IF(Q1-Q2)147,147,148
147     Q=Q2*(10.0**PY)
        GO TO 149
148     Q=Q1*(10.0**PY)
149     IF(WM-Q)150,150,151
151     IF(N9-1)110,152,153
152     IF(N10-4)146,110,110
153     IF(N9-2)110,154,155
154     IF(N10-3)146,110,110
155     IF(N10-2)146,110,110
150     IF(YN)156,157,157
156     QR=YN+O
        O=-O
        GO TO 158
157     QR=YN-O
158     GO TO (159,160,161,162),N13
159     N1A=QR*(10.0**PY)
        N1D=P1*(10.0**PY)
        N1P=WA/100.0+1.0
        SF1=10.0**PY
        NN1=0
        A=1.0
        GO TO 146
160     N5A=QR*(10.0**PY)
        N5D=P5*(10.0**PY)
        N5P=WA/100.0+1.0
        SF5=10.0**PY
        NN5=0
        B=1.0
        GO TO 146
161     N6A=QR*(10.0**PY)
        N6D=P6*(10.0**PY)
        N6P=WA/100.0+1.0
        SF6=10.0**PY
        NN6=0
```

```
        C=1.0
        GO TO 146
162     N7A=QR*(10.0**PY)
        N7D=P7*(10.0**PY)
        N7P=WA/100.0+1.0
        SF7=10.0**PY
        NN7=0
        D=1.0
        GO TO 146
110     CONTINUE
163     P2=100.0*(Y2M-Y2N)/HA
        DO 164 I=1,20
        PX=I
        Q1=SQR(P2*P2)
        Q2=SQR(Y2N*Y2N)
        NQ2=Q2
        NN2=0
        O=0.0
        DO 165 J=1,10000
        IF(NQ2-J)166,167,165
167     NN2=J
        O=J
        Q2=Q2-0
        GO TO 166
165     CONTINUE
166     IF(Q1-Q2)168,168,169
168     Q=Q2*(10.0**PX)
        GO TO 170
169     Q=Q1*(10.0**PX)
170     IF(WM-Q)171,171,164
171     IF(Y2N)172,173,173
172     QR=Y2N+0
        NN2=-0
        GO TO 174
173     QR=Y2N-0
174     N2A=QR*(10.0**PX)
        N2D=P2*(10.0**PX)
        N2P=HA/100.0+1.0
        SF2=10.0**PX
        GO TO 175
164     CONTINUE
175     IF(PD1)176,177,176
177     PD1=1.0/Y1M
        GO TO 178
176     PD1=1.0/PD1
178     IF(PD2)179,180,179
180     PD2=1.0/Y2M
        GO TO 181
179     PD2=1.0/PD2
181     IF(N9-1)192,182,185
182     IF(PD7)183,184,183
184     PD7=1.0/Y7M
        GO TO 185
183     PD7=1.0/PD7
185     IF(N9-2)186,186,189
186     IF(PD6)187,188,187
188     PD6=1.0/Y6M
        GO TO 189
187     PD6=1.0/PD6
189     IF(PD5)190,191,190
191     PD5=1.0/Y5M
        GO TO 192
```

```
190    PD5=1.0/PD5
192      DO 193 I=1,20
         IF(Y(I,2))194,193,194
194      Y(I,1)=Y(I,1)*PD1
         Y(I,2)=Y(I,2)*PD2
         Y(I,3)=Y(I,3)*PD2
         Y(I,4)=Y(I,4)*PD2
         IF(NLS-5)193,195,196
195      Y(I,5)=Y(I,5)*PD2
         GO TO 193
196      Y(I,5)=Y(I,5)*PD5
         Y(I,6)=Y(I,6)*PD6
         Y(I,7)=Y(I,7)*PD7
193      CONTINUE
         Y1M=Y1M*PD1
         Y1N=Y1N*PD1
         Y2N=Y2N*PD2
         Y2M=Y2M*PD2
         Y5M=Y5M*PD5
         Y5N=Y5N*PD5
         Y6M=Y6M*PD6
         Y6N=Y6N*PD6
         Y7M=Y7M*PD7
         Y7N=Y7N*PD7
         D1=(Y1M-Y1N)/WA
         IF(NLS-7)198,197,197
197      D5=(Y5M-Y5N)/WA
         D6=(Y6M-Y6N)/WA
         D7=(Y7M-Y7N)/WA
198      D2=(Y2M-Y2N)/HA
         IF(D1)199,200,199
200      D1=Y1M/WA
199      IF(NLS-6)206,206,201
201      IF(D5)202,203,202
203      D5=Y5M/WA
202      IF(D6)204,205,204
205      D6=Y6M/WA
204      IF(D7)206,207,206
207      D7=Y7M/WA
206      IF(D2)208,209,208
209      D2=Y2M/HA
208      DO 210 I=1,20
         IF(Y(I,1))211,210,211
211      NY(I,1)=(Y(I,1)-Y1N)/D1
         NY(I,2)=(Y(I,2)-Y2N)/D2
         IF(NLS-6)212,212,210
212      GO TO (210,210,214,215,216,215),NLS
216      NY(I,5)=(Y(I,5)-Y2N)/D2
215      NY(I,4)=(Y(I,4)-Y2N)/D2
214      NY(I,3)=(Y(I,3)-Y2N)/D2
210      CONTINUE
         NQR=1
         N12=0
         N11=NLS-4
249      N11=N11-1
213      IF(N12)223,223,224
224      IF(N11)1,1,225
225      DO 251 I=1,20
         IF(Y(I,1))217,251,217
217      GO TO (218,219,220,1),N12
220      NY(I,1)=(Y(I,7)-Y7N)/D7
         NN1=NN7
```

```
          SF1=SF7
          N1P=N7P
          N1A=N7A
          N1D=N7D
          NQR=4
          GO TO 251
219       NY(I,1)=(Y(I,6)-Y6N)/D6
          NN1=NN6
          SF1=SF6
          N1P=N6P
          N1A=N6A
          N1D=N6D
          NQR=3
          GO TO 251
218       NY(I,1)=(Y(I,5)-Y5N)/D5
          NN1=NN5
          SF1=SF5
          N1P=N5P
          N1A=N5A
          N1D=N5D
          NQR=2
251       CONTINUE
223       NH=H
          NW=W
          M=AM
          PUNCH 300,1,NW,NH,M,M,0,0
          IF(NLS-6)226,227,227
226       GO TO (228,229,230,231,232),NLS
228       PUNCH 300,2,01,00
233       DO 234 I=1,20
          IF(Y(I,1))235,234,235
235       PUNCH 300,3,NY(I,1),NY(I,2)
234       CONTINUE
          GO TO 244
229       PUNCH 300,2,31,00
          GO TO 233
230       PUNCH 300,2,42,00,01
236       DO 237 I=1,20
          IF(Y(I,1))238,237,238
238       PUNCH 300,3,NY(I,1),NY(I,2),NY(I,3)
237       CONTINUE
          GO TO 244
231       PUNCH 300,2,43,00,01,10
239       DO 240 I=1,20
          IF(Y(I,1))241,240,241
241       PUNCH 300,3,NY(I,1),NY(I,2),NY(I,3),NY(I,4)
240       CONTINUE
          GO TO 244
232       PUNCH 300,2,44,00,01,10,11
          DO 242 I=1,20
          IF(Y(I,1))243,242,243
243       PUNCH 300,3,NY(I,1),NY(I,2),NY(I,3),NY(I,4),NY(I,5)
242       CONTINUE
          GO TO 244
227       PUNCH 300,2,33,00,01,01
          GO TO 239
244       NXL=-50
          PUNCH 300,4,155,NXL,01
          IF(NLS-7)245,246,246
245       GO TO (246,246,247,247,247,246),NLS
246       PUNCH 305,NQR,NN1,SF1
          NXL=-100
```

```
          PUNCH 300,4,NXL,800,11
          PUNCH 304,NN2,SF2
          GO TO 248
247       PUNCH 304,NN1,SF1
          NXL=-100
          PUNCH 300,4,NXL,800,11
          PUNCH 305,NQR,NN2,SF2
248       NL=-100
          PUNCH 300,4,155,NL,00
          PUNCH 301,PROGN,L,RUN,TEMP
          NL=-125
          PUNCH 300,4,155,NL,00
          PUNCH 302,OPER,INSTR,WAVEL
          NL=-150
          PUNCH 300,4,155,NL,00
          PUNCH 303,G1,G
          NS1=-25
          NS2=0
          PUNCH 300,5,NS2,NS1,N1P,N1A,N1D,00
          PUNCH 300,5,NS1,NS2,N2P,N2A,N2D,10
          PUNCH300,6
          IF(N11)1,1,250
250       N12=N12+1
          GO TO 249
          END
```

ALGOL 60 FOR PROGRAM NUMBER 501

PROCEDURE AEEEE(w,h,am,wm,nLs,ji,progn,feedp); ARRAY y[1:20,1:10],
ny[1:20,1:6]; REAL w,h,am,wm; INTEGER nLs,ji,progn,feedp; SWITCH
sw1:=x3,x4,x5,x6; SWITCH sw2:=x10,x9,x8,x7; SWITCH sw3:=x19,x13,x18,x17,
x16,x15,x14,x12; SWITCH sw4:=x20,x20,x21,x22,x23,x24,x24,x24,x24; SWITCH
sw5:=x28,x27,x26,x25; SWITCH sw6:=x33,x32,x31,x30; SWITCH sw7:=x48,x49,
x50; SWITCH sw8:=x67,x68,x69,x70; SWITCH sw9:=x89,x89,x88,x87,x86,x87;
SWITCH sw10:=x93,x92,x91,w9; SWITCH sw11:=x96,x98,x99,w1,w3; SWITCH
sw12:=w6,w6,w7,w7,w7,w6;

    BEGIN INTEGER k,ka,kb,kc,kd,ke,kf,kq,i,j,jj,L,m,n,nq,nq2,nq4,nq6,nq8,nqr,
n1x,n6x,n7x,n8x,n9,n10,n11,n12,n13,nn1,nn2,nn5,nn6,nn7,n1a,n1d,n1p,n5a,
n5d,n5p,n6a,n6d,n6p,n7a,n7d,n7p,npr,oper,instr,run; REAL q,qr,q1,q2,q3,
q4,q5,q6,q7,q8,q99,O,o1,o5,o6,o7,o8,d1,d2,d3,d4,d5,d6,d7,a,b,c,d,ha,wa,yn,
y1n,y1m,y2n,y2m,y5n,y5m,y6n,y6m,y7n,y7m,p1,p5,p6,p7,px,py,pd1,pd2,pd5,
pd6,pd7,sf1,sf5,sf6,sf7,temp,waveL;

X1:   nLs:=q99;
      y5m:=y5n:=y6m:=y6n:=y7m:=y7n:=0;
      npr:=progn;
      IF npr>100 THEN npr:=npr−300;
      IF npr>26 THEN GO TO W9
      ELSE IF npr=26 THEN
      BEGIN
         READ ka,kb,kc,kd,ke,kf;
         READ jj; GO TO X2END;
      READ ka,kb,kc,kd;
X2:   READ j;
      IF npr>4 THEN npr:=4;
      FOR i:=1 STEP 1 UNTIL 20 DO
      FOR j:=1 STEP 1 UNTIL 20 DO y[i,j]=0;
      GO TO sw1[npr];
X3:   IF nLs<7 THEN GO TO X6;
      nLs:=6; GO TO X6;
X4:   IF nLs<8 THEN GO TO X6;
      nLs:=7; GO TO X6;
X5:   IF nLs≥9 THEN nLs:=8;
X6:   IF nLs>9 THEN nLs:=9;
      READ k,L,m;
      READ d1,d2,d3,d4;
      READ d1,d2,d3,d4;
      GO TO sw2[npr];
X7:   READ d1,d2,d3,d4;
X8:   READ d1,d2,d3,d4;
X9:   READ d1,d2,d3,d4;
X10:   npr:=2Xnpr+2;
      FOR i:=1 STEP 1 UNTIL ji DO
      FOR j:=1 STEP 1 UNTIL npr DO READ y[i,j];
      npr:=(npr−2)/2;
      kq:=ka+2;
      IF kq≤8 THEN GO TO X11;
      kq:=kq−8;
      IF kq>8 THEN kq:=kq−8;

```
X11:   GO TO sw3[kq];
X12:   FOR i:=kd STEP 1 UNTIL ke DO y[i,1]:=0;
X13:   FOR i:=kb STEP 1 UNTIL kc DO y[i,1]:=0;
       GO TO X19;
X14:   y[kf,1]:=0;
X15:   y[ke,1]:=0;
X16:   y[kd,1]:=0;
X17:   y[kc,1]:=0;
X18:   y[kb,1]:=0;
X19:   READ g; g1:=20;
       READ oper,instr;
       READ run,temp,waveL;
       FOR i:=1 STEP 1 UNTIL 20 DO
       BEGIN
          IF y[i,1]=0 THEN
          BEGIN
             g1:=g1-1;
             FOR j:=2 STEP 1 UNTIL 10 DO y[i,j]:=0END
       END;
       GO TO sw4[nLs];
X20:   FOR i:=1 STEP 1 UNTIL 20 DO
       BEGIN
          y[i,2]:=y[i,1]; y[i,1]:=y[i,3]
       END;
       nq:=3; GO TO X24;
X21:   IF npr< 1 THEN GO TO W9;
       ELSE IF npr=1 THEN
       BEGIN
          nLs:=2; GO TO X20END;
       FOR i:=1 STEP 1 UNTIL 20 DO
       BEGIN
          y[i,2]:=y[i,3]; y[i,3]:=y[i,5]
       END;
       nq:=4; GO TO X24;
X22:   IF npr< 2 THEN
       BEGIN
          nLs:=3; GO TO X21END;
       FOR i:=1 STEP 1 UNTIL 20 DO
       BEGIN
          y[i,2]:=y[i,3]; y[i,3]:=y[i,5];
          y[i,4]:=y[i,7]
       END;
       nq:=5; GO TO X24;
X23:   IF npr≤ 3 THEN
       BEGIN
          nLs:=4; GO TO X22END;
       FOR i:=1 STEP 1 UNTIL 20 DO
       BEGIN
          y[i,2]:=y[i,3]; y[i,3]:=y[i,5];
          y[i,4]:=y[i,7]; y[i,5]:=y[i,9]
       END;
       nq:=6;
X24:   FOR i:=1 STEP 1 UNTIL 20 DO
```

```
        FOR j:=nq STEP 1 UNTIL 10 DO y[i,j]:=0;
        GO TO X29;
        FOR i:=1 STEP 1 UNTIL 20 DO
        BEGIN
            y[i,8]:=y[i,9];  y[i,6]:=y[i,5];
            y[i,5]:=y[i,3];  y[i,3]:=y[i,1]+y[i,2];
            y[i,4]:=y[i,1]-y[i,2];  y[i,2]:=y[i,1];
            y[i,1]:=y[i,5];  y[i,5]:=y[i,6];
            y[i,6]:=y[i,7];  y[i,7]:=y[i,8]
        END;
        nq:=0;
        GO TO sw5[npr];
X25:    nq:=nq+1;
X26:    nq:=nq+1;
X27:    nq:=nq+1;
X28:    nq:=nq+5;  GO TO X24;
X29:    FOR i:=1 STEP 1 UNTIL 20 DO
        BEGIN
            IF y[i,1]=0 THEN GO TO X33;
            y1m:=y[i,1];  y2m:=y[i,2];
            y1n:=y[i,1];  y2n:=y[i,2];
            GO TO sw6[npr];
X30:        y7m:=y[i,7];  y7n:=y[i,7];
X31:        y6m:=y[i,6];  y6n:=y[i,6];
X32:        y5m:=y[i,5];  y5n:=y[i,5];  GO TO X34
X33:    END;
X34:    FOR i:=1 STEP 1 UNTIL 20 DO
        BEGIN
            IF y[i,1]=0 THEN GO TO X36;
            IF y1m<y[i,1] THEN y1m:=y[i,1];
            IF y1n>y[i,1] THEN y1n:=y[i,1];
            mm:=4;
            IF nLs=5 THEN mm:=5;
            FOR j:=2 STEP 1 UNTIL mm DO
            BEGIN
                IF y[i,j]=0 THEN GO TO X35;
                IF y2m<y[i,j] THEN y2m:=y[i,j];
                IF y2n>y[i,j] THEN y2n:=y[i,j]
X35:        END
X36:    END;
        IF nLs< 7 THEN GO TO X44
        ELSE IF nLs>7 THEN GO TO X39;
X37:    FOR i:=1 STEP 1 UNTIL 20 DO
        BEGIN
            IF y[i,1]=0 THEN GO TO X38;
            IF y5m<y[i,5] THEN y5m:=y[i,5];
            IF y5n>y[i,5] THEN y5n:=y[i,5]
X38:    END;
        GO TO X44;
X39:    IF nLs< 8 THEN GO TO X37
        ELSE IF nLs>8 THEN GO TO X42;
X40:    FOR i:=1 STEP 1 UNTIL 20 DO
        BEGIN
```

```
              IF y[i,1]=0 THEN GO TO X41;
              IF y6m<y[i,6] THEN y6m:=y[i,6];
              IF y6n>y[i,6] THEN y6n:=y[i,6]
X41:  END;
      GO TO X37;
X42:  FOR i:=1 STEP 1 UNTIL 20 DO
      BEGIN
              IF y[i,1]=0 THEN GO TO X44;
              IF y7m<y[i,7] THEN y7m:=y[i,7];
              IF y7n>y[i,7] THEN y7n:=y[i,7]
X43:  END;
      GO TO X40
X44:  pd1:=(y1m−y1n)X0.1;
      y1m:=y1m+pd1;  y1n:=y1n−pd1;
      pd2:=(y2m−y2n)X0.1;
      y2m:=y2m+pd2;  y2n:=y2n−pd2;
      pd5:=pd6:=pd7:=0
      IF nLs< 7 THEN GO TO X45;
      pd5:=(y5m−y5n)X0.1;
      y5m:=y5m+pd5;
      y5n:=y5n−pd5;
      IF nLs< 8 THEN GO TO X45;
      pd6:=(y6m−y6n)X0.1;
      y6m:=y6m+pd6;
      y6n:=y6n−pd6
      IF nLs< 9 THEN GO TO X45;
      pd7:=(y7m−y7n)X0.1;
      y7m:=y7m+pd7;
      y7n:=y7n−pd7;
X45:  wa:=w−am;
      n:=wa/100;  wa:=nX100;  ha:=h−am;
      n:=ha/100;  ha=nX100;
      a:=b:=c:=d:=0;
      p1:=100X(y1m−y1n)/wa;
      IF nLs< 8 THEN GO TO X46
      ELSE IF nLs>8 THEN p7:=100X(y7m−y7n)/wa;
      p6:=100X(y6m−y6n)/wa;
X46:  IF nLs≥ 7 THEN p5:=100X(y5m−y5n)/wa;
      FOR i:=1 STEP 1 UNTIL 20 DO
      BEGIN
        py:=i
        IF a<0 THEN GO TO W9
        ELSE IF a=0 THEN
        BEGIN
          q1:=abs(p1);  q2:=abs(y1n);
          nq2:=q2;  yn:=n1x:=o1:=0;  O:=o1END;
        IF nLs< 8 THEN GO TO X47
        ELSE IF nLs>8 THEN
        BEGIN
          IF d<0 THEN GO TO W9
          ELSE IF d=0 THEN
          BEGIN
            q3:=abs(p7);  q4:=abs(y7n);
```

```
            nq4:=q4;  nX7:=o7:=0END END;
        IF c< 0 THEN GO TO W9
        ELSE IF c=0 THEN
        BEGIN
            q5:=abs(p6);  q6:=abs(y6n);
            nq6:=q6;  n6x:=o6:=0END
X47:    IF nLs≥7∧b< 0 THEN GO TO W9
        ELSE IF nLs≥ 7∧b=0 THEN
        BEGIN
            q7:=abs(p5);  q8:=abs(y5n);
            nq8:=q8;  n5x:=o5:=0END;
        n9:=0;
        IF nLs≤6 THEN GO TO X51;
        nq:=nLs − 6;
        GO TO sw7[nq];
X48:    n9:=n9+1;
X49:    n9:=n9+1;
X50:    n9:=n9+1;
X51:    IF a< 0 THEN GO TO W9
        ELSE IF a=0 THEN
        BEGIN
            FOR j:=1 STEP 1 UNTIL 10000 DO
            BEGIN
                IF nq2>j THEN GO TO X52
                ELSE IF nq2< j THEN GO TO X53;
                nn1:=o1:=j;  O:=o1;  q2:=q2−o1;
                yn:=y1n;  GO TO X53
X52:        END END;
X53:    IF n9< 1 THEN GO TO X57
        ELSE IF n9>1 THEN GO TO X54;
        IF d< 0 THEN GO TO W9
        ELSE IF d>0 THEN GO TO X54;
        FOR j:=1 STEP 1 UNTIL 10000 DO
        BEGIN
            IF nq4< j THEN GO TO X54 ELSE IF nq4=j THEN
            BEGIN
                nn7:=o7:=j;  q4:=q4−o7;  GO TO X55END
        END;
X54:    IF n9>2 THEN GO TO X56;
X55:    IF c< 0 THEN GO TO W9
        ELSE IF c>0 THEN GO TO X56;
        FOR j:=1 STEP 1 UNTIL 10000 DO
        BEGIN
            IF nq6< j THEN GO TO X56 ELSE IF nq6=j THEN
            BEGIN
                nn6:=o6:=j;  q6:=q6−o6;  GO TO X56END
        END;
X56:    IF b< 0 THEN GO TO W9
        ELSE IF b=0 THEN
        FOR j:=1 STEP 1 UNTIL 10000 DO
        BEGIN
            IF nq8< j THEN GO TO X57 ELSE IF nq8=j THEN
            BEGIN
```

```
              nn5:=o5:=j;  a8:=q8-o5;  GO TO X57END
          END;
X57:      n10:=0;  n13:=1;  n11:=nLs-5;
X58:      IF a<0 THEN GO TO W9 ELSE IF a=0 THEN GO TO X61;
          IF n9<1 THEN GO TO X72 ELSE IF n9>1 THEN GO TO X59;
          IF d<0 THEN GO TO W9 ELSE IF d=0 THEN
          BEGIN
              q1:=q3;  q2:=q4;  O:=o7;  yn:=y7n;
              n13:=4;  GO TO X61END;
X59:      IF n9>2 THEN GO TO X60;
          IF c<0 THEN GO TO W9 ELSE IF c=0 THEN
          BEGIN
              q1:=q5;  q2:=q6;  O:=o6;  yn:=y6n;
              n13:=3;  GO TO X61END;
X60:      IF b<0 THEN GO TO W9 ELSE IF b>0 THEN GO TO X72;
          q1:=q7;  q2:=q8;  O:=o5;  yn:=y5n;
          n13:=2;
X61:      n10:=n10+1;
          IF q1≤q2 THEN
          BEGIN
              q:=q2X(10↑py);  GO TO X62END;
          q:=q1X(10↑py);
X62:      IF wn≤q THEN GO TO X65;
          IF n9<1 THEN GO TO X71 ELSE IF n9>1 THEN GO TO X63;
          IF n10<4 THEN GO TO X58 ELSE GO TO X71;
X63:      IF n9<2 THEN GO TO X71 ELSE IF n9>2 THEN GO TO X64;
          IF n10<3 THEN GO TO X58 ELSE GO TO X71;
X64:      IF n10<2 THEN GO TO X58 ELSE GO TO X71;
X65:      IF yn<0 THEN
          BEGIN
              qr:=yn+O;  O:=-O;  GO TO X66END;
          qr:=yn-O;
X66:      GO TO sw8(n13);
X67:      n1a:=qrX(10↑py);  n1d:=p1X(10↑py);
          n1p:=wa/100+1;  sf1:=10↑py
          nn1:=0;  a:=1;  GO TO X58;
X68:      n5a:=qrX(10↑py);  n5d:=p5X(10↑py);
          n5p:=wa/100+1;  sf5:=10↑py;
          nn5:=0;  b:=1;  GO TO X58;
X69:      n6a:=qrX(10↑py);  n6d:=p6X(10↑py);
          n6p:=wa/100+1;  sf6:=10↑py;
          nn6:=0;  c:=1;  GO TO X58;
X70:      n7a:=qrX(10↑py);  n7d:=p7X(10↑py);
          n7p:=wa/100+1;  sf7:=10↑py;
          nn7:=0;  d:=1;  GO TO X58
X71:      END;
X72:      p2:=100X(y2m-y2n)/ha;
          FOR i:=1 STEP 1 UNTIL 20 DO
          BEGIN
              px:=i;
              q1:=abs(p2);  q2:=abs(y2n);
              nq2:=q2;  nn2:=O:=0;
              FOR j:=1 STEP 1 UNTIL 10000 DO
```

```
        BEGIN
          IF nq2<j THEN GO TO X74 ELSE IF nq2>j THEN
            GO TO X73;
          nn2:=O:=j; q2:=q2−O; GO TO X74
X73:    END;
X74:    IF q1≤q2 THEN
        BEGIN
          q:=q2X(10ᵗpx); GO TO X75END;
        q:=q1X(10ᵗpx);
X75:    IF wm>q THEN GO TO X77;
        IF y2n<0 THEN
        BEGIN
          qr:=y2n+O; nn2:=−O; GO TO X76END;
        qr:=y2n−O;
X76:    n2a:=qrX(10ᵗpx); n2d:=p2X(10ᵗpx);
        n2p:=ha/100+1; sf2:=10ᵗpx;
        GO TO X78
X77:    END;
X78:    IF pd1=0 THEN
        BEGIN
          pd1:=1/y1m; GO TO X79END;
        pd1:=1/pd1;
X79:    IF pd2=0 THEN
        BEGIN
          pd2:=1/y2m; GO TO X80END;
        pd2:=1/pd2;
X80:    IF n9<1 THEN GO TO X83;
        ELSE IF n9=1 THEN
        BEGIN
          IF pd7=0 THEN
          BEGIN
            pd7:=1/y7m; GO TO X81END;
          pd7:=1/pd7END;
X81:    IF (n9≤2)∧pd6=0 THEN
        BEGIN
          pd6:=1/y6m; GO TO X82END;
        IF (n9≤2)∧pd6≠0 THEN pd6:=1/pd6;
X82:    IF pd5=0 THEN
        BEGIN
          pd5:=1/y5m; GO TO X83END;
        pd5:=1/pd5;
X83:    FOR i:=1 STEP 1 UNTIL 20 DO
        BEGIN
          IF y[i,2]=0 THEN GO TO X84;
          y[i,1]:=y[i,1]Xpd1; y[i,2]:=y[i,2]Xpd2;
          y[i,3]:=y[i,3]Xpd2; y[i,4]:=y[i,4]Xpd2;
          IF nLs<5 THEN GO TO X84
          ELSE IF nLs=5 THEN
          BEGIN
            y[i,5]:=y[i,5]Xpd2; GO TO X84END;
          y[i,5]:=y[i,5]Xpd5; y[i,6]:=y[i,6]Xpd6;
          y[i,7]:=y[i,7]Xpd7
X84:    END;
```

```
        y1m:=y1mXpd1;  y1n:=y1nXpd1;
        y2m:=y2mXpd2;  y2n:=y2nXpd2;
        y5m:=y5mXpd5;  y5n:=y5nXpd5;
        y6m:=y6mXpd6;  y6n:=y6nXpd6;
        y7m:=y7mXpd7;  y7n:=y7nXpd7;
        d1:=(y1m−y1n)/wa;
        IF nLs≥7 THEN
        BEGIN
           d5:=(y5m−y5n)/wa;  d6:=(y6m−y6n)/wa;
           d7:=(y7m−y7n)/waEND;
        d2:=(y2m−y2n)/ha;
        IF d1=0 THEN d1:=y1m/wa;
        IF nLs≤6 THEN GO TO X85;
        IF d5=0 THEN d5:=y5m/wa;
        IF d6=0 THEN d6:=y6m/wa;
        IF d7=0 THEN d7:=y7m/wa;
X85:    IF d2=0 THEN d2:=y2m/ha;
        FOR i:=1 STEP 1 UNTIL 20 DO
        BEGIN
           IF y[i,2]=0 THEN GO TO X89;
           ny[i,1]:=(y[i,1]−y1n)/d1;
           ny[i,2]:=(y[i,2]−y2n)/d2;
           IF nLs>6 THEN GO TO X89;
           GO TO sw9[nLs];
X86:       ny[i,5]:=(y[i,5]−y2n)/d2;
X87:       ny[i,4]:=(y[i,4]−y2n)/d2;
X88:       ny[i,3]:=(y[i,3]−y2n)/d2;
X89:    END;
        nqr:=1;  n12:=0;  n11:=nLs−4;
X90:    n11:=n11−1;
        IF n12≤0 THEN GO TO X95;
        IF n11≤0 THEN GO TO W9;
        FOR i:=1 STEP 1 UNTIL 20 DO
        BEGIN
           IF y[i,1]=0 THEN GO TO X94;
           GO TO sw10[n12];
X91:       ny[i,1]:=(y[i,7]−y7n)/d7;
           nn1:=nn7; sf1:=sf7; n1p:=n7p;
           n1a:=n7a; n1d:=n7d; nqr:=4;
           GO TO X94;
X92:       ny[i,1]:=(y[i,6]−y6n)/d6;
           nn1:=nn6; sf1:=sf6; n1p:=n6p;
           n1a:=n6a; n1d:=n6d; nqr:=3;
           GO TO X94;
X93:       ny[i,1]:=(y[i,5]−y5n)/d5;
           nn1:=nn5; sf1:=sf5; n1p:=n5p;
           n1a:=n5a; n1d:=n5d; nqr:=2
X94:    END;
X95:    nh:=h; nw:=w; m:=am;
        PUNCH 1,nw,nh,m,m,0,0;
        IF nLs≥6 THEN GO TO W4;
        GO TO sw11[nLs];
X96:    PUNCH 2,1,0;
```

```
X97:   FOR i:=1 STEP 1 UNTIL 20 DO
       IF y[i,1]≠0 THEN PUNCH 3,ny[i,1],ny[i,2];
       GO TO W5;
X98:   PUNCH 2,31,0;
       GO TO X97;
X99:   PUNCH 2,42,0,1;
       FOR i:=1 STEP 1 UNTIL 20 DO
       IF y[i,1]≠0 THEN PUNCH 3,ny[i,2],ny[i,3];
       GO TO W5;
W1:    PUNCH 2,43,0,1,10;
W2:    FOR i:=1 STEP 1 UNTIL 20 DO
       IF y[i,1]≠0 THEN PUNCH 3,ny[i,1],ny[i,2],ny[i,3],ny[i,4];
       GO TO W5;
W3:    PUNCH 2,44,0,1,10,11;
       FOR i:=1 STEP 1 UNTIL 20 DO
       IF y[i,1]≠0 THEN PUNCH 3,ny[i,1],ny[i,2],ny[i,3],ny[i,4],ny[i,5];
       GO TO W5;
W4:    PUNCH 2,33,0,1,1;
       GO TO W2;
W5:    nxL:=-50;
       PUNCH 4,155,nxL,1;
       IF nLs<7 THEN GO TO sw12[nLs];
W6:    PUNCH nqr,nn1,sf1;
       nxL:=-100;
       PUNCH 4,nxL,800,11;
       PUNCH nn2,sf2;
       GO TO W8;
W7:    PUNCH nn1,sf1;
       nxL:=-100;
       PUNCH 4,nxL,800,11;
       PUNCH nqr,nn2,sf2;
W8:    nL:=-100;
       PUNCH 4,155,nL,0;
       PUNCH progn,L,run,temp;
       nL:=-125
       PUNCH 4,155,nL,0;
       PUNCH oper,instr,waveL;
       nL:=-150;
       PUNCH 4,155,nL,0;
       PUNCH g1,g;
       ns1:=-25; ns2:=0;
       PUNCH 5,ns2,ns1,n1p,n1a,n1d,0;
       PUNCH 5,ns1,ns2,n2p,n2a,n2d,10;
       PUNCH 6;
       IF n11≤0 THEN GO TO W9;
       n12:=n12+1;
       GO TO X90;
W9:    END(AEEEE);
W10:   READ w,h,am,wm,nLs,ji; q99:=nLs;
W11:   READ progn,feedp;
       PROCEDURE(w,h,am,wm,nLs,ji,progn,feedp);
       GO TO W11;
```

AUTOPLOTTER PROGRAM NUMBER 502

CALL WORD BEEEE

```
C   C   AUTOPLOTTER PROGRAM NUMBER 502(CALL WORD BEEEE)
300     FORMAT (15,15,15,15,15,15,15,15)
301     FORMAT (8HPROGRAM ,13,4H L ,12,6H  RUN ,F5.1,7H  TEMP ,F4.1)
302     FORMAT (14HWAVELENGTH IS ,12,11H  OPERATOR ,F9.0)
303     FORMAT (F4.1,28H POINTS ARE RETAINED OUT OF ,F4.1)
304     FORMAT (8HYMINUS ,16,7H TIMES ,F12.3)
305     FORMAT (9HX1 MINUS ,16,7H TIMES ,F12.3)
306     FORMAT (17HWAVELENGTHS FROM ,12,4H TO ,12,11H  OPERATOR ,F9.0)
        DIMENSION Y(20,10),NY(20,5),AI1(5),WAC(5)
        READ,W,H,AM,WM,NLS
        Q99=NLS
1       READ,NQR
        NNR=NQR
        M4=0
        NPR=NQR
        IF(NQR-300)2,3,3
3       NPR=NQR-300
2       IF(NPR-9)1,4,5
5       NPR=NPR-12
4      NPR=NPR-8
        IF(NPR-1)1,6,7
6       READ,NPROG,FEEDP
        GO TO 8
7       READ,PROGN,FEEDP
8       IF(NPR-5)500,501,501
501     READ,KA,KB,KC,KD,KE,KF
        READ,JJ
        GO TO 502
500     READ,KA,KB,KC,KD
502     READ,J
        READ,M6
        M5=M6
        READ,K,L,M
        LL=L
       READ,D1,WL1,WU1
        READ,D1,WL2,WU2
        GO TO (9,9,10,10),K
9       READ,DEVF1
        GO TO 12
10      DO 11 I=1,20,4
11      READ,Y(I,8),Y(I+1,8),Y(I+2,8),Y(I+3,8)
12      GO TO (13,14,13,14),K
13      READ,DEVF2
        GO TO 15
14      DO 16 I=1,20,4
16      READ,DEV,DEV,DEV,DEV
15      NLS=Q99
        M3=0
        Y5M=0.0
        Y5N=0.0
        Y6M=0.0
        Y6N=0.0
        Y7M=0.0
        DO 17 I=1,20
        DO 18 J=2,5
        NY(I,J)=0
18      Y(I,J)=0.0
17      CONTINUE
        Y7N=0.0
```

```
           IF(NLS-6)264,264,257
257        NLS=6
264        IF(NPR-1)1,20,23
20         GO TO (23,23,24,25,26,23),NLS
26         M3=M3+1
25         M3=M3+1
24         M3=M3+1
23         M3=M3+2
           JJ=0
           M10=2
           M9=0
           IF(M4)1,378,379
378        M9=M3
           M3=2
379        DO 21 J=M10,M3
           M5=M5-1
           IF(M5)368,22,22
368        M3=JJ+1
           NLS=JJ+1
           IF(JJ)1,1,29
22         JJ=JJ+1
           DO 27 I=1,20,4
27         READ,Y(I,J),Y(I+1,J),Y(I+2,J),Y(I+3,J)
           AI1(J)=0.0
           WAC(J)=0.0
           IF(L-5)21,28,28
28         READ,AI1(J),WAC(J)
21         CONTINUE
29         IF(M6-1-M5)1,30,380
30         M3=M3+1
           DO 31 J=M3,10
           DO 32 I=1,20
32         Y(I,J)=0.0
31         CONTINUE
           M3=M3-1
           IF(NPR-6)509,510,510
510        DO 511 I=1,20
511        Y(I,9)=1.0
           NPR=5
           L=3
           GO TO 277
509        DO 33 I=1,20,4
33         READ,Y(I,9),Y(I+1,9),Y(I+2,9),Y(I+3,9)
           DO 275 I=1,20
275        Y(I,10)=Y(I,9)
           GO TO (276,276,277,276,276,277,277),L
277        DO 278 I=1,20,4
278        READ,Y(I,10),Y(I+1,10),Y(I+2,10),Y(I+3,10)
276        READ,OPER,INSTR
           READ,RUN,TEMP,WAVEL
           IF(M9-2)380,380,381
381        M10=3
           M3=M9
           GO TO 379
380        DO 279 I=1,20
           IF(Y(I,10)-WL2)280,281,281
281        IF(Y(I,10)-WU2)285,285,280
285        GO TO (287,287,287,287,288,287,289),L
287        AAA=Y(I,10)
           GO TO 290
288        AAA=LOG(Y(I,10))
           GO TO 290
```

```
289      AAA=1.0/Y(I,10)
290      IF(NPR-1)1,291,292
291      Y(I,1)=AAA
         GO TO 279
292      GO TO (291,291,293,293,293,297,297,297,297),NLS
297      GO TO (298,299,307,308,383),NPR
383      NPR=NPR-1
308      Y(I,7)=AAA*AAA*AAA*AAA
307      Y(I,6)=AAA*AAA*AAA
299      Y(I,5)=AAA*AAA
298      Y(I,1)=AAA
         GO TO 279
293      Y(I,1)=Y(I,2)
         IF(NLS-4)294,295,296
296      Y(I,5)=AAA*AAA*AAA*AAA
295      Y(I,4)=AAA*AAA*AAA
294      Y(I,3)=AAA*AAA
         Y(I,2)=AAA
         GO TO 279
280      Y(I,10)=0.0
         Y(I,9)=0.0
279      CONTINUE
309      G1=20.0
         G=0.0
         M3=M3-1
         M4=M4+1
         DO 310 I=1,20
         IF(NPR-1)1,311,313
311      IF(Y(I,2))310,310,312
312      G=G+1.0
         GO TO 310
313      GO TO (311,311,315,315,315,311,311,311,311),NLS
315      IF(Y(I,1))310,310,312
310      CONTINUE
         KQ=KA+2
         IF(KQ-8)384,384,385
385      KQ=KQ-8
         IF(KQ-8)384,384,505
505      KQ=KQ-8
384      GO TO (316,317,318,319,320,386,503,504),KQ
504      DO 508 I=KD,KE
508      Y(I,9)=0.0
317      DO 321 I=KB,KC
321      Y(I,9)=0.0
         GO TO 316
503      Y(KF,9)=0.0
386      Y(KE,9)=0.0
320      Y(KD,9)=0.0
319      Y(KC,9)=0.0
318      Y(KB,9)=0.0
316      DO 322 I=1,20
         IF(Y(I,9))323,323,324
324      IF(Y(I,10))323,323,322
323      DO 325 J=2,10
325      Y(I,J)=0.0
322      CONTINUE
         DO 470 I=1,20
         IF(Y(I,2))471,472,471
471      GO TO (470,470,473,474,475,470),NLS
475      IF(Y(I,5))474,472,474
474      IF(Y(I,4))473,472,473
473      IF(Y(I,3))470,472,470
```

```
472     Y(I,2)=0.0
470     CONTINUE
        IF(NLS-6)347,348,348
348     GO TO (344,344,347,347),K
344     DO 346 I=1,20
346     Y(I,8)=Y(I,2)*DEVF1
347     DO 326 I=1,20
        IF(NLS-6)328,327,327
327     IF(Y(I,2)-WL1)329,330,330
330     IF(Y(I,2)-WU1)331,331,329
352     CONTINUE
329     G1=G1-1.0
        DO 332 J=1,7
332     Y(I,J)=0.0
        GO TO 326
331     IF(NLS-2)333,333,339
333     Y(I,2)=Y(I,2)/Y(I,9)
        IF(Y(I,2)-WAC(2)*Y(I,2)-AI1(2))329,334,334
334     Y(I,2)=Y(I,2)-AI1(2)
        IF(L-5)326,335,336
335     Y(I,2)=LOG(Y(I,2))
        GO TO 326
336     IF(L-6)326,337,338
337     Y(I,2)=Y(I,10)/Y(I,2)
        GO TO 326
338     Y(I,2)=1.0/Y(I,2)
        GO TO 326
339     Y(I,3)=Y(I,2)
        Y(I,2)=(Y(I,3)+Y(I,8))/Y(I,9)-AI1(2)
        Y(I,4)=(Y(I,3)-Y(I,8))/Y(I,9)-AI1(2)
        Y(I,3)=Y(I,3)/Y(I,9)
        IF(Y(I,3)-WAC(2)*Y(I,3)-AI1(2))329,340,340
340     Y(I,3)=Y(I,3)-AI1(2)
        IF(L-5)326,341,342
341     Y(I,2)=LOG(Y(I,2))
        Y(I,3)=LOG(Y(I,3))
        Y(I,4)=LOG(Y(I,4))
        GO TO 326
342     Y(I,2)=1.0/Y(I,2)
        Y(I,3)=1.0/Y(I,3)
        Y(I,4)=1.0/Y(I,4)
        IF(L-6)326,343,326
343     Y(I,2)=Y(I,2)*Y(I,10)
        Y(I,3)=Y(I,3)*Y(I,10)
        Y(I,4)=Y(I,4)*Y(I,10)
        GO TO 326
328     IF(NLS-2)327,327,349
349     IF(NPR-1)1,350,359
350     M88=M3+1
        DO 356 J=2,M88
        IF(Y(I,J)-WL1)352,353,353
353     IF(Y(I,J)-WU1)354,354,352
354     IF(Y(I,9))352,352,351
351     Y(I,J)=Y(I,J)/Y(I,9)
        IF(Y(I,J)-AI1(J)-WAC(J)*Y(I,J))352,355,355
355     Y(I,J)=Y(I,J)-AI1(J)
        IF(L-5)356,357,399
357     Y(I,J)=LOG(Y(I,J))
        GO TO 356
399     Y(I,J)=1.0/Y(I,J)
        IF(L-6)356,358,356
358     Y(I,J)=Y(I,J)*Y(I,10)
```

```
356     CONTINUE
        GO TO 326
359     IF(Y(I,1)-WL1)329,360,360
360     IF(Y(I,1)-WU1)361,361,329
361     IF(Y(I,9))329,329,362
362     Y(I,1)=Y(I,1)/Y(I,9)
        IF(Y(I,1)-AI1(2)-WAC(2)*Y(I,1))329,363,363
363     Y(I,1)=Y(I,1)-AI1(2)
326     CONTINUE
        IF(NLS-6)431,432,432
432     DO 433 I=1,20
433     Y(I,5)=0.0
431     DO 36 I=1,20
        IF(Y(I,1))37,36,37
37      Y1M=Y(I,1)
        Y1N=Y(I,1)
        IF(Y(I,2))430,36,430
430     Y2M=Y(I,2)
        Y2N=Y(I,2)
        GO TO 42
36      CONTINUE
42      DO 41 I=1,20
        IF(Y(I,1))41,41,425
425     IF(Y1M-Y(I,1))44,43,43
44      Y1M=Y(I,1)
43      IF(Y1N-Y(I,1))46,46,45
45      Y1N=Y(I,1)
46      DO 47 J=2,5
        IF(Y(I,J))47,47,426
426     IF(Y2M-Y(I,J))48,49,49
48      Y2M=Y(I,J)
49      IF(Y2N-Y(I,J))47,47,50
50      Y2N=Y(I,J)
47      CONTINUE
41      CONTINUE
        PD1=(Y1M-Y1N)*0.1
        Y1M=Y1M+PD1
        Y1N=Y1N-PD1
        PD2=(Y2M-Y2N)*0.1
        Y2M=Y2M+PD2
        Y2N=Y2N-PD2
        WA=W-AM
        N=WA/100.0
        WA=N*100
        HA=H-AM
        N=HA/100.0
        HA=N*100
        P1=100.0*(Y1M-Y1N)/WA
        DO 110 I=1,20
        PY=I
        Q1=SQR(P1*P1)
        Q2=SQR(Y1N*Y1N)
        NQ2=Q2
        N1X=0
        O=0.0
        YN=0.0
        DO 116 J=1,10000
        IF(NQ2-J)117,118,116
118     NN1=J
        O=J
        Q2=Q2-O
        YN=Y1N
```

```
         GO TO 117
116      CONTINUE
117      IF(Q1-Q2)147,147,148
147      Q=Q2*(10.0**PY)
         GO TO 149
148      Q=Q1*(10.0**PY)
149      IF(WM-Q)150,150,110
150      IF(YN)156,157,157
156      QR=YN+O
         O=-O
         GO TO 158
157      QR=YN-O
158      N1A=QR*(10.0**PY)
         N1D=P1*(10.0**PY)
         NN1=O
         N1P=WA/100.0+1.0
         SF1=10.0**PY
         GO TO 163
110      CONTINUE
163      P2=100.0*(Y2M-Y2N)/HA
         DO 164 I=1,20
         PX=I
         Q1=SQR(P2*P2)
         Q2=SQR(Y2N*Y2N)
         NQ2=Q2
         NN2=O
         YN=0.0
         O=0.0
         DO 165 J=1,10000
         IF(NQ2-J)166,167,165
167      NN2=J
         YN=Y2N
         O=J
         Q2=Q2-O
         GO TO 166
165      CONTINUE
166      IF(Q1-Q2)168,168,169
168      Q=Q2*(10.0**PX)
         GO TO 170
169      Q=Q1*(10.0**PX)
170      IF(WM-Q)171,171,164
171      IF(YN)172,173,173
172      QR=Y2N+O
         O=-O
         GO TO 174
173      QR=Y2N-O
174      N2A=QR*(10.0**PX)
         N2D=P2*(10.0**PX)
         NN2=O
         N2P=HA/100.0+1.0
         SF2=10.0**PX
         GO TO 175
164      CONTINUE
175      IF(PD1)176,177,176
177      PD1=1.0/Y1M
         GO TO 178
176      PD1=1.0/PD1
178      IF(PD2)179,180,179
180      PD2=1.0/Y2M
         GO TO 181
179      PD2=1.0/PD2
181      DO 193 I=1,20
```

```
          IF(Y(I,1))194,193,194
194       GO TO (185,185,184,183,182,183),NLS
182       Y(I,5)=Y(I,5)*PD2
183       Y(I,4)=Y(I,4)*PD2
184       Y(I,3)=Y(I,3)*PD2
185       Y(I,2)=Y(I,2)*PD2
          Y(I,1)=Y(I,1)*PD1
193       CONTINUE
          Y1M=Y1M*PD1
          Y1N=Y1N*PD1
          Y2M=Y2M*PD2
          Y2N=Y2N*PD2
          D1=(Y1M-Y1N)/WA
          D2=(Y2M-Y2N)/HA
          IF(D1)199,200,199
200       D1=Y1M/WA
199       IF(D2)208,209,208
209       D2=Y2M/HA
208       DO 210 I=1,20
          IF(Y(I,2))211,210,211
211       NY(I,1)=(Y(I,1)-Y1N)/D1
          NY(I,2)=(Y(I,2)-Y2N)/D2
          GO TO (210,210,212,213,214,213),NLS
214       NY(I,5)=(Y(I,5)-Y2N)/D2
213       NY(I,4)=(Y(I,4)-Y2N)/D2
212       NY(I,3)=(Y(I,3)-Y2N)/D2
210       CONTINUE
          NH=H
          NW=W
          M=AM
          L=LL
          PUNCH 300,1,NW,NH,M,M,0,0
          IF(NPR-1)1,450,451
451       GO TO (228,229,230,231,232,227),NLS
450       GO TO (228,229,452,455,454,227),NLS
452       PUNCH 300,2,32,00,01
          GO TO 236
454       PUNCH 300,2,34,00,01,10,11
          GO TO 453
455       PUNCH 300,2,33,00,01,10
          GO TO 239
228       PUNCH 300,2,01,00
233       DO 234 I=1,20
          IF(Y(I,1))235,234,235
235       PUNCH 300,3,NY(I,1),NY(I,2)
234       CONTINUE
          GO TO 244
229       PUNCH 300,2,31,00
          GO TO 233
230       PUNCH 300,2,42,00,01
236       DO 237 I=1,20
          IF(Y(I,1))238,237,238
238       PUNCH 300,3,NY(I,1),NY(I,2),NY(I,3)
237       CONTINUE
          GO TO 244
231       PUNCH 300,2,43,00,01,10
239       DO 240 I=1,20
          IF(Y(I,1))241,240,241
241       PUNCH 300,3,NY(I,1),NY(I,2),NY(I,3),NY(I,4)
240       CONTINUE
          GO TO 244
232       PUNCH 300,2,44,00,01,10,11
```

```
453     DO 242 I=1,20
        IF(Y(I,1))243,242,243
243     PUNCH 300,3,NY(I,1),NY(I,2),NY(I,3),NY(I,4),NY(I,5)
242     CONTINUE
        GO TO 244
227     PUNCH 300,2,33,01,00,01
        GO TO 239
244     NXL=-50
        PUNCH 300,4,155,NXL,01
        IF(NPR-1)1,374,375
374     PUNCH 305,NN1,SF1
        NXL=-100
        PUNCH 300,4,NXL,800,11
        PUNCH 304,NN2,SF2
        GO TO 376
375     GO TO (374,374,377,377,377,374),NLS
377     PUNCH 304,NN1,SF1
        NXL=-100
        PUNCH 300,4,NXL,800,11
        PUNCH305,NN2,SF2
376     NL=-100
        PUNCH300,4,155,NL,00
        PUNCH 301,NQR,L,RUN,TEMP
        NL=-125
        M3=JJ+M4-1
        PUNCH 300,4,155,NL,00
        IF(NPR-1)1,19,371
19      GO TO (371,371,372,372,372,371),NLS
371     PUNCH 302,M4,OPER
        GO TO 373
372     PUNCH 306,M4,M3,OPER
373     NL=-150
        PUNCH 300,4,155,NL,00
        PUNCH 303,G1,G
        NS1=-25
        NS2=0
        PUNCH 300,5,NS2,NS1,N1P,N1A,N1D,00
        PUNCH 300,5,NS1,NS2,N2P,N2A,N2D,10
        PUNCH300,6
        M4=M3
        IF(M5)1,15,15
        END
```

ALGOL 60 FOR PROGRAM NUMBER 502

```
PROCEDURE BEEEE(w,h,am,wm,nLs,nqr); ARRAY y[1:20,1:10],ny[1:20,1:5],
ail,wac[1:5]; REAL w,h,am,wm; INTEGER nLs,nqr; SWITCH sw1:=x3,x3,x4,x4;
SWITCH sw2:=x6,x7,x6,x7; SWITCH sw3:=x12,x12,x11,x10,x9,x12; SWITCH
sw4:=xxx,xxx,x15,xxx,xxx,x15,x15; SWITCH sw5:=x17,x17,x17,x17,x18,x17,x19;
SWITCH sw6:=xxy,xxy,x27,x27,x27,x21,x21,x21,x21; SWITCH sw7:=x26,x25,x24,
x23,x22; SWITCH sw8:=x32,x32,x35,x35,x35,x32,x32,x32,x32; SWITCH sw9:=x45,
x39,x44,x43,x42,x41,x40,x38; SWITCH sw10:=x50,x50,x48,x47,x46,x50; SWITCH
sw11:=x51,x51,x52,x52; SWITCH sw12:=x77,x77,x76,x75,x74,x75; SWITCH
sw13:=x82,x82,x81,x80,x79,x80; SWITCH sw14:=x86,x88,x89,x91,x93,x95;
SWITCH sw15:=x86,x88,x83,x85,x84,x95; SWITCH sw16:=x97,x97,x98,x98,x98,x97;
SWITCH sw17:=w1,w1,w2,w2,w2,w1;
     BEGIN INTEGER i,j,jj,k,ka,kb,kc,kd,ke,kf,kq,L,LL,m,m3,m4,m5,m6,m88,
     m9,m10,n,npr,nq2,n1x,nn1,nxL,nL,n1a,n1d,n1p,nn2,n2a,n2d,n2p,nh,nw,ns1,
     ns2,nprogn,feedp,g1,g,oper,run,instr; REAL aaa,d1,d2,devf1,devf2,dev,ha,
     O,pd1,pd2,p1,p2,px,py,q,q1,q2,q99,qr,sf1,sf2,wL1,wu1,wa,wm,yn,y1m,y1n,
     y2m,y2n,y5m,y5n,y6m,y6n,y7m,y7n,temp,waveL;
X1:  nnr:=nqr; m4:=o; npr:=nqr;
     IF nqr≥300 THEN npr:=nqr−300;
     IF npr<9 THEN GO TO W4
     ELSE IF npr>9 THEN npr:=npr−12;
     npr:=npr−8;
     IF npr<1 THEN GO TO W4;
     READ nprog,feedp;
     IF npr≥5 THEN
     BEGIN
         READ ka,kb,kc,kd,ke,kf;
         READ jj; GO TO X2 END;
     READ ka,kb,kc,kd;
X2:  READ j; READ m6;
     m5:=m6;
     READ k,L,m;
     LL:=L
     READ d1,wL1,wu1;
     READ d1,wL2,wu2;
     GO TO sw1[k];
X3:  READ devf1;
     GO TO X5;
X4:  FOR i:=1 STEP 1 UNTIL 20 DO READ y[i,8];
X5:  GO TO sw2[k];
X6:  READ devf2;
     GO TO X8;
X7:  FOR i:=1 STEP 1 UNTIL 20 DO READ dev,dev,dev,dev;
X8:  nLs:=q99;
     m3:=y5m:=y5n:=y6m:=y6n:=y7m:=0;
     FOR i:=1 STEP 1 UNTIL 20 DO
     FOR j:=2 STEP 1 UNTIL 5 DO
     ny[i,j]:=y[i,j]:=0;
     y7n:=0;
     IF nLs>6 THEN nLs:=6;
     IF npr<1 THEN GO TO W4
```

```
        ELSE IF npr=1 THEN
        BEGIN
           GO TO sw3[nLs];
X9:        m3:=m3+1;
X10:       m3:=m3+1;
X11:       m3:=m3+1; END;
X12:       m3:=m3+2
        jj:=m9:=0; m10:=2;
        IF m4<0 THEN GO TO W4
        ELSE IF m4=0 THEN
        BEGIN
           m9:=m3; m3:=2END;
X13:    FOR j:=m10 STEP 1 UNTIL m3 DO
        BEGIN
          m5:=m5-1;
          IF m5<0 THEN
          BEGIN
           m3:=jj+1; nLs:=jj+1;
            IF jj≤0 THEN GO TO W4
            ELSE GO TO X14END;
          jj:=jj+1;
          FOR i:=1 STEP 1 UNTIL 20 DO READ y[i,j];
          ai1[j]:=wac[j]:=0;
          IF L≥5 THEN READ ai1[j],wac[j]
        END;
X14:    IF m6<(m5+1) THEN GO TO W4
        ELSE IF m6>(m5+1) THEN GO TO X16;
        m3:=m3+1;
        FOR j:=m3 STEP 1 UNTIL 10 DO
        FOR i:=1 STEP 1 UNTIL 20 DO
        y[i,j]:=0;
        m3:=m3-1;
        IF npr≥6 THEN
        BEGIN
           FOR i:=1 STEP 1 UNTIL 20 DO y[i,9]:=1
           npr:=5; L:=3;
           GO TO X15END;
        FOR i:=1 STEP 1 UNTIL 20 DO READ y[i,9];
        FOR i:=1 STEP 1 UNTIL 20 DO y[i,10]:=y[i,9];
        GO TO sw4[L];
X15:    FOR i:=1 STEP 1 UNTIL 20 DO READ y[i,10];
XXX:    READ oper,instr;
        READ run,temp,waveL;
        IF m9>2 THEN
        BEGIN
           m10:=3,m3:=m9; GO TO X13END;
X16:    FOR i:=1 STEP 1 UNTIL 20 DO
        BEGIN
           IF y[i,10]<wL2∨y[i,10]>wu2 THEN GO TO X30;
           GO TO sw5[L];
X17:       aaa:=y[i,10];
           GO TO X20;
X18:       aaa:=Ln(y[i,10]);
```

```
              GO TO X20;
X19:          aaa:=1/y[i,10];
X20:          IF npr<1 THEN GO TO W4
              ELSE IF npr=1 THEN
              BEGIN
XXY:              y[i,1]:=aaa; GO TO X31END;
              GO TO sw6[nLs];
X21:          GO TO sw7[npr];
X22:          npr:=npr-1;
X23:          y[i,7]:=aaa↑4;
X24:          y[i,6]:=aaa↑3;
X25:          y[i,5]:=aaa↑2;
X26:          y[i,1]:=aaa;
              GO TO X31;
X27:          y[i,1]:=y[i,2];
              IF nLs<4 THEN GO TO X29
              ELSE IF nLs=4 THEN GO TO X28;
              y[i,5]:=aaa↑4;
X28:          y[i,4]:=aaa↑3;
X29:          y[i,3]:=aaa↑2;
              y[i,2]:=aaa
              GO TO X31;
X30:          y[i,10]:=y[i,9]:=0;
X31:          END;
              g1:=20;  g:=0;
              m3:=m3-1;  m4:=m4+1;
              FOR i:=1 STEP 1 UNTIL 20 DO
              BEGIN
                  IF npr<1 THEN GO TO W4
                  ELSE IF npr>1 THEN GO TO X34;
X32:              IF y[i,2]>0 THEN
                  BEGIN
X33:                  g:=g+1;  GO TO X36
X34:                  GO TO sw8[nLs];
X35:                  IF y[i,1]>0 THEN GO TO X33
X36:          END END;
              kq:=ka+2;
              IF kq≤8 THEN GO TO X37;
              kq:=kq-8;
              IF kq>8 THEN kq:=kq-8;
X37:          GO TO sw9[kq];
X38:          FOR i:=kd STEP 1 UNTIL ke DO y[i,9]:=0;
X39:          FOR i:=kb STEP 1 UNTIL kc DO y[i,9]:=0;
              GO TO X45;
X40:          y[kf,9]:=0;
X41:          y[ke,9]:=0;
X42:          y[kd,9]:=0;
X43:          y[kc,9]:=0;
X44:          y[kb,9]:=0;
X45:          FOR i:=1 STEP 1 UNTIL 20 DO
              BEGIN
                  IF y[i,9]≤0Vy[i,10]≤0 THEN
                  FOR j:=2 STEP 1 UNTIL 10 DO y[i,j]:=0
```

```
        END;
        FOR i:=1 STEP 1 UNTIL 20 DO
        BEGIN
          IF y[i,2]≠0 THEN
          BEGIN
            GO TO sw10[nLs];
X46:        IF y[i,5]=0 THEN GO TO X49;
X47:        IF y[i,4]=0 THEN GO TO X49;
X48:        IF y[i,3]≠0 THEN GO TO X50END;
X49:      y[i,2]:=0
X50:    END;
        IF nLs≥6 THEN
        BEGIN
          GO TO sw11[k];
X51:      FOR i:=1 STEP 1 UNTIL 20 DO y[i,8]:=y[i,2]Xdevf1
        END;
X52:    FOR i:=1 STEP 1 UNTIL 20 DO
        BEGIN
          IF nLs<6 THEN GO TO X56;
X53:      IF y[i,2]<wL1Vy[i,2]>wu1 THEN
          BEGIN
X54:        g1:=g1-1;
            FOR j:=1 STEP 1 UNTIL 7 DO y[i,j]=0;
            GO TO X59END;
          IF nLs>2 THEN GO TO X55;
          y[i,2]:=y[i,2]/y[i,9];
          IF y[i,2]<(wac[2]Xy[i,2]+ai1) THEN GO TO X54;
          y[i,2]:=y[i,2]-ai1[2];
          IF L<5 THEN GO TO X59
          ELSE IF L=5 THEN
          BEGIN
            y[i,2]:=Ln(y[i,2]); GO TO X59END;
          IF L=6 THEN
          BEGIN
            y[i,2]:=y[i,10]/y[i,2]; GO TO X59END;
          y[i,2]:=1/y[i,2]; GO TO X59;
X55:      y[i,3]:=y[i,2];
          y[i,2]:=(y[i,3]+y[i,8])/y[i,9]-ai1[2];
          y[i,4]:=(y[i,3]-y[i,8])/y(i,9)-ai1; y[i,3]:=y[i,3]/y[i,9];
          IF y[i,3]<(wac[2]Xy[i,3]+ai1[2]) THEN
          GO TO X54;
          y[i,3]:=y[i,3]-ai1[2];
          IF L<5 THEN GO TO X59
          ELSE IF L=5 THEN
          BEGIN
            y[i,2]:=Ln(y[i,2]);
            y[i,3]:=Ln(y[i,3]);
            y[i,4]:=Ln(y[i,4]);
            GO TO X59END;
          y[i,2]:=1/y[i,2];
          y[i,3]:=1/y[i,3];
          y[i,4]:=1/y[i,4];
          IF L≠6 THEN GO TO X59
```

```
          y[i,2]:=y[i,2]Xy[i,10];
          y[i,3]:=y[i,3]Xy[i,10];
          y[i,4]:=y[i,4]Xy[i,10];
          GO TO X59;
X56:      IF nLs≤2 THEN GO TO X53;
          IF npr<1 THEN GO TO W4
          ELSE IF npr=1 THEN
          BEGIN
             FOR j:=2 STEP 1 UNTIL m3 DO
             BEGIN m88:=m3+1;
                IF y[i,j]<wL1Vy[i,j]>wu1Vy[i,9]≤0 THEN
                GO TO X54;
                y[i,j]:=y[i,j]/y[i,9];
                IF y[i,j]<(wac[j]Xy[i,j]+ai1) THEN
                GO TO X54;
                y[i,j]:=ai1[j];
                IF L<5 THEN GO TO X57
                ELSE IF L=5 THEN
                BEGIN
                   y[i,j]:=Ln(y[i,j]); GO TO X57END;
                y[i,j]:=1/y[i,j];
                IF L=6 THEN y[i,j]:=y[i,j]Xy[i,10]
X57:      END END; GO TO X59;
X58:      IF y[i,1]<wL1Vy[i,1]>wu1Vy[i,9]≤0 THEN
          GO TO X54;
          y[i,1]:=y[i,1]/y[i,9];
          IF y[i,1]<(wac[2]Xy[i,1]+ai1[2]) THEN GO TO X54;
          y[i,1]:=y[i,1]−ai1[2]
X59:      END;
          IF nLs≥6 THEN
          FOR i:=1 STEP 1 UNTIL 20 DO y[i,5]:=0;
          FOR i:=1 STEP 1 UNTIL 20 DO
          BEGIN
             IF y[i,1]≠0 THEN
             BEGIN
             y1m:=y[i,1]; y1n:=y[i,1]
                IF y[i,2]≠0 THEN
                BEGIN
                   y2m:=y[i,2]; y2n:=y[i,2]; GO TO X60
          END END END;
X60:      FOR i:=1 STEP 1 UNTIL 20 DO
          BEGIN
             IF y[i,1]≤0 THEN GO TO X61;
             IF y1m<y[i,1] THEN y1m:=y[i,1];
             IF y1n>y[i,1] THEN y1n:=y[i,1];
             FOR j:=2 STEP 1 UNTIL 5 DO
             BEGIN
                IF y[i,j]≤0 THEN GO TO X61;
                IF y2m<y[i,j] THEN y2m:=y[i,j];
                IF y2n>y[i,j] THEN y2n:=y[i,j]
X61:      END END;
          pd1:=(y1m−y1n)X0.1;
          y1m:=y1m+pd1; y1n:=y1n−pd1
```

```
pd2:=(y2m−y2n)X0.1;
y2m:=y2m+pd2;  y2n:=y2n−pd2;
wa:=w−am;
n:=wa/100;
wa:=nX100;
ha:=h−am;
n:=ha/100;
ha:=nX100;
p1:=100X(y1m−y1n)/wa;
FOR i:=1 STEP 1 UNTIL 20 DO
BEGIN
  py:=i;
  q1:=abs(p1);  q2:=abs(y1n);
  nq2:=q2;  n1x:=O:=yn:=0;
  FOR j:=1 STEP 1 UNTIL 20 DO
  BEGIN
    IF nq2<j THEN GO TO X62
    ELSE IF nq2=j THEN
    BEGIN
      nn1:=j;  O:=j;  q2:=q2−O;
      yn:=y1n;  GO TO X62
  END END;
```

X62:
```
      IF q1≤q2 THEN
      BEGIN
        q:=q2X10↑py;  GO TO X63END;
      q:=q1X10↑py;
```

X63:
```
      IF wm≤q THEN
      BEGIN
        IF yn≥0 THEN
        BEGIN
          qr:=yn−O;  GO TO X64END;
        qr:=yn+O;  O:=−O;
```

X64:
```
      n1a:=qrX10↑py;
      n1d:=p1X10↑py;
      nn1:=0;
      n1p:=wa/100+1;
      sf1:=10↑py;
      GO TO X66
```

X65: `END END;`
X66:
```
      p2:=100X(y2m−y2n)/ha;
      FOR i:=1 STEP 1 UNTIL 20 DO
      BEGIN
        px:=i;
        q1:=abs(p2);  q2:=abs(y2n);
        nq2:=q2;  nn2:=yn:=O:=0;
        FOR j:=1 STEP 1 UNTIL 10000 DO
        BEGIN
          IF nq2<j THEN GO TO X67
          ELSE IF nq2=j THEN
          BEGIN
            nn2:=j;  yn:=y2n;  O:=j;
            q2:=q2−O;  GO TO X67
        END END;
```

```
X67:    IF q1≤q2 THEN
        BEGIN
            q:=q2X10ᵗpx;  GO TO X68END;
        q:=q1X10ᵗpx;
X68:    IF wm≤q THEN
        BEGIN
            IF yn≤0 THEN
            BEGIN
                qr:=y2n+O;  O:=-O;  GO TO X69END;
            qr:=y2n-O;
X69:        n2a:=qrX10ᵗpx;
            n2d:=qrX10ᵗpx;
            nn2:=0;
            n2p:=ha/100+1;
            sf2:=10ᵗpx
            GO TO X71
X70:    END END;
X71:    IF pd1=0 THEN
        BEGIN
            pd1:=1/y1m;  GO TO X72END;
        pd1:=1/pd1;
X72:    IF pd2=0 THEN
        BEGIN
            pd2:=1/y2m;  GO TO X73END;
        pd2:=1/pd2;
X73:    FOR i:=1 STEP 1 UNTIL 20 DO
        BEGIN
            IF y[i,1]=0 THEN GO TO X78;
            GO TO sw12[nLs];
X74:    y[i,5]:=y[i,5]Xpd2;
X75:    y[i,4]:=y[i,4]Xpd2;
X76:    y[i,3]:=y[i,3]Xpd2;
X77:    y[i,2]:=y[i,2]Xpd2;
        y[i,1]:=y[i,1]Xpd1;
X78:    END;
        y1m:=y1mXpd1;  y1n:=y1nXpd1;
        y2m:=y2mXpd2;  y2n:=y2nXpd2;
        d1:=(y1m-y1n)/wa;
        d2:=(y2m-y2n)/ha;
        IF d1=0 THEN d1:=y1m/wa;
        IF d2=0 THEN d2:=y2m/ha;
        FOR i:=1 STEP 1 UNTIL 20 DO
        BEGIN
            IF y[i,2]=0 THEN GO TO X82;
            ny[i,1]:=(y[i,1]-y1n)/d1;
            ny[i,2]:=(y[i,2]-y2n)/d2;
            GO TO sw13[nLs];
X79:    ny[i,5]:=(y[i,5]-y2n)/d2;
X80:    ny[i,4]:=(y[i,4]-y2n)/d2;
X81:    ny[i,3]:=(y[i,3]-y2n)/d2
X82:    END;
        nh:=h;  nw:=w;  m:=am;  L:=LL;
        PUNCH 1,nw,nh,m,m,0,0;
```

```
          IF npr<1 THEN GO TO W4
          ELSE IF npr>1 THEN GO TO sw14[nLs];
          GO TO sw15[nLs];
X83:      PUNCH 2,32,0,1;
          GO TO X90;
X84:      PUNCH 2,34,0,1,10,11;
          GO TO X94;
X85:      PUNCH 2,33,0,1,10;
          GO TO X92;
X86:      PUNCH 2,1,0;
X87:      FOR i:=1 STEP 1 UNTIL 20 DO
          BEGIN
              IF y[i,1]≠0 THEN
              PUNCH 3,ny[i,1],ny[i,2]
          END;
          GO TO X96;
X88:      PUNCH 2,31,0;
          GO TO X87;
X89;      PUNCH 2,42,0,1;
X90:      FOR i:=1 STEP 1 UNTIL 20 DO
          BEGIN
              IF y[i,1]≠0 THEN
              PUNCH 3,ny[i,1],ny[i,2],ny[i,3]
          END;
          GO TO X96;
X91:      PUNCH 2,43,0,1,10;
X92:      FOR i:=1 STEP 1 UNTIL 20 DO
          BEGIN
              IF y[i,1]≠0 THEN
              PUNCH 3,ny[i,1],ny[i,2],ny[i,3],ny[i,4]
          END;
          GO TO X96;
X93:      PUNCH 2,44,0,1,10,11;
X94:      FOR i:=1 STEP 1 UNTIL 20 DO
          BEGIN
              IF y[i,1]≠0 THEN
              PUNCH 3,ny[i,1],ny[i,2],ny[i,3],ny[i,4],ny[i,5]
          END;
          GO TO X96;
X95:      PUNCH 2,33,1,0,1;
          GO TO X92;
X96:      nxL:=-50;
          PUNCH 4,155,nxL,1;
          IF npr<1 THEN GO TO W4
          ELSE IF npr=1 THEN
          BEGIN
X97:          PUNCH nn1,sf1;
              nxL:=-100;
              PUNCH 4,nxL,800,11;
              PUNCH nn2,sf2;
              GO TO X99END;
          GO TO sw16[nLs];
X98:      PUNCH nn1,sf1;
```

```
        nxL:=-100;
        PUNCH 4,nxL,800,11;
        PUNCH nn2,sf2;
X99:    nL:=-100;
        PUNCH 4,155,nL,0;
        PUNCH nqr,L,run,temp;
        nL:=-125;
        m3:=jj+m4-1;
        PUNCH 4,155,nL,0;
        IF npr<1 THEN GO TO W4
        ELSE IF npr=1 THEN GO TO sw17[nLs];
W1:     PUNCH m4,oper;
        GO TO W3;
W2:     PUNCH m4,m3,oper;
W3:     nL:=-150;
        PUNCH 4,155,nL,0;
        PUNCH g1,g;
        ns1:=-25; ns2:=0;
        PUNCH 5,ns2,ns1,n1p,n1a,n1d,0;
        PUNCH 5,ns1,ns2,n2p,n2a,n2d,10;
        PUNCH 6;
        m4:=m3;
        IF m5≥0 THEN GO TO X8
W4:     END(BEEEE);
W5:     READ w,h,am,wm,nLs; q99:=nLs;
W6:     READ nqr;
        PROCEDURE(w,h,am,wm,nLs,nqr);
        GO TO W6;
```

AUTOPLOTTER PROGRAM NUMBER 503

CALL WORD CEEEE

```
C  C   AUTOPLOTTER PROGRAM NUMBER 503(CALL WORD CEEEE)
300    FORMAT(I5,I5,I5,I5,I5,I5,I5,I5)
301    FORMAT (8HPROGRAM ,I3,4H  L ,I2,6H  RUN ,F5.1,7H  TEMP ,F4.1)
302    FORMAT(14HWAVELENGTH IS ,I2,11H  OPERATOR ,F9.0)
303    FORMAT (F4.1,28H POINTS ARE RETAINED OUT OF ,F4.1)
304    FORMAT (8HY MINUS ,I6,7H TIMES ,F12.3)
305    FORMAT (9HX1 MINUS ,I6,7H TIMES ,F12.3)
306    FORMAT(17HWAVELENGTHS FROM ,I2,4H TO ,I2,11H  OPERATOR ,F9.0)
       DIMENSION Y(20,10),NY(20,6),A1(5),A2(5),A3(5),A4(5),B1(5),B2(5)
       DIMENSION B3(5),B4(5),AIAX(5),AIBX(5)
       READ,W,H,AM,WM,NLS
       Q99=NLS
1      READ,NQR
       NLS=Q99
       NPR=NQR
       IF(NQR-300)2,3,3
3      NPR=NQR-300
       IF(NPR-100)2,1,506
506    NPR=NPR-100
2      IF(NPR-14)4,5,14
14     NPR=NPR-13
5      NPR=NPR-2
4      NPR=NPR-9
       M4=0
       DO 6 I=1,20
       DO 7 J=1,10
7      Y(I,J)=0.0
       DO 8 J=1,5
8      NY(I,J)=0
6      CONTINUE
       IF(NPR-3)10,10,11
11     READ,PROGN,FEEDP
       GO TO 387
10     READ,NPROG,FEEDP
       IF(NPR-2)387,388,389
389    READ,QQ2
       READ,QQ1L,QQ1U
       READ,PPQQ
       GO TO 387
388    READ,QQ1,QQ2
387    IF(NQR-400)507,1,508
507    READ,J
       GO TO509
508    READ,J,WACRR
509    IF(NPR-4)476,450,450
476    READ,EQO
       IF(NPR-1)1,450,451
451    READ,PP
450    READ,M6
       M5=M6
       READ,K,L,M
       IF(NPR-4)500,501,501
500    READ,KA,KB,KC,KD
       GO TO 502
501    READ,KA,KB,KC,KD,KE,KF
502    READ,D1,WAC1,WL1,WU1
       READ,D1,WAC2,WL2,WU2
       QNR=L
       QNR=QNR/10.0
```

```
          DO 13 J=1,20
          P=J
          IF(QNR-P)16,16,13
16        LL=J
          GO TO 15
13        CONTINUE
15        NLS=Q99
          DO 9 J=1,5
          A1(J)=0.0
          A2(J)=0.0
          A3(J)=0.0
          A4(J)=0.0
          B1(J)=0.0
          B2(J)=0.0
          B3(J)=0.0
          B4(J)=0.0
          AIAX(J)=0.0
9         AIBX(J)=0.0
          M3=0
          DO 17 I=1,20
          Y(I,1)=Y(I,7)
          DO 18 J=2,5
          NY(I,J)=0
18        Y(I,J)=0.0
17        CONTINUE
          IF(NLS-6)264,264,257
257       NLS=6
264       GO TO (23,23,24,25,26,23),NLS
26        M3=M3+1
25        M3=M3+1
24        M3=M3+1
23        M3=M3+2
          JJ=0
          M9=0
          M10=2
          IF(M4)1,378,379
378       M9=M3
          M3=2
379       DO 21 J=M10,M3
          M5=M5-1
          IF(M5)368,22,22
368       M3=JJ+1
          NLS=JJ+1
          IF(JJ)1,1,29
22        JJ=JJ+1
          DO 27 I=1,20,4
27        READ,Y(I,J),Y(I+1,J),Y(I+2,J),Y(I+3,J)
          IF(NPR-4)390,390,21
390       IF(LL-4)391,391,392
391       READ,AIAX(J)
          GO TO 393
392       READ,AIAX(J),AIBX(J)
393       GO TO (394,395,394,395,394,395,394,395),LL
395       READ,A1(J),A2(J),A3(J),A4(J)
394       IF(LL-6)21,21,396
396       READ,B1(J),B2(J),B3(J),B4(J)
21        CONTINUE
29        IF(M6-1-M5)1,30,380
30        DO 31 I=1,20,4
31        READ,Y(I,6),Y(I+1,6),Y(I+2,6),Y(I+3,6)
          IF(NPR-4)397,398,397
397       IF(LL-2)399,399,398
```

```
399      DO 400 I=1,20
400      Y(I,1)=Y(I,6)
         GO TO 401
398      DO 32 I=1,20,4
32       READ,Y(I,1),Y(I+1,1),Y(I+2,1),Y(I+3,1)
401      DO 434 I=1,20
434      Y(I,7)=Y(I,1)
         GO TO (283,283,284,284),K
283      READ,DEVF1
         GO TO 286
284      DO 285 I=1,20,4
285      READ,Y(I,9),Y(I+1,9),Y(I+2,9),Y(I+3,9)
286      GO TO (287,288,287,288),K
287      READ,DEVF2
         DO 289 I=1,20
289      Y(I,10)=DEVF2*Y(I,1)
         GO TO 290
288      DO 291 I=1,20,4
291      READ,Y(I,10),Y(I+1,10),Y(I+2,10),Y(I+3,10)
290      READ,OPER,INSTR
         READ,RUN,TEMP,WAVEL
         IF(M9-2)380,380,381
381      M10=3
         M3=M9
         GO TO 379
380      DO 292 I=1,20
         IF(Y(I,1)-WL2)293,294,294
294      IF(Y(I,1)-WU2)292,292,293
293      DO 279 J=1,10
279      Y(I,J)=0.0
292      CONTINUE
         G=20.0
         G1=20.0
         M3=M3-1
         M4=M4+1
         DO 296 J=2,5
         DO 299 I=1,20
         IF(Y(I,1))297,297,298
298      IF(Y(I,J)-WL1)297,308,308
308      IF(Y(I,J)-WU1)299,299,297
297      Y(I,J)=0.0
299      CONTINUE
296      CONTINUE
         DO 309 I=1,20
         IF(Y(I,2))310,310,309
310      G=G-1.0
309      CONTINUE
         KQ=KA+2
         IF(KQ-8)382,382,383
383      KQ=KQ-8
         IF(KQ-8)382,382,505
505      KQ=KQ-8
382      GO TO (311,312,313,314,315,385,403,404),KQ
404      DO 405 I=KD,KE
405      Y(I,2)=0.0
312      DO 319 I=KB,KC
319      Y(I,2)=0.0
         GO TO 320
403      Y(KF,2)=0.0
385      Y(KE,2)=0.0
315      Y(KD,2)=0.0
314      Y(KC,2)=0.0
```

```
313     Y(KB,2)=0.0
320     DO 316 I=1,20
        DO 317 J=2,5
        IF(Y(I,2))316,318,316
318     Y(I,J)=0.0
317     CONTINUE
316     CONTINUE
311     DO 323 I=1,20
        IF(Y(I,6))323,323,325
325     IF(NLS-6)409,410,1
410     IF(K-2)411,411,412
411     Y(I,9)=DEVF1*Y(I,2)
412     Y(I,3)=Y(I,2)
        Y(I,2)=Y(I,3)+Y(I,9)
        Y(I,4)=Y(I,3)-Y(I,9)
409     DO 413 J=2,5
        IF(NLS-6)481,482,1
482     IF(J-2)1,481,480
481     AAA=Y(I,6)
        AA=Y(I,6)*Y(I,6)*Y(I,6)
        XX=AIAX(J)+A1(J)*AAA+A2(J)*AAA*AAA+A3(J)*AA+A4(J)*AA*AAA
        XX=XX*AAA
        AAA=Y(I,1)
        AA=Y(I,1)*Y(I,1)*Y(I,1)
        YY=AIBX(J)+B1(J)*AAA+B2(J)*AAA*AAA+B3(J)*AA+B4(J)*AA*AAA
        YY=YY*AAA
        IF(NLS-6)477,478,1
478     IF(J-2)1,479,480
479     AA=Y(I,3)*WAC1
        Y(I,2)=Y(I,2)-XX-YY
        BB=Y(I,3)-XX-YY
        IF(BB-AA)414,415,415
480     Y(I,J)=Y(I,J)-XX-YY
        GO TO 415
477     AA=Y(I,J)*WAC1
        Y(I,J)=Y(I,J)-XX-YY
        IF(Y(I,J)-AA)414,415,415
415     Y(I,J)=Y(I,J)/Y(I,6)
        GO TO 413
414     Y(I,J)=0.0
413     CONTINUE
        IF(NPR-4)323,416,323
416     Y(I,1)=Y(I,1)/Y(I,6)
323     CONTINUE
        DO 470 I=1,20
        IF(Y(I,2))471,472,471
471     GO TO (470,470,473,474,475,470),NLS
475     IF(Y(I,5))474,472,474
474     IF(Y(I,4))473,472,473
473     IF(Y(I,3))470,472,470
472     Y(I,1)=0.0
470     CONTINUE
        DO 321 I=1,20
        IF(Y(I,2))322,322,321
322     G1=G1-1.0
321     CONTINUE
        DO 36 I=1,20
        IF(Y(I,1))37,36,37
37      Y1M=Y(I,1)
        Y1N=Y(I,1)
        IF(Y(I,2))430,36,430
430     Y2M=Y(I,2)
```

```
         Y2N=Y(I,2)
         GO TO 42
36       CONTINUE
42       DO 41 I=1,20
         IF(Y(I,1))425,41,425
425      IF(Y1M-Y(I,1))44,43,43
44       Y1M=Y(I,1)
43       IF(Y1N-Y(I,1))46,46,45
45       Y1N=Y(I,1)
46       DO 47 J=2,5
         IF(Y(I,J))47,47,426
426      IF(Y2M-Y(I,J))48,49,49
48       Y2M=Y(I,J)
49       IF(Y2N-Y(I,J))47,47,50
50       Y2N=Y(I,J)
47       CONTINUE
41       CONTINUE
         PD1=(Y1M-Y1N)*0.1
         Y1M=Y1M+PD1
         Y1N=Y1N-PD1
         PD2=(Y2M-Y2N)*0.1
         Y2M=Y2M+PD2
         Y2N=Y2N-PD2
         WA=W-AM
         N=WA/100.0
         WA=N*100
         HA=H-AM
         N=HA/100.0
         HA=N*100
         P1=100.0*(Y1M-Y1N)/WA
         DO 110 I=1,20
         PY=I
         Q1=SQR(P1*P1)
         Q2=SQR(Y1N*Y1N)
         NQ2=Q2
         N1X=0
         O=0.0
         YN=0.0
         DO 116 J=1,10000
         IF(NQ2- J)117,118,116
118      NN1=J
         O=J
         Q2=Q2-O
         YN=Y1N
         GO TO 117
116      CONTINUE
117      IF(Q1-Q2)147,147,148
147      Q=Q2*(10.0**PY)
         GO TO 149
148      Q=Q1*(10.0**PY)
149      IF(WM-Q)150,150,110
150      IF(YN)156,157,157
156      QR=YN+O
         O=-O
         GO TO 158
157      QR=YN-O
158      N1A=QR*(10.0**PY)
         N1D=P1*(10.0**PY)
         NN1=0
         N1P=WA/100.0+1.0
         SF1=10.0**PY
         GO TO 163
```

```
110       CONTINUE
163       P2=100.0*(Y2M-Y2N)/HA
          DO 164 I=1,20
          PX=I
          Q1=SQR(P2*P2)
          Q2=SQR(Y2N*Y2N)
          NQ2=Q2
          NN2=0
          YN=0.0
          O=0.0
          DO 165 J=1,10000
          IF(NQ2-J)166,167,165
167       NN2=J
          O=J
          YN=Y2N
          Q2=Q2-O
          GO TO 166
165       CONTINUE
166       IF(Q1-Q2)168,168,169
168       Q=Q2*(10.0**PX)
          GO TO 170
169       Q=Q1*(10.0**PX)
170       IF(WM-Q)171,171,164
171       IF(YN)172,173,173
172       QR=Y2N+O
          O=-O
          GO TO 174
173       QR=Y2N-O
174       N2A=QR*(10.0**PX)
          N2D=P2*(10.0**PX)
          NN2=O
          N2P=HA/100.0+1.0
          SF2=10.0**PX
          GO TO 175
164       CONTINUE
175       IF(PD1)176,177,176
177       PD1=1.0/Y1M
          GO TO 178
176       PD1=1.0/PD1
178       IF(PD2)179,180,179
180       PD2=1.0/Y2M
          GO TO 181
179       PD2=1.0/PD2
181       DO 193 I=1,20
          IF(Y(I,1))194,193,194
194       GO TO (185,185,184,183,182,183),NLS
182       Y(I,5)=Y(I,5)*PD2
183       Y(I,4)=Y(I,4)*PD2
184       Y(I,3)=Y(I,3)*PD2
185       Y(I,2)=Y(I,2)*PD2
          Y(I,1)=Y(I,1)*PD1
193       CONTINUE
          Y1M=Y1M*PD1
          Y1N=Y1N*PD1
          Y2M=Y2M*PD2
          Y2N=Y2N*PD2
          D1=(Y1M-Y1N)/WA
          D2=(Y2M-Y2N)/HA
          IF(D1)199,200,199
200       D1=Y1M/WA
199       IF(D2)208,209,208
209       D2=Y2M/HA
```

```
208     DO 210 I=1,20
        IF(Y(I,1))211,210,211
211     NY(I,1)=(Y(I,1)-Y1N)/D1
        NY(I,2)=(Y(I,2)-Y2N)/D2
        GO TO (210,210,212,213,214,213),NLS
214     NY(I,5)=(Y(I,5)-Y2N)/D2
213     NY(I,4)=(Y(I,4)-Y2N)/D2
212     NY(I,3)=(Y(I,3)-Y2N)/D2
210     CONTINUE
        NH=H
        NW=W
        M=AM
        PUNCH 300,1,NW,NH,M,M,0,0
        GO TO (228,229,230,231,232,227),NLS
228     PUNCH 300,2,01,00
233     DO 234 I=1,20
        IF(Y(I,1))235,234,235
235     PUNCH 300,3,NY(I,1),NY(I,2)
234     CONTINUE
        GO TO 244
229     PUNCH 300,2,31,00
        GO TO 233
230     PUNCH 300,2,42,00,01
236     DO 237 I=1,20
        IF(Y(I,1))238,237,238
238     PUNCH 300,3,NY(I,1),NY(I,2),NY(I,3)
237     CONTINUE
        GO TO 244
231     PUNCH 300,2,43,00,01,10
239     DO 240 I=1,20
        IF(Y(I,1))241,240,241
241     PUNCH 300,3,NY(I,1),NY(I,2),NY(I,3),NY(I,4)
240     CONTINUE
        GO TO 244
232     PUNCH 300,2,44,00,01,10,11
        DO 242 I=1,20
        IF(Y(I,1))243,242,243
243     PUNCH 300,3,NY(I,1),NY(I,2),NY(I,3),NY(I,4),NY(I,5)
242     CONTINUE
        GO TO 244
227     PUNCH 300,2,33,01,00,01
        GO TO 239
244     NXL=-50
        PUNCH 300,4,155,NXL,01
        PUNCH305,NN1,SF1
        NXL=-100
        PUNCH 300,4,NXL,800,11
        PUNCH304,NN2,SF2
        NL=-100
        PUNCH 300,4,155,NL,00
        PUNCH 301,NQR,L,RUN,TEMP
        NL=-125
        M3=JJ+M4-1
        PUNCH 300,4,155,NL,00
        GO TO (371,371,372,372,372,371),NLS
371     PUNCH 302,M4,OPER
        GO TO 373
372     PUNCH 306,M4,M3,OPER
373     NL=-150
        PUNCH 300,4,155,NL,00
        PUNCH 303,G1,G
        NS1=-25
```

```
NS2=0
PUNCH 300,5,NS2,NS1,N1P,N1A,N1D,00
PUNCH 300,5,NS1,NS2,N2P,N2A,N2D,10
PUNCH 300,6
M4=M3
IF(M5)1,15,15
END
```

ALGOL 60 FOR PROGRAM NUMBER 503

```
PROCEDURE CEEEE(w,h,am,wm,nLs,nqr); ARRAY y[1:20,1:10],ny[1:20,1:6],
a1,a2,a3,a4,b1,b2,b3,b4,aiax,aibx[1:5]; REAL w,h,am,wm; INTEGER nLs,nqr;
SWITCH sw1:=x13,x13,x12,x11,x10,x13; SWITCH sw2:=x17,x16,x17,x16,x17,x16,
x17,x16; SWITCH sw3:=x21,x21,x22,x22; SWITCH sw4:=x24,x25,x24,x25;
SWITCH sw5:=x37,x30,x35,x34,x33,x32,x31,x29; SWITCH sw6:=x48,x48,x46,x45,
x44,x48; SWITCH sw7:=x66,x66,x65,x64,x63,x64; SWITCH sw8:=xx4,xx4,xx3,
xx2,xx1,xx2; SWITCH sw9:=x68,x70,x71,x72,x74,x75; SWITCH sw10:=x77,x77,
x78,x78,x77;
       BEGIN INTEGER i,j,jj,k,ka,kb,kc,kd,ke,kf,kq,L,LL,m,m3,m4,m5,nprog,m6,
       m9,m10,n,npr,nq2,n1x,nn1,nn2,n14,n1d,n1p,n2a,n2d,n2p,nh,nw,nxL,nL,ns1,
       ns2,progn,feedp,oper,instr,run,g,g1; REAL aa,aaa,bb,d1,d2,devf1,devf2,eqo,
       ha,O,p,p1,p2,px,py,pd1,pd2,ppqq,pp,q,q1,q2,qq1,qq2,q99,qq1L,qq1u,qnr,qr,
       sf1,sf2,wa,wac1,wL1,wu1,wac2,wL2,wu2,wacrr,xx,xxx,yy,yyy,y1m,y1n,y2m,
       y2n,yn,temp,waveL;
X1:    nLs:=q99; npr:=nqr;
       IF nqr<300 THEN GO TO X2;
       npr:=nqr-300;
       IF npr=100 THEN GO TO X80
       ELSE IF npr>100 THEN npr:=npr-100;
X2:    IF npr<14 THEN GO TO X4
       ELSE IF npr=14 THEN GO TO X3;
       npr:=npr-13;
X3:    npr:=npr-2;
X4:    npr:=npr-9;
       m4:=0;
       FOR i:=1 STEP 1 UNTIL 20 DO
       BEGIN
           FOR j:=1 STEP 1 UNTIL 10 DO y[i,j]:=0;
           FOR j:=1 STEP 1 UNTIL 5 DO ny[i,j]:=0
       END;
       IF npr≤3 THEN GO TO X5;
       READ progn,feedp;
       GO TO X6;
X5:    READ nprog,feedp;
       IF npr<2 THEN GO TO X6
       ELSE IF npr>2 THEN
       BEGIN
           READ qq2;
           READ qq1L,qq1u;
           READ ppqq; GO TO X6END;
       READ qq1,qq2;
X6:    IF nqr=400 THEN GO TO X80
       ELSE IF nqr<400 THEN
       BEGIN
           READ j; GO TO X7END;
       READ j,wacrr;
X7:    IF npr<4 THEN
       BEGIN
           READ eqo;
           IF npr<1 THEN GO TO X80
```

```
        ELSE IF npr>1 THEN READ ppEND;
        READ m6;
        m5:=m6;
        READ k,L,m;
        IF npr<4 THEN
        BEGIN
          READ ka,kb,kc,kd
          GO TO X8END;
        READ ka,kb,kc,kd,ke,kf;
X8:     READ d1,wac1,wL1,wu1;
        READ d1,wac2,wL2,wu2;
        qnr:=L;  qnr:=qnr/10;
        FOR j:=1 STEP 1 UNTIL 20 DO
        BEGIN
          p:=j;
          IF qnr≤p THEN
          BEGIN
            LL:=j;  GO TO X9END
        END;
X9:     nLs:=q99;
        FOR j:=1 STEP 1 UNTIL 5 DO
          a1[j]:=a2[j]:=a3[j]:=a4[j]:=b1[j]:=b2[j]:=b3[j]:=b4[j]:=aiax[j]:=aibx[j]:=0;
        m3:=0;
        FOR i:=1 STEP 1 UNTIL 20 DO
        BEGIN
          y[i,1]:=y[i,7];
          FOR j:=2 STEP 1 UNTIL 5 DO ny[i,j]:=y[i,j]:=0
        END;
        IF nLs>6 THEN nLs:=6;
        GO TO sw1[nLs];
X10:    m3:=m3+1;
X11:    m3:=m3+1;
X12:    m3:=m3+1;
X13:    m3:=m3+2;
        jj:=m9:=0;  m10:=2;
        IF m4<0 THEN GO TO X80
        ELSE IF m4=0 THEN
        BEGIN
          m9:=m3;  m3:=2END;
X14:    FOR j:=m10 STEP 1 UNTIL m3 DO
        BEGIN
          m5:=m5-1;
          IF m5<0 THEN
          BEGIN
            m3:=jj+1;  nLs:=jj+1;
            IF jj≤0 THEN GO TO X80;
            GO TO XXX;
            jj:=jj+1END;
          FOR i:=1 STEP 1 UNTIL 20 DO READ y[i,j]
          IF npr>4 THEN GO TO X18;
          IF LL<4 THEN
          BEGIN
            READ aiax[j];  GO TO X15END;
```

```
        READ aiax[j],aibx[j];
X15:    GO TO sw2[LL];
X16:    READ a1[j],a2[j],a3[j],a4[j];
X17:    IF LL>6 THEN READ b1[j],b2[j],b3[j],b4[j]
X18:    END;
XXX:    IF m6<(1+m5) THEN GO TO X80
        ELSE IF m6>(1+m5) THEN GO TO X27;
        FOR i:=1 STEP 1 UNTIL 20 DO READ y[i,6];
        IF npr=4VLL>2 THEN GO TO X19;
        FOR i:=1 STEP 1 UNTIL 20 DO y[i,1]:=y[i,6];
        GO TO X20;
X19:    FOR i:=1 STEP 1 UNTIL 20 DO READ y[i,1]
X20:    FOR i:=1 STEP 1 UNTIL 20 DO y[i,7]:=y[i,1];
        GO TO sw3[k];
X21:    READ devf1; GO TO X23;
X22:    FOR i:=1 STEP 1 UNTIL 20 DO READ y[i,9];
X23:    GO TO sw4[k];
X24:    READ devf2;
        FOR i:=1 STEP 1 UNTIL 20 DO y[i,10]:=devf2Xy[i,1];
        GO TO X26;
X25:    FOR i:=1 STEP 1 UNTIL 20 DO READ y[i,10];
X26:    READ oper,instr;
        READ run,temp,waveL;
        IF m6>2 THEN
        BEGIN
           m10:=3; m3:=m9; GO TO X14END;
X27:    FOR i:=1 STEP 1 UNTIL 20 DO
        BEGIN
           IF y[i,1]<wL2Vy[i,1]>wu2 THEN
           FOR j:=1 STEP 1 UNTIL 10 DO y[i,j]:=0
        END;
        g:=g1:=20;
        m3:=m3-1; m4:=m4+1;
        FOR j:=2 STEP 1 UNTIL 5 DO
        FOR i:=1 STEP 1 UNTIL 20 DO
        IF y[i,1]≤0Vy[i,j]<wL1Vy[i,j]>wu1 THEN y[i,j]:=0;
        FOR i:=1 STEP 1 UNTIL 20 DO
        IF y[i,2]≤0 THEN g:=g-1;
        kq:=ka+2;
        IF kq>8 THEN kq:=kq-8;
        IF kq>8 THEN kq:=kq-8;
X28:    GO TO sw5[kq];
X29:    FOR i:=kd STEP 1 UNTIL ke DO y[i,2]:=0;
X30:    FOR i:=kb STEP 1 UNTIL kc DO y[i,2]:=0;
        GO TO X36;
X31:    y[kf,2]:=0;
X32:    y[ke,2]:=0;
X33:    y[kd,2]:=0;
X34:    y[kc,2]:=0;
X35:    y[kb,2]:=0;
X36:    FOR i:=1 STEP 1 UNTIL 20 DO
        FOR j:=2 STEP 1 UNTIL 5 DO
        IF y[i,2]=0 THEN y[i,j]:=0;
```

```
X37:    FOR i:=1 STEP 1 UNTIL 20 DO
        BEGIN
           IF y[i,6]≤0 THEN GO TO X43;
           IF nLs>6 THEN GO TO X80
           ELSE IF nLs=6 THEN
           BEGIN
              IF k≤2 THEN y[i,9]:=devf1Xy[i,2];
              y[i,3]:=y[i,2];
              y[i,2]:=y[i,3]+y[i,9];
              y[i,4]:=y[i,3]-y[i,9]END;
           FOR j:=2 STEP 1 UNTIL 5 DO
           BEGIN
              IF nLs>6 THEN GO TO X80
              ELSE IF nLs=6∧j<2 THEN GO TO X80
              ELSE IF nLs=6∧j>2 THEN GO TO X38;
              aaa:=y[i,6];
              aa:=y[i,6]↑3;
              xx:=aiax[j]+a1[j]Xaaa+a2[j]Xaaa↑2+a3[j]Xaa+a4[j]XaaXaaa;
              xx:=xxXaaa;
              aaa:=y[i,1];
              aa:=y[i,1]↑3;
              yy:=aibx[j]+b1[j]Xaaa+b2[j]Xaaa↑2+b3[j]Xaa+b4[j]XaaXaaa;
              yy:=yyXaaa;
              IF nLs>6∨(nLs=6∧j<2) THEN GO TO X80
              ELSE IF nLs<6 THEN GO TO X39;
              ELSE IF nLs=6∧j>2 THEN GO TO X38;
              aa:=y[i,3]Xwac1;
              y[i,2]:=y[i,2]-xx-yy;
              bb:=y[i,3]-xx-yy;
              IF bb<aa THEN GO TO X41;
              GO TO X40;
X38:          y[i,j]:=y[i,j]-xx-yy; GO TO X40;
X39:          aa:=y[i,j]Xwac1;
              y[i,j]:=y[i,j]-xx-yy;
              IF y[i,j]≥aa THEN
              BEGIN
X40:             y[i,j]:=y[i,j]/y[i,6]; GO TO X42END;
X41:          y[i,j]:=0
X42:       END;
           IF npr=4 THEN y[i,1]:=y[i,1]/y[i,6]
X43:    END;
        FOR i:=1 STEP 1 UNTIL 20 DO
        BEGIN
           IF y[i,2]=0 THEN GO TO X47;
           GO TO sw6[nLs];
X44:       IF y[i,5]=0 THEN GO TO X47;
X45:       IF y[i,4]=0 THEN GO TO X47;
X46:       IF y[i,3]≠0 THEN GO TO X48;
X47:       y[i,1]:=0
X48:    END;
        FOR i:=1 STEP 1 UNTIL 20 DO
        IF y[i,2]≤0 THEN g1:=g1-1;
        FOR i:=1 STEP 1 UNTIL 20 DO
```

```
      BEGIN
        IF y[i,1]≠0 THEN
        BEGIN
          y1m:=y[i,1]; y1n:=y[i,1];
          IF y[i,2]≠0 THEN
          BEGIN
            y2m:=y[i,2]; y2n:=y[i,2];
            GO TO X49END END
      END;
X49:  FOR i:=1 STEP 1 UNTIL 20 DO
      BEGIN
          IF y[i,1]≤0 THEN GO TO X50;
          IF y1m<y[i,1] THEN y1m:=y[i,1];
          IF y1n>y[i,1] THEN y1n:=y[i,1];
          FOR j:=2 STEP 1 UNTIL 5 DO
          BEGIN
            IF y[i,j]≤0 THEN GO TO X50;
            IF y2m<y[i,j] THEN y2m:=y[i,j];
            IF y2n>y[i,j] THEN y2n:=y[i,j]
X50:  END END;
      pd1:=(y1m-y1n)X0.1;
      y1m:=y1m+pd1; y1n:=y1n-pd1;
      pd2:=(y2m-y2n)X0.1;
      y2m:=y2m+pd2; y2n:=y2n-pd2;
      wa:=w-am; n:=wa/100; wa:=nX100;
      ha:=h-am; n:=ha/100; ha:=nX100;
      p1:=100X(y1m-y1n)/wa;
      FOR i:=1 STEP 1 UNTIL 20 DO
      BEGIN
        py:=i;
        q1:=abs(p1); q2:=abs(y1n);
        nq2:=q2; n1x:=O:=yn:=0;
        FOR j:=1 STEP 1 UNTIL 10000 DO
        BEGIN
          IF nq2<j THEN GO TO X51
          ELSE IF nq2=j THEN
          BEGIN
            nn1:=O:=j; q2:=q2-O;
            yn:=y1n; GO TO X51
        END;
X51:  IF q1≤q2 THEN
      BEGIN
          q:=q2X10↑py; GO TO X52END;
        q:=q1X10↑py
X52:  IF wm>q THEN GO TO X54;
      IF yn<0 THEN
      BEGIN
        qr:=yn+O; O:=-O;
        GO TO X53END;
      qr:=yn-O;
X53:  n1a:=qrX10↑py;
      n1d:=p1X10↑py; nn1:=0;
      n1p:=wa/100+1; sf1:=10↑py;
      GO TO X55
X54:  END;
```

```
X55:    p2:=100X(y2m−y2n)/ha;
        FOR i:=1 STEP 1 UNTIL 20 DO
        BEGIN
          px:=i;
          q1:=abs(p2); q2:=abs(y2n);
          nq2:=q2; nn2:=O:=yn:=0;
          FOR j:=1 STEP 1 UNTIL 10000 DO
          BEGIN
            IF nq2<j THEN GO TO X56
            ELSE IF nq2=j THEN
            BEGIN
              nn2:=O:=j;
              yn:=y2n; q2:=q2−O;
              GO TO X56END
          END;
X56:      IF q1≤q2 THEN
          BEGIN
            q:=q2X10↑px; GO TO X57END;
          q:=q1X10↑px;
X57:      IF wm>q THEN GO TO X59;
          IF yn<0 THEN
          BEGIN
            qr:=y2n+O; O:=−O;
            GO TO X58END;
          qr:=y2n−O;
X58:      n2a:=qrX10↑px;
          n2d:=p2X10↑px; nn2:=0;
          n2p:=ha/100+1; sf2:=10↑px;
          GO TO X60
X59:    END;
X60:    IF pd1=0 THEN
        BEGIN
          pd1:=1/y1m; GO TO X61END;
        pd1:=1/pd1;
X61:    IF pd2=0 THEN
        BEGIN
          pd2:=1/y2m; GO TO X62END;
        pd2:=1/pd2;
X62:    FOR i:=1 STEP 1 UNTIL 20 DO
        BEGIN
          IF y[i,1]=0 THEN GO TO X67;
          GO TO sw7[nLs];
X63:    y[i,5]:=y[i,5]Xpd2;
X64:    y[i,4]:=y[i,4]Xpd2;
X65:    y[i,3]:=y[i,3]Xpd2;
X66:    y[i,2]:=y[i,2]Xpd2;
        y[i,1]:=y[i,1]Xpd1
X67:    END;
        y1m:=y1mXpd1;
        y1n:=y1nXpd1;
        y2m:=y2mXpd2;
        y2n:=y2nXpd2;
        d1:=(y1m−y1n)/wa;
```

```
        d2:=(y2m−y2n)/ha;
        IF d1=0 THEN d1:=y1m/wa;
        IF d2=0 THEN d2:=y2m/ha;
        FOR i:=1 STEP 1 UNTIL 20 DO
        BEGIN
            IF y[i,1]≠0 THEN
            BEGIN
                ny[i,1]:=(y[i,1]−y1n)/d1;
                ny[i,2]:=(y[i,2]−y2n)/d2;
                GO TO sw8[nLs];
XX1:            ny[i,5]:=(y[i,5]−y2n)/d2;
XX2:            ny[i,4]:=(y[i,4]−y2n)/d2;
XX3:            ny[i,3]:=(y[i,3]−y2n)/d2END;
XX4:    END;
        nh:=h; nw:=w; m:=am;
        PUNCH 1,nw,nh,m,m,0,0;
        GO TO sw9[nLs];
X68:    PUNCH 2,1,0;
X69:    FOR i:=1 STEP 1 UNTIL 20 DO
        IF y[i,1]≠0 THEN PUNCH 3,ny[i,1],ny[i,2];
        GO TO X76;
X70:    PUNCH 2,31,0;
        GO TO X69;
X71:    PUNCH 2,42,0,1;
        FOR i:=1 STEP 1 UNTIL 20 DO
        IF y[i,1]≠0 THEN PUNCH 3,ny[i,1],ny[i,2],ny[i,3];
        GO TO X76;
X72:    PUNCH 2,43,0,1,10;
X73:    FOR i:=1 STEP 1 UNTIL 20 DO
        IF y[i,1]≠0 THEN
        PUNCH 3,ny[i,1],ny[i,2],ny[i,3],ny[i,4];
        GO TO X76;
X74:    PUNCH 2,44,0,1,10,11;
        FOR i:=1 STEP 1 UNTIL 20 DO
        IF y[i,1]≠0 THEN
        PUNCH 3,ny[i,1],ny[i,2],ny[i,3],ny[i,4],ny[i,5];
        GO TO X76;
X75:    PUNCH 2,33,1,0,1;
        GO TO X73;
X76:    nxL:=−50;
        PUNCH 4,155,nxL,1;
        PUNCH nn1,sf1;
        nxL:=−100;
        PUNCH 4,nxL,800,11;
        PUNCH nn2,sf2;
        nL:=−100;
        PUNCH 4,155,nL,0;
        PUNCH nqr,run,temp;
        nL:=−125;
        m3:=jj+m4−1;
        PUNCH 4,155,nL,0;
        GO TO sw10[nLs];
X77:    PUNCH m4,oper;
```

```
            GO TO X79;
X78:    PUNCH m4,m3,oper;
X79:    nL:=-150;
        PUNCH 4,155,nL,0;
        PUNCH g1,g;
        ns1:=-25; ns2:=0;
        PUNCH 5,ns2,ns1,n1p,n1a,n1d,0;
        PUNCH 5,ns1,ns2,n2p,n2a,n2d,10;
        PUNCH 6; m4:=m3;
        IF m5≥0 THEN GO TO X9
X80: END(CEEEE);
X81: READ w,h,am,wm,nLs; q99:=nLs;
X82: READ nqr;
        PROCEDURE(w,h,am,wm,nLs,nqr);
        GO TO X82;
```

AUTOPLOTTER PROGRAM NUMBER 504

CALL WORD DEEEE

```
C  C  AUTOPLOTTER PROGRAM NUMBER 504 (CALL WORD DEEEE)
300    FORMAT(I5,I5,I5,I5,I5,I5,I5,I5)
301    FORMAT (8HPROGRAM ,I3,4H L ,I3,6H  RUN ,F5.1,7H  TEMP ,F4.1)
302    FORMAT(14HWAVELENGTH IS ,I2,11H  OPERATOR ,F9.0)
303    FORMAT (F4.1,28H POINTS ARE RETAINED OUT OF ,F4.1)
304    FORMAT (8HY MINUS ,I6,7H TIMES ,F12.3)
305    FORMAT (9HX1 MINUS ,I6,7H TIMES ,F12.3)
306    FORMAT (17HWAVELENGTHS FROM ,I2,4H TO ,I2,11H  OPERATOR ,F9.0)
       DIMENSION Y(20,10),NY(20,5),A1(5),A2(5),A3(5),A4(5),B1(5),B2(5)
       DIMENSION B3(5),B4(5),CA1(5),CA2(5),CA3(5),CA4(5),CB1(5),CB2(5)
       DIMENSION CB3(5),CB4(5),AIAX(5),AIBX(5),AIC1X(5),AIC2X(5),C(20,2)
       READ,W,H,AM,WM,NLS
       Q99=NLS
1      READ,NQR
       NLS=Q99
       NPR=NQR
       IF(NQR-300)2,3,3
3      NPR=NQR-300
       IF(NPR-100)2,1,506
506    NPR=NPR-100
2      IF(NPR-15)4,5,1
5      NPR=NPR-1
4      NPR=NPR-11
       M4=0
       DO 6 I=1,20
       DO 7 J=1,10
7      Y(I,J)=0.0
       DO 8 J=1,5
8      NY(I,J)=0
6      CONTINUE
       IF(NPR-3)10,11,1
11     READ,QNR,FEEDP
       NQR=QNR
       READ,QQ1,QQ2,QQ3
       READ,QQ4L,QQ4U
       READ,PPQQ
       GO TO 12
10     READ,NQR,FEEDP
       IF(NPR-2)12,14,1
14     READ,QQ1,QQ2,QQ3,QQ4
12     IF(NQR-400)507,1,508
507    READ,J
       GO TO 509
508    READ,J,WACRR
509    READ,EQ0,EQ1,EQ2
       READ,PP
       READ,M6
       M5=M6
       READ,K,L,M
       READ,KA,KB,KC,KD
       READ,D1,WAC1,WL1,WU1
       READ,D1,WAC2,WL2,WU2
       QNR=L
       QNR=QNR/10.0
       DO 13 J=1,20
       P=J
       IF(QNR-P)16,16,13
16     LL=J
       GO TO 15
```

```
13      CONTINUE
15      NLS=Q99
        DO 9 J=1,5
        A1(J)=0.0
        A2(J)=0.0
        A3(J)=0.0
        A4(J)=0.0
        B1(J)=0.0
        B2(J)=0.0
        B3(J)=0.0
        B4(J)=0.0
        AIAX(J)=0.0
        AIBX(J)=0.0
        AIC1X(J)=0.0
        AIC2X(J)=0.0
        CA1(J)=0.0
        CA2(J)=0.0
        CA3(J)=0.0
        CA4(J)=0.0
        CB1(J)=0.0
        CB2(J)=0.0
        CB3(J)=0.0
9       CB4(J)=0.0
        DO 17 I=1,20
        Y(I,1)=Y(I,7)
        DO 18 J=2,5
        NY(I,J)=0
18      Y(I,J)=0.0
17      CONTINUE
        M3=0
        IF(NLS-6)264,264,257
257     NLS=6
264     GO TO (23,23,24,25,26,23),NLS
26      M3=M3+1
25      M3=M3+1
24      M3=M3+1
23      M3=M3+2
        JJ=0
        M9=0
        M10=2
        IF(M4)1,378,379
378     M9=M3
        M3=2
379     DO 21 J=M10,M3
        M5=M5-1
        IF(M5)368,22,22
368     M3=JJ+1
        NLS=JJ+1
        IF(JJ)1,1,29
22      JJ=JJ+1
        DO 27 I=1,20,4
27      READ,Y(I,J),Y(I+1,J),Y(I+2,J),Y(I+3,J)
        READ,AIAX(J),AIC1X(J),AIBX(J),AIC2X(J)
        IF(LL-9)389,390,390
389     GO TO (387,387,387,387,388,388,388,388),LL
390     LX=LL-8
        GO TO (387,387,387,387,388,388,388),LX
388     READ,A1(J),A2(J),A3(J),A4(J)
387     IF(LL-9)391,392,392
391     GO TO (393,393,393,394,394,393,394,394),LL
392     LX=LL-8
        GO TO (394,394,394,393,393,393,394),LX
```

```
394      READ,B1(J),B2(J),B3(J),B4(J)
393      IF(LL-9)395,396,396
395      GO TO (397,397,398,398,398,397,397,398),LL
396      LX=LL-8
         GO TO (397,398,397,398,398,398,397),LX
398      READ,CA1(J),CA2(J),CA3(J),CA4(J)
397      IF(LL-9)399,400,400
399      GO TO (401,402,402,402,402,401,401,401),LL
400      LX=LL-8
         GO TO (401,401,402,401,401,402,402),LX
402      READ,CB1(J),CB2(J),CB3(J),CB4(J)
401      CONTINUE
21       CONTINUE
29       IF(M6-1-M5)1,30,380
30       DO 31 I=1,20,4
31       READ,Y(I,6),Y(I+1,6),Y(I+2,6),Y(I+3,6)
         DO 32 I=1,20,4
32       READ,Y(I,1),Y(I+1,1),Y(I+2,1),Y(I+3,1)
         IF(NPR-1)1,483,484
483      QQ1=2.0
         QQ2=2.0
484      PPT=0.0
         XAA=0.0
         R=0.0
         DO 485I=1,20
         IF(Y(I,6))485,485,486
486      IF(Y(I,1))485,485,487
487      IF(XAA)1,489,492
489      AA=Y(I,6)
         EQR=EQ1
         QQ4=QQ1
         GO TO 490
492      AA=Y(I,1)
         EQR=EQ2
         QQ4=QQ2
490      IF(XAA)1,501,502
502      IF(QQ2-2.0)499,500,499
501      IF(QQ1-2.0)499,500,499
500      BB=((4.0*EQR*AA+1.0)-SQR(8.0*EQR*AA+1.0)))/(8.0*EQR)
         GO TO 495
499      R=R+1.0
         RR=1.0/(2.0**R)
488      PPT=PPT+RR
493      BB=PPT*AA
         BR=EQR*((AA-QQ4*BB)**QQ4)
         IF(BR-BB)494,495,488
494      IF(RR-PP)495,495,498
495      IF(XAA)1,496,497
496      C(I,1)=BB
         XAA=XAA+1.0
         R=0.0
         PPT=0.0
         GO TO 492
497      XAA=0.0
         C(I,2)=BB
         R=0.0
         PPT=0.0
         GO TO 485
498      PPT=PPT-RR
         GO TO 490
485      CONTINUE
         DO 434 I=1,20
```

```
434    Y(I,7)=Y(I,1)
       GO TO (283,283,284,284),K
283    READ,DEVF1
       GO TO 286
284    DO 285 I=1,20,4
285    READ,Y(I,9),Y(I+1,9),Y(I+2,9),Y(I+3,9)
286    GO TO (287,288,287,288),K
287    READ,DEVF2
       DO 289 I=1,20
289    Y(I,10)=DEVF2*Y(I,1)
       GO TO 290
288    DO 291 I=1,20,4
291    READ,Y(I,10),Y(I+1,10),Y(I+2,10),Y(I+3,10)
290    READ,OPER,INSTR
       READ,RUN,TEMP,WAVEL
       IF(M9-2)380,380,381
381    M10=3
       M3=M9
       GO TO 379
380    DO 292 I=1,20
       IF(Y(I,1)-WL2)293,294,294
294    IF(Y(I,1)-WU2)292,292,293
293    DO 279 J=1,10
279    Y(I,J)=0.0
292    CONTINUE
       G=20.0
       G1=20.0
       M3=M3-1
       M4=M4+1
       DO 296 J=2,5
       DO 299 I=1,20
       IF(Y(I,1))297,297,298
298    IF(Y(I,J)-WL1)297,308,308
308    IF(Y(I,J)-WU1)299,299,297
297    Y(I,J)=0.0
299    CONTINUE
296    CONTINUE
       DO 309 I=1,20
       IF(Y(I,2))310,310,309
310    G=G-1.0
309    CONTINUE
       KE=KA+2
       GO TO (311,312,313,314,315),KE
312    DO 319 I=KB,KC
       DO 320 J=2,5
320    Y(I,J)=0.0
319    CONTINUE
       GO TO 311
315    DO 316 J=2,5
316    Y(KD,J)=0.0
314    DO 317 J=2,5
317    Y(KC,J)=0.0
313    DO 318 J=2,5
318    Y(KB,J)=0.0
311    DO 323 I=1,20
       IF(Y(I,6))323,323,325
325    IF(NLS-6)419,420,1
420    IF(K-2)421,421,422
421    Y(I,9)=DEVF1*Y(I,2)
422    Y(I,3)=Y(I,2)
       Y(I,2)=Y(I,3)+Y(I,9)
       Y(I,4)=Y(I,3)-Y(I,9)
```

```
419      DO 423 J=2,5
         IF(NLS-6)481,482,1
482      IF(J-2)1,481,480
481      AAA=Y(I,6)-QQ1*C(I,1)
         AA=AAA*AAA*AAA
         XX=AIAX(J)+A1(J)*AAA+A2(J)*AAA*AAA+A3(J)*AA+A4(J)*AA*AAA
         XX=XX*AAA
         AAA=Y(I,1)-QQ2*C(I,2)
         AA=AAA*AAA*AAA
         YY=AIBX(J)+B1(J)*AAA+B2(J)*AAA*AAA+B3(J)*AA+B4(J)*AA*AAA
         YY=YY*AAA
         XY=C(I,1)*AIC1X(J)
         YX=C(I,2)*AIC2X(J)
         IF(NLS-6)477,478,1
478      IF(J-2)1,479,480
479      AA=Y(I,3)*WAC1
         Y(I,2)=Y(I,2)-XX-YY-XY-YX
         BB=Y(I,3)-XX-YY-XY-YX
         IF(BB-AA)424,324,324
480      Y(I,J)=Y(I,J)-XX-YY-XY-YX
         GO TO 324
477      AA=Y(I,J)*WAC1
         Y(I,J)=Y(I,J)-XX-YY-XY-YX
         IF(Y(I,J)-AA)424,324,324
424      Y(I,J)=0.0
         GO TO 423
324      Y(I,J)=Y(I,J)/Y(I,6)
423      CONTINUE
323      CONTINUE
         DO 470 I=1,20
         IF(Y(I,2))471,472,471
471      GO TO (470,470,473,474,475,474),NLS
475      IF(Y(I,5))474,472,474
474      IF(Y(I,4))473,472,473
473      IF(Y(I,3))470,472,470
472      Y(I,1)=0.0
470      CONTINUE
         DO 321 I=1,20
         IF(Y(I,2))322,322,321
322      G1=G1-1.0
321      CONTINUE
         DO 36 I=1,20
         IF(Y(I,1))37,36,37
37       Y1M=Y(I,1)
         Y1N=Y(I,1)
         IF(Y(I,2))430,36,430
430      Y2M=Y(I,2)
         Y2N=Y(I,2)
         GO TO 42
36       CONTINUE
42       DO 41 I=1,20
         IF(Y(I,1))41,41,425
425      IF(Y1M-Y(I,1))44,43,43
44       Y1M=Y(I,1)
43       IF(Y1N-Y(I,1))46,46,45
45       Y1N=Y(I,1)
46       DO 47 J=2,5
         IF(Y(I,J))47,47,426
426      IF(Y2M-Y(I,J))48,49,49
48       Y2M=Y(I,J)
49       IF(Y2N-Y(I,J))47,47,50
50       Y2N=Y(I,J)
```

```
47      CONTINUE
41       CONTINUE
         PD1=(Y1M-Y1N)*0.1
         Y1M=Y1M+PD1
         Y1N=Y1N-PD1
         PD2=(Y2M-Y2N)*0.1
         Y2M=Y2M+PD2
         Y2N=Y2N-PD2
         WA=W-AM
        N=WA/100.0
         WA=N*100
         HA=H-AM
         N=HA/100.0
         HA=N*100
         P1=100.0*(Y1M-Y1N)/WA
         DO 110 I=1,20
         PY=I
         Q1=SQR(P1*P1)
         Q2=SQR(Y1N*Y1N)
         NQ2=Q2
         N1X=0
         O=0.0
         YN=0.0
         DO 116 J=1,10000
         IF(NQ2- J)117,118,116
118      NN1=J
         O=J
         Q2=Q2-O
         YN=Y1N
         GO TO 117
116      CONTINUE
117      IF(Q1-Q2)147,147,148
147      Q=Q2*(10.0**PY)
         GO TO 149
148      Q=Q1*(10.0**PY)
149      IF(WM-Q)150,150,110
150      IF(YN)156,157,157
156      QR=YN+O
         O=-O
         GO TO 158
157      QR=YN-O
158      N1A=QR*(10.0**PY)
         N1D=P1*(10.0**PY)
         N1P=WA/100.0+1.0
         SF1=10.0**PY
         NN1=0
         GO TO 163
110      CONTINUE
163      P2=100.0*(Y2M-Y2N)/HA
         DO 164 I=1,20
         PX=I
         Q1=SQR(P2*P2)
         Q2=SQR(Y2N*Y2N)
         NQ2=Q2
         NN2=0
         YN=0.0
         O=0.0
         DO 165 J=1,10000
         IF(NQ2-J)166,167,165
167      NN2=J
         O=J
         YN=Y2N
```

```
           Q2=Q2-0
            GO TO 166
165        CONTINUE
166        IF(Q1-Q2)168,168,169
168        Q=Q2*(10.0**PX)
            GO TO 170
169        Q=Q1*(10.0**PX)
170        IF(WM-Q)171,171,164
171        IF(YN)172,173,173
172        QR=Y2N+0
            O=-0
            GO TO 174
173        QR=Y2N-0
174        N2A=QR*(10.0**PX)
            N2D=P2*(10.0**PX)
            N2P=HA/100.0+1.0
            SF2=10.0**PX
            NN2=0
            GO TO 175
164        CONTINUE
175        IF(PD1)176,177,176
177        PD1=1.0/Y1M
            GO TO 178
176        PD1=1.0/PD1
178        IF(PD2)179,180,179
180        PD2=1.0/Y2M
            GO TO 181
179        PD2=1.0/PD2
181        DO 193 I=1,20
            IF(Y(I,1))194,193,194
194        GO TO (185,185,184,183,182,183),NLS
182        Y(I,5)=Y(I,5)*PD2
183        Y(I,4)=Y(I,4)*PD2
184        Y(I,3)=Y(I,3)*PD2
185        Y(I,2)=Y(I,2)*PD2
            Y(I,1)=Y(I,1)*PD1
193        CONTINUE
            Y1M=Y1M*PD1
            Y1N=Y1N*PD1
            Y2M=Y2M*PD2
            Y2N=Y2N*PD2
            D1=(Y1M-Y1N)/WA
            D2=(Y2M-Y2N)/HA
            IF(D1)199,200,199
200        D1=Y1M/WA
199        IF(D2)208,209,208
209        D2=Y2M/HA
208        DO 210 I=1,20
            IF(Y(I,1))211,210,211
211        NY(I,1)=(Y(I,1)-Y1N)/D1
            NY(I,2)=(Y(I,2)-Y2N)/D2
            GO TO (210,210,212,213,214,213),NLS
214        NY(I,5)=(Y(I,5)-Y2N)/D2
213        NY(I,4)=(Y(I,4)-Y2N)/D2
212        NY(I,3)=(Y(I,3)-Y2N)/D2
210        CONTINUE
            NH=H
            NW=W
            M=AM
            PUNCH 300,1,NW,NH,M,M,0,0
            GO TO (228,229,230,231,232,227),NLS
228        PUNCH 300,2,01,00
```

```
233     DO 234 I=1,20
        IF(Y(I,1))235,234,235
235     PUNCH 300,3,NY(I,1),NY(I,2)
234     CONTINUE
        GO TO 244
229     PUNCH 300,2,31,00
        GO TO 233
230     PUNCH 300,2,42,00,01
236     DO 237 I=1,20
        IF(Y(I,1))238,237,238
238     PUNCH 300,3,NY(I,1),NY(I,2),NY(I,3)
237     CONTINUE
        GO TO 244
231     PUNCH 300,2,43,00,01,10
239     DO 240 I=1,20
        IF(Y(I,1))241,240,241
241     PUNCH 300,3,NY(I,1),NY(I,2),NY(I,3),NY(I,4)
240     CONTINUE
        GO TO 244
232    PUNCH 300,2,44,00,01,10,11
        DO 242 I=1,20
        IF(Y(I,1))243,242,243
243     PUNCH 300,3,NY(I,1),NY(I,2),NY(I,3),NY(I,4),NY(I,5)
242     CONTINUE
        GO TO 244
227     PUNCH 300,2,33,01,00,01
        GO TO 239
244     NXL=-50
        PUNCH 300,4,155,NXL,01
        PUNCH 305,NN1,SF1
        NXL=-100
        PUNCH 300,4,NXL,800,11
        PUNCH 304,NN2,SF2
        NL=-100
        PUNCH 300,4,155,NL,00
        PUNCH 301,NQR,L,RUN,TEMP
        NL=-125
        M3=JJ+M4-1
        PUNCH 300,4,155,NL,00
        GO TO (371,371,372,372,372,371),NLS
371     PUNCH 302,M4,OPER
        GO TO 373
372     PUNCH 306,M4,M3,OPER
373     NL=-150
        PUNCH 300,4,155,NL,00
        PUNCH 303,G1,G
        NS1=-25
        NS2=0
        PUNCH 300,5,NS2,NS1,N1P,N1A,N1D,00
        PUNCH 300,5,NS1,NS2,N2P,N2A,N2D,10
        PUNCH 300,6
        M4=M3
        IF(M5)1,15,15
        END
```

ALGOL 60 FOR PROGRAM NUMBER 504

PROCEDURE DEEEE(w,h,am,wm,nLs,nqr), ARRAY y[1:20,1:10],ny[1:20,1:5],
c[1:20,1:2],a1,a2,a3,a4,b1,b2,b3,b4, ca1,ca2,ca3,ca4,cb1,cb2,cb3,cb4,aiax,aibx,
aic1x,aic2x[1:5]; REAL w,h,am,wm; INTEGER nLs,nqr; SWITCH sw1:=x9,x9
x8,x7,x6,x9; SWITCH sw2:=x11,x11,x11,x11,x10,x10,x10,x10; SWITCH sw3:=x11,
x11,x11,x11,x10,x10,x10; SWITCH sw4:=x13,x13,x13,x12,x12,x13,x12,x12;
SWITCH sw5:=x12,x12,x12,x13,x13,x13,x12; SWITCH sw6:=x15,x15,x14,x14,x14,
x15,x15,x14; SWITCH sw7:=x15,x14,x15,x14,x14,x14,x15; SWITCH sw8:=x17,x16,
x16,x16,x16,x17,x17,x17; SWITCH sw9:=x17,x17,x16,x17,x17,x16,x16; SWITCH
sw10:=x27,x27,x28,x28; SWITCH sw11:=x30,x31,x30,x31; SWITCH sw12:=x39,
x35,x38,x37,x36; SWITCH sw13:=xx1,xx1,x48,x47,x46,x47; SWITCH sw14:=x66,
x66,x65,x64,x63,x64; SWITCH sw15:=x71,x71,x70,x69,x68,x69; SWITCH sw16:
=x72,x74,x75,x76,x78,x79; SWITCH sw17:=x81,x81,x82,x82,x82,x81;
COMMENT: Autoplotter Program for Fortran Programs 12, 13, 15, 312, 313,
315, 412, 413, and 415
    BEGIN INTEGER i,j,jj,ka,kb,kc,kd,ke,L,LL,Lx,m,m3,m4,m5,m6,m9,m10,
    n,npr,nq2,n1x,nn1,n1a,n1d,n1p,nn2,n2a,n2p,nh,nw,nxL,feedp,oper,instr,run,
    g,g1;
    REAL aa,aaa,bb,br,d1,eqo,eq1,eq2,eqr,ha,O,pp,ppqq,p,ppt,pd1,pd2,p1,p2,
    py,px,q,q1,q2,q99,qnr,qq1,qq2,qq3,qq4,qq4L,qq4u,r,rr,sf1,sf2,temp,wac1,
    wac2,wL1,wL2,wu1,wu2,waveL,wa,wacrr,xxa,xx,xy,yx,yy,y1m,y2m,y1n,
    y2n,yn;
        nLs:=q99;
        npr:=nqr;
        IF nqr<300 THEN GO TO X1;
        npr:=nqr−300;
        IF npr=100 THEN GO TO X84
        ELSE IF npr>100 THEN npr:=npr−100;
X1:   IF npr>15 THEN GO TO X84
        ELSE IF npr=15 THEN npr:=npr−1;
        npr:=npr−11;
        m4:=0;
        FOR i:=1 STEP 1 UNTIL 20 DO
        BEGIN
            FOR j:=1 STEP 1 UNTIL 10 DO y[i,j]:=0;
            FOR j:=1 STEP 1 UNTIL 5 DO ny[i,j]=0
        END;
        IF npr>3 THEN GO TO X84
        ELSE IF npr<3 THEN GO TO X2;
        READ qnr,feedp;
        nqr:=qnr;
        READ qq1,qq2,qq3;
        READ qq4L,qq4u;
        READ ppqq; GO TO X3;
X2:   READ nqr,feedp;
        IF npr>2 THEN GO TO X84
        ELSE IF npr=2 THEN READ qq1,qq2,qq3,qq4;
X3:   IF nqr=400 THEN GO TO X84
        ELSE IF nqr<400 THEN
        BEGIN
            READ j; GO TO X4END;
        READ j,wacrr;

```
X4:     READ eq0,eq1,eq2;
        READ pp; READ m6; m5:=m6;
        READ k,L,m;
        READ ka,kb,kc,kd;
        READ d1,wac1,wL1,wu1;
        READ d1,wac2,wL2,wu2;
        qnr:=L/10;
        FOR j:=1 STEP 1 UNTIL 20 DO
        BEGIN
          p:=j;
          IF qnr≤p THEN
          BEGIN
            LL:=j; GO TO X5END
        END;
X5:     nLs:=q99;
        FOR j:=1 STEP 1 UNTIL 5 DO
          a1[j]:=a2[j]:=a3[j]:=a4[j]:=b1[j]:=b2[j]:=b3[j]:=b4[j]:=aiax[j]:=aibx[j]
             :=aic1x[j]:=aic2x[j]:=ca1[j]:=ca2[j]:=ca3[j]:=ca4[j]:=cb1[j]:=cb2[j]
             :=cb3[j]:=cb4[j]:=0;
        FOR i:=1 STEP 1 UNTIL 20 DO
        BEGIN
          y[i,1]:=y[i,7];
          FOR j:=2 STEP 1 UNTIL 5 DO ny[i,j]:=y[i,j]:=0
        END;
        m3:=0;
        IF nLs>6 THEN nLs=6;
        GO TO sw1[nLs];
X6:     m3:=m3+1;
X7:     m3:=m3+1;
X8:     m3:=m3+1;
X9:     m3:=m3+2;
        jj:=m9:=0; m10:=2;
        IF m4<0 THEN GO TO X84
        ELSE IF m4=0 THEN
        BEGIN
          m9:=m3; m3:=2END;
XZ:     FOR j:=m10 STEP 1 UNTIL m3 DO
        BEGIN
          m5:=m5−1;
          IF m5<0 THEN
          BEGIN
            m3:=jj+1; nLs:=jj+1;
            IF jj≤0 THEN GO TO X84
            ELSE GO TO X18END;
          jj:=jj+1;
          FOR i:=1 STEP 1 UNTIL 20 DO READ y[i,j];
          READ aiax[j],aic1x[j],aibx[j],aic2x[j];
          IF LL<9 THEN GO TO sw2[LL];
          Lx:=LL−8;
          GO TO sw3[Lx];
X10:      READ a1[j],a2[j],a3[j],a4[j];
X11:      IF LL<9 THEN GO TO sw4[LL];
          lx:=LL−8;
```

```
        GO TO sw5[Lx];
X12:    READ b1[j],b2[j],b3[j],b4[j];
X13:    IF LL<9 THEN GO TO sw6[LL];
        Lx:=LL−8;
        GO TO sw7[Lx];
X14:    READ ca1[j],ca2[j],ca3[j],ca4[j];
X15:    IF LL<9 THEN GO TO sw8[LL];
        Lx:=LL−8;
        GO TO sw9[Lx];
X16:    READ cb1[j],cb2[j],cb3[j],cb4[j]
X17:    END;
X18:    IF m6<(1+m5) THEN GO TO X84
        ELSE IF m6>(1+m5) THEN GO TO X34;
        FOR i:=1 STEP 1 UNTIL 20 DO READ y[i,6];
        FOR i:=1 STEP 1 UNTIL 20 DO READ y[i,1];
        IF npr<1 THEN GO TO X84
        ELSE IF npr=1 THEN qq1:=qq2:=2;
        ppt:=xaa:=r:=0;
        FOR i:=1 STEP 1 UNTIL 20 DO
        BEGIN
            IF y[i,6]≤0∨y[i,1]≤0 THEN GO TO X26;
            IF xaa<0 THEN GO TO X84
            ELSE IF xaa=0 THEN
            BEGIN
              aa:=y[i,6]; eqr:=eq1;
              qq4:=qq1; GO TO X20END;
X19.        aa:=y[i,1]; eqr:=eq2;
            qq4:=qq2;
X20:        IF xaa<0 THEN GO TO X84
            ELSE IF xaa>0 THEN
            BEGIN
                IF qq2=2 THEN GO TO X21
                ELSE GO TO X22END;
            IF qq1≠2 THEN GO TO X22
X21:        bb:=((4XeqrXaa+1)−sqrt(8XeqrXaa+1))/(8Xeqr);
            GO TO X24;
X22:        r:=r+1; rr:=1/2↑r;
X23;        ppt:=ppt+rr;
            bb:=pptXaa;
            br:=eqrX((aa−qq4Xbb)↑qq4);
            IF br>bb THEN GO TO X23
            ELSE IF br<bb∧rr>pp THEN GO TO X25;
X24:        IF xaa<0 THEN GO TO X84
            ELSE IF xaa=0 THEN
            BEGIN
              c[i,1]:=bb; xaa:=xaa+1;
              r:=ppt:=0; GO TO X19END;
            c[i,2]:=bb;
            r:=ppt:=xxa:=0;
            GO TO X26;
X25:        ppt:=ppt−rr;
            GO TO X20
X26:    END;
```

```
        FOR i:=1 STEP 1 UNTIL 20 DO y[i,7]:=y[i,1];
        GO TO sw10[k];
X27;    READ devf1; GO TO X29;
X28:    FOR i:=1 STEP 1 UNTIL 20 DO READ y[i,9];
X29:    GO TO sw11[k];
X30:    READ devf2;
        FOR i:=1 STEP 1 UNTIL 20 DO y[i,10]:=devf2Xy[i,1];
        GO TO X32;
X31:    FOR i:=1 STEP 1 UNTIL 20 DO READ y[i,10];
X32:    READ oper,instr;
        READ run,temp,waveL;
        IF m9≤2 THEN
        BEGIN
            m10:=3; m3:=m9; GO TO XZEND;
X34:    FOR i:=1 STEP 1 UNTIL 20 DO
        BEGIN
            IF y[i,1]<wL2Vy[i,1]>wu2 THEN
            FOR j:=1 STEP 1 UNTIL 10 DO y[i,j]:=0
        END;
        g:=g1:=20;
        m3:=m3−1; m4:=m4+1;
        FOR j:=2 STEP 1 UNTIL 5 DO
        FOR i:=1 STEP 1 UNTIL 20 DO
        IF y[i,1]≤0Vy[i,j]<wL1Vy[i,j]>wu1 THEN y[i,j]:=0;
        FOR i:=1 STEP 1 UNTIL 20 DO
        IF y[i,2]≤0 THEN g:=g−1;
        ke:=ka+2;
        GO TO sw12[ke];
X35:    FOR i:=kb STEP 1 UNTIL kc DO
        FOR j:=2 STEP 1 UNTIL 5 DO y[i,j]:=0;
        GO TO X39;
X36:    FOR j:=2 STEP 1 UNTIL 5 DO y[kd,j]:=0;
X37:    FOR j:=2 STEP 1 UNTIL 5 DO y[kc,j]:=0;
X38:    FOR j:=2 STEP 1 UNTIL 5 DO y[kb,j]:=0;
X39:    FOR i:=1 STEP 1 UNTIL 20 DO
        BEGIN
            IF y[i,6]≤0 THEN GO TO X45;
            IF nLs>6 THEN GO TO X84
            ELSE IF nLs=6 THEN
            BEGIN
                IF k≤2 THEN y[i,9]:=devf1Xy[i,2];
                y[i,3]:=y[i,2];
                y[i,2]:=y[i,3]+y[i,9];
                y[i,4]:=y[i,3]−y[i,9]END;
X40:    FOR j:=2 STEP 1 UNTIL 5 DO
        BEGIN
            IF nLs>6V[nLs=6∧j<2) THEN GO TO X84
            ELSE IF nLs=6∧j>2 THEN GO TO X41;
            aaa:=y[i,6]−qq1Xc[i,1];
            aa:=aaa↑3;
            xx:=aiax[j]+a1[j]Xaaa+a2[j]Xaaa↑2+a3[j]Xaa+a4[j]XaaXaaa;
            xx:=xxXaaa;
            aaa:=y[i,1]−qq2Xc[i,2];
```

```
           aa:=aaa↑3;
           yy:=aibx[j]+b1[j]Xaaa+b2[j]Xaaa↑2+b3[j]Xaa+b4[j]XaaXaaa;
           yy:=yyXaaa;
           xy:=c[i,1]Xaic1x[j];
           yx:=c[i,2]Xaic2x[j];
           IF nLs>6∨(nLs=6∧j<2) THEN GO TO X84
           ELSE IF nLs<6 THEN GO TO X42
           ELSE IF j=2 THEN
           BEGIN
               aa:=y[i,3]Xwac1;
               y[i,2]:=y[i,2]−xx−yy−xy−yx;
               bb:=y[i,3]−xx−yy−xy−yx;
               IF bb<aa THEN GO TO X43
               ELSE GO TO X44END
X41:           y[i,j]:=y[i,j]−xx−yy−xy−yx; GO TO X44;
X42:           aa:=y[i,j]Xwac1;
               y[i,j]:=y[i,j]−xx−yy−xy−yx;
               IF y[i,j]<aa THEN
               BEGIN
X43:               y[i,j]:=0; GO TO X45END;
X44:           y[i,j]:=y[i,j]/y[i,6]
X45:       END END;
           FOR i:=1 STEP 1 UNTIL 20 DO
           BEGIN
               IF y[i,2]=0 THEN GO TO X49;
               GO TO sw13[nLs];
X46:           IF y[i,5]=0 THEN GO TO X49;
X47:           IF y[i,4]=0 THEN GO TO X49;
X48:           IF y[i,3]=0 THEN
X49:           y[i,1]:=0
XX1:       END:
           FOR i:=1 STEP 1 UNTIL 20 DO
           IF y[i,2]≤0 THEN g1:=g1−1;
           FOR i:=1 STEP 1 UNTIL 20 DO
           BEGIN
               IF y[i,1]≠0 THEN
               BEGIN
                   y1m:=y[i,1]; y1n:=y[i,1];
                   IF y[i,2]≠0 THEN
                   BEGIN
                       y2m:=y[i,2]; y2n:=y[i,2];
                       GO TO X50END END
           END;
X50:       FOR i:=1 STEP 1 UNTIL 20 DO
           BEGIN
               IF y[i,1]≤0 THEN GO TO XZX;
               IF y1m<y[i,1] THEN y1m:=y[i,1];
               IF y1n>y[i,1] THEN y1n:=y[i,1];
               FOR j:=2 STEP 1 UNTIL 5 DO
               BEGIN
                   IF y[i,j]>0∧(y2m<y[i,j]) THEN y2m:=y[i,j];
                   IF y2n>y[i,j] THEN y2n:=y[i,j]END
XZX:       END;
```

```
        pd1:=(y1m−y1n)X0.1;
        y1m:=y1m+pd1;  y1n:=y1n−pd1;
        pd2:=(y2m−y2n)X0.1;
        y2m:=y2m+pd2;  y2n:=y2n−pd2;
        wa:=w−am;  n:=wa/100;
        wa:=nX100;  ha:=h−am;
        n:=ha/100;  ha:=nX100;
        p1:=100X(y1m−y1n)/wa;
        FOR i:=1 STEP 1 UNTIL 20 DO
        BEGIN
          py:=i;
          q1:=abs(p1);  q2:=abs(p2);
          nq2:=q2;  n1x:=O:=yn:=0;
          FOR i:=1 STEP 1 UNTIL 20 DO
          BEGIN
            IF nq2<j THEN GO TO X51
            ELSE IF nq2=j THEN
            BEGIN
              nn1:=j;  O:=j;  q2:=q2−O;
              yn:=y1n;  GO TO X51END
          END;
X51:      IF q1≤q2 THEN
          BEGIN
            q:=q2X10↑py;  GO TO X52END;
          q:=q1X10↑py;
X52:      IF wm>q THEN GO TO X54;
          IF yn<0 THEN
          BEGIN
            qr:=yn+O;  O:=−O;  GO TO X53END;
          qr:=yn−O;
X53:      n1a:=qrX10↑py;  n1d:=p1X10↑py;
          n1p:=wa/100+1;  sf1:=10↑py;
          nn1:=0;  GO TO X55
X54:      END;
X55:      p2:=100X(y2m−y2n)/ha;
          FOR i:=1 STEP 1 UNTIL 20 DO
          BEGIN
            px:=i;
            q1:=abs(p2);  q2:=abs(y2n);
            nq2:=q2;  nn2:=O:=yn:=0;
            FOR j:=1 STEP 1 UNTIL 20 DO
            BEGIN
              IF nq2<j THEN GO TO X56
              ELSE IF nq2=j THEN
              BEGIN
                nn2:=j;  O:=j;  q2:=q2−O;
                yn:=y2n;  GO TO X56END
X56:        END;
            IF q1≤q2 THEN
            BEGIN
              q:=q2X10↑px;  GO TO X57END;
            q:=q1X10↑px;
X57:        IF wm>q THEN GO TO X59;
```

```
          IF yn<0 THEN
          BEGIN
              qr:=y2n+O;  O:=-O;  GO TO X58END;
          qr:=y2n-O;
X58:      n2a:=qrX10↑px;  n2d:=p2X10↑px;
          n2p:=ha/100+1;  sf2:=10↑px;
          nn2:=0;  GO TO X60
X59:      END;
X60:      IF pd1=0 THEN
          BEGIN
              pd1:=1/y1m;  GO TO X61END;
          pd1:=1/pd1;
X61:      IF pd2=0 THEN
          BEGIN
              pd2:=1/y2n;  GO TO X62END;
X62:      FOR i:=1 STEP 1 UNTIL 20 DO
          BEGIN
              IF y[i.1]=0 THEN GO TO X67;
              GO TO sw14[nLs];
X63:      y[i,5]:=y[i,5]Xpd2;
X64:      y[i,4]:=y[i,4]Xpd2;
X65:      y[i,3]:=y[i,3]Xpd2;
X66:      y[i,2]:=y[i,2]Xpd2;
          y[i,1]:=y[i,1]Xpd1
X67:      END;
          y1m:=y1mXpd1;  y1n:=y1nXpd1;
          y2m:=y2mXpd2;  y2n:=y2nXpd2;
          d1:=(y1m-y1n)/wa;  d2:=(y2m-y2n)/ha;
          IF d1=0 THEN d1:=y1m/wa;
          IF d2=0 THEN d2:=y2m/ha;
          FOR i:=1 STEP 1 UNTIL 20 DO
          BEGIN
              IF y[i,1]≠0 THEN
              BEGIN
                  ny[i,1]:=(y[i,1]-y1n)/d1;
                  ny[i,2]:=(y[i,2]-y2n[/d2;
                  GO TO sw15[nLs];
X68:      ny[i,5]:=(y[i,5]-y2n)/d2;
X69:      ny[i,4]:=(y[i,4]-y2n)/d2;
X70:      ny[i,3]:=(y[i,3]-y2n)/d2END
X71:      END;
          nh:=h;  nw:=w;  m:=am;
          PUNCH 1,nw,nh,m,m,0,0;
          GO TO sw16[nLs];
X72:      PUNCH 2,1,0;
X73:      FOR i:=1 STEP 1 UNTIL 20 DO
          IF y[i,1]≠0 THEN PUNCH 3,ny[i,1],ny[i,2];
          GO TO X80;
X74:      PUNCH 2,31,0;
          GO TO X73;
X75:      PUNCH 2,42,0,1;
          FOR i:=1 STEP 1 UNTIL 20 DO
          IF y[i,1]≠0 THEN PUNCH 3,ny[i,1],ny[i,2],ny[i,3];
```

```
          GO TO X80;
X76:    PUNCH 2,43,0,1,10;
X77:    FOR i:=1 STEP 1 UNTIL 20 DO
          IF y[i,1]≠0 THEN
              PUNCH 3,ny[i,1],ny[i,2],ny[i,3],ny[i,4];
          GO TO X80;
X78:    PUNCH 2,44,0,1,10,11;
          IF y[i,1]≠0 THEN
              PUNCH 3,ny[i,1],ny[i,2],ny[i,3],ny[i,4],ny[i,5];
          GO TO X80;
X79:    PUNCH 2,33,1,0,1;
          GO TO X77;
X80:    nxL:=-50;
          PUNCH 4,155,nxL,1;
          PUNCH nn1,sf1;
          nxL:=-100;
          PUNCH 4,nxL,800,11;
          PUNCH nn2,sf2;
          nL:=-100;
          PUNCH 4,155,nL,0;
          PUNCH nqr,L,run,temp;
          nL:=-125
          m3:=jj+m4-1;
          PUNCH 4,155,nL,0;
          GO TO sw17[nLs];
X81:    PUNCH m4,oper;
          GO TO X83;
X82:    PUNCH m4,m3,oper;
X83:    nL:=-150;
          PUNCH 4,155,nL,0;
          PUNCH g1,g;
          ns1:=-25;  ns2:=0;
          PUNCH 5,ns2,ns1,n1p,n1s,n1d,0;
          PUNCH 5,ns1,ns2,n2p,n2a,n2d,10;
          PUNCH 6;  m4:=m3;
          IF m5>0 THEN GO TO X5
X84:END DEEEE
X85:READ w,h,am,wm,nLs; q99:=nLs;
X86:READ nqr;
          PROCEDURE(w,h,am,wm,nLs,nqr);
          GO TO X86;
```

CHAPTER II

EXPANSION PROGRAMS

Frequently in the physical sciences otherwise intractable problems can be easily solved by arbitrarily expanding sets of data points (x, y) thus:

$$y = B + A_1 x + A_2 x^2 + A_3 x^3 + A_4 x^4 + \cdots \tag{1}$$

The *self-judgment principle*[1,2] provides a method of calculating the constants in equation (1) for any preselected limits of error in x and y. In this chapter FORTRAN programs and their ALGOL 60 translations are given for solving the two-, three-, four-, five-, and N-dimensional forms of equation (1). The programs with variable dimensions (25 and 325) have been specifically designed for use with large computers. However, by suitable choice of the dimension commands JI and JJ, both programs may be used with medium (20K to 60K storage) computers. The *expansion programs* are extensively used in both the *method of limiting intercepts* and the *expansion method*. Smith,[3] Bell,[4] and Thompson[5] have described the use of the *expansion programs* in quantitative analyses of infrared and ultraviolet absorption spectra, and Menendez[6] has discussed their use in the analysis of polarization data.

With Programs 9, 22–25, 309, and 322–325 the measured absorbance (AM = OAM(I)) and the concentrations of either one (C_1 = C1(I)) or two (C_1 = C1(I); C_2 = C2(I)) components must be entered (see *input format* for Programs 9, 22–25, 309, and 322–325). In equation (1) x and y are related to the observables thus:

$$y = \text{AM}/C_1 \qquad x = C_1 \quad \text{or} \quad C_2$$

---

[1] P. A. D. de Maine and R. D. Seawright, *Digital Computer Programs for Physical Chemistry*, Vol. I (New York: The Macmillan Co., 1963).

[2] P. A. D. de Maine and R. D. Seawright, *Ind. Eng. Chem.*, 55, No. 4 (1963), 29.

[3] M. S. Smith, Jr., Ph.D. Thesis, University of Mississippi (1963).

[4] J. T. Bell, Ph.D. Thesis, University of Mississippi (1963).

[5] C. C. Thompson, Jr., Ph.D. Thesis, University of Mississippi (1964).

[6] J. S. Menendez, M.S. Thesis, University of Mississippi (in preparation).

For a *homogeneous expansion* $x = C_1$, and for a *heterogeneous expansion* $x = C_2$. In a homogeneous expansion the intercept, B, equals the absorbancy index at infinite dilution. In a heterogeneous expansion where C_1 is constant, the intercept, B, is the absorbancy index of component 1 when no component 2 is present.

Programs 9, 22, 23, 24, and 25 can be used to solve the two-, three-, four-, five-, and N-dimensional forms, respectively, of equation (1). These programs have similar input formats, and each has incorporated the *fail–safe procedure*, the *reject–restore* and *normalization mechanisms*, and the *self-judgment principle*.[1,2] Programs 9 and 22–24 also contain the *transposition mechanism*.[1,2] A special transposition technique used in Program 25 is discussed in Chapter III (see *Crout reduction method*). In each program the *fail–safe procedure* is applied twice to discard unreliable values of the measured absorbance (OAM(I)) and the concentration of one component (C1(I) or C2(I)). Then the ordinates (Y(I), X1(I), X2(I), $\cdots$) and the associated *maximum permitted errors* (YER(I), X1ER(I), X2ER(I) $\cdots$) are calculated. Next the *reject–restore mechanism* is activated, the ordinates are normalized, and the origin is transposed to the center of the coordinate system (Programs 9 and 22–24) or to the first quadrant (Program 25). After the *self-judgment principle* is applied in each dimension for each programmed cycle, the *maximum permitted error* for each parameter is computed. Detailed descriptions of these computer operations have been given in Chapter I of the preceding volume.[1]

Programs 9 (*call word* IAAAA) and 25 (*call word* YAAAA) can be used to solve the seven spectrophotometric equations discussed in Chapter III of the preceding volume[1] (also see *input commands* for L in this chapter). With adequate computer storage Program 25 (*call word* YAAAA), can be used in place of Programs 9 (*call word* IAAAA), 22 (*call word* VAAAA), 23 (*call word* WAAAA), and 24 (*call word* XAAAA).

SPECIAL MODIFICATIONS

Programs 309, 322, 323, 324, and 325 are the one-dimensional *self-judgment* forms of Programs 9, 22, 23, 24, and 25 respectively. Input commands, input formats, and output formats for the one-dimensional forms are identical with those for the respective parent program. In Programs 309, 322, 323, 324, and 325 the computer operations described above are executed, except that in each programmed cycle the *self-judgment principle* is applied only to the first dimension (Y(I)). However, the *error zone* is used to calculate the *maximum permitted error* for each parameter. Thus the *maximum permitted deviation* for the second observable (C1(I) or C2(I)) still has a realistic value.

Programs 309, 322, 323, 324, and 325 should be used if one or more of the A_1, A_2, A_3, etc., values in equation (1) is small (see Appendix I in reference 1).

SECONDARY CORRECTION FACTORS

Errors which arise from the neglect of temperature-volume changes and nonideal solution behavior can be eliminated if the concentrations of all components are calculated with Program 5, 6, or 7 (see Chapter II of reference 1).

Activity coefficients may be introduced into Programs 9, 22–25, 309, and 322–325 as described in the section entitled "Statistical Bias" in this chapter.

INSTRUMENT RELIABILITY FACTORS

For all values of L (see *input commands*) in Programs 9, 22–25, 309, and 322–325 there are two sets of *instrument reliability factors*. The first set, RLM1, WL1, WU1, and DEVF1 or DEV1(I) (in 9 and 309), RLM(1), WL(1), WU(1), and DEVF(1) or DEV1(I) (in 25 and 325), or RLM1, WL1, WU1, and DEVF1 or DEVY(I) (in 22–24 and 322–324), is associated exclusively with the measured absorbance (OAM(I) or Y(I, JJ)), whereas the second set, RLM2, WL2, WU2, and DEVF2 or DEV2(I) (9 and 309), or DEVX(I) (22–24 and 322–324), or RLM(2), WL(2), WU(2), and DEVF(2) or DEV2(I) (25 and 325), is associated with the concentration, C1(I), of the first component for L = 1, 2, 4, and 5, or the concentration, C2(I) of the second component for L = 3, 6, and 7. For L = 5, 6, or 7 an additional factor, WAC or WAC(JJ), must be entered.

The *maximum permitted deviation* for each observable can be entered as a fixed fraction (DEVF____) of the measured quantities, or in the same units as the value of each observable (DEV____(I)). Thus DEV1(I) is the *maximum permitted deviation* in the Ith value of the absorbance (OAM(I)), and DEVF1 is the *maximum permitted deviation* expressed as a fixed fraction of all OAM(I). The K value determines the form in which the *maximum permitted deviations* are entered.

RLM____ is the *measured limit of reproducibility* of the designated observable, which must be entered even if it is not actually used in the calculations.

WL____ and WU____ are the lowest and highest reliable values respectively for the designated observable.

WAC is the lowest fraction of the measured absorbance that can be used in calculations when L = 5, 6, or 7 (see *input commands* for L).

Table 8

Modifications Permitting Application of Self-judgment Principle in Only One Dimension

Special Program		Original Program		Replacement Statements to Convert the Original Program to the Special Program	
Number	Call Word	Number	Call Word	Original	Replacement

309	IAAAS	9†	IAAAA	1 READ,IAAAA,FEEDP
				NUM=9
				162 PUNCH,IAAAA,NUM,FEEDP
				IF(RR−YC(I))77,77,76
				IF(YC(I)−DEVY(I))61,62,62
					1 READ,IAAAS,FEEDP
					NUM=309
					162 PUNCH,IAAAS,NUM,FEEDP
					IF(RR−YC(I))163,163,76
					IF(YC(I)−DEVY(I))61,59,59

322	VAAAS	22	VAAAA	1 READ,VAAAA,FEEDP
				NUM=22
				PUNCH,VAAAA,NUM,FEEDP
				IF(RR−YC(I))404,404,402
				IF(YC(I)−DEV1(I))34,32,32
					1 READ,VAAAS,FEEDP
					NUM=322
					PUNCH,VAAAS,NUM,FEEDP
					IF(RR−YC(I))2222,2222,402
					IF(YC(I)−DEV1(I))34,36,36

323	WAAAS	23	WAAAA	1 READ,WAAAA,FEEDP
				NUM=23
				PUNCH,WAAAA,NUM,FEEDP
				IF(RR−YC(I))404,404,402
				IF(YC(I)−DEV1(I))34,35,35
					1 READ,WAAAS,FEEDP
					NUM=323
					PUNCH,WAAAS,NUM,FEEDP
					IF(RR−YC(I))2222,2222,402
					IF(YC(I)−DEV1(I))34,39,39

No.	Name	Code

324	XAAAAS	```
		1 READ,XAAAA,FEEDP
		NUM=324
		PUNCH,XAAAA,NUM,FEEDP
		IF(RR-C(I))Y2222,2222,902
		IF(YC(I)-DEV1(I))72,77,77
		``

24	XAAAA	```
		1 READ,XAAAA,FEEDP
		NUM=24
		PUNCH,XAAAA,NUM,FEEDP
		IF(RR-YC(I))904,904,902
		IF(YC(I)-DEV1(I))72,73,73
		``

325	YAAAAS	```
		1 READ,YAAAA,FEEDP
		NUM=325
		PUNCH,YAAAA,NUM,FEEDP
		IF(YY(I,JJ))127,130,127
		127 AA=SQR(YER(I,JJ)*YER(I,JJ))
		BB=SQR(DEV(I,JJ)*DEV(I,JJ))
		IF(AA-BB)129,128,128
		129 IF(NNN-1)1,130,132
		130 DO 9003 J=1,JJ
		Y(I,J)=0.0
		9003 DEV(I,J)=0.0
		GO TO 126
		128 IF(NNN-1)1,126,133
		131 DO 9001 J=1,JJ
		9001 Y(I,J)=YY(I,J)
		GO TO 126
		``

25	YAAAA	```
		1 READ,YAAAA,FEEDP
		NUM=25
		PUNCH,YAAAA,NUM,FEEDP
		JRK=0
		DO 126 J=1,JJ
		IF(YY(I,JJ))127,130,127
		127 AA=SQR(YER(I,J)*YER(I,J))
		BB=SQR(DEV(I,J)*DEV(I,J))
		IF(AA-BB)129,128,128
		129 IF(NNN-1)1,130,132
		130 Y(I,J)=0.0
		DEV(I,J)=0.0
		GO TO 126
		128 IF(NNN-1)1,126,133
		131 JRK=JRK+1
		IF(JRK-JJ)126,43,1
		43 DO 9001 JP=1,JJ
		9001 Y(I,JP)=YY(I,JP)
		GO TO 126
		``

---

† The modified version of Program 9 (*call word* IAAAA)[1] discussed in the section entitled "Two-Dimension Expansion," later in this chapter.

FAIL-SAFE PROCEDURE

If any single item of information is less than the lowest reliable value (WL1 or WL2) or greater than the highest reliable value (WU1 or WU2), the entire set of conjugate data is discarded and all members of the corresponding set of conjugate information are set equal to zero. Sets of conjugate data are also discarded if, for L = 5, 6, or 7, the absolute value of $(OAM(I) - AI1 * C1(I))$ is less than $(WAC * OAM(I))$. Here AI1 is the molar absorbancy index of the first component, whose initial concentration is C1(I).

The *maximum permitted deviations*, expressed either as DEVF____ or DEV____(I), are used to calculate the *maximum permitted errors* for all values of all ordinates (YER(I), X1ER(I), $\cdots$). These errors collectively define the *error zone*. If the one-dimensional *self-judgment* forms of Programs 9 and 22–25 are used, a realistic value for DEVF2 (or DEV2(I)) must be entered because the *maximum permitted error* in Y(I), designated YER(I), is determined by the value of both DEVF1 (or DEV1(I)) and DEVF2 (or DEV2(I)).

STATISTICAL BIAS

The one semiautomatic and two fully automatic devices for reducing statistical bias[1] due to gross errors in the data or to round-off errors, have been incorporated in Programs 9, 22–24, 309, and 322–324. In the two variable-dimension programs (25 and 325), a more sophisticated version of the *reject–restore mechanism*, entirely compatible with the earlier version, and additional normalization devices have been incorporated. In both programs maximum values of each of the ordinates are automatically normalized to $+1$. Then all elements of the *Crout* matrix, obtained by summing various combinations of the ordinates, are divided by the element which has the maximum numerical value. All normalization procedures are completely automatic. The normalization devices are described in Chapter III.

Activity coefficients, or weighting functions, can be introduced by replacing statements numbered 999, 1000, $\cdots$ by selected functions for each of Y(I), X1(I) $\cdots$ XN(I) in this order. The companion correction functions for each slope (SL1, SL2, $\cdots$ SLN) and the intercept (B or BB) must also be introduced by replacing statements 1110, 1111 $\cdots$ respectively.

For all practical purposes we have found unnecessary the introduction of special weighting functions and companion correction functions to reduce *statistical bias*.

INPUT COMMANDS FOR PROGRAMS 9, 22–25, 309, AND 322–325

The *input commands* for Programs 9, 22–25, 309, and 322–325 are designated by the symbols: KA, J (or JC), M6, K, L, and M. M6, K, L, and M define the actual *input format* and the mode of calculation. J (or JC) is the number of cycles to be completed before the *error analysis* is performed. During the first cycle the *self-judgment principle* is not applied. The value entered for KA activates the *reject–restore mechanism* and determines which sets of conjugate information are to be killed (i.e., removed from memory) or ignored during the first cycle. "Ignored" sets of conjugate information are restored after the first cycle if their *actual errors* are numerically smaller than the corresponding *maximum permitted errors*.[1] The values to be used for KA, J (or JC), M6, K, L, and M are listed in the following sections.

Reject–Restore Commands (KA)

For KA, only five values (−1, 0, 1, 2, 3) can be used with Programs 9, 22–24, 309, and 322–324. Twenty-two values for KA can be used with Programs 25 and 325. The abbreviations used are as follows.

Kill(KB–KC)	Means the KBth to KCth sets of conjugate information are to be removed from memory
K(KB,KC,KD) or Kill(KB,KC,KD)	Means the KBth, KCth, and KDth sets are to be removed from memory
Ignore(KB–KC)	Means the KBth to KCth sets are to be ignored during the first cycle
Ignore(KB,KC) or I(KB,KC)	Means the KBth and KCth sets are to be ignored during the first cycle

In the input format, values must be entered for all KA, KB, KC, and KD (Programs 9, 22–24, 309, and 322–324), or for all KA, KB, KC, KD, KE, and KF (Programs 25 and 325). Thus for Program 25 (*call word* YAAAA) a card with KA = −1, KB = 9, KC = 0, KD = 99, KE = 100, KF = 4 means no sets of conjugate information are to be ignored or killed during the first cycle.

KA	Meaning	KA	Meaning
−1	No sets are ignored or killed	11	Kill(KB,KC,KD)
0	Ignore(KB–KC)	12	Kill(KB,KC,KD,KE)
1	Ignore(KB)	13	Kill(KB,KC,KD,KE,KF)
2	Ignore(KB,KC)	14	Kill(KB–KC; KD–KE)
3	Ignore(KB,KC,KD)	15	No sets are ignored or killed
4	Ignore(KB,KC,KD,KE)	16	Kill(KB–KC)
5	Ignore(KB,KC,KD,KE,KF)	17	Kill(KB)
6	Ignore(KB–KC;KD–KE)	18	Kill(KB); ignore(KC)
7	No sets are ignored or killed	19	K(KB),I(KC),K(KD)
8	Kill(KB–KC)	20	K(KB),I(KC),K(KD),I(KE)
9	Kill(KB)	21	K(KB),I(KC),K(KD),I(KE),K(KF)
10	Kill(KB,KC)	22	Kill(KB–KC); ignore(KD–KE)

Input Commands J (or JC), M6, K, and M

J (or JC)	The number of cycles to be completed by the computer before the *error analysis*. The *self-judgment principle* is not applied during the first and the (J + 1)th (*error analysis*) cycles
M6	The number of wavelengths for which data are to be processed
K	Defines the form in which the *maximum permitted deviations* are to be entered. DEVF– and DEV___(I) have been defined under *instrument reliability factors*

K	Form	K	Form
1	DEVF1, DEVF2	3	DEV1(I), DEVF2
2	DEVF1, DEV2(I)	4	DEV1(I), DEV2(I)

M	M = 0 means that concentrations of all components are in moles/liter
	M = 1 means that the second component is in mole fraction units

Input Commands L

For Programs 22–24 and 322–324, the only values which can be entered for L are L = 1 for *homogeneous expansion* and L = 3 for *heterogeneous expansion*.

With Programs 9 and 309 the two-dimensional homogeneous (L = 1) and heterogeneous (L = 3) expansions are identical with the Beer's Law and Collison equations (see Chapter III of reference 1). In Programs 25 and 325 the dimension of the expansion, with L = 1 or 3, is determined by the value entered for JJ (see Special Input Commands for Programs 25 and 325).

For Programs 9 and 309 or Programs 25 and 325, with JJ = 2, the following seven two-dimensional spectrophotometric equations can be solved. Each equation has been discussed in detail in Chapter III of the preceding volume.[1]

L	Equation
1	Beer's Law equation
2	Simple Collison equation
3	Collision equation
4	de Maine-Koubek equation
5	Multiple Collision equation
6	Scott equation
7	Ketelaar equation

SPECIAL INPUT COMMANDS FOR PROGRAMS 25 AND 325

The maximum number of sets of conjugate information and the dimension of the expansion which can be handled by Programs 25 (*call word* YAAAA) and 325 (*call word* YAAAS) will be determined by the storage capacity of the computer. The values for JQ, JD, and JR, which appear only in the *dimension* statements of each program, must be selected before compilation. JI and JJ are selected to fit the input information to be processed. The meanings of these symbols are as follows.

JQ	Maximum number of sets of conjugate information which can be processed
JD	Maximum number of dimensions for the equations to be solved
JR = JD + 1	
JI	The actual number of sets of conjugate information (in multiples of four) for the data to be processed
JJ	The actual dimensions of the equation to be solved

INPUT FORMATS FOR PROGRAMS 9, 22–25, 309, AND 322–325

In the following, READ, X, Y, Z (L ≠ 7), means the information is to be entered only if L is not equal to seven.

READ, X, Y, Z (25, 325) means the information is entered only for Programs 25 and 325.

STATEMENT	PROGRAM	COMMENT
READ,JI	(25, 325)	

> The information for JI is entered once with the first deck of input information to be processed. Subsequent decks must have the same JI (number of sets of conjugate data in multiples of four). With *Autoplotter Program* 502 (*call word* BEEEE) the value for JI is not entered with the *data deck*. Input information for FORTRAN Programs 25 and 325 can be processed for the *autoplotter* with Program 502 only if JI = 20. Limited storage capacity of the IBM 1620 60K computer imposes this restriction.

STATEMENT	PROGRAM	COMMENT
READ,XXXXX,FEEDP		XXXXX = IAAAA,VAAAA,WAAAA, XAAAA,YAAAA,IAAAS,VAAAS, WAAAS,XAAAS, or YAAAS
READ,KA,KB,KC,KD,KE,KF	(25, 325)	*Reject–restore commands*
READ,JJ	(25, 325)	Dimension of equation or expansion
OR		
READ,KA,KB,KC,KD	(9, 22–24, 309, 322–324)	*Reject–restore commands*
READ,J or JC		Number of cycles before *error analysis*
READ,M6		Number of wavelengths to be processed
READ,K,L,M		*Input commands*
READ,RLM1,WL1,WU1 ⎫ READ,RLM2,WL2,WU2 ⎭	(Not 25 or 325)	*Instrument reliability factors*
OR		
READ,RLM(1),WL(1),WU(1) ⎫ READ,RLM(2),WL(2),WU(2) ⎭	(25, 325)	*Instrument reliability factors*

READ,DEVF1 or DEVF(1)
or
READ,DEV1(I),DEV1(I+1),DEV1(I+2),
    DEV1(I+3)
READ,DEVF2 or DEVF(2)
or
READ,DEV2(I),DEV2(I+1),DEV2(I+2),
    DEV2(I+3)

> *Maximum permitted deviations.* Form is selected by the value entered for K. For Programs 22–23 and 322–323, DEV1(I) and DEV2(I) are replaced by DEVY(I) and DEVX(I) respectively. See page 109 for changes in Programs 24 and 324

READ,OAM(I),OAM(I+1),OAM(I+2),
    OAM(I+3)   (Not 25 or 325)
or
READ,Y(I,JJ),Y(I+1,JJ),Y(I+2,JJ),
    Y(I+3,JJ)   (25, 325)

> Measured absorbancies

READ,AI1,WAC or WAC(JJ)   (L = 5, 6, or 7)

AI1, absorbancy index of first component; WAC or WAC(JJ), *instrument reliability factor*

READ,C1(I),C1(I+1),C1(I+2),C1(I+3)

Concentration of first component; X1(I) is used for Programs 24 and 324

READ,C2(I),C2(I+1),C2(I+2),   (All programs)
    C2(I+3)   (L = 3, 6, or 7)
or
READ,FM2(I),FM2(I+1),   (Not 25 or
    FM2(I+2),FM2(I+3)   325)

> Concentrations (mole/liter) or mole fractions of the second component

READ,OPER,INSTR
READ,RUN,TEMP,WAVEL

> Identification

READ,OAM(I),OAM(I+1),   (Not 25 or
    OAM(I+2),OAM(I+3)   325)
or
READ,Y(I,JJ),Y(I+1,JJ),   (25, 325)
    Y(I+2,JJ),Y(I+3,JJ)
READ,AI1,WAC or WAC(JJ)   (L = 5, 6, or 7)

> Entered (M6 − 1) times for all programs. These are data collected at different wavelengths

OPTIONAL EXTERNAL COMMANDS FOR PROGRAMS 9, 22–24, 309, AND 322–324

SWITCH 1 POSITION	SWITCH 2 POSITION	COMMAND EXECUTED
ON	ON or OFF	*Actual errors* in each accepted value for Y(I) and X1(I) are given after each application of the *self-judgment principle*. DEVY(I) and DEVX(I) (Programs 9 and 309) are the *actual errors* in the Ith value for Y(I) and X1(I). DEV1(I), DEV2(I), DEV3(I) ⋯ are the *actual errors* in the Ith values for Y(I), X1(I), X2(I) ⋯ respectively
OFF	ON	Each accepted set of conjugate information and the corresponding actual errors are given after each application of the *self-judgment principle*
OFF	OFF	Sets of conjugate information and the actual errors are *not* given after each application of the *self-judgment principle*

OPTIONAL EXTERNAL COMMANDS FOR PROGRAMS 25 AND 325

SWITCH POSITIONS				COMMANDS EXECUTED AND COMMENTS
1	2	3	4	

ON				PUNCH,EQ,AIC,AI1 (for L = 6 or 7) JJ = 2 PUNCH,SQRMS(1),SQRMS(2) or PUNCH,SL(J),SQRMS(J) (for L = 1 to 5) J = 1, 2, ... JJ These commands are executed at the end of each cycle. The SL(J)'s are the values for the parameters calculated in the preceding cycle and defined thus in equation (A): $$y = \mathrm{SL}(1)\,x + \mathrm{SL}(2)\,x^2 + \cdots \mathrm{SL}(JJ)$$ SQRMS(1), SQRMS(2) ··· SQRMS(JJ) are the standard deviations in the accepted x, x^2, ··· y respectively.
ON	ON			PUNCH,YY(I,JJ),YY(I+1,JJ),YY(I+2,JJ),YY(I+3,JJ) PUNCH,Y(I,JJ),Y(I+1,JJ),Y(I+2,JJ),Y(I+3,JJ) This command is executed at the end of each cycle. YY(I,JJ) is the Ith value of y (equation (A)) originally entered. Y(I,JJ) is the Ith value of y used in the preceding cycle
ON	OFF	ON		PUNCH,YY(I,J),YY(I+1,J), YY(I+2,J),YY(I+3,J) PUNCH,Y(I,J),Y(I+1,J),Y(I+2,J), Y(I+3,J) PUNCH,YER(I,J),YER(I+1,J), YER(I+2,J),YER(I+3,J) PUNCH,DEV(I,J),DEV(I+1,J), DEV(I+2,J),DEV(I+3,J) For I = 1,2 ··· JI and J = 1,2 ··· JJ This command is executed at the end of each cycle. YY(I,J) is the original information; Y(I,J) is the information used in the preceding cycle; YER(I,J) and DEV(I,J) are the *maximum permitted error* and the *actual error* in YY(I,J). These data tables have been rearranged. Y(I,1) refers to x in equation (A). Y(I,JJ) refers to y
			OFF	The commands with both *switches* 1 and 2 ON are executed at the end of the N(= JC)th cycle if G1 $\neq$ G2
			ON	The commands with *switches* 1, 2, and 3 ON, OFF, and ON respectively are executed at the end of the N(= JC)th cycle if G1 $\neq$ G2

OUTPUT FORMATS FOR PROGRAMS 9, 22–24, 309, AND 322–324

STATEMENT*	COMMENT
PUNCH,XXXXX,NUM,FEEDP	XXXXX = NUM if the correct program was used
PUNCH,J,M4	J is the number of cycles to be completed before doing the *error analysis* with data collected at the M4th wavelength
PUNCH,M6	The number of wavelengths for which data are processed
PUNCH,K,L,M	*Input commands*

PUNCH,DEVF1,RLM1,WL1,WU1
PUNCH,WAC   (9, 309)
PUNCH,DEVF2,RLM2,WL2,WU2
PUNCH,DEVF2,RLM2,WL2,WU2
  $\vdots$ $\vdots$ $\vdots$ $\vdots$ $\vdots$

} *Instrument reliability factors*

PRINT,CODE,M4,RUN
PUNCH,CODE,M4
PUNCH,OPER,INSTR
PUNCH,RUN,TEMP,WAVEL

} Executed only if CODE = 88888888.0 or 99999999.0. If executed, the calculations are terminated

The following statements which lie between the double horizontal lines are punched J times.

PUNCH,EQ,AIC,AI1,G1,G,J,M4   (9, 309)   (for L = 6 or 7)
      or
PUNCH,SL1,SL2 $\cdots$, B or BB,G1,G,J,M4   (for L = 1 to 5)
PUNCH,SQRM1,SQRM2 $\cdots$

DEFINITIONS

EQ   Equilibrium constant
AIC   Molar absorbancy index of the complex
AI1   Molar absorbancy index of the first component (*input data*)
SL1, SL2, etc.   Slopes
B or BB   Intercept   } For the equation $y = SL1x + SL2x^2 + \cdots B$
SQRM1   Square-root-mean-square deviation in accepted Y(I)
SQRM2, SQRM3, etc.   Square-root-mean-square deviations in accepted
  X1(I), X2(I), etc., respectively

These values are calculated in the Jth cycle with data collected at the M4th wavelength. G1 is the number of accepted sets of conjugate information used in the Jth cycle to calculate the parameters, EQ, AIC, SL1, SL2 $\cdots$, and B or BB. G is the number of accepted sets of conjugate data.

PUNCH,DEV1(I),DEV1(I+1),DEV1(I+2),DEV1(I+3) PUNCH,DEV2(I),DEV2(I+1),DEV2(I+2),DEV2(I+3) ⋮ ⋮ ⋮ ⋮ ⋮	DEV1(I), DEV2(I) ··· are the actual errors in Y(I), X1(I), ··· in accepted sets of conjugate information

or

PUNCH,Y(I),Y(I+1)Y(I+2),Y(I+3) PUNCH,YER(I),YER(I+1),YER(I+2),YER(I+3) PUNCH,DEV1(I),DEV1(I+1),DEV1(I+2),DEV1(I+3) PUNCH,X1(I),X1(I+1),X1(I+2),X1(I+3) PUNCH,X1ER(I),X1ER(I+1),X1ER(I+2),X1ER(I+3) PUNCH,DEV2(I),DEV2(I+1),DEV2(I+2),DEV2(I+3) ⋮ ⋮ ⋮ ⋮ ⋮	Accepted sets of conjugate information and the actual errors used in the Jth cycle. If a set of conjugate information is rejected during application of the *self-judgment principle*, Y(I), X1(I), DEV1(I), DEV2(I) ··· are set equal to zero. YER(I), X1ER(I) ··· are not set equal to zero

---

* In Programs 22, 23, 322, and 323, DEV1(I) and DEV2(I) are replaced by DEVY(I) and DEVX(I) respectively. In Programs 24 and 324, YER(I) and X1ER(I) replace DEV1(I) and DEV2(I) respectively. The actual data generated at the end of each cycle will be determined by the choice of *switch* positions (see the section "Optional External Commands for Programs 9, 22–24, 309, and 322–324 earlier in this chapter). If DEV1(I) is positive, Y(I) is greater than it should be.

The results for the *error analysis* are given at the end of the (J + 1)th cycle thus.

STATEMENT	COMMENT
PUNCH,DEVEQ,DEAIC,G1,G,J,M4 (9, 309)	(For L = 6 or 7)
or PUNCH,DESL1,DESL2, ··· ,DEVB,G1,G,J,M4	(For L = 1 through 5)

DEFINITIONS

DEVEQ,DEAIC,DESL1,DESL2, ··· DEVB are the *maximum permitted errors* for EQ, AIC, SL1, SL2, ··· and B (or BB) calculated during the (J − 1)th cycle with data collected at the M4th wavelength. G1 is the number of sets of conjugate information used in the *error analysis*. G is the number of sets of conjugate data not rejected during the two successive applications of the *fail-safe procedure*.

PUNCH,OPER,INSTR PUNCH,RUN,TEMP,WAVEL	Identification

The entire format will be repeated M6 times. M6 is the number of wavelengths for which data are processed.

OUTPUT FORMATS FOR PROGRAMS 25 AND 325

STATEMENT	COMMENT
PUNCH,XXXXX,NUM,FEEDP	XXXXX = NUM if the correct program was used
PUNCH,JJ,JI,JC,M4	JJ Dimension of equation solved JI Maximum number of *sets of conjugate data* JC Number of cycles before doing the *error analysis* with data collected at the M4th wavelength
PUNCH,M6	The number of wavelengths for which data are to be processed
PUNCH,K,L,M	Input commands
PUNCH,DEVF(1),RLM(1),WL(1),WU(1) PUNCH,WAC(JJ) PUNCH,DEVF(2),RLM(2),WL(2),WU(2)	Instrument reliability factors
PRINT,CODE,M4,RUN PUNCH,CODE,M4 PUNCH,OPER,INSTR PUNCH,RUN,TEMP,WAVEL	Executed only if *code* = 88888888.0 or 99999999.0. The calculation is terminated and processing of new data automatically begins

The following statements which lie between the double horizontal lines are punched JC times.

PUNCH,JC,M4,G,G1,G2
PUNCH,EQ,AIC,AI1   (for L = 6 or 7, JJ = 2)
PUNCH,SQRMS(1),SQRMS(2)
  or
PUNCH,SL(1),SQRMS(1) ⎫
PUNCH,SL(2),SQRMS(2) ⎬ (L = 1 to 5, JJ = 2) (L = 1 or 3, JJ ≥ 2) Executed at the end of each cycle if *switch 1* is ON
 ⋮   ⋮   ⋮ ⎭
PUNCH,SL(JJ),SQRMS(JJ)

DEFINITIONS

EQ   Equilibrium constant

AIC   Molar absorbancy index of the complex

AI1   Molar absorbancy index of the first component (*input data*)

$SL(1),SL(2),SL(3) \cdots SL(JJ)$ The slopes and intercept for the equation $y = SL(1)x + SL(2)x^2 + \cdots + SL(JJ)$, calculated during the JCth cycle with data collected at the M4th wavelength

$SQRMS(1),SQRMS(2), \cdots SQRMS(JJ)$ The *standard deviations* in the accepted values for $X1(I), X2(I) \cdots Y(I)$ respectively

G   Number of sets of conjugate data after two applications of the *fail–safe procedure*

G1   Number of sets of conjugate data after two applications of the *fail–safe procedure* and execution of the *reject–restore commands*

G2   The number of sets of conjugate information actually used to calculate the parameters (EQ, AIC, and SL(1), SL(2) ···) during the JCth cycle with data collected at the M4th wavelength

PUNCH,YY(I,JJ),YY(I+1,JJ),YY(I+2,JJ),YY(I+3,JJ) } Only information for the
PUNCH,Y(I,JJ),Y(I+1,JJ),Y(I+2,JJ),Y(I+3,JJ) } JJth ordinate is punched
   or
PUNCH,YY(I,J),YY(I+1,J),YY(I+2,J),YY(I+3,J) } Information for all ordin-
PUNCH,Y(I,J),Y(I+1,J),Y(I+2,J),Y(I+3,J) } ates (J = 1, 2, ⋯ JJ) is
PUNCH,YER(I,J),YER(I+1,J),YER(I+2,J)YER(I+3,J) } punched
PUNCH,DEV(I,J),DEV(I+1,J),DEV(I+2,J),DEV(I+3,J) }

DEFINITIONS

YY(I,J)   The Ith value for the Jth ordinate calculated from the original
data. Information rejected during the first two applications of the *fail–
safe procedure*, or killed (see *reject–restore commands*) is replaced by zero

Y(I,J)   The Ith value for the Jth ordinate used in the JCth cycle to calculate the parameters

YER(I,J)   The *maximum permitted error* in Y(I,J)

DEV(I,J)   The *actual error* in Y(I,J). If DEV(I,J) is positive Y(I,J) is
greater than it should be

Note: In Programs 25 and 325 the ordinates are defined thus:
$$Y(I,JJ) = SL(1)*Y(I,1) + SL(2)*Y(I,2) + \cdots + SL(JJ)$$
In Programs 9, 22–24, 309, and 322–324 they are defined thus:
$$Y(I) = SL1*X1(I) + SL(2)*X2(I) + \cdots + B \text{ or } BB$$
Their order of appearance should be carefully considered.

The positions of *switches* 2, 3, and 4 determine the amount of information generated
(see "Optional External Commands for Programs 25 and 325" earlier in this chapter).

At the end of the (JC + 1)th cycle the results of the *error analysis* are
given as follows.

PUNCH,JC,M4,G,G1,G2
PUNCH,EQ,DEVEQ,AIC,DEAIC,AI1   (for L = 6 or 7; JJ = 2)
PUNCH,SQRMS(1),SQRMS(2)
   or
PUNCH,SL(1),DEVSL(1),SQRMS(1) }
PUNCH,SL(2),DEVSL(2),SQRMS(2) }   (L = 1 to 5; JJ = 2)   } (L = 1 or 3,
⋮   ⋮   ⋮   ⋮   } JJ ≥ 2)
PUNCH,SL(JJ),DEVSL(JJ),SQRMS(JJ)

DEFINITIONS

DEVEQ, DEAIC, and DEVSL(J) are the *maximum permitted errors* in EQ,
AIC, and SL(J), respectively, calculated with the G2 *accepted sets of conjugate
information* during the JCth (N + 1) cycle. EQ, AIC, SL(1), SL(2) ⋯ SL(JJ),
SQRMS(1), SQRMS(2) ⋯ SQRMS(JJ) comprise the information calculated
during the preceding cycle. Other symbols have already been defined.

After the *error analysis* has been completed, the identification information is punched thus
               PUNCH,OPER,INSTR
               PUNCH,RUN,TEMP,WAVEL

The entire format is repeated M6 − 1 times. M6 is the number of wavelengths for which data are to be processed.

RELIABILITY LIMITS FOR PROGRAMS 9, 22–25, 309, AND 322–325

In the preceding volume[1] it was pointed out that round-off errors always appear first in the final step (*error analysis*). Thus the occurrence of round-off errors is first evident in absurd values for the *maximum permitted errors*. The additional procedures for eliminating round-off error (see Chapter I of reference 1) can be used. However, for all practical purposes round-off errors in Programs 9, 22–25, 309, and 322–325 do not occur. Even with measured absorbancies of 200.0 and concentrations of 10^{-4} moles per liter we have been unable to induce round-off errors. In Chapter III (see the *Crout reduction method*) the problem of eliminating round-off error in the *Crout* reduction is discussed in detail.

TWO-DIMENSION EXPANSION (Call Word IAAAA)

Programs 9 (*call word* IAAAA) and 309 (*call word* IAAAS) in this chapter are slight modifications of the programs with the same numbers in the first volume.[1] These modifications do not change the basic structure of the earlier programs, but they make the *output formats* similar to those for Programs 22–24 and 322–324. The changes necessary to convert Program 9 to Program 309 have been given. Here are the changes for converting Program 9 (*call word* IAAAA) in the first volume[1] to its new form.

STATEMENT IN THE OLD PROGRAM 9	REPLACEMENTS
32 PRINT, CODE	32 PRINT, CODE, M4, RUN
PUNCH, CODE	PUNCH, CODE, M4
	PUNCH, OPER, INSTR
	PUNCH, RUN, TEMP, WAVEL
41 DO 42 I = 1, 20, 4	41 IF (SENSE SWITCH 2) 640, 58
	640 DO 42 I = 1, 20, 4

In this table M4 is the number of the wavelength for which data have been processed. OPER, INSTR, RUN, TEMP, and WAVEL are identifications.

FORTRAN FOR PROGRAM NUMBER 22

CALL WORD VAAAA

```
DIMENSION Y(20),YER(20),X1(20),X1ER(20),X2(20),X2ER(20),X3(20),X3ER(20)
DIMENSION X4(20),X4ER(20),P(6),DEV1(20),DEV2(20),DEV3(20),DEV4(20)
DIMENSION DEV5(20),OAM(20),C1(20),DEVY(20),DEVX(20),XX1(20),XX2(20)
DIMENSION XX3(20),XX4(20),YY(20),YC(20),A(5),C2(20),C(5),T(5)
M4=1
1  IF(M4-1)4000,4000,4012
4000 READ,VAAAA,FEEDP
READ,KA,KB,KC,KD
READ,J
READ,M6
M5=M6
N=J
READ,K,L,M
READ,RLM1,WL1,WU1
READ,RLM2,WL2,WU2
IF(K-1)1,4001,4002
4001 READ,DEVF1
READ,DEVF2
4002 IF(K-2)4012,4003,4005
4003 READ,DEVF1
DO 4004 I=1,20,4
4004 READ,DEVX(I),DEVX(I+1),DEVX(I+2),DEVX(I+3)
DEVF2=5555.0
4005 IF(K-3)4012,4006,4008
4006 DO 4007 I=1,20,4
4007 READ,DEVY(I),DEVY(I+1),DEVY(I+2),DEVY(I+3)
DEVF1=5555.0
READ,DEVF2
4008 IF(K-4)4012,4009,1
4009 DO 4010 I=1,20,4
4010 READ,DEVY(I),DEVY(I+1),DEVY(I+2),DEVY(I+3)
DEVF1=5555.0
DO 4011 I=1,20,4
4011 READ,DEVX(I),DEVX(I+1),DEVX(I+2),DEVX(I+3)
DEVF2=5555.0
4012 DO 4013 I=1,20,4
4013 READ,OAM(I),OAM(I+1),OAM(I+2),OAM(I+3)
G=20.0
J=N
IF(M6-M5)4014,4014,4016
4014 DO 4015 I=1,20,4
4015 READ,C1(I),C1(I+1),C1(I+2),C1(I+3)
IF(L-3)4050,4051,1
4051 DO 4052 I=1,20,4
4052 READ,C2(I),C2(I+1),C2(I+2),C2(I+3)
GO TO 4054
4050 DO 4053 I=1,20
4053 C2(I)=C1(I)
4054 READ,OPER,INSTR
READ,RUN,TEMP,WAVEL
4016 IF(K-2)4017,4017,4019
4017 DO 4018 I=1,20
4018 DEVY(I)=DEVF1*OAM(I)
4019 IF(K-1)1,4020,4021
4021 IF(K-3)4023,4020,4023
4020 DO 4022 I=1,20
4022 DEVX(I)=DEVF2*C2(I)
4023 DO 4024 I=1,20
IF(OAM(I)-WL1)4025,4026,4026
```

```
4025 Y(I)=0.0
     YER(I)=0.0
     X1(I)=0.0
     X1ER(I)=0.0
     X2(I)=0.0
     X2ER(I)=0.0
     X3(I)=0.0
     X3ER(I)=0.0
     X4(I)=0.0
     X4ER(I)=0.0
     G=G-1.0
     GO TO 4024
4026 IF(OAM(I)-WU1)4027,4027,4025
4027 IF(C2(I)-WL2)4025,4028,4028
4028 IF(C2(I)-WU2)4029,4029,4025
4029 X1(I)=C2(I)
     X1ER(I)=DEVX(I)
     X2(I)=C2(I)*C2(I)
     X2ER(I)=(C2(I)+DEVX(I))*(C2(I)+DEVX(I))
     X3(I)=X2(I)*C2(I)
     X3ER(I)=X2ER(I)*(C2(I)+DEVX(I))
     X4(I)=X3(I)*C2(I)
     X4ER(I)=X3ER(I)*(C2(I)+DEVX(I))-X4(I)
     X3ER(I)=X3ER(I)-X3(I)
     X2ER(I)=X2ER(I)-X2(I)
     Y(I)=OAM(I)/C1(I)
     YER(I)=DEVY(I)/C1(I)
4024 CONTINUE
     RLM3=RLM2
     DEVF3=DEVF2
     DEVF4=DEVF2
     DEVF5=DEVF2
     RLM4=RLM2
     RLM5=RLM2
     WL3=WL2
     WL4=WL2
     WL5=WL2
     WU3=WU2
     WU4=WU2
     WU5=WU2
     NUM=22
     PUNCH,VAAAA,NUM,FEEDP
     PUNCH,M6,M4
     PUNCH,J
     PUNCH,K,L,M
     PUNCH,DEVF1,RLM1,WL1,WU1
     PUNCH,DEVF2,RLM2,WL2,WU2
     PUNCH,DEVF3,RLM3,WL3,WU3
     DO 400 I=1,20
     YY(I)=Y(I)
     XX1(I)=X1(I)
400  XX2(I)=X2(I)
     P(1)=SQR(Y(1)*Y(1))
     P(2)=SQR(X1(1)*X1(1))
     P(3)=SQR(X2(1)*X2(1))
     DO 40 I=2,20
     IF(P(1)-SQR(Y(I)*Y(I)))41,42,42
41   P(1)=SQR(Y(I)*Y(I))
42   IF(P(2)-SQR(X1(I)*X1(I)))43,44,44
43   P(2)=SQR(X1(I)*X1(I))
44   IF(P(3)-SQR(X2(I)*X2(I))) 45,40,40
45   P(3)=SQR(X2(I)*X2(I))
```

```
40 CONTINUE
NA=0
46 NA=NA+1
IF(P(NA)-1.0) 47,48,49
47 IF(P(NA)-0.1) 49,48,48
48 A(NA)=1.0
GO TO 56
49 DO 50 I=1,10
M=10-I
MA=-M
IF(P(NA)-10.0**MA)52,52,53
52 A(NA)=10.0**MA
GO TO 56
53 IF(P(NA)-10.0**M) 50,55,54
54 M=M+1
55 A(NA)=10.0**M
GO TO 56
50 CONTINUE
56 IF(NA-3) 46,57,57
57 A1=A(1)
A2=A(2)
A3=A(3)
N=J
J=0
IF(KA)3,300,302
300 DO 301 I=KB,KC
301 Y(I)=0.0
302 IF(KA-1)3,303,303
303 Y(KB)=0.0
IF(KA-2)3,304,304
304 Y(KC)=0.0
IF(KA-3)3,305,305
305 Y(KD)=0.0
3 DO 4 I=1,20
Y(I)=Y(I)/A1
YY(I)=YY(I)/A1
X1(I)=X1(I)/A2
XX1(I)=XX1(I)/A2
X2(I)=X2(I)/A3
XX2(I)=XX2(I)/A3
YER(I)=YER(I)/A1
X1ER(I)=X1ER(I)/A2
4 X2ER(I)=X2ER(I)/A3
NA=0
401 NA=NA+1
G1=20.0
SQRM1=0.0
SQRM2=0.0
SQRM3=0.0
PY=0.0
PZ2=0.0
PX=0.0
PZ=0.0
PX2=0.0
PXY=0.0
PXZ=0.0
PZY=0.0
DO 796 I=1,20
IF(Y(I))797,796,797
797 IF(X1(I))798,796,798
798 IF(X2(I))815,796,815
815 X1MIN=X1(I)
```

```
X1MAX=X1(I)
YMIN=Y(I)
YMAX=Y(I)
X2MIN=X2(I)
X2MAX=X2(I)
GO TO 799
796 CONTINUE
799 DO 800 I=1,20
999 FUNY=1.0
1000 FUNX1=1.0
1001 FUNX2=1.0
Y(I)=FUNY*Y(I)
X1(I)=FUNX1*X1(I)
X2(I)=FUNX2*X2(I)
IF(Y(I))801,800,801
801 IF(X1(I))802,800,802
802 IF(X2(I))803,800,803
803 IF(X1MIN-X1(I))804,805,805
805 X1MIN=X1(I)
804 IF(X1MAX-X1(I))806,806,807
806 X1MAX=X1(I)
807 IF(X2MIN-X2(I))808,809,809
809 X2MIN=X2(I)
808 IF(X2MAX-X2(I))810,810,811
810 X2MAX=X2(I)
811 IF(YMIN-Y(I))812,813,813
813 YMIN=Y(I)
812 IF(YMAX-Y(I))814,814,800
814 YMAX=Y(I)
800 CONTINUE
X1A=(X1MAX+X1MIN)/2.0
X2A=(X2MAX+X1MIN)/2.0
YA=(YMAX+YMIN)/2.0
DO 7 I=1,20
IF(Y(I)) 6,5,6
5 X1(I)=0.0
X2(I)=0.0
DEV1(I)=0.0
DEV2(I)=0.0
DEV3(I)=0.0
G1=G1-1.0
GO TO 7
6 Y(I)=Y(I)-YA
X1(I)=X1(I)-X1A
X2(I)=X2(I)-X2A
PY=PY+Y(I)
PZ2=PZ2+X2(I)*X2(I)
PX=PX+X1(I)
PX2=PX2+X1(I)*X1(I)
PZ=PZ+X2(I)
PXY=PXY+Y(I)*X1(I)
PXZ=PXZ+X1(I)*X2(I)
PZY=PZY+X2(I)*Y(I)
Y(I)=Y(I)+YA
X1(I)=X1(I)+X1A
X2(I)=X2(I)+X2A
Y(I)=Y(I)/FUNY
X1(I)=X1(I)/FUNX1
X2(I)=X2(I)/FUNX2
7 CONTINUE
D=PX*(PXZ*PZ-PX*PZ2)-PZ*(PX2*PZ-PX*PXZ)+G1*(PX2*PZ2-PXZ*PXZ)
IF(D) 10,8,10
```

```
8 CODE=88888888.
9 PRINT,CODE,M4,RUN
PUNCH,CODE,M4
PUNCH,OPER,INSTR
PUNCH,RUN,TEMP,WAVEL
GO TO 4030
10 S1=PY*(PXZ*PZ-PX*PZ2)-PZ*(PXY*PZ-PX*PZY)+G1*(PXY*PZ2-PXZ*PZY)
S2=PX*(PXY*PZ-PX*PZY)-PY*(PX2*PZ-PX*PXZ)+G1*(PX2*PZY-PXY*PXZ)
SL1=S1/D
SL2=S2/D
IF(G1-4.0) 11,11,12
11 CODE=99999999.
GO TO 9
12 B=(PY-SL1*PX-SL2*PZ)/G1
B=B-SL1*X1A-SL2*X2A+YA
1110 FNSL1=1.0
1111 FNSL2=1.0
1112 FUNB=1.0
SL1=SL1*FNSL1
SL2=SL2*FNSL2
B=B*FUNB
DO 402 I=1,20
IF(YY(I))406,402,406
406 RR=SL1*XX1(I)+SL2*XX2(I)+B
RR=SQR((YY(I)-RR)*(YY(I)-RR))
YC(I)=SQR(YER(I)*YER(I))
IF(RR-YC(I))404,404,402
2222 Y(I)=YY(I)
X1(I)=XX1(I)
X2(I)=XX2(I)
GO TO 402
404 RR=(YY(I)-SL2*XX2(I)-B)/SL1
RR=SQR((XX1(I)-RR)*(XX1(I)-RR))
YC(I)=SQR(X1ER(I)*X1ER(I))
IF(RR-YC(I))403,403,402
403 RR=(YY(I)-SL1*XX1(I)-B)/SL2
YC(I)=SQR(X2ER(I)*X2ER(I))
RR=SQR((RR-XX2(I))*(RR-XX2(I)))
IF(RR-YC(I))2222,2222,402
402 CONTINUE
IF(NA-2)401,405,405
405 J=J+1
IF(N-J) 13,19,19
13 DESL1=SL1*A4/A2
DESL2=SL2*A4/A3
DEVB=B*A4
PUNCH,DESL1,DESL2,DEVB,G1,G,J,M4
PUNCH,OPER,INSTR
PUNCH,RUN,TEMP,WAVEL
GO TO 4030
14 DO 18 I=1,20
IF(Y(I)) 15,18,15
15 Y(I)=YER(I)-SL1*X1ER(I)-SL2*X2ER(I)
IF(Y(I))18,16,18
16 Y(I)=0.000001
18 CONTINUE
P(4)=SQR(Y(1)*Y(1))
DO 58 I=2,20
IF(P(4)-SQR(Y(I)*Y(I))) 59,58,58
59 P(4)=SQR(Y(I)*Y(I))
58 CONTINUE
IF(P(4)-1.0) 60,61,62
```

```
   60 IF(P(4)-0.1) 62,61,61
   61 A(4)=1.0
      GO TO 69
   62 DO 63 I=1,10
      M=10-I
      MA=-M
      IF(P(4)-10.0**MA)65,65,66
   65 A(4)=10.0**MA
      GO TO 69
   66 IF(P(4)-10.0**M)63,68,67
   67 M=M+1
   68 A(4)=10.0**M
      GO TO 69
   63 CONTINUE
   69 A4=A(4)
      DO 70 I=1,20
   70 Y(I)=Y(I)*A1/A4
      GO TO 3
   19 DO 24 I=1,20
      IF(Y(I)) 21,24,21
   21 DEV1(I)=SQR((SL1*X1(I)+SL2*X2(I)+B)*(SL1*X1(I)+SL2*X2(I)+B))
      DEV1(I)=(DEV1(I)-SQR(Y(I)*Y(I)))*A1
      SQRM1=SQRM1+DEV1(I)*DEV1(I)
      IF(SL1) 23,22,23
   22 DEV2(I)=0.0
      GO TO 24
   23 DEV2(I)=SQR((Y(I)-SL2*X2(I)-B)*(Y(I)-SL2*X2(I)-B)/(SL1*SL1))
      DEV2(I)=(DEV2(I)-SQR(X1(I)*X1(I)))*A2
      SQRM2=SQRM2+DEV2(I)*DEV2(I)
      IF(SL2)98,99,98
   99 DEV3(I)=0.0
      GO TO 24
   98 DEV3(I)=SQR((Y(I)-SL1*X1(I)-B)*(Y(I)-SL1*X1(I)-B)/(SL2*SL2))
      DEV3(I)=(DEV3(I)-SQR(X2(I)*X2(I)))*A3
      SQRM3=SQRM3+DEV3(I)*DEV3(I)
   24 CONTINUE
      SQRM1=SQR(SQRM1/G1)
      SQRM2=SQR(SQRM2/G1)
      SQRM3=SQR(SQRM3/G1)
      SL1=SL1*A1/A2
      SL2=SL2*A1/A3
      B=B*A1
      DO 25 I=1,20
      YY(I)=YY(I)*A1
      XX1(I)=XX1(I)*A2
      XX2(I)=XX2(I)*A3
      Y(I)=Y(I)*A1
      X1(I)=X1(I)*A2
      X2(I)=X2(I)*A3
      YER(I)=YER(I)*A1
      X1ER(I)=X1ER(I)*A2
   25 X2ER(I)=X2ER(I)*A3
      PUNCH,SL1,SL2,B,G1,G,J,M4
      PUNCH,SQRM1,SQRM2,SQRM3
      IF(SENSE SWITCH 1) 26,28
   26 DO 27 I=1,20,4
      PUNCH,DEV1(I),DEV1(I+1),DEV1(I+2),DEV1(I+3)
      PUNCH,DEV2(I),DEV2(I+1),DEV2(I+2),DEV2(I+3)
   27 PUNCH,DEV3(I),DEV3(I+1),DEV3(I+2),DEV3(I+3)
      GO TO 30
   28 IF(SENSE SWITCH 2)640,30
  640 DO 29 I=1,20,4
```

```
PUNCH,Y(I),Y(I+1),Y(I+2),Y(I+3)
PUNCH,YER(I),YER(I+1),YER(I+2),YER(I+3)
PUNCH,DEV1(I),DEV1(I+1),DEV1(I+2),DEV1(I+3)
PUNCH,X1(I),X1(I+1),X1(I+2),X1(I+3)
PUNCH,X1ER(I),X1ER(I+1),X1ER(I+2),X1ER(I+3)
PUNCH,DEV2(I),DEV2(I+1),DEV2(I+2),DEV2(I+3)
PUNCH,X2(I),X2(I+1),X2(I+2),X2(I+3)
PUNCH,X2ER(I),X2ER(I+1),X2ER(I+2),X2ER(I+3)
29 PUNCH,DEV3(I),DEV3(I+1),DEV3(I+2),DEV3(I+3)
30 DO 36 I=1,20
IF(Y(I)) 31,36,31
31 YC(I)=SQR(YER(I)*YER(I))
DEV1(I)=SQR(DEV1(I)*DEV1(I))
IF(YC(I)-DEV1(I))34,32,32
32 YC(I)=SQR(X1ER(I)*X1ER(I))
DEV2(I)=SQR(DEV2(I)*DEV2(I))
IF(YC(I)-DEV2(I))34,33,33
33 YC(I)=SQR(X2ER(I)*X2ER(I))
DEV3(I)=SQR(DEV3(I)*DEV3(I))
IF(YC(I)-DEV3(I))34,36,36
34 Y(I)=0.0
X1(I)=0.0
X2(I)=0.0
36 CONTINUE
IF(N-J)4030,14,3
4030 M4=M4+1
M5=M5-1
IF(M5)4031,4031,4012
4031 M4=1
GO TO 1
END
```

ALGOL 60 FOR PROGRAM NUMBER 22

PROCEDURE VAAAA(m4); ARRAY y,yer,x1,x1er,x2,x2er,x3,x3er,x4,x4er,dev1,
dev2,dev3,dev4,dev5,oam,c1,devy,devx,xx1,xx2,xx3,xx4,yy,yc,c2[1:20],p[1:6],a,
c,t[1:5]; INTEGER m4;
COMMENT: Three Dimensional Expansion Program
  BEGIN INTEGER i,n,num,ma,m,g,g1,code,na,oper,instr,run,k,L,ka,kb,kc,
  kd,j,m4,m5,m6,feedp; REAL a1,a2,a3,a4,sqrm1,sqrm2,sqrm3,py,pz2,px,
  pz,pxy,pxz,pzy,d,s1,s2,sL1,sL2,b,rr,desL1,desL2,devb,ymin,ymax,x1min,
  x1max,x2min,x2max,funy,funx1,funx2,ya,x1a,x2a,fnsL1,fnsL2,funb,run,
  temp,rLm1,wL1,wu1,rLm2,wL2,wu2,devf1,devf2,devf3,devf4,devf5,rLm3,
  rLm4,rLm5,wL3,wL4,wL5,wu3,wu4,wu5
    IF m4>1 THEN GO TO X1;
    READ VAAAA,feedp;
    READ ka,kb,kc,kd;
    READ j; READ m6;
    m5:=m6; n:=j;
    READ k,L,m;
    READ rLm1,wL1,wu1;
    READ rLm2,wL2,wu2;
    IF k<1 THEN GO TO X25
    ELSE IF k=1 THEN
    BEGIN
     READ devf1; READ devf2END;
    IF k<2 THEN GO TO X1
    ELSE IF k=2 THEN
    BEGIN
     READ devf1;
     FOR i:=1 STEP 1 UNTIL 20 DO READ devx[i];
     devf2:=5555END;
    IF k<3 THEN GO TO X1
    ELSE IF k=3 THEN
    BEGIN
     READ devf2;
     FOR i:=1 STEP 1 UNTIL 20 DO READ devy[i];
     devf1:=5555END;
    IF k>4 THEN GO TO X25
    ELSE IF k=4 THEN
    BEGIN
     FOR i:=1 STEP 1 UNTIL 20 DO READ devy[i];
     FOR i:=1 STEP 1 UNTIL 20 DO READ devx[i];
     devf1:=devf2:=5555END;
X1: FOR i:=1 STEP 1 UNTIL 20 DO READ oam[i];
  g:=20; j:=n;
  IF m6>m5 THEN GO TO X3;
  FOR i:=1 STEP 1 UNTIL 20 DO READ c1[i];
  IF L>3 THEN GO TO X25
  ELSE IF L=3 THEN
  BEGIN
   FOR i:=1 STEP 1 UNTIL 20 DO READ c2[i];
   GO TO X2END;
  c2[i]:=c1[i];
X2: READ oper,instr;

```
       READ run,temp,waveL;
X3:    IF k≤2 THEN
          FOR i:=1 STEP 1 UNTIL 20 DO devy[i]:=devf1Xoam[i];
       IF k<1 THEN GO TO X25
       ELSE IF k=1Vk=3 THEN
          FOR i:=1 STEP 1 UNTIL 20 DO devx[i]:=devf2Xc2[i];
       FOR i:=1 STEP 1 UNTIL 20 DO
       BEGIN
          IF oam[i]<wL1 THEN
          BEGIN
X4:          y[i]:=yer[i]:=x1[i]:=x1er[i]:=x2[i]:=x2er[i]:=x3[i]:=x3er[i]:=x4[i]
             :x3er[i]:=x4[i]:=x4er[i]:=0;
             g:=g−1; GO TO X5END;
          IF(oam[i]>wu1)V(c2[i]<wL2)V(c2[i]>wu2)
             THEN GO TO X4;
          x1[i]:=c2[i]; x1er[i]:=devx[i];
          x2[i]:=c2[i]↑2; x2er[i]:=(c2[i]+devx[i]↑2;
          x3[i]:=x2[i]Xc2[i]; x3er[i]:=x2er[i]X(c2[i]+devx[i]);
          x4[i]:=x3[i]Xc2[i]; x4er[i]:=x3er[i]X(c2[i]+devx[i]−x4[i]);
          x3er[i]:=x3er[i]−x3[i];
          x2er[i]:=x2er[i]−x2[i]
          y[i]:=oam[i]/c1[i]; yer[i]:=devy[i]/c1[i]
X5:    END;
       rLm3:=rLm4:=rLm5:=rLm2;
       devf3:=devf4:=devf5:=devf2;
       wL3:=wL4:=wL5:=wL2;
       wu3:=wu4:=wu5:=wu2;
       PUNCH VAAAA,num,feedp;
       PUNCH m6,m4,PUNCH j;
       PUNCH k,L,m;
       PUNCH devf1,rLm1,wL1,wu1;
       PUNCH devf2,rLm2,wL2,wu2;
       PUNCH devf3,rLm3,wL3,wu3;
       FOR i:=1 STEP 1 UNTIL 20 DO
       BEGIN
          yy[i]:=y[i]; xx1[i]:=x1[i]; xx2[i]:=x2[i]END;
       p[1]:=abs(y[1]);
       p[2]:=abs(x1[1]);
       p[3]:=abs(x2[1]);
       FOR i:=2 STEP 1 UNTIL 20 DO
       BEGIN
          IF p[1]<abs(y[i]) THEN p[1]:=abs(y[i]);
          IF p[2]<abs(x1[i]) THEN p[2]:=abs[x1[i]);
          IF p[3]<abs(x2[i]) THEN p[3]:=abs(x2[i])
       END;
       na:=0;
X6:    na:=na+1;
       IF p[na]≤1Λp[na]≥0.1 THEN
       BEGIN
          a[na]:=1; GO TO X8END;
       FOR i:=1 STEP 1 UNTIL 10 DO
       BEGIN
          m:=10−i; ma:=− m;
```

```
         IF p[na]≤₁₀ma THEN
         BEGIN
           a[na]:=₁₀ma;  GO TO X8END;
         IF p[na]<₁₀m THEN GO TO X7
         ELSE IF p[na]>₁₀m THEN m:=m+1;
         a[na]:=₁₀m;  GO TO X8
X7       END;
X8:      IF na<3 THEN GO TO X6;
         a1:=a[1];  a2:=a[2];  a3:=a[3];
         n:=j;  j:=0;
         IF ka<0 THEN GO TO X9
         ELSE IF ka=0 THEN
         BEGIN
           FOR i:=kb STEP 1 UNTIL kc DO y[i]:=0;
           GO TO X9END;
         IF ka<1 THEN GO TO X9;
         y[kb]:=0;
         IF ka<2 THEN GO TO X9;
         y[kc]:=0;
         IF ka<3 THEN GO TO X9;
         y[kd]:=0;
X9:      FOR i:=1 STEP 1 UNTIL 20 DO
         BEGIN
           y[i]:=y[i]/a1;  yy[i]:=yy[i]/a1;
           x1[i]:=x1[i]/a2;  xx1[i]:=xx1[i]/a2;
           x2[i]:=x2[i]/a3;  xx2[i]:=xx2[i]/a3;
           yer[i]:=yer[i]/a1;  x1er[i]:=x1er[i]/a2;
           x2er[i]:=2er[i]/a3
         END;
         na:=0;
X10:     na:=na+1;  g1:=20;
         sqrm1:=sqrm2:=sqrm3:=py:=pz2:=px:=pz:=px2:=pxy:=pxz:=pzy:=0;
         FOR i:=1 STEP 1 UNTIL 20 DO
         IF (y[i]≠0)∧(x1[i]≠0)∧(x2[i]≠0) THEN
         BEGIN
           x1min:=x1max:=x1[i];
           ymin:=ymax:=y[i];
           x2min:=x2max:=x2[i];  GO TO X11
         END;
X11:     FOR i:=1 STEP 1 UNTIL 20 DO
         BEGIN
           funy:=funx1:=funx2:=1;
           y[i]:=y[i]Xfuny;  x1[i]:=x1[i]Xfunx1;
           x2[i]:=x2[i]Xfunx2;
           IF(y[i]≠0)∧(x1[i]≠0)∧(x2[i]≠0) THEN
           BEGIN
             IF ymin≥y[i] THEN ymin:=y[i];
             IF ymax≤y[i] THEN ymax:=y[i];
             IF x1min≥x1[i] THEN x1min:=x1[i];
             IF x1max≤x1[i] THEN x1max:=x1[i];
             IF x2min≥x2[i] THEN x2min:=x2[i];
             IF x2max≤x2[i] THEN x2max:=x2[i]END
         END;
```

```
         x1a:=(x1max+x1min)/2.0;
         x2a:=(x2max+x2min)/2.0;
         ya:=(ymax+ymin)/2.0;
         FOR i:=1 STEP 1 UNTIL 20 DO
         BEGIN
             IF y[i]=0 THEN
             BEGIN
                 x1[i]:=x2[i]:=dev1[i]:=dev2[i]:=dev3[i]:=0;
                 g1:=g1-1; GO TO X12END;
             y[i]:=y[i]-ya; x1[i]:=x1[i]-x1a; x2[i]:=x2[i]-x2a;
             py:=py+y[i]; pz2:=pz2+x2[i]↑2; px:=px+x1[i];
             px2:=px2+x1[i]↑2; pz:=pz+x2[i]; pxy:=pxy+y[i]Xx1[i];
             pxz:=pxz+x1[i]Xx2[i]; pzy:=pzy+x2[i]Xy[i];
             y[i]:=y[i]+ya; x1[i]:=x1[i]+x1a; x2[i]:=x2[i]+x2a;
             y[i]:=y[i]/funy; x1[i]:=x1[i]/funx1; x2[i]:=x2[i]/funx2
X12:     END;
         d:=pxX(pxzXpz-pxXpz2)-pzX(px2Xpz-pxXpxz)+g1X(px2Xpz2-pxzXpxz);
         IF d≠0 THEN GO TO X14;
         code:=88888888;
X13:     PUNCH code;
         PUNCH oper,instr;
         PUNCH run,temp,waveL;
         GO TO X24;
X14:     s1:=pyX(pxzXpz-pxXpz2)-pzX(pxyXpz-pxXpzy)+g1X(pxyXpz2-pxzXpzy);
         s2:=pxX(pxyXpz-pxXpzy)-pyX(px2Xpz-pxXpxz)+g1X(px2Xpzy-pxyXpxz);
         sL1:=s1/d; sL2:=s2/d;
         IF g1≤4 THEN
         BEGIN
             code:=99999999; GO TO X13END;
         b:=(py-sL1Xpx-sL2Xpz)/g1-sL1Xx1a-sL2Xx2a+ya;
         fnsL1:=fnsL2:=funb:=1;
         sL1:=sL1XfnsL1; sL2:=sL2XfnsL2; b:=bXfunb;
         FOR i:=1 STEP 1 UNTIL 20 DO
         BEGIN
             IF yy[i]=0 THEN GO TO X15;
             rr:=abs(yy[i]-(sL1Xxx1[i]+sL2Xxx2[i]+b));
             yc[i]:=abs(yer[i]);
             IF rr>yc[i] THEN GO TO X15
             rr:=abs(xx1[i]-((yy[i]-sL2Xxx2[i]-b)/sL1));
             yc[i]:=abs(x1er[i]);
             IF rr>yc[i] THEN GO TO X15;
             rr:=abs(xx2[i]-((yy[i]-sL1Xxx1[i]-b)/sL2));
             yc[i]:=abs(x2er[i]);
             IF rr≤yc [i] THEN
             BEGIN
                 y[i]:=yy[i]; x1[i]:=xx1[i]; x2[i]:=xx2[i]END
X15:     END;
         IF na<2 THEN GO TO X10; j:=j+1;
         IF m<j THEN
         BEGIN
             desL1:=sL1Xa4/a2; desL2:=sL2Xa4/a3; devb:=bXa4;
             PUNCH desL1,desL2,devb,g1,g,j,m4;
             PUNCH oper,instr;
```

```
            PUNCH run,temp,waveL, GO TO X24END
            ELSE GO TO X20;
X16:    FOR i:=1 STEP 1 UNTIL 20 DO
        BEGIN
            IF y[i]=0 THEN GO TO X17;
            y[i]:=yer[i]- sL1Xx1er[i]- sL2Xx2er[i];
            IF y[i]=0 THEN y[i]:=0.000001
X17:    END;
        p[4]:=abs(y[1]);
        FOR i:=1 STEP 1 UNTIL 20 DO
        BEGIN
            IF 1[4]<abs (y[i]) THEN p[4]:=abs(y[i])
        END;
        IF p[4]≤1∧p[4]≥0.1 THEN
        BEGIN
            a[4]:=1;  GO TO X19END
        ELSE FOR i:=1 STEP 1 UNTIL 10 DO
        BEGIN
            m:=10-i;  ma:=- m;
            IF p[4]≤ ₁₀ma THEN
            BEGIN
            a[4]:= ₁₀ma;  GO TO X19END;
            IF p[4]< ₁₀m THEN GO TO X18
            ELSE IF p[4]> ₁₀m THEN m:=m+1;
            a[4]:= ₁₀m;  GO TO X19
X18:    END;
X19:    a4:=a[4];
        FOR i:=1 STEP 1 UNTIL 20 DO y[i]:=y[i]Xa1/a4
        GO TO X9;
X20:    FOR i:=1 STEP 1 UNTIL 20 DO
        BEGIN
            IF y[i]=0 THEN GO TO X21;
            dev1[i]:=(abs(sL1Xx1[i]+sL2Xx2[i]+b)- abs(y[i]))Xa1;
            sqrm1:=sqrm1+dev1[i]↑2;
            IF sL1=0 THEN
            BEGIN
            dev2[i]:=0;  GO TO X21END;
            dev2[i]:=(abs((y[i]- sL2Xx2[i]- b)/sL1)- abs(x1[i]))Xa2;
            sqrm2:=sqrm2+dev2[i]↑2;
            IF sL2=0 THEN
            BEGIN
            dev3[i]:=0;  GO TO X21END;
            dev3[i]:=(abs((y[i]- sL1Xx1[i]- b)/sL2)- abs(x2[i]))Xa3;
            sqrm3:=sqrm3+dev3[i]↑2
X21:    END;
        sqrm1:=sqrt(sqrm1/g1);
        sqrm2:=sqrt(sqrm2/g1);
        sqrm3:=sqrt(sqrm3/g1);
        sL1:=sL1Xa1/a2;  sL2:=sL2Xa1/a3;  b:=bXa1;
        FOR i:=1 STEP 1 UNTIL 20 DO
        BEGIN
            y[i]:=y[i]Xa1;  x1[i]:=x1[i]Xa2;  x2[i]:=x2[i]Xa3;
            yer[i]:=yer[i]Xa1;  x1er[i]:=x1er[i]Xa2;
```

```
        x2er[i]:=x2er[i]Xa3; yy[i]:=yy[i]Xa1; xx1[i]:=xx1[i]Xa2;
        xx2[i]:=xx2[i]Xa3
      END;
      PUNCH sL1,sL2,b,g1,g,j,m4;
      PUNCH sqrm1,sqrm2,sqrm3;
      FOR i:=1 STEP 1 UNTIL 20 DO PUNCH y[i];
      FOR i:=1 STEP 1 UNTIL 20 DO PUNCH yer[i];
      FOR i:=1 STEP 1 UNTIL 20 DO PUNCH dev1[i];
      FOR i:=1 STEP 1 UNTIL 20 DO PUNCH x1[i];
      FOR i:=1 STEP 1 UNTIL 20 DO PUNCH x1er[i];
      FOR i:=1 STEP 1 UNTIL 20 DO PUNCH dev2[i];
      FOR i:=1 STEP 1 UNTIL 20 DO PUNCH x2[i];
      FOR·i:=1 STEP 1 UNTIL 20 DO PUNCH x2er[i];
      FOR i:=1 STEP 1 UNTIL 20 DO PUNCH dev3[i];
      FOR i:=1 STEP 1 UNTIL 20 DO
      BEGIN
        IF y[i]=0 THEN GO TO X23;
        dev1[i]:=abs(dev1[i]); yc[i]:=abs(yer[i]);
        IF yc[i]<dev1[i] THEN GO TO X22;
        dev2[i]:=abs(dev2[i]); yc[i]:=abs(x1er[i]);
        IF yc[i]<dev2[i] THEN GO TO X22;
        dev3[i]:=abs(dev3[i]); yc[i]:=abs(x2er[i]);
        IF yc[i]≧dev3[i] THEN GO TO X23;
X22:    y[i]:=x1[i]:=x2[i]:=0
X23:    END;
        IF n>j THEN GO TO X9
        ELSE IF n=j THEN GO TO X16;
X24:    m4:=m4+1; m5:=m5-1;
        IF m5>0 THEN GO TO X1;
        m4:=1
X25:END VAAAA;
        m4:=1;
X26:PROCEDURE VAAAA(m4);
        GO TO X26;
```

FORTRAN FOR PROGRAM NUMBER 23

CALL WORD WAAAA

```
DIMENSION Y(20),YER(20),X1(20),X1ER(20),X2(20),X2ER(20),X3(20),X3ER(20)
DIMENSION X4(20),X4ER(20),P(6),DEV1(20),DEV2(20),DEV3(20),DEV4(20)
DIMENSION DEV5(20),OAM(20),C1(20),DEVY(20),DEVX(20),XX1(20),XX2(20)
DIMENSION XX3(20),XX4(20),YY(20),YC(20),D(6),C2(20),C(5),T(5),A(5)
M4=1
1  IF(M4-1)4000,4000,4012
4000 READ,WAAAA,FEEDP
READ,KA,KB,KC,KD
READ,J
READ,M6
M5=M6
N=J
READ,K,L,M
READ,RLM1,WL1,WU1
READ,RLM2,WL2,WU2
IF(K-1)1,4001,4002
4001 READ,DEVF1
READ,DEVF2
4002 IF(K-2)4012,4003,4005
4003 READ,DEVF1
DO 4004 I=1,20,4
4004 READ,DEVX(I),DEVX(I+1),DEVX(I+2),DEVX(I+3)
DEVF2=5555.0
4005 IF(K-3)4012,4006,4008
4006 DO 4007 I=1,20,4
4007 READ,DEVY(I),DEVY(I+1),DEVY(I+2),DEVY(I+3)
DEVF1=5555.0
READ,DEVF2
4008 IF(K-4)4012,4009,1
4009 DO 4010 I=1,20,4
4010 READ,DEVY(I),DEVY(I+1),DEVY(I+2),DEVY(I+3)
DEVF1=5555.0
DO 4011 I=1,20,4
4011 READ,DEVX(I),DEVX(I+1),DEVX(I+2),DEVX(I+3)
DEVF2=5555.0
4012 DO 4013 I=1,20,4
4013 READ,OAM(I),OAM(I+1),OAM(I+2),OAM(I+3)
G=20.0
J=N
IF(M6-M5)4014,4014,4016
4014 DO 4015 I=1,20,4
4015 READ,C1(I),C1(I+1),C1(I+2),C1(I+3)
IF(L-3)4050,4051,1
4051 DO 4052 I=1,20,4
4052 READ,C2(I),C2(I+1),C2(I+2),C2(I+3)
GO TO 4054
4050 DO 4053 I=1,20
4053 C2(I)=C1(I)
4054 READ,OPER,INSTR
READ,RUN,TEMP,WAVEL
4016 IF(K-2)4017,4017,4019
4017 DO 4018 I=1,20
4018 DEVY(I)=DEVF1*OAM(I)
4019 IF(K-1)1,4020,4021
4021 IF(K-3)4023,4020,4023
4020 DO 4022 I=1,20
4022 DEVX(I)=DEVF2*C2(I)
4023 DO 4024 I=1,20
IF(OAM(I)-WL1)4025,4026,4026
```

```
4025 Y(I)=0.0
YER(I)=0.0
X1(I)=0.0
X1ER(I)=0.0
X2(I)=0.0
X2ER(I)=0.0
X3(I)=0.0
X3ER(I)=0.0
X4(I)=0.0
X4ER(I)=0.0
G=G-1.0
GO TO 4024
4026 IF(OAM(I)-WU1)4027,4027,4025
4027 IF(C2(I)-WL2)4025,4028,4028
4028 IF(C2(I)-WU2)4029,4029,4025
4029 X1(I)=C2(I)
X1ER(I)=DEVX(I)
X2(I)=C2(I)*C2(I)
X2ER(I)=(C2(I)+DEVX(I))*(C2(I)+DEVX(I))
X3(I)=X2(I)*C2(I)
X3ER(I)=X2ER(I)*(C2(I)+DEVX(I))
X4(I)=X3(I)*C2(I)
X4ER(I)=X3ER(I)*(C2(I)+DEVX(I))-X4(I)
X2ER(I)=X2ER(I)-X2(I)
X3ER(I)=X3ER(I)-X3(I)
Y(I)=OAM(I)/C1(I)
YER(I)=DEVY(I)/C1(I)
4024 CONTINUE
RLM3=RLM2
DEVF3=DEVF2
DEVF4=DEVF2
DEVF5=DEVF2
RLM5=RLM2
RLM4=RLM2
WL3=WL2
WL4=WL2
WL5=WL2
WU3=WU2
WU4=WU2
WU5=WU2
NUM=23
PUNCH,WAAAA,NUM,FEEDP
PUNCH,M6,M4
PUNCH,J
PUNCH,K,L,M
PUNCH,DEVF1,RLM1,WL1,WU1
PUNCH,DEVF2,RLM2,WL2,WU2
PUNCH,DEVF3,RLM3,WL3,WU3
PUNCH,DEVF4,RLM4,WL4,WU4
DO 400 I=1,20
YY(I)=Y(I)
XX1(I)=X1(I)
XX2(I)=X2(I)
400 XX3(I)=X3(I)
P(1)=SQR(Y(1)*Y(1))
P(2)=SQR(X1(1)*X1(1))
P(3)=SQR(X2(1)*X2(1))
P(4)=SQR(X3(1)*X3(1))
DO 40 I=2,20
IF(P(1)-SQR(Y(I)*Y(I)))41,42,42
41 P(1)=SQR(Y(I)*Y(I))
42 IF(P(2)-SQR(X1(I)*X1(I)))43,44,44
```

```
   43 P(2)=SQR(X1(I)*X1(I))
   44 IF(P(3)-SQR(X2(I)*X2(I)))45,46,46
   45 P(3)=SQR(X2(I)*X2(I))
   46 IF(P(4)-SQR(X3(I)*X3(I)))47,40,40
   47 P(4)=SQR(X3(I)*X3(I))
   40 CONTINUE
      NA=0
   48 NA=NA+1
      IF(P(NA)-1.0)49,50,51
   49 IF(P(NA)-0.1)51,50,50
   50 A(NA)=1.0
      GO TO 57
   51 DO 52 I=1,10
      M=10-I
      MA=-M
      IF(P(NA)-10.0**MA)53,53,54
   53 A(NA)=10.0**MA
      GO TO 57
   54 IF(P(NA)-10.0**M)52,56,55
   55 M=M+1
   56 A(NA)=10.0**M
      GO TO 57
   52 CONTINUE
   57 IF(NA-4)48,58,58
   58 A1=A(1)
      A2=A(2)
      A3=A(3)
      A4=A(4)
      N=J
      J=0
      IF(KA) 3,300,302
  300 DO 301 I=KB,KC
  301 Y(I)=0.0
      GO TO 3
  302 IF(KA-1) 3,303,303
  303 Y(KB)=0.0
      IF(KA-2) 3,304,304
  304 Y(KC)=0.0
      IF(KA-3) 3,305,305
  305 Y(KD)=0.0
    3 DO 4 I=1,20
      Y(I)=Y(I)/A1
      YY(I)=YY(I)/A1
      X1(I)=X1(I)/A2
      XX1(I)=XX1(I)/A2
      X2(I)=X2(I)/A3
      XX2(I)=XX2(I)/A3
      X3(I)=X3(I)/A4
      XX3(I)=XX3(I)/A4
      YER(I)=YER(I)/A1
      X1ER(I)=X1ER(I)/A2
      X2ER(I)=X2ER(I)/A3
    4 X3ER(I)=X3ER(I)/A4
      NN=0
  401 NN=NN+1
      G1=20.0
      SQRM1=0.0
      SQRM2=0.0
      SQRM3=0.0
      SQRM4=0.0
      PY=0.0
      PX=0.0
```

```
PZ=0.0
PW=0.0
PX2=0.0
PXZ=0.0
PZ2=0.0
PWY=0.0
PWZ=0.0
PXY=0.0
PW2=0.0
PXW=0.0
PZY=0.0
    DO 796 I=1,20
    IF(Y(I))797,796,797
797 IF(X1(I))798,796,798
798 IF(X2(I))799,796,799
799 IF(X3(I))800,796,800
800 X1MIN=X1(I)
    X1MAX=X1(I)
    X2MIN=X2(I)
    X2MAX=X2(I)
    X3MIN=X3(I)
    X3MAX=X3(I)
    YMIN=Y(I)
    YMAX=Y(I)
    GO TO 801
796 CONTINUE
801 DO 802 I=1,20
999 FUNY=1.0
1000 FUNX1=1.0
1001 FUNX2=1.0
1002 FUNX3=1.0
    Y(I)=Y(I)*FUNY
    X1(I)=X1(I)*FUNX1
    X2(I)=X2(I)*FUNX2
    X3(I)=X3(I)*FUNX3
    IF(Y(I))803,802,803
803 IF(X1(I))804,802,804
804 IF(X2(I))805,802,805
805 IF(X3(I))806,802,806
806 IF(X1MIN-X1(I))807,808,808
808 X1MIN=X1(I)
807 IF(X1MAX-X1(I))809,809,810
809 X1MAX=X1(I)
810 IF(X2MIN-X2(I))811,812,812
812 X2MIN=X2(I)
811 IF(X2MAX-X2(I))813,813,814
813 X2MAX=X2(I)
814 IF(X3MIN-X3(I))815,816,816
816 X3MIN=X3(I)
815 IF(X3MAX-X3(I))817,817,818
817 X3MAX=X3(I)
818 IF(YMIN-Y(I))819,820,820
820 YMIN=Y(I)
819 IF(YMAX-Y(I))821,821,802
821 YMAX=Y(I)
802 CONTINUE
    X1A=(X1MAX+X1MIN)/2.0
    X2A=(X2MAX+X2MIN)/2.0
    YA=(YMAX+YMIN)/2.0
    X3A=(X3MAX+X3MIN)/2.0
    DO 7 I=1,20
    IF(Y(I)) 6,5,6
```

```
5 Y(I)=0.0
X1(I)=0.0
X2(I)=0.0
X3(I)=0.0
DEV1(I)=0.0
DEV2(I)=0.0
DEV3(I)=0.0
DEV4(I)=0.0
G1=G1-1.0
GO TO 7
6 Y(I)=Y(I)-YA
X1(I)=X1(I)-X1A
X2(I)=X2(I)-X2A
X3(I)=X3(I)-X3A
PY=PY+Y(I)
PX=PX+X1(I)
PZ=PZ+X2(I)
PW=PW+X3(I)
PXY=PXY+X1(I)*Y(I)
PX2=PX2+X1(I)*X1(I)
PXZ=PXZ+X1(I)*X2(I)
PXW=PXW+X1(I)*X3(I)
PZY=PZY+X2(I)*Y(I)
PZ2=PZ2+X2(I)*X2(I)
PWZ=PWZ+X3(I)*X2(I)
PWY=PWY+X3(I)*Y(I)
PW2=PW2+X3(I)*X3(I)
Y(I)=Y(I)+YA
X1(I)=X1(I)+X1A
X2(I)=X2(I)+X2A
X3(I)=X3(I)+X3A
Y(I)=Y(I)/FUNY
X1(I)=X1(I)/FUNX1
X2(I)=X2(I)/FUNX2
X3(I)=X3(I)/FUNX3
7 CONTINUE
D1=PXZ*(PWZ*PW-PZ*PW2)-PXW*(PZ2*PW-PZ*PWZ)+PX*(PZ2*PW2-PWZ*PWZ)
D2=PX2*(PWZ*PW-PZ*PW2)-PXW*(PXZ*PW-PZ*PXW)+PX*(PXZ*PW2-PWZ*PXW)
D3=PX2*(PZ2*PW-PZ*PWZ)-PXZ*(PXZ*PW-PXW*PZ)+PX*(PXZ*PWZ-PZ2*PXW)
D4=PX2*(PZ2*PW2-PWZ*PWZ)-PXZ*(PW2*PXZ-PWZ*PXW)+PXW*(PXZ*PWZ-PZ2*PXW)
D=PX*D1-PZ*D2+PW*D3-G1*D4
IF(D) 10,8,10
8 CODE=88888888.
9 PRINT,CODE,M4,RUN
PUNCH,CODE,M4
PUNCH,OPER,INSTR
PUNCH,RUN,TEMP,WAVEL
GO TO 4030
10 D1=PXZ*(PWZ*PW-PW2*PZ)-PXW*(PZ2*PW-PWZ*PZ)+PX*(PZ2*PW2-PWZ*PWZ)
D2=PXY*(PWZ*PW-PW2*PZ)-PXW*(PZY*PW-PWY*PZ)+PX*(PZY*PW2-PWY*PWZ)
D3=PXY*(PZ2*PW-PWZ*PZ)-PXZ*(PZY*PW-PWY*PZ)+PX*(PZY*PWZ-PWY*PZ2)
D4=PXY*(PZ2*PW2-PWZ*PWZ)-PXZ*(PZY*PW2-PWY*PWZ)+PXW*(PZY*PWZ-PWY*PZ2)
S1=PY*D1-PZ*D2+PW*D3-G1*D4
D1=PXY*(PWZ*PW-PW2*PZ)-PXW*(PZY*PW-PWY*PZ)+PX*(PZY*PW2-PWY*PWZ)
D2=PX2*(PWZ*PW-PW2*PZ)-PXW*(PXZ*PW-PXW*PZ)+PX*(PXZ*PW2-PXW*PWZ)
D3=PX2*(PZY*PW-PWY*PZ)-PXY*(PXZ*PW-PXW*PZ)+PX*(PXZ*PWY-PXW*PZY)
D4=PX2*(PZY*PW2-PWY*PWZ)-PXY*(PXZ*PW2-PXW*PWZ)+PXW*(PXZ*PWY-PXW*PZY)
S2=PX*D1-PY*D2+PW*D3-G1*D4
D1=PXZ*(PZY*PW-PWY*PZ)-PXY*(PZ2*PW-PWZ*PZ)+PX*(PZ2*PWY-PWZ*PZY)
D2=PX2*(PZY*PW-PWY*PZ)-PXY*(PXZ*PW-PXW*PZ)+PX*(PXZ*PWY-PXW*PZY)
D3=PX2*(PZ2*PW-PWZ*PZ)-PXZ*(PXZ*PW-PXW*PZ)+PX*(PXZ*PWZ-PXW*PZ2)
D4=PX2*(PZ2*PWY-PWZ*PZY)-PXZ*(PXZ*PWY-PXW*PZY)+PXY*(PXZ*PWZ-PXW*PZ2),
```

```
S3=PX*D1-PZ*D2+PY*D3-G1*D4
SL1=S1/D
SL2=S2/D
SL3=S3/D
IF(G1-5.0) 11,11,12
11 CODE=99999999.
GO TO 9
12 B=(PY-SL1*PX-SL2*PZ-SL3*PW)/G1
B=B-SL1*X1A-SL2*X2A-X3A*SL3+YA
1110 FNSL1=1.0
1111 FNSL2=1.0
1112 FNSL3=1.0
1113 FUNB=1.0
SL1=SL1*FNSL1
SL2=SL2*FNSL2
SL3=SL3*FNSL3
B=B*FUNB
DO 402 I=1,20
IF(YY(I))407,402,407
407 RR=SL1*XX1(I)+SL2*XX2(I)+SL3*XX3(I)+B
RR=SQR((RR-YY(I))*(RR-YY(I)))
YC(I)=SQR(YER(I)*YER(I))
IF(RR-YC(I))404,404,402
2222 Y(I)=YY(I)
X1(I)=XX1(I)
X2(I)=XX2(I)
X3(I)=XX3(I)
GO TO 402
404 RR=(YY(I)-SL2*XX2(I)-SL3*XX3(I)-B)/SL1
RR=SQR((RR-XX1(I))*(RR-XX1(I)))
YC(I)=SQR(X1ER(I)*X1ER(I))
IF(RR-YC(I)) 405,405,402
405 RR=(YY(I)-SL1*XX1(I)-SL3*XX3(I)-B)/SL2
RR=SQR((RR-XX2(I))*(RR-XX2(I)))
YC(I)=SQR(X2ER(I)*X2ER(I))
IF(RR-YC(I))403,403,402
403 RR=(YY(I)-SL1*XX1(I)-SL2*XX2(I)-B)/SL3
RR=SQR((RR-XX3(I))*(RR-XX3(I)))
YC(I)=SQR(X3ER(I)*X3ER(I))
IF(RR-YC(I))2222,2222,402
402 CONTINUE
IF(NN-2)401,406,406
406 J=J+1
IF(N-J) 13,19,19
13 DESL1=SL1*A5/A2
DESL2=SL2*A5/A3
DESL3=SL3*A5/A4
DEVB=B*A5
PUNCH,DESL1,DESL2,DESL3,DEVB,G1,G,J,M4
PUNCH,OPER,INSTR
PUNCH,RUN,TEMP,WAVEL
GO TO 4030
14 DO 18 I=1,20
IF(Y(I)) 15,18,15
15 Y(I)=YER(I)-SL1*X1ER(I)-X2ER(I)*SL2-SL3*X3ER(I)
IF(Y(I)) 18,16,18
16 Y(I)=0.000001
18 CONTINUE
P(5)=SQR(Y(1)*Y(1))
DO 59 I=2,20
IF(P(5)-SQR(Y(I)*Y(I)))60,59,59
60 P(5)=SQR(Y(I)*Y(I))
```

```
59 CONTINUE
   IF(P(5)-1.0)60,61,62
60 IF(P(5)-0.1)62,61,61
61 A(5)=1.0
   GO TO 68
62 DO 63 I=1,10
   M=10-I
   MA=-M
   IF(P(5)-10.0**MA)64,64,65
64 A(5)=10.0**MA
   GO TO 68
65 IF(P(5)-10.0**M)63,67,66
66 M=M+1
67 A(5)=10.0**M
   GO TO 68
63 CONTINUE
68 A5=A(5)
   DO 69 I=1,20
69 Y(I)=Y(I)*A1/A5
   GO TO 3
19 IF(G1-5.0) 11,11,20
20 DO 26 I=1,20
   IF(Y(I)) 21,26,21
21 DEV1(I)=SL1*X1(I)+SL2*X2(I)+SL3*X3(I)+B
   DEV1(I)=(SQR(DEV1(I)*DEV1(I))-SQR(Y(I)*Y(I)))*A1
   SQRM1=SQRM1+DEV1(I)*DEV1(I)
   IF(SL1) 23,22,23
22 DEV2(I)=0.0
   GO TO 26
23 DEV2(I)=(Y(I)-SL2*X2(I)-SL3*X3(I)-B)/SL1
   DEV2(I)=(SQR(DEV2(I)*DEV2(I))-SQR(X1(I)*X1(I)))*A2
   SQRM2=SQRM2+DEV2(I)*DEV2(I)
   IF(SL2) 25,24,25
24 DEV3(I)=0.0
   GO TO 26
25 DEV3(I)=(Y(I)-SL1*X1(I)-SL3*X3(I)-B)/SL2
   DEV3(I)=(SQR(DEV3(I)*DEV3(I))-SQR(X2(I)*X2(I)))*A3
   SQRM3=SQRM3+DEV3(I)*DEV3(I)
   IF(SL3) 98,99,98
99 DEV4(I)=0.0
   GO TO 26
98 DEV4(I)=(Y(I)-SL1*X1(I)-SL2*X2(I)-B)/SL3
   DEV4(I)=(SQR(DEV4(I)*DEV4(I))-SQR(X3(I)*X3(I)))*A4
   SQRM4=SQRM4+DEV4(I)*DEV4(I)
26 CONTINUE
   SQRM1=SQR(SQRM1/G1)
   SQRM2=SQR(SQRM2/G1)
   SQRM3=SQR(SQRM3/G1)
   SQRM4=SQR(SQRM4/G1)
   SL1=SL1*A1/A2
   SL2=SL2*A1/A3
   SL3=SL3*A1/A4
   B=B*A1
   DO 27 I=1,20
   Y(I)=Y(I)*A1
   YY(I)=YY(I)*A1
   X1(I)=X1(I)*A2
   XX1(I)=XX1(I)*A2
   X2(I)=X2(I)*A3
   XX2(I)=XX2(I)*A3
   X3(I)=X3(I)*A4
   XX3(I)=XX3(I)*A4
```

```
    YER(I)=YER(I)*A1
    X1ER(I)=X1ER(I)*A2
    X2ER(I)=X2ER(I)*A3
27  X3ER(I)=X3ER(I)*A4
    PUNCH,SL1,SL2,SL3,B,G1,G,J,M4
    PUNCH,SQRM1,SQRM2,SQRM3,SQRM4
    IF(SENSE SWITCH 1) 28,30
28  DO 29 I=1,20,4
    PUNCH,DEV1(I),DEV1(I+1),DEV1(I+2),DEV1(I+3)
    PUNCH,DEV2(I),DEV2(I+1),DEV2(I+2),DEV2(I+3)
    PUNCH,DEV3(I),DEV3(I+1),DEV3(I+2),DEV3(I+3)
29  PUNCH,DEV4(I),DEV4(I+1),DEV4(I+2),DEV4(I+3)
    GO TO 32
30  IF(SENSE SWITCH 2)640,32
640 DO 31 I=1,20,4
    PUNCH,Y(I),Y(I+1),Y(I+2),Y(I+3)
    PUNCH,YER(I),YER(I+1),YER(I+2),YER(I+3)
    PUNCH,DEV1(I),DEV1(I+1),DEV1(I+2),DEV1(I+3)
    PUNCH,X1(I),X1(I+1),X1(I+2),X1(I+3)
    PUNCH,X1ER(I),X1ER(I+1),X1ER(I+2),X1ER(I+3)
    PUNCH,DEV2(I),DEV2(I+1),DEV2(I+2),DEV2(I+3)
    PUNCH,X2(I),X2(I+1),X2(I+2),X2(I+3)
    PUNCH,X2ER(I),X2ER(I+1),X2ER(I+2),X2ER(I+3)
    PUNCH,DEV3(I),DEV3(I+1),DEV3(I+2),DEV3(I+3)
    PUNCH,X3(I),X3(I+1),X3(I+2),X3(I+3)
    PUNCH,X3ER(I),X3ER(I+1),X3ER(I+2),X3ER(I+3)
31  PUNCH,DEV4(I),DEV4(I+1),DEV4(I+2),DEV4(I+3)
32  DO 39 I=1,20
    IF(Y(I)) 33,39,33
33  YC(I)=SQR(YER(I)*YER(I))
    DEV1(I)=SQR(DEV1(I)*DEV1(I))
    IF(YC(I)-DEV1(I))34,35,35
35  YC(I)=SQR(X1ER(I)*X1ER(I))
    DEV2(I)=SQR(DEV2(I)*DEV2(I))
    IF(YC(I)-DEV2(I)) 34,36,36
36  YC(I)=SQR(X2ER(I)*X2ER(I))
    DEV3(I)=SQR(DEV3(I)*DEV3(I))
    IF(YC(I)-DEV3(I)) 34,37,37
37  YC(I)=SQR(X3ER(I)*X3ER(I))
    DEV4(I)=SQR(DEV4(I)*DEV4(I))
    IF(YC(I)-DEV4(I)) 34,39,39
34  Y(I)=0.0
    X1(I)=0.0
    X2(I)=0.0
    X3(I)=0.0
39  CONTINUE
    IF(N-J)4030,14,3
4030 M4=M4+1
    M5=M5-1
    IF(M5)4031,4031,4012
4031 M4=1
    GO TO 1
    END
```

ALGOL 60 FOR PROGRAM NUMBER 23

```
PROCEDURE WAAA(m4); ARRAY y,yer,x1,x1er,x2,x2er,x3,x3er,x4,x4er,dev1,
dev2,dev3,dev4,dev5,oam,devy,devx,xx1,xx2,xx3,xx4,yy,yc,c2[1:20],p,d[1:6],c,t,
a[1:5]; INTEGER m4;
COMMENT: FOUR DIMENSION EXPANSION PROGRAM
    BEGIN INTEGER i,n,nn,na,num,ma,g,g1,code,oper,instr,feedp,run,ka,kb,
    kc,kd,k,L,m,m5,m6;  REAL a1,a2,a3,a4,a5,sqrm1,sqrm2,sqrm3,sqrm4,
    py,px,pz,pw,px2,pxz,pz2,pwy,pwz,pw2,pxw,pzy,d,d1,d2,d3,d4,s1,s2,s3,sL1,
    sL2,sL3,b,rr,desL1,desL2,desL3,devb,ymin,ymax,x1min,x1max,x2min,
    x2max,x3min,x3max,funy,funx1,funx2,funx3,ya,x1a,x2a,x3a,fnsL1,fnsL2,
    fnsL3,funb,devf1,devf2,rLm1,rLm2,rLm3,rLm4,rLm5,wL1,wL2,wL3,wL4,wL5,
    wL5,wu1,wu2,wu3,wu4,wu5,temp,waveL,devf3,devf4,devf5;
        IF m4>1 THEN GO TO X1;
        READ feedp;
        READ ka,kb,kc,kd;
        READ j: READ m6;
        m5:=m6; n:=j;
        READ k,L,m;
        READ rLm1,wL1,wu1;
        READ rLm2,wL2,wu2;
        IF k<1 THEN GO TO X24
        ELSE IF k=1 THEN
        BEGIN
            READ devf1;
            READ devf2END;
        IF k<2 THEN GO TO X1
        ELSE IF k=2 THEN
        BEGIN
            READ devf1;
            FOR i:=1 STEP 1 UNTIL 20 DO READ devx[i];
            devf2:=5555END;
        IF k<3 THEN GO TO X1
        ELSE IF k=3 THEN
        BEGIN
            READ devf2;
            FOR i:=1 STEP 1 UNTIL 20 DO READ devy[i];
            devf1:=5555END;
        IF k>4 THEN GO TO X24
        ELSE IF k=4 THEN
        BEGIN
            FOR i:=1 STEP 1 UNTIL 20 DO READ devy[i];
            FOR i:=1 STEP 1 UNTIL 20 DO READ devx[i];
            devf1:=devf2:=5555END;
X1:     FOR i:=1 STEP 1 UNTIL 20 DO READ oam[i];
        g:=20; j:=n;
        IF m6≤m5 THEN
        BEGIN
            FOR i:=1 STEP 1 UNTIL 20 DO READ c1[i];
            IF L>3 THEN GO TO X24
            ELSE IF L=3 THEN
            BEGIN
                FOR i:=1 STEP 1 UNTIL 20 DO READ c2[i];
```

```
        GO TO X2END;
        FOR i:=1 STEP 1 UNTIL 20 DO c2[i]:=c1[i];
X2:        READ oper,instr;
           READ run,temp,waveL
        END;
        IF k≤2 THEN
        FOR i:=1 STEP 1 UNTIL 20 DO devy[i]:=devf1Xoam[i];
        IF k<1 THEN GO TO X24
        ELSE IF k=1∨k=3 THEN
        FOR i:=1 STEP 1 UNTIL 20 DO devx[i]:=devf2Xc2[i];
        FOR i:=1 STEP 1 UNTIL 20 DO
        BEGIN
           IF oam[i]<wL1 THEN
           BEGIN
X3:           y[i]:=yer[i]:=x1[i]:=x1er[i]:=x2[i]:=x2er[i]:=x3[i]:=x3er[i]:=x4[i]
                :=x4er[i]:=0; g:=g-1;
              GO TO X4END;
           IF(oam[i]>wu1)∨(c2[i]<wL2)∨(c2[i]>wu2) THEN
              GO TO X3;
           x1[i]:=c2[i]; x1er[i]:=devx[i]; x2[i]:=c2[i]↑2;
           x2er[i]:=(c2[i]+devx[i]↑2;
           x3[i]:=x2[i]Xc2[i]; x3er[i]:=x2er[i]X(c2[i]+devx[i]);
           x4[i]:=x3[i]Xc2[i];
           x4er[i]:=x3er[i]X(c2[i]+devx[i])-x4[i];
           x2er[i]:=x2er[i]-x2[i];
           x3er[i]:=x3er[i]-x3[i];
           y[i]:=oam[i]/c1[i];
           yer[i]:=devy[i]/c1[i]
X4:        END;
        rLm3:=rLm4:=rLm5:=rLm2; wL3:=wL4:=wL5:=wL2;
        devf3:=devf4:=devf5:=devf2;
        wu3:=wu4:=wu5:=wu2;
        num:=23;
        PUNCH num,feedp;
        PUNCH m6,m4;
        PUNCH j;
        PUNCH k,L,m;
        PUNCH devf1,rLm1,wL1,wu1;
        PUNCH devf2,rLm2,wL2,wu2;
        PUNCH devf3,rLm3,wL3,wu3;
        PUNCH devf4,rLm4,wL4,wu4;
        FOR i:=1 STEP 1 UNTIL 20 DO
        BEGIN
           yy[i]:=y[i]; xx1[i]:=x1[i]; xx2[i]:=x2[i]; xx3[i]:=x3[i]
        END;
        p[1]:=abs(y[1]); p[2]:=abs(x1[1]);
        p[3]:=abs(x2[1]); p[4]:=abs(x3[1]);
        FOR i:=1 STEP 1 UNTIL 20 DO
        BEGIN
           IF p[1]<abs(y[i] THEN p[1]:=abs(y[i]);
           IF p[2]<abs(x1[i]) THEN p[2]:=abs(x1[i]);
           IF p[3]<abs(x2[i]) THEN p[3]:=abs(x2[i]);
           IF p[4]<abs(x3[i]) THEN p[4]:=abs(x3[i])
```

```
        END;
        na:=0;
X5:     na:=na+1;
        IF p[na]≤1∧p[na]≥0.1 THEN
        BEGIN
            a[na]:=1;  GO TO X7END
        ELSE FOR i:=1 STEP 1 UNTIL 10 DO
        BEGIN
            m:=10-i;  ma:=-m;
            IF p[na]≤₁₀ma THEN
            BEGIN
                a[na]:=₁₀ma;  GO TO X7END;
                IF p[na]<₁₀m THEN GO TO X6
                ELSE IF p[na]>₁₀m THEN m:=m+1;
                a[na]:=₁₀m;  GO TO X7
X6:     END;
X7:     IF na<4 THEN GO TO X5;
        a1:=a[1];  a2:=a[2];  a3:=a[3];  a4:=a[4];
        n:=j;  j:=0;
        IF ka<0 THEN GO TO X8
        ELSE IF ka=0 THEN
        FOR i:=kb STEP 1 UNTIL kc DO
        BEGIN
            y[i]:=0;  GO TO X8
        END;
        IF ka<1 THEN GO TO X8;
        y[kb]:=0;
        IF ka<2 THEN GO TO X8;
        y[kc]:=0;
        IF ka<3 THEN GO TO X8;
        y[kd]:=0;
X8:     FOR i:=1 STEP 1 UNTIL 20 DO
        BEGIN
            y[i]:=y[i]/a1;  yy[i]:=yy[i]/a1;  x1[i]:=x1[i]/a2;
            xx1[i]:=xx1[i]/a2;  x2[i]:=x2[i]/a3;  xx2[i]:=xx2[i]/a3;
            x3[i]:=x3[i]/a4;  xx3[i]:=xx3[i]/a4;  yer[i]:=yer[i]/a1;
            x1er[i]:=x1er[i]/a2;  x2er[i]:=x2er[i]/a3;
            x3er[i]:=3er[i]/a4
        END;
        nn:=0;
X9:     nn:=nn+1;  g1:=20;
        sqrm1:=sqrm2:=sqrm3:=sqrm4:=py:=px:=pz:=pw:=px2:=pxz:=pz2:=pwy
          :=pwz:=pxy:=pw2:=pxw:=pzy:=0;
        FOR i:=1 STEP 1 UNTIL 20 DO
        BEGIN
            IFy[i]≠0∧x1[i]≠0∧x2[i]≠0∧x3[i]≠0 THEN
            BEGIN
                ymin:=ymax:=y[i];  x1min:=x1max:=x1[i];
                x2min:=x2max:=x2[i];  x3min:=x3max:=x3[i];
                GO TO X10END
        END;
X10:    FOR i:=1 STEP 1 UNTIL 20 DO
        BEGIN
```

```
        funy:=funx1:=funx2:=funx3:=1;
        y[i]:=y[i]Xfuny;  x1[i]:=x1[i]Xfunx1;
        x2[i]:=x2[i]Xfunx2;  x3[i]:=x3[i]Xfunx3;
        IF y[i]≠0∧x1[i]≠0∧x2[i]≠0∧x3[i]≠0 THEN
        BEGIN
            IF ymin≥y[i] THEN ymin:=y[i];
            IF ymax≤y[i] THEN ymax:=y[i];
            IF x1min≥x1[i] THEN x1min:=x1[i];
            IF x1max≤x1[i] THEN x1max:=x1[i];
            IF x2min≥x2[i] THEN x2min:=x2[i];
            IF x2max≤x2[i] THEN x2max:=x2[i];
            IF x3min≥x3[i] THEN x3min:=x3[i];
            IF x3max≤x3[i] THEN x3max:=x3[i]END
        END;
        ya:=(ymax+ymin)/2.0;
        x1a:=(x1max+x1min)/2.0;
        x2a:=(x2max+x2min)/2.0
        x3a:=(x3max+x3min)/2.0;
        FOR i:=1 STEP 1 UNTIL 20 DO
        BEGIN
            IF y[i]=0 THEN
            BEGIN
                x1[i]:=x2[i]:=x3[i]:=dev1[i]:=dev2[i]:=dev3[i]:=dev4[i]:=0;  g1:=g1−1;
                GO TO X11END;
            y[i]:=y[i]−ya;  x1[i]:=x1[i]−x1a;  x2[i]:=x2[i]−x2a;
            x3[i]:=x3[i]−x3a;  py:=py+y[i];  px:=px+x1[i];
            pz:=pz+x2[i];  pw:=pw+x3[i];  pxy:=pxy+x1[i]Xy[i];
            px2:=px2+x1[i]↑2;  pxz:=pxz+x1[i]Xx2[i];
            pxw:=pxw+x1[i]Xx3[i];  pzy:=pzy+x2[i]Xy[i];
            pz2:=pz2+x2[i]↑2;  pwz:=pwz+x3[i]Xx2[i];
            pwy:=pwy+x3[i]Xy[i];  pw2:=pw2+x3[i]↑2;
            y[i]:=y[i]+ya;  x1[i]:=x1[i]+x1a;
            x2[i]:=x2[i]+x2a;  x3[i]:=x3[i]+x3a;
            y[i]:=y[i]/funy;  x1[i]:=x1[i]/funx1;
            x2[i]:=x2[i]/funx2;  x3[i]:=x3[i]/funx3
X11:    END;
        d1:=pxzX(pwzXpw−pzXpw2)−pxwX(pz2Xpw−pzXpwz)+pxX(pz2Xpw2−
            pwzXpwz);
        d2:=px2X(pwzXpw−pzXpw2)−pxwX(pxzXpw−pzXpxw)+pxX(pxzXpw2−
            pwzXpxw);
        d3:=px2X(pz2Xpw−pzXpwz)−pxzX(pxzXpw−pxwXpz)+pxX(pxzXpwz−
            pz2Xpxw);
        d4:=px2X(pz2Xpw2−pwzXpwz)−pxzX(pw2Xpxz−pwzXpxw)+pxwX
            (pxzXpwz−pz2Xpxw);
        d:=pxXd1−pzXd2+pwXd3−g1Xd4;
        IF d≠0 THEN GO TO X13;
        code:=88888888;
X12:    PUNCH code,m4;
        PUNCH oper,instr;
        PUNCH run, temp,waveL;
        GO TO X23;
X13:    d1:=pxzX(pwzXpw−pw2Xpz)−pxwX(pz2Xpw−pwzXpz)+pxX(pz2Xpw2−
            pwzXpwz);
```

```
      d2:=pxyX(pwzXpw-pw2Xpz)-pxwX(pzyXpw-pwyXpz)+pxX(pzyXpw2-
      pwyXpwz);
      d3:=pxyX(pz2Xpw-pwzXpz)-pxzX(pxyXpw-pwyXpz)+pxX(pzyXpwz-
      pwyXpz2);
      d4:=pxyX(pz2Xpw2-pwxXpwz)-pxzX(pzyXpw2-pwyXpwz)+pxwX(pzyXpwz
      -pwyXpz2);
      s1:=pyXd1-pzXd2+pwXd3-g1Xd4;
      d1:=pxyX(pwzXpw-pw2Xpz)-pxwX(pzyXpw-pwyXpz)+pxX(pzyXpw2-
      pwyXpwz);
      d2:=px2X(pwzXpw-pw2Xpz)-pxwX(pxzXpw-pxwXpz)+pxX(pxzXpw2-
      pxwXpwz);
      d3:=px2X(pzyXpw-pwyXpz)-pxyX(pxzXpw-pxwXpz)+pxX(pxzXpwy-
      pxwXpzy);
      d4:=px2X(pzyXpw2-pwyXpwz)-pxyX(pxzXpw2-pxwXpwz)+pxyX(pxzXpwy
      -pxwXpzy);
      s2:=pxXd1-pyXd2+pwXd3-g1Xd4;
      d1:=pxzX(pzyXpw-pwyXpz)-pxyX(pz2Xpw-pwzXpz)+pxX(pz2Xpwy-
      pwzXpzy);
      d2:=px2X(pzyXpw-pwyXpz)-pxyX(pxzXpw-pxwXpz)+pxX(pxzXpwy-
      pxwXpzy);
      d3:=px2X(pz2Xpw-pwzXpz)-pxzX(pxzXpw-pxwXpz)+pxX(pxzXpwz-
      pxwXpz2);
      d4:=px2X(pz2Xpwy-pwzXpzy)-pxzX(pxzXpwy-pxwXpzy)+pxyX(pxzXpwz
      -pxwXpz2);
      s3:=pxXd1-pzXd2+pyXd3-g1Xd4;
      sL1:=s1/d;  sL2:=s2/d;  sL3:=s3/d;
      IF g1≤5 THEN
      BEGIN
        code:=99999999;  GO TO X12END;
      b:=(py-sL1Xpx-sL2Xpz-sL3Xpw)/g1-sL1Xx1a-sL2Xx2a-sL3Xx3a+ya;
      fnsL1:=fnsL2:=fnsL3:=funb:=1;
      sL1:=sL1XfnsL1;  sL2:=sL2XfnsL2;
      sL3:=sL3XfnsL3;  b:=bXfunb;
      FOR i:=1 STEP 1 UNTIL 20 DO
      BEGIN
        IF yy[i]=0 THEN GO TO X14;
        rr:=abs(yy[i]-(sL1Xxx1[i]+sL2Xxx2[i]+sL3Xxx3[i]+b));
        yc[i]:=abs(yer[i]);
        IF rr>yc[i] THEN GO TO X14;
        rr:=abs(xx1[i]-((yy[i]-sL2Xxx2[i]-sL3Xxx3[i]-b)/sL1));
        yc[i]:=abs(x1er[i]);
        IF rr>yc[i] THEN GO TO X14;
        rr:=abs(xx2[i]-((yy[i]-sL1Xxx1[i]-sL3Xxx3[i]-b)/sL2));
        yc[i]:=abs(x2er[i]);
        IF rr>yc[i] THEN GO TO X14;
        rr:=abs(xx3[i]-((yy[i]-sL1Xxx1[i]-sL2Xxx2[i]-b)/sL3));
        yc[i]:=abs(x3er[i]);
        IF rr≤yc[i] THEN
        BEGIN
          y[i]:=yy[i];  x1[i]:=xx1[i];  x2[i]:=xx2[i];
          x3[i]:=xx3[i]END
X14:  END;
      IF nn<2 THEN GO TO X9;
```

```
       j:=j+1;
       IF n<j THEN
       BEGIN
          desL1:=sL1Xa5/a2;  desL2:=sL2Xa5/a3;
          desL3:=sL3Xa5/a4;  devb:=bXa5;
          PUNCH desL1,desL2,desL3,devb,g1,g,j,m4;
          PUNCH oper,instr;
          PUNCH run,temp,waveL;  GO TO X23END
       ELSE GO TO X19;
X15:   FOR i:=1 STEP 1 UNTIL 20 DO
       BEGIN
          IF y[i]=0 THEN GO TO X16;
          y[i]:=yer[i]-sL1Xx1er[i]-sL2Xx2er[i]-sL3Xx3er[i];
          IF y[i]=0 THEN y[i]:=0.000001
X16:   END;
       p[5]:=abs(y[i]);
       FOR i:=1 STEP 1 UNTIL 20 DO
       BEGIN
          IF p[5]<abs(y[i]) THEN p[5]:=abs(y[i])
       END;
       IF p[5]≤1∧p[5]≥0.1 THEN
       BEGIN
          a[5]:=1; GO TO X18END
       ELSE FOR i:=1 STEP 1 UNTIL 10 DO
       BEGIN
          m:=10-i;  ma:=-m;
          IF p[5]≤₁₀ma THEN
          BEGIN
             a[5]:=₁₀ma;  GO TO X18END;
          IF p[5]<₁₀m THEN GO TO X17
          ELSE IF p[5]>₁₀m THEN m:=m+1;
          a[5]:=₁₀m;  GO TO X18
X17:   END;
X18:   a5:=a[5];
       FOR i:=1 STEP 1 UNTIL 20 DO y[i]:=y[i]Xa1/a5;
       GO TO X8;
X19:   IF g1≤5 THEN
       BEGIN
          code:=99999999;  GO TO X12END;
       FOR i:=1 STEP 1 UNTIL 20 DO
       BEGIN
          IF y[i]=0 THEN GO TO X20;
          dev1:=(abs(sL1Xx1[i]+sL2Xx2[i]+sL3Xx3[i]+b)-abs(y[i]))Xa1;
          sqrm1:=sqrm1+dev1[i]↑2;
          IF sL1=0 THEN
          BEGIN
             dev2[i]:=0;  GO TO X20END;
          dev2[i]:=(abs((y[i]-sL2Xx2[i]-sL3Xx3[i]-b)/sL1)-abs(x1[i]))Xa2;
          sqrm2:=sqrm2+dev2[i]↑2;
          IF sL2=0 THEN
          BEGIN
             dev3[i]:=0;  GO TO X20END;
          dev3[i]:=(abs((y[i]-sL1Xx1[i]-sL3Xx3[i]-b)/sL2)-abs(x2[i]))Xa3;
```

```
            sqrm3:=sqrm3+dev3[i]↑2;
            IF sL3=0 THEN
            BEGIN
               dev4[i]:=0;  GO TO X20END;
            dev4[i]:=(abs(([y[i]− sL1Xx1[i]− sL2Xx2[i]− b)/sL3)−abs(x3[i]))Xa4;
            sqrm4:=sqrm4+dev4[i]↑2
X20:        END;
            sqrm1:=sqrt(sqrm1/g1);
            sqrm2:=sqrt(sqrm2/g1);
            sqrm3:=sqrt(sqrm3/g1);
            sqrm4:=sqrt(sqrm4/g1);
            sL1:=sL1Xa1/a2;  sL2:=sL2Xa1/a3;  sL3:=sL3Xa1/a4;
            b:=bXa1;
            FOR i:=1 STEP 1 UNTIL 20 DO
            BEGIN
               y[i]:=y[i]Xa1;  yy[i]:=yy[i]Xa1;  x1[i]:=x1[i]Xa2;
               xx1[i]:=xx1[i]Xa2;  x2[i]:=x2[i]Xa3;
               xx2[i]:=xx2[i]Xa3;  x3[i]:=x3[i]Xa4;
               xx3[i]:=xx3[i]Xa4;  yer[i]:=yer[i]Xa1;
               x1er[i]:=x1er[i]Xa2;  x2er[i]:=x2er[i]Xa3;
               x3er[i]:=x3er[i]Xa4
            END;
            PUNCH sL1,sL2,sL3,b,g1,g,j,m4;
            PUNCH sqrm1,sqrm2,sqrm3,sqrm4;
            FOR i:=1 STEP 1 UNTIL 20 DO PUNCH y[i];
            FOR i:=1 STEP 1 UNTIL 20 DO PUNCH yer[i];
            FOR i:=1 STEP 1 UNTIL 20 DO PUNCH dev1[i];
            FOR i:=1 STEP 1 UNTIL 20 DO PUNCH x1[i];
            FOR i:=1 STEP 1 UNTIL 20 DO PUNCH x1er[i];
            FOR i:=1 STEP 1 UNTIL 20 DO PUNCH dev2[i];
            FOR i:=1 STEP 1 UNTIL 20 DO PUNCH x2[i];
            FOR i:=1 STEP 1 UNTIL 20 DO PUNCH x2er[i];
            FOR i:=1 STEP 1 UNTIL 20 DO PUNCH dev3[i];
            FOR i:=1 STEP 1 UNTIL 20 DO PUNCH x3[i];
            FOR i:=1 STEP 1 UNTIL 20 DO PUNCH x3er[i];
            FOR i:=1 STEP 1 UNTIL 20 DO PUNCH dev4[i];
            FOR i:=1 STEP 1 UNTIL 20 DO
            BEGIN
               IF y[i]=0 THEN GO TO X22;
               dev1[i]:=abs(dev1[i]);  yc[i]:=abs(yer[i]);
               IF yc[i]<dev1[i] THEN GO TO X21;
               dev2[i]:=abs(dev2[i]);  yc[i]:=abs(x1er[i]);
               IF yc[i]<dev2[i] THEN GO TO X21;
               dev3[i]:=abs(dev3[i]);  yc[i]:=abs(x2er[i]);
               IF yc[i]<dev3[i] THEN GO TO X21;
               dev4[i]:=abs(dev4[i]);  yc[i]:=abs(x3er[i]);
               IF yc[i]≥dev4[i] THEN GO TO X22;
X21:           y[i]:=x1[i]:=x2[i]:=x3[i]:=0
X22:        END;
            IF n>j THEN GO TO X8
            ELSE IF n=j THEN GO TO X15
X23:        m4:=m4+1;
            m5:=m5−1;
```

```
       IF m5>0 THEN GO TO X1;
       m4:=1
X24:END WAAAA;
     m4:=1;
X25:WAAAA(m4);
     GO TO X25;
```

FORTRAN FOR PROGRAM NUMBER 24

CALL WORD XAAAA

```
DIMENSION Y(20),YER(20),X1(20),X1ER(20),X2(20),X2ER(20),X3(20),X3ER(20)
DIMENSION X4(20),X4ER(20),P(6),DEV1(20),DEV2(20),DEV3(20),DEV4(20)
DIMENSION DEV5(20),XX1(20),XX2(20)
DIMENSION XX3(20),XX4(20),YY(20),YC(20),D(6),B(4,4),C(5),T(5),A(5,5)
DIMENSION C2(20)
M4=1
1 IF(M4-1)4000,4000,4012
4000 READ,XAAAA,FEEDP
READ,KA,KB,KC,KD
READ,J
READ,M6
M5=M6
N=J
READ,K,L,M
READ,RLM1,WL1,WU1
READ,RLM2,WL2,WU2
GO TO (4001,4001,4002,4002),K
4001 READ,DEVF1
GO TO 4004
4002 DO 4003 I=1,20,4
4003 READ,YER(I),YER(I+1),YER(I+2),YER(I+3)
DEVF1=5555.0
4004 GO TO (4005,4006,4005,4006),K
4005 READ,DEVF2
GO TO 4012
4006 DO 4007 I=1,20,4
4007 READ,X1ER(I),X1ER(I+1),X1ER(I+2),X1ER(I+3)
DEVF2=5555.0
4012 DO 4013 I=1,20,4
4013 READ,Y(I),Y(I+1),Y(I+2),Y(I+3)
G=20.0
J=N
IF(M6-M5)4014,4014,4016
4014 DO 4015 I=1,20,4
4015 READ,X1(I),X1(I+1),X1(I+2),X1(I+3)
IF(L-3)4050,4051,1
4051 DO 4052 I=1,20,4
4052 READ,C2(I),C2(I+1),C2(I+2),C2(I+3)
DO 4055 I=1,20
A=X1(I)
X1(I)=C2(I)
XX1(I)=X1(I)
4055 C2(I)=A
GO TO 4054
4050 DO 4053 I=1,20
XX1(I)=X1(I)
4053 C2(I)=X1(I)
4054 READ,OPER,INSTR
READ,RUN,TEMP,WAVEL
4016 GO TO (4008,4008,4009,4009),K
4008 DO 4010 I=1,20
4010 YER(I)=Y(I)*DEVF1
4009 GO TO (4011,4023,4011,4023),K
4011 DO 4018 I=1,20
4018 X1ER(I)=X1(I)*DEVF2
4023 DO 4024 I=1,20
IF(Y(I)-WL1)4025,4026,4026
4025 Y(I)=0.0
X1(I)=0.0
```

```
X2(I)=0.0
X2ER(I)=0.0
X3(I)=0.0
X3ER(I)=0.0
X4(I)=0.0
X4ER(I)=0.0
G=G-1.0
GO TO 4024
4026 IF(Y(I)-WU1)4027,4027,4025
4027 IF(X1(I)-WL2)4025,4028,4028
4028 IF(X1(I)-WU2)4029,4029,4025
4029 X2(I)=X1(I)*X1(I)
X2ER(I)=(X1(I)+X1ER(I))*(X1(I)+X1ER(I))
X3(I)=X2(I)*X1(I)
X3ER(I)=X2ER(I)*(X1(I)+X1ER(I))
X4(I)=X3(I)*X1(I)
X4ER(I)=X3ER(I)*(X1(I)+X1ER(I))-X4(I)
X3ER(I)=X3ER(I)-X3(I)
Y(I)=Y(I)/C2(I)
X2ER(I)=X2ER(I)-X2(I)
YER(I)=YER(I)/C2(I)
4024 CONTINUE
RLM3=RLM2
DEVF3=DEVF2
DEVF4=DEVF2
DEVF5=DEVF2
RLM5=RLM2
RLM4=RLM2
WL3=WL2
WL4=WL2
WL5=WL2
WU3=WU2
WU4=WU2
WU5=WU2
NUM=24
PUNCH,XAAAA,NUM,FEEDP
PUNCH,M6,M4
PUNCH,J
PUNCH,K,L,M
PUNCH,DEVF1,RLM1,WL1,WU1
PUNCH,DEVF2,RLM2,WL2,WU2
PUNCH,DEVF3,RLM3,WL3,WU3
PUNCH,DEVF4,RLM4,WL4,WU4
PUNCH,DEVF5,RLM5,WL5,WU5
DO 900 I=1,20
YY(I)=Y(I)
XX2(I)=X2(I)
XX3(I)=X3(I)
900 XX4(I)=X4(I)
P(1)=SQR(Y(1)*Y(1))
P(2)=SQR(X1(1)*X1(1))
P(3)=SQR(X2(1)*X2(1))
P(4)=SQR(X3(1)*X3(1))
P(5)=SQR(X4(1)*X4(1))
DO 200 I=2,20
IF(P(1)-SQR(Y(I)*Y(I)))201,202,202
201 P(1)=SQR(Y(I)*Y(I))
202 IF(P(2)-SQR(X1(I)*X1(I)))203,204,204
203 P(2)=SQR(X1(I)*X1(I))
204 IF(P(3)-SQR(X2(I)*X2(I)))205,206,206
205 P(3)=SQR(X2(I)*X2(I))
206 IF(P(4)-SQR(X3(I)*X3(I)))207,208,208
```

```
207 P(4)=SQR(X3(I)*X3(I))
208 IF(P(5)-SQR(X4(I)*X4(I)))209,200,200
209 P(5)=SQR(X4(I)*X4(I))
200 CONTINUE
NA=0
210 NA=NA+1
IF(P(NA)-1.0)211,212,213
211 IF(P(NA)-0.1)213,212,212
212 D(NA)=1.0
GO TO 219
213 DO 214 I=1,10
M=10-I
MA=-M
IF(P(NA)-10.0**MA)215,215,216
215 D(NA)=10.0**MA
GO TO 219
216 IF(P(NA)-10.0**M)214,218,217
217 M=M+1
218 D(NA)=10.0**M
GO TO 219
214 CONTINUE
219 IF(NA-5) 210,220,220
220 A1=D(1)
A2=D(2)
A3=D(3)
A4=D(4)
A5=D(5)
N=J
J=0
IF(KA) 3,300,302
300 DO 301I=KB,KC
301 Y(I)=0.0
GO TO 3
302 IF(KA-1) 3,303,303
303 Y(KB)=0.0
IF(KA-2) 3,304,304
304 Y(KC)=0.0
IF(KA-3) 3,305,305
305 Y(KD)=0.0
3 DO 4 I=1,20
Y(I)=Y(I)/A1
YY(I)=YY(I)/A1
X1(I)=X1(I)/A2
XX1(I)=XX1(I)/A2
X2(I)=X2(I)/A3
XX2(I)=XX2(I)/A3
X3(I)=X3(I)/A4
XX3(I)=XX3(I)/A4
X4(I)=X4(I)/A5
XX4(I)=XX4(I)/A5
YER(I)=YER(I)/A1
X1ER(I)=X1ER(I)/A2
X2ER(I)=X2ER(I)/A3
X3ER(I)=X3ER(I)/A4
4 X4ER(I)=X4ER(I)/A5
NN=0
901 NN=NN+1
G1=20.0
SQRM1=0.0
SQRM2=0.0
SQRM3=0.0
SQRM4=0.0
```

```
SQRM5=0.0
PY=0.0
PX=0.0
PZ=0.0
PW=0.0
PXY=0.0
PX2=0.0
PXZ=0.0
PXW=0.0
PZ2=0.0
PWZ=0.0
PWY=0.0
PW2=0.0
PQ=0.0
PXQ=0.0
PZQ=0.0
PWQ=0.0
PQ2=0.0
PQY=0.0
PZY=0.0
      DO 790 I=1,20
      IF(Y(I))791,790,791
791   IF(X1(I))792,790,792
792   IF(X2(I))793,790,793
793   IF(X3(I))794,790,794
794   IF(X4(I))795,790,795
795   X1MIN=X1(I)
      X1MAX=X1(I)
      X2MIN=X2(I)
      X2MAX=X2(I)
      X3MIN=X3(I)
      X3MAX=X3(I)
      X4MIN=X4(I)
      X4MAX=X4(I)
      YMIN=Y(I)
      YMAX=Y(I)
      GO TO 796
790   CONTINUE
796   DO 797 I=1,20
999   FUNY=1.0
1000  FUNX1=1.0
1001  FUNX2=1.0
1002  FUNX3=1.0
1003  FUNX4=1.0
      Y(I)=Y(I)*FUNY
      X1(I)=X1(I)*FUNX1
      X2(I)=X2(I)*FUNX2
      X3(I)=X3(I)*FUNX3
      X4(I)=X4(I)*FUNX4
      IF(Y(I))798,797,798
798   IF(X1(I))799,797,799
799   IF(X2(I))800,797,800
800   IF(X3(I))801,797,801
801   IF(X4(I))802,797,802
802   IF(X4MIN-X4(I))803,804,804
804   X4MIN=X4(I)
803   IF(X4MAX-X4(I))805,805,806
805   X4MAX=X4(I)
806   IF(X3MIN-X3(I))807,808,808
808   X3MIN=X3(I)
807   IF(X3MAX-X3(I))809,809,810
809   X3MAX=X3(I)
```

```
810 IF(X2MIN-X2(I))811,812,812
812 X2MIN=X2(I)
811 IF(X2MAX-X2(I))813,813,814
813 X2MAX=X2(I)
814 IF(X1MIN-X1(I))815,816,816
816 X1MIN=X1(I)
815 IF(X1MAX-X1(I))817,817,818
817 X1MAX=X1(I)
818 IF(YMIN-Y(I))819,820,820
820 YMIN=Y(I)
819 IF(YMAX-Y(I))821,821,797
821 YMAX=Y(I)
797 CONTINUE
YA=(YMAX+YMIN)/2.0
X1A=(X1MAX+X1MIN)/2.0
X2A=(X2MAX+X2MIN)/2.0
X3A=(X3MAX+X3MIN)/2.0
X4A=(X4MAX+X4MIN)/2.0
DO 5 I=1,20
IF(Y(I))50,49,50
49 Y(I)=0.0
X1(I)=0.0
X2(I)=0.0
X3(I)=0.0
X4(I)=0.0
DEV1(I)=0.0
DEV2(I)=0.0
DEV3(I)=0.0
DEV4(I)=0.0
DEV5(I)=0.0
G1=G1-1.0
GO TO 5
50 Y(I)=Y(I)-YA
X1(I)=X1(I)-X1A
X2(I)=X2(I)-X2A
X3(I)=X3(I)-X3A
X4(I)=X4(I)-X4A
PY=PY+Y(I)
PZ=PZ+X2(I)
PX=PX+X1(I)
PW=PW+X3(I)
PQ=PQ+X4(I)
PXY=PXY+Y(I)*X1(I)
PX2=PX2+X1(I)*X1(I)
PXZ=PXZ+X1(I)*X2(I)
PXW=PXW+X1(I)*X3(I)
PZY=PZY+X2(I)*Y(I)
PZ2=PZ2+X2(I)*X2(I)
PWZ=PWZ+X2(I)*X3(I)
PWY=PWY+Y(I)*X3(I)
PW2=PW2+X3(I)*X3(I)
PXQ=PXQ+X1(I)*X4(I)
PZQ=PZQ+X2(I)*X4(I)
PWQ=PWQ+X3(I)*X4(I)
PQ2=PQ2+X4(I)*X4(I)
PQY=PQY+Y(I)*X4(I)
Y(I)=Y(I)+YA
X1(I)=X1(I)+X1A
X2(I)=X2(I)+X2A
X3(I)=X3(I)+X3A
X4(I)=X4(I)+X4A
Y(I)=Y(I)/FUNY
```

```
X1(I)=X1(I)/FUNX1
X2(I)=X2(I)/FUNX2
X3(I)=X3(I)/FUNX3
X4(I)=X4(I)/FUNX4
5 CONTINUE
A(1,1)=PX
A(1,2)=PZ
A(1,3)=PW
A(1,4)=PQ
A(1,5)=G1
A(2,1)=PX2
A(2,2)=PXZ
A(2,3)=PXW
A(2,4)=PXQ
A(2,5)=PX
A(3,1)=PXZ
A(3,2)=PZ2
A(3,3)=PWZ
A(3,4)=PZQ
A(3,5)=PZ
A(4,1)=PXW
A(4,2)=PWZ
A(4,3)=PW2
A(4,4)=PWQ
A(4,5)=PW
A(5,1)=PXQ
A(5,2)=PZQ
A(5,3)=PWQ
A(5,4)=PQ2
A(5,5)=PQ
C(1)=PY
C(2)=PXY
C(3)=PZY
C(4)=PWY
C(5)=PQY
JA=1
6 GO TO (21,7,10,14,18),JA
7 DO 8 IA=1,5
8 T(IA)=A(IA,1)
DO 9 IA=1,5
9 A(IA,1)=C(IA)
GO TO 21
10 DO 11 IA=1,5
11 A(IA,1)=T(IA)
DO 12 IA=1,5
12 T(IA)=A(IA,2)
DO 13 IA=1,5
13 A(IA,2)=C(IA)
GO TO 21
14 DO 15 IA=1,5
15 A(IA,2)=T(IA)
DO 16 IA=1,5
16 T(IA)=A(IA,3)
DO 17 IA=1,5
17 A(IA,3)=C(IA)
GO TO 21
18 DO 19 IA=1,5
19 A(IA,3)=T(IA)
DO 20 IA=1,5
20 A(IA,4)=C(IA)
21 KA=1
DO 36 IC=1,5
```

```
GO TO (22,24,27,30,33),KA
22 AK2=0.0
DO 23 IA=2,5
DO 23 IB=2,5
23 B(IA-1,IB-1)=A(IA,IB)
KA=KA+1
GO TO 35
24 DO 25 IA=2,5
25 B(IA-1,1)=A(IA,1)
DO 26 IA=2,5
DO 26 IB=3,5
26 B(IA-1,IB-1)=A(IA,IB)
KA=KA+1
GO TO 35
27 DO 28 IA=2,5
DO 28 IB=1,2
28 B(IA-1,IB)=A(IA,IB)
DO 29 IA=2,5
DO 29 IB=4,5
29 B(IA-1,IB-1)=A(IA,IB)
KA=KA+1
GO TO 35
30 DO 31 IA=2,5
DO 31 IB=1,3
31 B(IA-1,IB)=A(IA,IB)
DO 32 IA=2,5
32 B(IA-1,4)=A(IA,5)
KA=KA+1
GO TO 35
33 DO 34 IA=2,5
DO 34 IB=1,4
34 B(IA-1,IB)=A(IA,IB)
KA=KA+1
35 D1=B(2,2)*(B(3,3)*B(4,4)-B(3,4)*B(4,3))
D1=D1-B(2,3)*(B(3,2)*B(4,4)-B(3,4)*B(4,2))
D1=D1+B(2,4)*(B(3,2)*B(4,3)-B(3,3)*B(4,2))
D2=B(2,1)*(B(3,3)*B(4,4)-B(3,4)*B(4,3))
D2=D2-B(2,3)*(B(3,1)*B(4,4)-B(3,4)*B(4,1))
D2=D2+B(2,4)*(B(3,1)*B(4,3)-B(3,3)*B(4,1))
D3=B(2,1)*(B(3,2)*B(4,4)-B(3,4)*B(4,2))
D3=D3-B(2,2)*(B(3,1)*B(4,4)-B(3,4)*B(4,1))
D3=D3+B(2,4)*(B(3,1)*B(4,2)-B(3,2)*B(4,1))
D4=B(2,1)*(B(3,2)*B(4,3)-B(3,3)*B(4,2))
D4=D4-B(2,2)*(B(3,1)*B(4,3)-B(3,3)*B(4,1))
D4=D4+B(2,3)*(B(3,1)*B(4,2)-B(3,2)*B(4,1))
AK1=B(1,1)*D1-B(1,2)*D2+B(1,3)*D3-B(1,4)*D4
GO TO(1,500,501,500,501,500),KA
500 AK2=AK2+A(1,KA-1)*AK1
GO TO 36
501 AK2=AK2-A(1,KA-1)*AK1
36 CONTINUE
GO TO (37,40,41,42,43),JA
37 JA=JA+1
DD=AK2
IF(DD)6,38,6
38 CODE=88888888.
39 PRINT,CODE,M4,RUN
PUNCH,CODE,M4
PUNCH,OPER,INSTR
PUNCH,RUN,TEMP,WAVEL
GO TO 4030
40 JA=JA+1
```

```
S1=AK2
GO TO 6
41  JA=JA+1
S2=AK2
GO TO 6
42  JA=JA+1
S3=AK2
GO TO 6
43  JA=JA+1
S4=AK2
SL1=S1/DD
SL2=S2/DD
SL3=S3/DD
SL4=S4/DD
IF(G1-6.0)44,44,45
44  CODE=99999999.
GO TO 39
45  BB=(PY-SL1*PX-SL2*PZ-SL3*PW-SL4*PQ)/G1
BB=BB-SL1*X1A-SL2*X2A-SL3*X3A-SL4*X4A+YA
1110  FNSL1=1.0
1111  FNSL2=1.0
1112  FNSL3=1.0
1113  FNSL4=1.0
1114  FUNB=1.0
SL1=SL1*FNSL1
SL2=SL2*FNSL2
SL3=SL3*FNSL3
SL4=SL4*FNSL4
BB=FUNB*BB
DO 902 I=1,20
IF(YY(I))905,902,905
905  RR=SL1*XX1(I)+SL2*XX2(I)+SL3*XX3(I)+SL4*XX4(I)+BB
RR=SQR((RR-YY(I))*(RR-YY(I)))
YC(I)=SQR(YER(I)*YER(I))
IF(RR-YC(I))904,904,902
2222  Y(I)=YY(I)
X1(I)=XX1(I)
X2(I)=XX2(I)
X3(I)=XX3(I)
X4(I)=XX4(I)
GO TO 902
904  RR=(YY(I)-SL2*XX2(I)-SL3*XX3(I)-SL4*XX4(I)-BB)/SL1
RR= SQR((RR-XX1(I))*(RR-XX1(I)))
YC(I)=SQR(X1ER(I)*X1ER(I))
IF(RR-YC(I))906,906,902
906  RR=(YY(I)-SL1*XX1(I)-SL3*XX3(I)-SL4*XX4(I)-BB)/SL2
RR=SQR((RR-XX2(I))*(RR-XX2(I)))
YC(I)=SQR(X2ER(I)*X2ER(I))
IF(RR-YC(I))907,907,902
907  RR=(YY(I)-SL1*XX1(I)-SL2*XX2(I)-SL4*XX4(I)-BB)/SL3
RR=SQR((RR-XX3(I))*(RR-XX3(I)))
YC(I)=SQR(X3ER(I)*X3ER(I))
IF(RR-YC(I))903,903,902
903  RR=(YY(I)-SL1*XX1(I)-SL2*XX2(I)-SL3*XX3(I)-BB)/SL4
YC(I)=SQR(X4ER(I)*X4ER(I))
RR=SQR((RR-XX4(I))*(RR-XX4(I)))
IF(RR-YC(I))2222,2222,902
902  CONTINUE
IF(NN-2)901,908,908
908  J=J+1
IF(N-J)52,233,233
52  DESL1=SL1*A6/A2
```

```
DESL2=SL2*A6/A3
DESL3=SL3*A6/A4
DESL4=SL4*A6/A5
DEVB=BB*A6
PUNCH,DESL1,DESL2,DESL3,DESL4,DEVB,G1,G,J,M4
PUNCH,OPER,INSTR
PUNCH,RUN,TEMP,WAVEL
GO TO 4030
53 DO 56 I=1,20
IF(Y(I))54,56,54
54 Y(I)=YER(I)-SL1*X1ER(I)-SL2*X2ER(I)-SL3*X3ER(I)-SL4*X4ER(I)
IF(Y(I))56,55,56
55 Y(I)=.000001
56 CONTINUE
P(6)=SQR(Y(1)*Y(1))
DO 221 I=2,20
IF(P(6)-SQR(Y(I)*Y(I)))222,221,221
222 P(6)=SQR(Y(I)*Y(I))
221 CONTINUE
IF(P(6)-1.0)223,224,225
223 IF(P(6)-0.1)225,224,224
224 D(6)=1.0
GO TO 231
225 DO 226 I=1,10
M=10-I
MA=-M
IF(P(6)-10.0**MA)227,227,228
227 D(6)=10.0**MA
GO TO 231
228 IF(P(6)-10.0**M)226,230,229
229 M=M+1
230 D(6)=10.0**M
GO TO 231
226 CONTINUE
231 A6=D(6)
DO 232I=1,20
232 Y(I)=Y(I)*A1/A6
GO TO 3
233 IF(G1-6.0)44,44,57
57 DO 62 I=1,20
IF(Y(I))58,62,58
58 DEV1(I)=SL1*X1(I)+SL2*X2(I)+SL3*X3(I)+SL4*X4(I)+BB
DEV1(I)=(SQR(DEV1(I)*DEV1(I))-SQR(Y(I)*Y(I)))*A1
SQRM1=SQRM1+DEV1(I)*DEV1(I)
IF(SL1) 59,400,59
400 DEV2(I)=0.0
GO TO 62
59 DEV2(I)=(Y(I)-SL2*X2(I)-SL3*X3(I)-SL4*X4(I)-BB)/SL1
DEV2(I)=(SQR(DEV2(I)*DEV2(I))-SQR(X1(I)*X1(I)))*A2
SQRM2=SQRM2+DEV2(I)*DEV2(I)
IF(SL2) 60,401,60
401 DEV3(I)=0.0
GO TO 62
60 DEV3(I)=(Y(I)-SL1*X1(I)-SL3*X3(I)-SL4*X4(I)-BB)/SL2
DEV3(I)=(SQR(DEV3(I)*DEV3(I))-SQR(X2(I)*X2(I)))*A3
SQRM3=SQRM3+DEV3(I)*DEV3(I)
IF(SL3) 61,402,61
402 DEV4(I)=0.0
GO TO 62
61 DEV4(I)=(Y(I)-SL1*X1(I)-SL2*X2(I)-SL4*X4(I)-BB)/SL3
DEV4(I)=(SQR(DEV4(I)*DEV4(I))-SQR(X3(I)*X3(I)))*A4
SQRM4=SQRM4+DEV4(I)*DEV4(I)
```

```
      IF(SL4) 306,403,306
  403 DEV5(I)=0.0
      GO TO 62
  306 DEV5(I)=(Y(I)-SL1*X1(I)-SL2*X2(I)-SL3*X3(I)-BB)/SL4
      DEV5(I)=(SQR(DEV5(I)*DEV5(I))-SQR(X4(I)*X4(I)))*A5
      SQRM5=SQRM5+DEV5(I)*DEV5(I)
   62 CONTINUE
      IF(G1-6.0)44,44,64
   64 SQRM1=SQR(SQRM1/G1)
      SQRM2=SQR(SQRM2/G1)
      SQRM3=SQR(SQRM3/G1)
      SQRM4=SQR(SQRM4/G1)
      SQRM5=SQR(SQRM5/G1)
      SL1=SL1*A1/A2
      SL2=SL2*A1/A3
      SL3=SL3*A1/A4
      SL4=SL4*A1/A5
      BB=BB*A1
      DO 65 I=1,20
      Y(I)=Y(I)*A1
      YY(I)=YY(I)*A1
      X1(I)=X1(I)*A2
      XX1(I)=XX1(I)*A2
      X2(I)=X2(I)*A3
      XX2(I)=XX2(I)*A3
      X3(I)=X3(I)*A4
      XX3(I)=XX3(I)*A4
      X4(I)=X4(I)*A5
      XX4(I)=XX4(I)*A5
      YER(I)=YER(I)*A1
      X1ER(I)=X1ER(I)*A2
      X2ER(I)=X2ER(I)*A3
      X3ER(I)=X3ER(I)*A4
   65 X4ER(I)=X4ER(I)*A5
      PUNCH,SL1,SL2,SL3,SL4,BB,G1,G,J,M4
      PUNCH,SQRM1,SQRM2,SQRM3,SQRM4,SQRM5
      IF(SENSE SWITCH 1)66,68
   66 DO 67 I=1,20,4
      PUNCH,DEV1(I),DEV1(I+1),DEV1(I+2),DEV1(I+3)
      PUNCH,DEV2(I),DEV2(I+1),DEV2(I+2),DEV2(I+3)
      PUNCH,DEV3(I),DEV3(I+1),DEV3(I+2),DEV3(I+3)
      PUNCH,DEV4(I),DEV4(I+1),DEV4(I+2),DEV4(I+3)
   67 PUNCH,DEV5(I),DEV5(I+1),DEV5(I+2),DEV5(I+3)
      GO TO 70
   68 IF(SENSE SWITCH 2)640,70
  640 DO 69 I=1,20,4
      PUNCH,Y(I),Y(I+1),Y(I+2),Y(I+3)
      PUNCH,YER(I),YER(I+1),YER(I+2),YER(I+3)
      PUNCH,DEV1(I),DEV1(I+1),DEV1(I+2),DEV1(I+3)
      PUNCH,X1(I),X1(I+1),X1(I+2),X1(I+3)
      PUNCH,X1ER(I),X1ER(I+1),X1ER(I+2),X1ER(I+3)
      PUNCH,DEV2(I),DEV2(I+1),DEV2(I+2),DEV2(I+3)
      PUNCH,X2(I),X2(I+1),X2(I+2),X2(I+3)
      PUNCH,X2ER(I),X2ER(I+1),X2ER(I+2),X2ER(I+3)
      PUNCH,DEV3(I),DEV3(I+1),DEV3(I+2),DEV3(I+3)
      PUNCH,X3(I),X3(I+1),X3(I+2),X3(I+3)
      PUNCH,X3ER(I),X3ER(I+1),X3ER(I+2),X3ER(I+3)
      PUNCH,DEV4(I),DEV4(I+1),DEV4(I+2),DEV4(I+3)
      PUNCH,X4(I),X4(I+1),X4(I+2),X4(I+3)
      PUNCH,X4ER(I),X4ER(I+1),X4ER(I+2),X4ER(I+3)
   69 PUNCH,DEV5(I),DEV5(I+1),DEV5(I+2),DEV5(I+3)
   70 DO 77 I=1,20
```

```
IF(Y(I))71,72,71
71 YC(I)=SQR(YER(I)*YER(I))
DEV1(I)=SQR(DEV1(I)*DEV1(I))
IF(YC(I)-DEV1(I))72,73,73
73 YC(I)=SQR(X1ER(I)*X1ER(I))
DEV2(I)=SQR(DEV2(I)*DEV2(I))
IF(YC(I)-DEV2(I))72,74,74
74 YC(I)=SQR(X2ER(I)*X2ER(I))
DEV3(I)=SQR(DEV3(I)*DEV3(I))
IF(YC(I)-DEV3(I))72,75,75
75 YC(I)=SQR(X3ER(I)*X3ER(I))
DEV4(I)=SQR(DEV4(I)*DEV4(I))
IF(YC(I)-DEV4(I))72,76,76
76 YC(I)=SQR(X4ER(I)*X4ER(I))
DEV5(I)=SQR(DEV5(I)*DEV5(I))
IF(YC(I)-DEV5(I)) 72,77,77
72 Y(I)=0.0
X1(I)=0.0
X2(I)=0.0
X3(I)=0.0
X4(I)=0.0
77 CONTINUE
IF(N-J)4030,53,3
4030 M4=M4+1
DO 4019 I=1,20
X1ER(I)=X1ER(I)*A2
XX1(I)=XX1(I)*A2
X1(I)=XX1(I)
4019 YER(I)=YER(I)*C2(I)*A1
M5=M5-1
IF(M5)4031,4031,4012
4031 M4=1
GO TO 1
END
```

ALGOL 60 FOR PROGRAM NUMBER 24

```
PROCEDURE XAAAA(m4); ARRAY y,yer,x1,x1er,x2,x2er,x3,x3er,x4,x4er,dev1,
dev2,dev3,dev4,dev5,yy,xx1,xx2,xx3,xx4,yc,c2[1:20],p,d[i:6],c,t[i:5],b[1:4,1:4],
a[1:5,1:5]; INTEGER m4; SWITCH sw1:=x1,x1,x2,x2; SWITCH sw2:=x4,x5,x4,x5;
SWITCH sw3:=x9,x9,x10,x10; SWITCH sw4:=x11,x12,x11,x12; SWITCH sw5:=x27,
x23,x24,x25,x26; SWITCH sw6:=x28,x29,x30,x31,x32; SWITCH sw7:=x53,x34,
x35,x34,x35,x34; SWITCH sw8:=x37,x38,x40,x41,x42;
COMMENT: FIVE DIMENSION EXPANSION PROGRAM
     BEGIN INTEGER i,ia,ib,ic,n,na,nn,num,j,ma,g1,code,ja,g,k,L,m,m5,m6,
     feedp,run,oper,ka,kb,kc,kd; REAL a1,a2,a3,a4,a5,a6,sqrm1,sqrm2,sqrm3,
     sqrm4,sqrm5,py,px,pz,pw,pq,pxy,px2,pxz,pxw,pz2,pwz,pwy,pw2,pxq,pzq,
     pwq,pq2,pqy,pzy,dd,d1,d2,d3,d4,ak1,ak2,s1,s2,s3,s4,sL1,sL2,sL3,sL4,rr,
     desL1,desL2,desL3,desL4,devb,bb,ymin,ymax,x1min,x1max,x2min,x2max,
     x3min,x3max,x4min,x4max,funy,funx1,funx2,funx3,funx4,ya,x1a,x2a,x3a,x4a,
     fnsL1,fnsL2,fnsL3,fnsL4,funb,devf1,devf2,devf3,devf4,devf5,rLm1,rLm2,
     rLm3,rLm4,rLm5,wL1,wL2,wL3,wL4,wL5,wu1,wu2,wu3,wu4,wu5;
          IF m4>1 THEN GO TO X6;
          READ feedp;
          READ ka,kb,kc,kd;
          READ j; READ m6;
          m5:=m6; n:=j;
          READ k,L,m;
          READ rLm1,wL1,wu1;
          READ rLm2,wL2,wu2;
          GO TO sw1[k];
X1:       READ devf1;
          GO TO X3;
X2;       FOR i:=1 STEP 1 UNTIL 20 DO READ yer[i];
          devf1:=5555;
X3:       GO TO sw2[k];
X4:       READ devf2;
          GO TO X6;
X5:       FOR i:=1 STEP 1 UNTIL 20 DO READ x1er[i];
          devf2:=5555;
X6:       FOR i:=1 STEP 1 UNTIL 20 DO READ y[i];
          g:=20; y:=n;
          IF m6>m5 THEN GO TO X8;
          FOR i:=1 STEP 1 UNTIL 20 DO READ x1[i];
          IF L>3 THEN GO TO X53
          ELSE IF L=3 THEN
          BEGIN
               FOR i:=1 STEP 1 UNTIL 20 DO READ c2[i];
               FOR i:=1 STEP 1 UNTIL 20 DO
               BEGIN
                    a:=x1[i]; x1[i]:=c2[i];
                    xx1[i]:=x1[i]; c2[i]:=a
               END;
               GO TO X7END;
          FOR i:=1 STEP 1 UNTIL 20 DO xx1[i]:=c2[i]:=x1[i];
X7:       READ oper,instr;
          READ run,temp,waveL;
X8:       GO TO sw3[k];
```

```
X9:     FOR i:=1 STEP 1 UNTIL 20 DO yer[i]:=y[i]Xdevf1;
X10:    GO TO sw4[k];
X11:    FOR i:=1 STEP 1 UNTIL 20 DO x1er[i]:=x1[i]Xdevf2;
X12:    FOR i:=1 STEP 1 UNTIL 20 DO
        BEGIN
          IF y[i]≥wL1 THEN GO TO X14;
X13:      y[i]:=x1[i]:=x2[i]:=x2er[i]:=x3[i]:=x3er[i]:=x4[i]:=x4er[i]:=0;
            g:=g-1;  GO TO XYX;
X14:      IF(y[i]>wL1)∨(x1[i]<wL2)∨(x1[i]>wu2) THEN GO TO X13;
          x2[i]:=x1[i]↑2;
          x2er[i]:=(x1[i]+x1er[i])↑2;
          x3[i]:=x2[i]Xx1[i];
          x3er[i]:=x2er[i]X(x1[i]+x1er[i]);
          x4[i]:=x3[i]Xx1[i];
          x4er[i]:=x3er[i]X(x1[i]+x1er[i])-x4[i];
          x3er[i]:=x3er[i]-x3[i];
          y[i]:=y[i]/c2[i];
          x2er[i]:=x2er[i]-x2[i];
          yer[i]:=yer[i]/c2[i]
XYX:    END;
        rLm3:=rLm4:=rLm5:=rLm2;
        devf3:=devf4:=devf5:=devf2;
        wL3:=wL4:=wL5:=wL2;
        wu3:=wu4:=wu5:=wu2;
        PUNCH num,feedp;
        PUNCH m6,m4;
        PUNCH j;
        PUNCH k,L,m;
        PUNCH devf1,rLm1,wL1,wu1;
        PUNCH devf2,rLm2,wL2,wu2;
        PUNCH devf3,rLm3,wL3,wu3;
        PUNCH devf4,rLm4,wL4,wu4;
        PUNCH devf5,rLm5,wL5,wu5;
        FOR i:=1 STEP 1 UNTIL 20 DO
        BEGIN
          yy[i]:=y[i];  xx2[i]:=x2[i];
          xx3[i]:=x3[i];  xx4[i];=x4[i]
        END;
        p[1]:=abs(y[1]);  p[2]:=abs(x1[1]);
        p[3]:=abs(x2[1]);  p[4]:=abs(x3[1]);
        p[5]:=abs(x4[1]);
        FOR i:=1 STEP 1 UNTIL 20 DO
        BEGIN
          IF p[1]<abs(y[i]) THEN p[1]:=abs(y[i]);
          IF p[2]<abs(x1[i]) THEN p[2]:=abs(x1[i]);
          IF p[3]<abs(x2[i]) THEN p[3]:=abs(x2[i]);
          IF p[4]<abs(x3[i]) THEN p[4]:=abs(x3[i]);
          IF p[5]<abs(x4[i]) THEN p[5]:=abs(x4[i])
        END;
        na:=0;
X15:    na:=na+1;
        IF p[na]≤1∧p[na]≥0.1 THEN
```

```
        BEGIN
          d[na]:=1; GO TO X17END
        ELSE FOR i:=1 STEP 1 UNTIL 10 DO
        BEGIN
          m:=10-i; ma:=-m;
          IF p[na]≤₁₀ma THEN
          BEGIN
            d[na]:=₁₀ma; GO TO X17END;
          IF p[na]<₁₀m THEN GO TO X16
          ELSE IF p[na]>₁₀m THEN m:=m+1;
          d[na]:=₁₀m; GO TO X17
X16:    END;
X17:    IF na<5 THEN GO TO X15;
        a1:=d[1]; a2:=d[2]; a3:=d[3]; a4:=d[4]; a5:=d[5];
        n:=j; j:=0;
        IF ka<0 THEN GO TO X18
        ELSE IF ka=0 THEN FOR i:=kb STEP 1 UNTIL kc DO
        BEGIN
          y[i]:=0; GO TO X18
        END;
        IF ka<1 THEN GO TO X18;
        y[kb]:=0;
        IF ka<2 THEN GO TO X18;
        y[kc]:=0;
        IF ka<3 THEN GO TO X18;
        y[kd]:=0;
X18:    FOR i:=1 STEP 1 UNTIL 20 DO
        BEGIN
          y[i]:=y[i]/a1; yy[i]:=yy[i]/a1; x1[i]:=x1[i]/a2;
          xx1[i]:=xx1[i]/a2; x2[i]:=x2[i]/a3; xx2[i]:=xx2[i]/a3;
          x3[i]:=x3[i]/a4; xx3[i]:=xx3[i]/a4; x4[i]:=x4[i]/a5;
          xx4[i]:=xx4[i]/a5; yer[i]:=yer[i]/a1; x1er[i]:=x1er[i]/a2;
          x2er[i]:=x2er[i]/a3; x3er[i]:=x3er[i]/a4; x4er[i]:=x4er[i]/a5
        END;
        nn:=0;
X19:    nn:=nn+1; g1:=20;
        sqrm1:=sqrm2:=sqrm3:=sqrm4:=sqrm5:=py:=px:=pz:=pw:=pq:=pzq:=pxy
          :=px2:=pxz:=pxw:=pz2:=pwz:=pwy:=pw2:=pxq:=pwq:=pq2:=pqy:=pzy:=0;
        FOR i:=1 STEP 1 UNTIL 20 DO
        BEGIN
          IF y[i]≠0∧x1[i]≠0∧x2[i]≠0∧x3[i]≠0∧x4[i]≠0 THEN
          BEGIN
            ymin:=ymax:=y[i]; x1min:=x1max:=x1[i];
            x2min:=x2max:=x2[i]; x3min:=x3max:=x3[i];
            x4min:=x4max:=x4[i]; GO TO X20END
        END;
X20:    FOR i:=1 STEP 1 UNTIL 20 DO
        BEGIN
          funy:=funx1:=funx2:=funx3:=funx4:=1;
          y[i]:=y[i]Xfuny; x1[i]:=x1[i]Xfunx1;
          x2[i]:=x2[i]Xfunx2; x3[i]:=x3[i]Xfunx3;
          x4[i]:=x4[i]Xfunx4;
          IF y[i]≠0∧x1[i]≠0∧x2[i]≠0∧x3[i]≠0∧x4[i]≠0 THEN
```

```
            BEGIN
               IF ymin≥y[i] THEN ymin:=y[i];
               IF ymax≤y[i] THEN ymax:=y[i];
               IF x1min≥x1[i] THEN x1min:=x1[i];
               IF x1max≤x1[i] THEN x1max:=x1[i];
               IF x2min≥x2[i] THEN x2min:=x2[i];
               IF x2max≤x2[i] THEN x2max:=x2[i];
               IF x3min≥x3[i] THEN x3min:=x3[i];
               IF x3max≤ x3[i] THEN x3max:=x3[i];
               IF x4min≥x4[i] THEN x4min:=x4[i];
               IF x4max≤ x4[i] THEN x4max:=x4[i]END
         END;
         ya:=(ymax+ymin)/2.0;
         x1a:=(x1max+x1min)/2.0;
         x2a:=(x2max+x2min)/2.0;
         x3a:=(x3max+x3min)/2.0;
         x4a:=(x4max+x4min)/2.0;
         FOR i:=1 STEP 1 UNTIL 20 DO
         BEGIN
            IF y[i]=0 THEN
            BEGIN
               x1[i]:=x2[i]:=x3[i]:=x4[i]:=dev1[i]:=dev2[i]:=dev3[i]:=dev4[i]:=dev5[i]
                  :=0; g1:=g1−1;
               GO TO X21END;
            y[i]:=y[i]−ya; x1[i]:=x1[i]−x1a; x2[i]:=x2[i]−x2a;
            x3[i]:=x3[i]−x3a; x4[i]:=x4[i]−x4a; py:=py+y[i];
            pz:=pz+x2[i]; px:=px+x1[i]; pw:=pw+x3[i];
            pq:=pq+x4[i]; pxy:=pxy+y[i]Xx1[i]; px2:=px2+x1[i]↑2;
            pxz:=pxz+x1[i]Xx2[i]; pxw:=pxw+x1[i]Xx3[i];
            pzy:=pzy+x2[i]Xy[i]; pz2:=pz2+x2[i]↑2;
            pwz:=pwz+x2[i]Xx3[i]; pwy:=pwy+y[i]Xx3[i];
            pw2:=pw2+x3[i]↑2; pxq:=pxq+x1[i]Xx4[i];
            pzq:=pzq+x2[i]Xx4[i]; pwq:=pwq+x3[i]Xx4[i];
            pq2:=pq2+x4[i]↑2; pqy:=pqy+y[i]Xx4[i];
            y[i]:=y[i]+ya; x1[i]:=x1[i]+x1a; x2[i]:=x2[i]+x2a;
            x3[i]:=x3[i]+x3a; x4[i]:=x4[i]+x4a;
            y[i]:=y[i]/funy; x1[i]:=x1[i]/funx1; x2[i]:=x2[i]/funx2;
            x3[i]:=x3[i]/funx3; x4[i]:=x4[i]/funx4
X21:     END;
         a[1,1]:=px; a[1,2]:=pz; a[1,3]:=pw; a[1,4]:=pq; a[1,5]:=g1;
         a[2,1]:=px2; a[2,2]:=pxz; a[2,3]:=pxw; a[2,4]:=pxq; a[2,5]:=px;
         a[3,1]:=pxz; a[3,2]:=pz2; a[3,3]:=pwz; a[3,4]:=pzq; a[3,5]:=pz;
         a[4,1]:=pxw; a[4,2]:=pwz; a[4,3]:=pw2; a[4,4]:=pwq; a[4,5]:=pw;
         a[5,1]:=pxq; a[5,2]:=pzq; a[5,3]:=pwq; a[5,4]:=pq2; a[5,5]:=pq;
         c[1]:=py; c[2]:=pxy; c[3]:=pzy; c[4]:=pwy; c[5]:=pqy;
         ja:=1;
X22:     GO TO sw5[ja];
X23:     FOR i:=1 STEP 1 UNTIL 5 DO
         BEGIN
            t[ia]:=a[ia,1]; a[ia,1]:=c[ia]
         END;
         GO TO X27;
X24:     FOR ia:=1 STEP 1 UNTIL 5 DO
```

```
      BEGIN
         a[ia,1]:=t[ia];  t[ia]:=a[ia,2];  a[ia,2]:=c[ia]
      END;
      GO TO X27;
X25:  FOR ia:=1 STEP 1 UNTIL 5 DO
      BEGIN
         a[ia,2]:=t[ia];  t[ia]:=a[ia,3];  a[ia,3]:=c[ia]
      END;
      GO TO X27;
X26:  FOR ia:=1 STEP 1 UNTIL 5 DO
      BEGIN
         a[ia,3]:=t[ia];  a[ia,4]:=c[ia]
      END;
X27:  ka:=1;
      FOR ic:=1 STEP 1 UNTIL 5 DO
      BEGIN
         GO TO sw6[ka];
X28:  ak2:=0;
      FOR ia:=2 STEP 1 UNTIL 5 DO
      FOR ib:=2 STEP 1 UNTIL 5 DO b[ia−1,ib−1]:=a[ia,ib];
      ka:=ka+1;  GO TO X33;
X29:  FOR ia:=2 STEP 1 UNTIL 5 DO
      FOR ib:=3 STEP 1 UNTIL 5 DO
      BEGIN
         b[ia−1,1]:=a[ia,1];  b[ia−1,ib−1]:=a[ia,ib]
      END;
      ka:=ka+1;  GO TO X33;
X30:  FOR ia:=2 STEP 1 UNTIL 5 DO
      FOR ib:=1 STEP 1 UNTIL 2 DO b[ia−1,ib]:=a[ia,ib];
      FOR ia:=2 STEP 1 UNTIL 5 DO
      FOR ib:=4 STEP 1 UNTIL 5 DO b[ia−1,ib−1]:=a[ia,ib];
      ka:=ka+1;  GO TO X33;
X31:  FOR ia:=2 STEP 1 UNTIL 5 DO
      FOR ib:=1 STEP 1 UNTIL 3 DO
      BEGIN
         b[ia−1,4]:=a[ia,5];  b[ia−1,ib]:=a[ia,ib]
      END;
      ka:=ka+1;  GO TO X33;
X32:  FOR ia:=2 STEP 1 UNTIL 5 DO
      FOR ib:=1 STEP 1 UNTIL 4 DO b[ia−1,ib]:=a[ia,ib];
      ka:=ka+1;
X33:  d1:=b[2,2]X(b[3,3]Xb[4,4]−b[3,4]Xb[4,3]);
      d1:=d1−b[2,3]X(b[3,2]Xb[4,4]−b[3,4]Xb[4,2]);
      d1:=d1+b[2,4]X(b[3,2]Xb[4,3]−b[3,3]Xb[4,2]);
      d2:=b[2,1]X(b[3,3]Xb[4,4]−b[3,4]Xb(4,3));
      d2:=d2−b[2,3]X(b[3,1]Xb[4,4]−b[3,4]Xb[4,1]);
      d2:=d2+b[2,4]X(b[3,1]Xb[4,3]−b[3,3]Xb[4,1]);
      d3:=b[2,1]X(b[3,2]Xb[4,4]−b[3,4]Xb[4,2]);
      d3:=d3−b[3,3]X(b[3,1]Xb[4,4]−b[3,4]Xb[4,1]);
      d3:=d3+b[2,4]X(b[3,1]Xb[4,2]−b[3,2]Xb[4,1]);
      d4:=b[2,1]X(b[3,2]Xb[4,3]−b[3,3]Xb[4,2]);
      d4:=d4−b[2,2]X(b[3,1]Xb[4,3]−b[3,3]Xb[4,1]);
      d4:=d4+b[2,3]X(b[3,1]Xb[4,2]−b[3,2]Xb[4,1]);
```

```
          GO TO sw7[ka];
X34:      ak2:=ak2+a[i,ka−1]Xak1;  GO TO X36;
X35:      ak2:=ak2−a[1,ka−1]Xak1
X36:      END;
          GO TO sw8[ja];
X37:      ja:=ja+1; dd:=ak2;
          IF dd≠0 THEN GO TO X22;
          code:=88888888;
X38:      PUNCH code,m4;
          PUNCH oper,instr;
          PUNCH run,temp,waveL;  GO TO X52;
X39:      ja:=ja+1; s1:=ak2;  GO TO X22;
X40:      ja:=ja+1; s2:=ak2;  GO TO X22;
X41:      ja:=ja+1; s3:=ak2;  GO TO X22;
X42:      ja:=ja+1; s4:=ak2;
          sL1:=s1/dd; sL2:=s2/dd; sL3:=s3/dd; sL4:=s4/dd;
          IF g1≤6 THEN
          BEGIN
             code:=99999999;  GO TO X38END;
          bb:=(py−sL1Xpx−sL2Xpz−sL3Xpw−sL4Xpq)/g1−sL1Xx1a−sL2Xx2a−sL3Xx3a
             −sL4Xx4a+ya;
          fnsL1:=fnsL2:=fnsL3:=fnsL4:=funb:=1;
          sL1:=sL1XfnsL1; sL2:=sL2XfnsL2; sL3:=sL3XfnsL3;
          sL4:=sL4XfnsL4; bb:=bbXfunb;
          FOR i:=1 STEP 1 UNTIL 20 DO
          BEGIN
             IF yy[i]=0 THEN GO TO X43;
             rr:=abs(yy[i]−(sL1Xxx1[i]+sL2Xxx2[i]+sL3Xxx3[i]+sL4Xxx4[i]+bb));
             yc[i]:=abs(yer[i]);
             IF rr>yc[i] THEN GO TO X43;
             rr:=abs(xx1[i]−((yy[i]−sL2Xxx2[i]−sL3Xxx3[i]−sL4Xxx4[i]−bb)/sL1));
             yc[i]:=abs(x1er[i]);
             IF rr>yc[i] THEN GO TO X43;
             rr:=abs(xx2[i]−((yy[i]−sL1Xxx1[i]−sL3Xxx3[i]−sL4Xxx4[i]−bb)/sL2));
             yc[i]:=abs(x2er[i]);
             IF rr>yc[i] THEN GO TO X43;
             rr:=abs(xx3[i]−((yy[i]−sL1Xxx1[i]−sL2Xxx2[i]−sL4Xxx4[i]−bb)/sL3));
             yc[i]:=abs(x3er[i]);
             IF rr>yc[i] THEN GO TO X43;
             rr:=abs(xx4[i]−((yy[i]−sL1Xxx1[i]−sL2Xxx2[i]−sL3Xxx3[i]−bb)/sL4));
             yc[i]:=abs(x4er[i]);
             IF rr≤yc[i] THEN
             BEGIN
                y[i]:=yy[i]; x1[i]:=xx1[i]; x2[i]:=xx2[i];
                x3[i]:=xx3[i]; x4[i]:=xx4[i]END
X43:      END;
          IF nn<2 THEN GO TO X19;
          j:=j+1;
          IF n<j THEN
          BEGIN
             desL1:=sL1Xa6/a2; desL2:=sL2Xa6/a3;
             desL3:=sL3Xa6/a4; desL4:=sL4Xa6/a5;
             devb:=bbXa6;
```

```
        PUNCH desL1,desL2,desL3,desL4,devb,g1,g,j,m4;
        PUNCH oper,instr;
        PUNCH run,temp,waveL; GO TO X52END
        ELSE GO TO X48;
X44:    FOR i:=1 STEP 1 UNTIL 20 DO
        BEGIN
          IF y[i]=0 THEN GO TO X45;
          y[i]:=yer[i]−sL1Xx1er[i]−sL2Xx2er[i]−sL3Xx3er[i]−sL4Xx4er[i];
          IF y[i]=0 THEN y[i]:=0.000001
X45:    END;
        p[6]:=abs(y[1]);
        FOR i:=2 STEP 1 UNTIL 20 DO
        BEGIN
          IF p[6]<abs(y[i]) THEN p[6]:=abs(y[i])
        END;
        IF p[6]≤1∧p[6]≥0.1 THEN
        BEGIN
          d[6]:=1; GO TO X47END
        ELSE FOR i:=1 STEP 1 UNTIL 10 DO
        BEGIN
          m:=10−i; ma:=−m;
          IF p[6]≤₁₀ma THEN
          BEGIN
            d[6]:=₁₀ma; GO TO X47END;
          IF p[6]<₁₀m THEN GO TO X46
          ELSE IF p[6]>₁₀m THEN m:=m+1;
          d[6]:=₁₀m; GO TO X47
X46:    END;
X47:    a6:=d[6];
        FOR i:=1 STEP 1 UNTIL 20 DO y[i]:=y[i]Xa1/a6;
        GO TO X18;
X48:    IF g1≤6 THEN
        BEGIN
          code:=99999999; GO TO X38END;
        FOR i:=1 STEP 1 UNTIL 20 DO
        BEGIN
          IF y[i]=0 THEN GO TO X49
          dev1[i]:=sL1Xx1[i]+sL2Xx2[i]+sL3Xx3[i]+sL4Xx4[i]+bb;
          dev1[i]:=(abs(dev1[i])−abs(y[i]))Xa1;
          sqrm1:=sqrm1+dev1[i]↑2;
          IF sL1=0 THEN
          BEGIN
            dev2[i]:=0; GO TO X49END;
          dev2[i]:=(y[i]−sL2Xx2[i]−sL3Xx3[i]−sL4Xx4[i]−bb)/sL1;
          dev2[i]:=(abs(dev2[i])−abs(x1[i]))Xa2;
          sqrm2:=sqrm2+dev2[i]↑2;
          IF sL2=0 THEN
          BEGIN
            dev3[i]:=0; GO TO X49END;
          dev3[i]:=(y[i]−sL1Xx1[i]−sL3Xx3[i]−sL4Xx4[i]−bb)/sL2;
          dev3[i]:=(abs(dev3[i])−abs(x2[i]))Xa3;
          sqrm3:=sqrm3+dev3[i]↑2;
          IF sL3=0 THEN
```

```
       BEGIN
          dev4[i]:=0; GO TO X49END;
       dev4[i]:=(y[i]−sL1Xx1[i]−sL2Xx2[i]−sL4Xx4[i]−bb)/sL3;
       dev4[i]:=(abs(dev4[i])−abs(x3[i]))Xa4;
       sqrm4:=sqrm4+dev4[i]↑2;
       IF sL4=0 THEN
       BEGIN
          dev5[i]:=0; GO TO X49END;
       dev5[i]:=(y[i]−sL1Xx1[i]−sL2Xx2[i]−sL3Xx3[i]−bb)/sL4;
       dev5[i]:=(abs(dev5[i])−abs(x4[i]))Xa5;
       sqrm5:=sqrm5+dev5[i]↑2; IF g1≤6 THEN GO TO X48
X49:   END;
       sqrm1:=sqrt(sqrm1/g1);
       sqrm2:=sqrt(sqrm2/g1);
       sqrm3:=sqrt(sqrm3/g1);
       sqrm4:=sqrt(sqrm4/g1);
       sqrm5:=sqrt(sqrm5/g1);
       sL1:=sL1Xa1/a2; sL2:=sL2Xa1/a3; sL3:=sL3Xa1/a4;
       sL4:=sL4Xa1/a5; bb:=bbXa1;
       FOR i:=1 STEP 1 UNTIL 20 DO
       BEGIN
          y[i]:=y[i]Xa1; yy[i]:=yy[i]Xa1; x1[i]:=x1[i]Xa2;
          xx1[i]:=xx1[i]Xa2; x2[i]:=x2[i]Xa3; xx2[i]:=xx2[i]Xa3;
          x3[i]:=x3[i]Xa4; xx3[i]:=xx3[i]Xa4; x4[i]:=x4[i]Xa5;
          xx4[i]:=xx4[i]Xa5; yer[i]:=yer[i]Xa1; x1er[i]:=x1er[i]Xa2;
          x2er[i]:=x2er[i]Xa3; x3er[i]:=x3er[i]Xa4; x4er[i]:=x4er[i]Xa5
       END;
       PUNCH sL1,sL2,sL3,sL4,bb,g1,g,j,m4;
       PUNCH sqrm1,sqrm2,sqrm3,sqrm4,sqrm5;
       FOR i:=1 STEP 1 UNTIL 20 DO PUNCH y[i];
       FOR i:=1 STEP 1 UNTIL 20 DO PUNCH yer[i];
       FOR i:=1 STEP 1 UNTIL 20 DO PUNCH dev1[i];
       FOR i:=1 STEP 1 UNTIL 20 DO PUNCH x1[i];
       FOR i:=1 STEP 1 UNTIL 20 DO PUNCH x1er[i];
       FOR i:=1 STEP 1 UNTIL 20 DO PUNCH dev2[i];
       FOR i:=1 STEP 1 UNTIL 20 DO PUNCH x2[i];
       FOR i:=1 STEP 1 UNTIL 20 DO PUNCH x2er[i];
       FOR i:=1 STEP 1 UNTIL 20 DO PUNCH dev3[i];
       FOR i:=1 STEP 1 UNTIL 20 DO PUNCH x3[i];
       FOR i:=1 STEP 1 UNTIL 20 DO PUNCH x3er[i];
       FOR i:=1 STEP 1 UNTIL 20 DO PUNCH dev4[i];
       FOR i:=1 STEP 1 UNTIL 20 DO PUNCH x4[i];
       FOR i:=1 STEP 1 UNTIL 20 DO PUNCH x4er[i];
       FOR i:=1 STEP 1 UNTIL 20 DO PUNCH dev5[i];
       FOR i:=1 STEP 1 UNTIL 20 DO
       BEGIN
          IF y[i]=0 THEN GO TO X50;
          dev1[i]:=abs(dev1[i]); yc[i]:=abs(yer[i]);
          IF yc[i]<dev1[i] THEN GO TO X50;
          dev2[i]:=abs(dev2[i]); yc[i]:=abs(x1er[i]);
          IF yc[i]<dev2[i] THEN GO TO X50;
          dev3[i]:=abs(dev3[i]); yc[i]:=abs(x2er[i]);
          IF yc[i]<dev3[i] THEN GO TO X50;
```

```
          dev4[i]:=abs(dev4[i]);  yc[i]:=abs(x3er[i]);
          IF yc[i]<dev4[i] THEN GO TO X50;
          dev5[i]:=abs(dev5[i]);  yc[i]:=abs(x4er[i]);
          IF yc[i]≥dev5[i] THEN GO TO X51;
X50:      y[i]:=x1[i]:=x2[i]:=x3[i]:=x4[i]:=0
X51:      END;
          IF n>j THEN GO TO X18
          ELSE IF n=j THEN GO TO X44;
X52:      m4:=m4+1;
          FOR i:=1 STEP 1 UNTIL 20 DO
          BEGIN
            x1er[i]:=x1er[i]Xa2;  xx1[i]:=xx1[i]Xa2;
            x1[i]:=xx1[i];  yer[i]:=yer[i]Xc2[i]Xa1
          END;
          m5:=m5-1;
          IF m5>0 THEN GO TO X6;
          m4:=1
X53:END XAAAA;
          m4:=1;
X54:XAAAA(m4);
          GO TO X54;
```

FORTRAN FOR PROGRAM NUMBER 25

CALL WORD YAAAA

```
DIMENSION Y(JQ,JD),DEV(JQ,JD),YER(JQ,JD),YY(JQ,JD)
DIMENSION A(JR,JR),RLM(JD),WL(JD),DEVF(JD),WU(JD)
DIMENSION YM(JD),YA(JD),SL(JD),C1(JQ),YN(JD),YB(JD)
DIMENSION DEV1(JQ),SQRMS(JD),DEV2(JQ),C2(JQ),DEVSL(JD)
DIMENSION WAC(JD),FUNY(JD),FUSL(JD)
READ,JI
IJ=4
1 READ,YAAAA,FEEDP
READ,KA,KB,KC,KD,KE,KF
READ,JJ
READ,JC
READ,M6
READ,K,L,M
GO TO (144,145,144,145,145,145,145),L
145 JJ=2
144 JK=JJ-1
N=JC
READ,RLM(1),WL(1),WU(1)
READ,RLM(2),WL(2),WU(2)
IF(K-2)2,2,3
2 READ,DEVF(1)
GO TO 5
3 DO 4 I=1,JI,4
4 READ,DEV1(I),DEV1(I+1),DEV1(I+2),DEV1(I+3)
DEVF(1)=5555.0
5 GO TO (6,7,6,7),K
6 READ,DEVF(2)
GO TO 9
7 DO 8 I=1,JI,4
8 READ,DEV2(I),DEV2(I+1),DEV2(I+2),DEV2(I+3)
DEVF(2)=5555.0
9 M5=M6
M4=0
10 DO 11 I=1,JI,4
11 READ,Y(I,JJ),Y(I+1,JJ),Y(I+2,JJ),Y(I+3,JJ)
WAC(JJ)=0.0
A11=0.0
IF(L-5)12,13,13
13 READ,A11,WAC(JJ)
12 G=0.0
JK=JJ-1
DO 4337 I=1,JI
DO 4337 J=1,JK
4337 Y(I,J)=YY(I,J)
G1=0.0
G2=0.0
IF(M4)1,14,153
14 DO 15 I=1,JI,4
15 READ,C1(I),C1(I+1),C1(I+2),C1(I+3)
GO TO (16,16,17,16,16,17,17),L
17 DO 18 I=1,JI,4
18 READ,C2(I),C2(I+1),C2(I+2),C2(I+3)
GO TO 19
16 DO 20 I=1,JI
20 C2(I)=C1(I)
19 GO TO (21,22,21,22,22,22,22),L
22 JJ=2
21 GO TO (23,24,23,24),K
23 DO 25 I=1,JI
```

```
25 DEV2(I)=DEVF(2)*C2(I)
24 KQ=KA+2
IF(KQ-8)26,26,27
27 IF(KQ-16)28,28,29
28 KQ=KQ-8
GO TO (26,30,31,32,33,34,35,36),KQ
36 DO 37 I=KD,KE
37 C2(I)=0.0
30 DO 38 I=KB,KC
38 C2(I)=0.0
GO TO 26
35 C2(KF)=0.0
34 C2(KE)=0.0
33 C2(KD)=0.0
32 C2(KC)=0.0
31 C2(KB)=0.0
GO TO 26
29 IF(KQ-24)39,39,40
40 KA=-1
GO TO 26
39 KQ=KQ-16
GO TO (26,41,42,42,4333,4333,44,41),KQ
41 DO 45 I=KB,KC
45 C2(I)=0.0
GO TO 26
44 C2(KF)=0.0
4333 C2(KD)=0.0
42 C2(KB)=0.0
26 DO 46 I=1,JI
IF(C2(I)-WL(2))47,48,48
48 IF(C2(I)-WU(2))49,49,47
47 C2(I)=0.0
C1(I)=0.0
DO 143 J=1,JJ
YER(I,J)=0.0
Y(I,J)=0.0
143 YY(I,J)=0.0
GO TO 46
49 GO TO (146,146,146,146,147,146,148),L
146 Y(I,1)=C2(I)
YER(I,1)=C2(I)+DEV2(I)
GO TO 149
147 Y(I,1)=LOG(C2(I))
YER(I,1)=LOG(C2(I)+DEV2(I))
GO TO 149
148 Y(I,1)=1.0/C2(I)
YER(I,1)=1.0/(C2(I)-DEV2(I))
149 IF(JJ-2)1,150,152
150 YER(I,1)=YER(I,1)-Y(I,1)
YY(I,1)=Y(I,1)
GO TO 46
JK=JJ-1
152 DO 151 J=2,JK
JRP=J-1
Y(I,J)=Y(I,1)*Y(I,JRP)
YER(I,J)=YER(I,1)*YER(I,JRP)
YER(I,J)=YER(I,J)-Y(I,J)
151 YY(I,J)=Y(I,J)
GO TO 150
46 CONTINUE
READ,OPER,INSTR
READ,RUN,TEMP,WAVEL
```

```
NUM=25
153 M4=M4+1
M5=M5-1
JC=N
PUNCH,YAAAA,NUM,FEEDP
PUNCH,JJ,JI,JC,M4
PUNCH,M6
PUNCH,K,L,M
PUNCH,DEVF(1),RLM(1),WL(1),WU(1)
PUNCH,WAC(JJ)
PUNCH,DEVF(2),RLM(2),WL(2),WU(2)
JC=0.0
DO 154 I=1,JI
IF(C2(I))155,155,4335
4335 IF(Y(I,JJ)-WL(1))155,156,156
156 IF(Y(I,JJ)-WU(1))157,157,155
155 Y(I,JJ)=0.0
YER(I,JJ)=0.0
YY(I,JJ)=0.0
DEV(I,JJ)=0.0
GO TO 154
157 G=G+1.0
PQR=Y(I,JJ)-C1(I)*AI1
PQR=SQR(PQR*PQR)
IF(PQR-WAC(JJ)*Y(I,JJ))155,158,158
158 YY(I,JJ)=Y(I,JJ)
154 CONTINUE
DO 175 I=1,JI
IF(YY(I,1))176,177,176
177 YY(I,JJ)=0.0
178 YER(I,JJ)=0.0
Y(I,JJ)=0.0
DEV(I,JJ)=0.0
GO TO 175
176 IF(YY(I,JJ))179,178,179
179 G1=G1+1.0
IF(K-2)181,181,182
181 DEV1(I)=YY(I,JJ)*DEVF(1)
182 GO TO (183,183,183,184,185,185),L
183 YER(I,JJ)=(YY(I,JJ)+DEV1(I))/C1(I)
YY(I,JJ)=YY(I,JJ)/C1(I)
YER(I,JJ)=YER(I,JJ)-YY(I,JJ)
GO TO 186
184 YER(I,JJ)=LOG((YY(I,JJ)+DEV1(I))/C1(I)-AI1)
YY(I,JJ)=LOG(YY(I,JJ)/C1(I)-AI1)
YER(I,JJ)=YER(I,JJ)-YY(I,JJ)
GO TO 186
185 YER(I,JJ)=1.0/((YY(I,JJ)-DEV1(I))/C1(I)-AI1)
YY(I,JJ)=1.0/(YY(I,JJ)/C1(I)-AI1)
IF(L-6)186,187,188
187 YER(I,JJ)=(C2(I)+DEV2(I))*YER(I,JJ)
YY(I,JJ)=YY(I,JJ)*C2(I)
188 YER(I,JJ)=YER(I,JJ)-YY(I,JJ)
186 CONTINUE
175 CONTINUE
KQ=KA+2
IF(KQ-8)159,159,160
159 GO TO (161,162,163,164,165,166,167,168),KQ
168 DO 169 I=KD,KE
169 Y(I,JJ)=0.0
162 DO 170 I=KB,KC
170 Y(I,JJ)=0.0
```

```
   GO TO 161
167 Y(KF,JJ)=0.0
166 Y(KE,JJ)=0.0
165 Y(KD,JJ)=0.0
164 Y(KC,JJ)=0.0
163 Y(KB,JJ)=0.0
   GO TO 161
160 KQ=KQ-16
   IF(KQ)161,161,207
207 GO TO (161,161,161,171,171,172,172,173),KQ
173 DO 174 I=KD,KE
174 Y(I,JJ)=0.0
   GO TO 161
172 Y(KE,JJ)=0.0
171 Y(KC,JJ)=0.0
161 CONTINUE
50 JC=JC+1
   NNN=1
51 DO 52 J=1,JJ
   YM(J)=-10000000.0
   YN(J)=10000000.0
999 FUNY(J)=1.0
   DO 53 I=1,JI
   Y(I,J)=Y(I,J)*FUNY(J)
   IF(Y(I,JJ))54,53,54
54 IF(YM(J)-Y(I,J))55,56,56
55 YM(J)=Y(I,J)
56 IF(YN(J)-Y(I,J))53,53,57
57 YN(J)=Y(I,J)
53 CONTINUE
   IF(YN(J))6666,8892,8893
8892 YA(J)=-YM(J)/10.0
   GO TO 8891
8893 YA(J)=-YN(J)/10.0
   GO TO 8891
6666 YA(J)=2.0*YN(J)
8891 AA=YM(J)-YA(J)
   BB=YN(J)-YA(J)
   AA=SQR(AA*AA)
   BB=SQR(BB*BB)
   IF(AA-BB)58,60,59
60 IF(AA)61,61,59
61 CODE=88888888.0
62 PRINT,CODE,M4,RUN
   PUNCH,CODE,M4
   PUNCH,OPER,INSTR
   PUNCH,RUN,TEMP,WAVEL
   IF(M6-M4)1,1,10
58 YB(J)=BB
   GO TO 63
59 YB(J)=AA
63 DO 52 I=1,JI
   IF(Y(I,JJ))64,52,64
64 Y(I,J)=Y(I,J)-YA(J)
   IF(Y(I,J))65,66,65
66 Y(I,J)=(YN(J)-YA(J))/(10.0**6.0)
65 Y(I,J)=Y(I,J)/YB(J)
52 CONTINUE
   JR=JJ+1
   DO 208 J=1,JR
   DO 208 I=1,JR
208 A(I,J)=0.0
```

```
   DO 67 J=1,JJ
   DO 67 JB=1,JJ
   DO 67 I=1,JI
   IF(Y(I,JJ))68,67,68
68 IF(JB-1)1,70,69
69 JP=JB-1
   A(JB,J)=A(JB,J)+Y(I,J)*Y(I,JP)
   GO TO 67
70 A(JB,J)=A(JB,J)+Y(I,J)
67 CONTINUE
   G2=0.0
   YAA=0.0
   DO 71 J=1,JJ
71 A(J,JR)=A(J,JJ)
   DO 72 I=1,JI
   IF(Y(I,JJ))73,72,73
73 G2=G2+1.0
72 CONTINUE
   A(1,JJ)=G2
   G9=JJ+2
   IF(G2-G9)74,75,75
74 CODE=99999999.0
   GO TO 62
75 DO 76 J=2,JJ
   JB=J-1
76 A(J,JJ)=A(1,JB)
   DO 77 J=1,JR
   DO 77 I=1,JJ
   AA=SQR(A(I,J)*A(I,J))
   IF(YAA-AA)78,77,77
78 YAA=AA
77 CONTINUE
   DO 79 J=1,JR
   DO 79 I=1,JJ
79 A(I,J)=A(I,J)/YAA
   DO 80 J=1,JR
   DO 80 I=1,JJ
   IF(J-1)80,80,82
82 IF(J-I)83,83,84
83 JA=J-1
   GO TO 85
84 JA=I-1
85 SET=0.0
   SUM=0.0
   IF(JA)86,86,87
87 DO 88 JK=1,JA
88 SUM=SUM+A(I,JK)*A(JK,J)
86 SET=A(I,J)-SUM
   IF(J-I)89,89,90
89 A(I,J)=SET
   GO TO 80
90 SOB=A(I,I)
   IF(SOB)94,8889,94
8889 SOB=10.0**(-18.0)
94 A(I,J)=SET/SOB
80 CONTINUE
   DO 81 I=1,JJ
   JAN=JR-I
   SUM2=0.0
   IA=I-1
   IF(IA)81,81,91
91 DO 93 JK=1,IA
```

```
JOB=JR-JK
93 SUM2=SUM2+A(JAN,JOB)*SL(JOB)
81 SL(JAN)=A(JAN,JR)-SUM2
DO 95 I=1,JI
DO 95 J=1,JJ
IF(Y(I,JJ))96,95,96
96 Y(I,J)=YB(J)*Y(I,J)
Y(I,J)=Y(I,J)+YA(J)
Y(I,J)=Y(I,J)/FUNY(J)
95 CONTINUE
SL(JJ)=SL(JJ)*YB(JJ)
AXYZ=0.0
JK=JJ-1
DO 205 J=1,JK
SL(J)=SL(J)*YB(JJ)/YB(J)
205 AXYZ=AXYZ+SL(J)*YA(J)
SL(JJ)=SL(JJ)-AXYZ+YA(JJ)
DO 206 J=1,JJ
1110 FUSL(J)=1.0
206 SL(J)=SL(J)*FUSL(J)
G3=G2-1.0
IF(N-JC)123,124,124
124 DO 8894 J=1,JJ
SQRMS(J)=0.0
DO 8894 I=1,JI
8894 DEV(I,J)=0.0
JK=JJ-1
DO 97 I=1,JI
RR=0.0
IF(YY(I,JJ))99,97,99
99 DO 98 J=1,JJ
IF(JJ-J)1,101,100
100 RR=RR+SL(J)*YY(I,J)
98 CONTINUE
101 QQ=RR+SL(JJ)
DEV(I,JJ)=YY(I,JJ)-QQ
DO 102JP=1,JK
IF(SL(JP))103,104,103
104 DEV(I,JP)=0.0
GO TO 102
103 DEV(I,JP)=YY(I,JP)-(YY(I,JJ)-QQ+SL(JP)*YY(I,JP))/SL(JP)
102 CONTINUE
97 CONTINUE
DO 105 J=1,JJ
DO 105 I=1,JI
105 SQRMS(J)=SQRMS(J)+DEV(I,J)*DEV(I,J)
DO 8895 J=1,JJ
8895 SQRMS(J)=SQR(SQRMS(J)/G3)
123 IF(JC-1)1,107,122
107 PUNCH,JC,G,G1,G2
IF(N-JC)119,109,109
109 IF(L-5)190,190,191
191 DO 192 I=1,JJ
EQ=SL(JJ)/SL(1)
IF(L-6)192,194,202
194 AIC=1.0/SL(1)+AI1
EQ=1.0/EQ
GO TO 192
202 AIC=1.0/SL(JI)+AI1
192 CONTINUE
190 IF(SENSE SWITCH 1)110,142
110 IF(L-5)203,203,204
```

```
204 PUNCH,EQ,AIC,AI1
PUNCH,SQRMS(1),SQRMS(2)
GO TO 142
203 DO 111 J=1,JJ
111 PUNCH,SL(J),SQRMS(J)
142 IF(N-JC)1,118,112
112 IF(SENSE SWITCH 2)113,115
113 DO 114 I=1,JI,4
PUNCH,YY(I,JJ),YY(I+1,JJ),YY(I+2,JJ),YY(I+3,JJ)
114 PUNCH,Y(I,JJ),Y(I+1,JJ),Y(I+2,JJ),Y(I+3,JJ)
IF(N-JC)1,119,50
115 IF(SENSE SWITCH 3)116,50
116 DO 117 I=1,JI,4
DO 117 J=1,JJ
PUNCH,YY(I,J),YY(I+1,J),YY(I+2,J),YY(I+3,J)
PUNCH,Y(I,J),Y(I+1,J),Y(I+2,J),Y(I+3,J)
PUNCH,YER(I,J),YER(I+1,J),YER(I+2,J),YER(I+3,J)
117 PUNCH,DEV(I,J),DEV(I+1,J),DEV(I+2,J),DEV(I+3,J)
IF(N-JC)1,119,50
118 IF(G1-G2)9002,119,9002
9002 IF(SENSE SWITCH 4)116,113
120 IF(L-5)193,193,195
195 PUNCH,EQ,DEVEQ,AIC,DEAIC,AI1
PUNCH,SQRMS(1),SQRMS(2)
GO TO 196
193 DO 121 J=1,JJ
121 PUNCH,SL(J),DEVSL(J),SQRMS(J)
196 PUNCH,OPER,INSTR
PUNCH,RUN,TEMP,WAVEL
IF(M6-M4)1,1,10
122 IF(N-JC)107,9999,9999
9999 IF(NNN-IJ)125,107,1
125 DO 126 I=1,JI
JRK=0
DO 126 J=1,JJ
IF(YY(I,JJ))127,130,127
127 AA=SQR(YER(I,J)*YER(I,J))
BB=SQR(DEV(I,J)*DEV(I,J))
IF(AA-BB)129,128,128
129 IF(NNN-1)1,130,132
130 Y(I,J)=0.0
DEV(I,J)=0.0
GO TO 126
128 IF(NNN-1)1,126,133
131 JRK=JRK+1
IF(JRK-JJ)126,43,1
43 DO 9001 JP=1,JJ
9001 Y(I,JP)=YY(I,JP)
GO TO 126
132 IF(NNN-4)126,130,126
133 IF(NNN-4)131,126,131
126 CONTINUE
NNN=NNN+1
GO TO 51
119 DO 134 J=1,JJ
IF(N-JC)136,135,1
135 IF(L-5)197,197,198
197 DEVSL(J)=SL(J)
GO TO 137
198 DEVEQ=EQ
DEAIC=AIC
GO TO 137
```

```
136 IF(L-6)199,200,201
199 AAA=DEVSL(J)
DEVSL(J)=SL(J)
SL(J)=AAA
GO TO 134
200 AAA=DEVEQ
BBB=DEAIC-AI1
DEAIC=-SL(1)*BBB*BBB
DEVEQ=(-SL(JJ)+SL(1)/AAA)*AAA*AAA*BBB
AIC=BBB+AI1
EQ=AAA
GO TO 134
201 AAA=DEVEQ
BBB=DEAIC-AI1
DEAIC=-SL(JJ)*BBB*BBB
DEVEQ=(-SL(1)+SL(JJ)/AAA)*AAA*AAA*BBB
AIC=BBB+AI1
EQ=AAA
GO TO 134
137 DO 134 I=1,JI
IF(Y(I,JJ))138,134,138
138 Y(I,JJ)=0.0
IF(JJ-J)1,139,140
140 JK=JJ-1
DO 141JQ=1,JK
YER(I,JQ)=-SQR(YER(I,JQ)*YER(I,JQ))
141 Y(I,JJ)=Y(I,JJ)+SL(JQ)*YER(I,JQ)
139 Y(I,JJ)=YER(I,JJ)-Y(I,JJ)
134 CONTINUE
IF(N-JC)120,50,1
END
```

ALGOL 60 FOR PROGRAM NUMBER 25

```
PROCEDURE YAAAA(ji); ARRAY y,dev,yer,yy[1:jq,1:jd],a[1:jr,1:jr],rLm,wL,
devf,wu,ym,ya,sL,yn,yb,sqrms,devsL,wac,funy,fusL[1:jd],c1,dev1,dev2,c2[1:jq];
INTEGER ji: SWITCH sw1:=x2,x1,x2,x1,x1,x1,x1; SWITCH sw2:=x4,x5,x4,x5;
SWITCH sw3:=x8,x8,x7,x8,x8,x7,x7; SWITCH sw4:=x11,x10,x11,x10,x10,x10,x10;
SWITCH sw5:=x12,x13,x12,x13; SWITCH sw6:=x25,x15,x20,x19,x18,x17,x16,x14;
SWITCH sw7:=x25,x21,x24,x24,x23,x23,x22,x21; SWITCH sw8:=x27,x27,x27,x27,
x28,x27,x29; SWITCH sw9:=x38,x38,x38,x38,x39,x40,x40; SWITCH sw10:=x53,x43,
x48,x47,x46,x45,x44,x42; SWITCH sw11:=x53,x53,x53,x52,x52,x51,x51,x50;
COMMENT: VARIABLE DIMENSION EXPANSION AND SPECTROPHOTOMET-
RIC PROGRAM;
        BEGIN INTEGER i,ia,j,jj,jc,jb,jk,jr,jp,jrp,jrk,jan,ka,kb,kc,kd,ke,kf,k,kq,
        L,m,m4,m5,m6,n,nnn,num,g,g1,g2,g3,g9,feedp,run,oper,instr,code,jq,job;
        REAL aa,aaa,ai1,aic,axyz,bbb,bb,devic,deveq,eq,pqr,qq,run,rr,sob,set,sum,
        sum2,temp,waveL,yaa;
        READ feedp;
        READ ka,kb,kc,kd,ke,kf;
        READ jj;
        READ jc;
        READ m6;
        READ k,L,m;
        GO TO sw1[L];
X1:     jj:=2;
X2:     jk:=jj−1;
        n:=jc;
        READ rLm[1],wL[1],wu[1];
        READ rLm[2],wL[2],wu[2];
    I   IF K≤2 THEN
        BEGIN
            READ devf[1]; GO TO X3END;
        FOR i:=1 STEP 1 UNTIL ji DO READ dev1[i];
        devf[1]:=5555;
X3:     GO TO sw2[k];
X4:     READ devf[2]; GO TO X6;
X5:     FOR i:=1 STEP 1 UNTIL ji DO READ dev2[i];
        devf[2]:=5555;
X6:     m5:=m6; m4:=0;
XZ:     FOR i:=1 STEP 1 UNTIL ji DO READ y[i,jj];
        wac[jj]:=ai1:=0;
        IF L≥5 THEN READ ai1,wac[jj];
        g:=0; jk:=jj−1;
        FOR i:=1 STEP 1 UNTIL ji DO
        FOR j:=1 STEP 1 UNTIL jk DO y[i,j]:=yy[i,j];
        g1:=g2:=0;
        IF m4<0 THEN GO TO X89
        ELSE IF m4>0 THEN GO TO X33;
        FOR i:=1 STEP 1 UNTIL ji DO READ c1[i];
        GO TO sw3[L];
X7:     FOR i:=1 STEP 1 UNTIL ji DO READ c2[i];
        GO TO X9;
X8:     FOR i:=1 STEP 1 UNTIL ji DO c2[i]:=c1[i];
X9:     GO TO sw4[L];
```

```
X10:    jj:=2;
X11:    GO TO sw5[k];
X12:    FOR i:=1 STEP 1 UNTIL ji DO dev2[i]:=devf[2]Xc2[i];
X13:    kq:=ka+2;
        IF kq ≤8 THEN GO TO X25;
        IF kq ≤16 THEN
        BEGIN
          kq:=kq-8;  GO TO sw6[kq];
X14:      FOR i:=kd STEP 1 UNTIL ke DO c2[i]:=0;
X15:      FOR i:=kb STEP 1 UNTIL kc DO c2[i]:=0;
          GO TO X25;
X16:      c2[kf]:=0;
X17:      c2[ke]:=0;
X18:      c2[kd]:=0;
X19:      c2[kc]:=0;
X20:      c2[kb]:=0;
          GO TO X25END;
        IF kq >24 THEN
        BEGIN
          ka:=-1;  GO TO X25END;
          kq:=kq-16;  GO TO sw7[kq];
X21:    FOR i:=kb STEP 1 UNTIL kc DO c2[i]:=0;
        GO TO X25;
X22:    c2[kf]:=0;
X23:    c2[kd]:=0;
X24:    c2[kb]:=0;
X25:    FOR i:=1 STEP 1 UNTIL ji DO
        BEGIN
          IF c2[i]≥wL[2]∧c2[i]≤wu[2] THEN GO TO X26;
          c2[i]:=c1[i]:=0;
          FOR j:=1 STEP 1 UNTIL jj DO yer[i,j]:=y[i,j]:=yy[i,j]:=0;
          GO TO X32;
X26:      GO TO sw8[L];
X27:      y[i,1]:=c2[i];  yer[i,1]:=c2[i]+dev2[i];  GO TO X30;
X28:      y[i,1]:=Ln(c2[i]);  yer[i]:=Ln(c2[i]+dev2[i]);
          GO TO X30;
X29:      y[i,1]:=1.0/c2[i];  yer[i]:=1.0/(c2[i]-dev2[i]);
X30:      IF jj <2 THEN GO TO X89
          ELSE IF jj=2 THEN
          BEGIN
X31:        yer[i,1]:=yer[i,1]-y[i,1];
            yy[i,1]:=y[i,1];  GO TO X32;
            jk:=jj-1 END;
          FOR j:=2 STEP 1 UNTIL jk DO
          BEGIN
            jrp:=j-1;  y[i,j]:=y[i,1]Xy[i,jrp];
            yer[i,j]:=yer[i,1]Xyer[i,jrp]-y[i,j];
            yy[i,j]:=y[i,j]
          END;
          GO TO X31
X32:    END;
        READ oper,instr;
        READ run,temp,waveL;
```

```
            num: =25;
X33:        m4:=m4+1;  m5:=m5-1;  jc:=n;
            PUNCH num,feedp
            PUNCH jj,ji,jc,m4;
            PUNCH m6;
            PUNCH k,L,m;
            PUNCH devf[1],rLm[1],wL[1],wu[1];
            PUNCH wac[jj];
            PUNCH devf[2],rLm[2],wL[2],wu[2];
            jc:=0;
            FOR i:=1 STEP 1 UNTIL ji DO
            BEGIN
              IF c2[i]>0∧y[i,jj]≥wL[1]∧y[i,jj]≤wu[1] THEN GO TO X35;
X34:          y[i,jj]:=yer[i,jj]:=yy[i,jj]:=dev[i,jj]:=0;
              GO TO X36;
X35:          g:=g+1;
              pqr:=y[i,jj]-c1[i]Xai1;  pqr:=abs(pqr);
              IF pqr<wac[jj]Xy[i,jj] THEN GO TO X34;
              yy[i,jj]:=y[i,jj]
X36:        END;
            FOR i:=1 STEP 1 UNTIL ji DO
            BEGIN
              IF yy[i,1]=0 THEN
              BEGIN
                yy[i,jj]:=0;
X37:            yer[i,jj]:=dev[i,jj]:=y[i,jj]:=0;  GO TO X41END;
              IF yy[i,jj]=0 THEN GO TO X37;
              g1:=g1+1;
              IF k≤2 THEN dev1[i]:=yy[i,jj]Xdevf[1];
              GO TO sw9[L];
X38:          yer[i,jj]:=(yy[i,jj]+dev1[i])/c1[i];
              yy[i,jj]:=yy[i,jj]/c1[i];
              yer[i,jj]:=yer[i,jj]-yy[i,jj];  GO TO X41;
X39:          yer[i,jj]:=Ln((yy[i,jj]+dev1[i])/c1[i]-ai1);
              yy[i,jj]:=Ln((yy[i,jj]/c1[i]-ai1);
              yer[i,jj]:=yer[i,jj]-yy[i,jj];  GO TO X41;
X40:          yer[i,jj]:=1/((yy[i,jj]-dev1[i])/c1[i]-ai1);
              yy[i,jj]:=1/(yy[i,jj]/c1[i]-ai1);
              IF L<6 THEN GO TO X41
              ELSE IF L=6 THEN
              BEGIN
                yer[i,jj]:=(c2[i]+dev2[i])Xyer[i,jj];
                yy[i,jj]:=yy[i,jj]Xc2[i]END;
              yer[i,jj]:=yer[i,jj]-yy[i,jj]
X41:        END;
            kq:=kq+2;
            IF kq≤8 THEN
            BEGIN
              GO TO sw10[kq];
X42:          FOR i:=kd STEP 1 UNTIL ke DO y[i,jj]:=0;
X43:          FOR i:=kb STEP 1 UNTIL kc DO y[i,jj]:=0;
              GO TO X53;
X44:          y[kf,jj]:=0;
```

```
X45:    y[ke,jj]:=0;
X46:    y[kd,jj]:=0;
X47:    y[kc,jj]:=0;
X48:    y[kb,jj]:=0;  GO TO X53END;
X49:    kq:=kq–16;
        IF kq>0 THEN
        BEGIN
            GO TO sw11[kq];
X50:        FOR i:=kd STEP 1 UNTIL ke DO y[i,jj]:=0;
            GO TO X53;
X51:        y[ke,jj]:=0;
X52:        y[kc,jj]:=0END;
X53:    jc:=jc+1; nnn:=1;
X54:    FOR i:=1 STEP 1 UNTIL jj DO
        BEGIN
            ym[j]:=-10000000.0; yn[j]:=10000000.0;
            funy[j]:=1;
            FOR i:=1 STEP 1 UNTIL ji DO
            BEGIN
                y[i,j]:=y[i,j]Xfuny[j];
                IF y[i,jj]=0 THEN GO TO X55;
                IF ym[j]<y[i,j] THEN ym[j]:=y[i,j];
                IF yn[j]>y[i,j] THEN yn[j]:=y[i,j]
X55:        END;
            IF yn[j]=0 THEN
            BEGIN
                ya[j]:=-ym[j]/10; GO TO X56END;
            ELSE IF yn[j]>0 THEN
            BEGIN
                ya[j]:=-yn[j]/10; GO TO X56END;
            ya[j]:=2Xyn[j];
X56:    aa:-ym[j]-ya[j]; bb:=yn[j]-ya[j];
        aa:=abs(aa);  bb:=abs(bb);
        IF (aa>bb)V(aa=bbΛaa>0) THEN GO TO X59
        ELSE IF aa≤0 THEN
        BEGIN
            code:=88888888;
X57:        PUNCH code,m4;
            PUNCH oper,instr;
            PUNCH run,temp,waveL;
            IF m6≤m4 THEN GO TO X89
            ELSE GO TO XZ END;
X58:    yb[j]:=bb; GO TO X60;
X59:    yb[j]:=aa;
X60:    FOR i:=1 STEP 1 UNTIL ji DO
        BEGIN
            IF y[i,jj]≠0 THEN y[i,j]:=y[i,j]-ya[j]
            ELSE GO TO X61;
            IF y[i,jj]=0 THEN y[i,j]:=(yn[j]-ya[j])/₁₀6
            y[i,j]:=y[i,j]/yb[j]
        END
X61:    END;
        jr:=jj+1;
```

```
         FOR j:=1 STEP 1 UNTIL jr DO
         FOR i:=1 STEP 1 UNTIL jr DO a[i,j]:=0;
         FOR j:=1 STEP 1 UNTIL jj DO
         FOR jb:=1 STEP 1 UNTIL jj DO
         FOR i:=1 STEP 1 UNTIL ji DO
         BEGIN
            IF y[i,jj]=0 THEN GO TO X62;
            IF jb<1 THEN GO TO X89
            ELSE IF jb>1 THEN
            BEGIN
               jp:=jb-1; a[jb,j]:=a[jb,j]+y[i,j]Xy[i,jp];
               GO TO X62END;
            a[jb,j]:=a[jb,j]+y[i,j]
X62:     END;
         g2:=yaa:=0;
         FOR j:=1 STEP 1 UNTIL jj DO a[j,jr]:=a[j,jj];
         FOR i:=1 STEP 1 UNTIL ji DO
         IF y[i,jj]≠0 THEN g2:=g2+1;
         a[1,jj]:=g2; g9:=jj+2;
         IF g2<g9 THEN
         BEGIN
            code:=99999999; GO TO X57END;
         FOR j:=2 STEP 1 UNTIL jj DO
         BEGIN
            jb:=j-1; a[j,jj]:=a[1,jb]
         END;
         FOR j:=1 STEP 1 UNTIL jr DO
         FOR i:=1 STEP 1 UNTIL jj DO
         BEGIN
            aa:=abs(a[i,j]);
            IF yaa<aa THEN yaa:=aa
         END;
         FOR j:=1 STEP 1 UNTIL jr DO
         FOR i:=1 STEP 1 UNTIL jj DO a[i,j]:=a[i,j]/yaa;
         FOR j:=1 STEP 1 UNTIL jr DO
         FOR i:=1 STEP 1 UNTIL jj DO
         BEGIN
            IF j≤1 THEN GO TO X64;
            IF j≤i THEN
            BEGIN
               ja:=j-1; GO TO X63END;
            ja:=i-1;
X63:     set:≥sum:=0;
         IF ja>0 THEN
         FOR jk:=1 STEP 1 UNTIL ja DO sum:=sum+a[i,jk]Xa[jk,j];
         set:=a[i,j]-sum;
         IF j≤i THEN
         BEGIN
            a[i,j]:=set; GO TO X64END;
         sob:=a[i,i];
         IF sob=0 THEN sob:=10(-18);
         a[i,j]:=set/sob
X64:     END;
```

```
FOR i:=1 STEP 1 UNTIL jj DO
BEGIN
    jan:=jr−i; sum2:=0; ia:=i−1;
    IF ia>0 THEN
    BEGIN
        FOR jk:=1 STEP 1 UNTIL ia DO
        BEGIN
            job:=jr−jk;
            sum2:=sum2+a[jan,job]XsL[job]
        END END;
    sL[jan]:=a[jan,jr]−sum2
END;
FOR i:=1 STEP 1 UNTIL ji DO
FOR j:=1 STEP 1 UNTIL jj DO
BEGIN
    IF y[i,jj]≠0 THEN
    BEGIN
        y[i,j]:=yb[j]Xy[i,j];
        y[i,j]:=y[i,j]+ya[j];
        y[i,j]:=y[i,j]/funy[j]
END END;
sL[jj]:=sL[jj]Xyb[jj];
axyz:=0; jk:=jj−1;
FOR j:=1 STEP 1 UNTIL jk DO
BEGIN
    sL[j]:=sL[j]Xyb[jj]/yb[j];
    axyz:=axyz+sL[j]Xya[j]
END;
sL[jj]:=sL[jj]−axyz+ya[jj];
FOR j:=1 STEP 1 UNTIL jj DO
BEGIN
    fusL[j]:=1; sL[j]:=sL[j]XfusL[j]
END;
g3:=g2−1;
IF n<jc THEN GO TO X66;
FOR j:=1 STEP 1 UNTIL jj DO
BEGIN
    sqrms[j]:=0;
    FOR i:=1 STEP 1 UNTIL ji DO dev[i,j]:=0
END;
jk:=jj−1;
FOR i:=1 STEP 1 UNTIL ji DO
BEGIN
    rr:=0;
    IF yy[i,jj]≠0 THEN
    BEGIN
        FOR j:=1 STEP 1 UNTIL jj DO
        BEGIN
            IF jj<j THEN GO TO X89
            ELSE IF jj>j THEN rr:=rr+sL[j]Xyy[i,j]
        END;
        qq:=rr+sL[jj]; dev[i,jj]:=yy[i,jj]−qq;
        FOR jp:=1 STEP 1 UNTIL jk DO
```

```
          BEGIN
            IF sL[jp]=0 THEN
            BEGIN
              dev[i,jp]:=0;  GO TO X65END;
            dev[i,jp]:=yy[i,jp]−(yy[i,jj]−qq+sL[jp]Xyy[i,jp])/sL[jp]
X65:      END
          END
        END;
        FOR j:=1 STEP 1 UNTIL jj DO
        FOR i:=1 STEP 1 UNTIL ji DO
        sqrms[j]:=sqrms[j]+dev[i,j]↑2;
        FOR j:=1 STEP 1 UNTIL jj DO sqrms[j]:=sqrt(sqrm[j]/g3);
X66:    IF jc<1 THEN GO TO X89
        ELSE IF jc>1 THEN GO TO X77;
X67:    PUNCH jc,g,g1,g2;
        IF n<jc THEN GO TO X84;
        IF L>5 THEN
        BEGIN
          FOR i:=1 STEP 1 UNTIL jj DO
          BEGIN
            eq:=sL[jj]/sL[1];
            IF L>6 THEN GO TO X68
            ELSE IF L<6 THEN GO TO X69;
            aic:=1/sL[1]+ai1
            eq:=1/eq;  GO TO X69;
X68:        aic:=1/sL[ji]+ai1
X69:    END END;
        COMMENT: At this point control either proceeds serially or is trans-
        ferred to label X70 (see OPTIONAL EXTERNAL COMMANDS FOR
        PROGRAM 25);
        IF L>5 THEN
        BEGIN
          PUNCH eq,aic,ai1;
          PUNCH sqrms[1],sqrms[2];  GO TO X70END;
        FOR j:=1 STEP 1 UNTIL jj DO PUNCH sL[j],sqrms[j];
X70:    IF n<jc THEN GO TO X89
        ELSE IF n=jc THEN GO TO X74;
        COMMENT: At this point control either proceeds serially or is trans-
        ferred to label X72 (see OPTIONAL EXTERNAL COMMANDS FOR
        PROGRAM 25);
X71:    FOR i:=1 STEP 1 UNTIL ji DO PUNCH yy[i,jj];
        FOR i:=1 STEP 1 UNTIL ji DO PUNCH y[i,jj];
        IF n<jc THEN GO TO X89
        ELSE IF n=jc THEN GO TO X84 ELSE GO TO X53;
X72:    COMMENT: At this point control either proceeds serially or is trans-
        ferred to label X53 (See OPTIONAL EXTERNAL COMMANDS FOR
        PROGRAM 25);
X73:    FOR i:=1 STEP 1 UNTIL ji DO
        FOR j:=1 STEP 1 UNTIL jj DO
        BEGIN
          PUNCH yy[i,j];
          PUNCH y[i,j];
          PUNCH yer[i,j];
```

```
          PUNCH dev[i,j]
       END;
       IF n<jc THEN GO TO X89
       ELSE IF n=jc THEN GO TO X84 ELSE GO TO X53;
X74:   IF g1=g2 THEN GO TO X84;
       COMMENT: At this point control is either transferred to label X71 or
       to label X73 (see OPTIONAL EXTERNAL COMMANDS FOR PROGRAM
       25);
X75:   IF L>5 THEN
       BEGIN
          PUNCH eq,deveq,aic,deaic,ai1;
          PUNCH sqrms[1],sqrms[2];
          GO TO X76END;
       FOR j:=1 STEP 1 UNTIL jj DO PUNCH sL[j],devsL[j],sqrms[j];
X76:   PUNCH oper,instr;
       PUNCH run,temp,waveL;
       IF m6≤m4 THEN GO TO X89 ELSE GO TO XZ;
X77:   IF n<jcVnnn=ij THEN GO TO X67
       ELSE IF nnn>ij THEN GO TO X89;
       FOR i:=1 STEP 1 UNTIL ji DO
       BEGIN
          jrk:=0;
          FOR j:=1 STEP 1 UNTIL jj DO
          BEGIN
             IF yy[i,jj]≠0 THEN
             BEGIN
                aa:=abs(yer[i,j]); bb:=abs(dev[i,j]);
                IF aa≥bb THEN GO TO X79;
                IF nnn<1 THEN GO TO X89
                ELSE IF nnn>1 THEN GO TO X81END;
X78:   dev[i,j]:=y[i,j]:=0;
       GO TO X83;
X79:   IF nnn<1 THEN GO TO X89
       ELSE IF nnn>1 THEN GO TO X82 ELSE GO TO X83;
X80:   jrk:=jrk+1;
       IF jrk>jj THEN GO TO X89
       ELSE IF jrk<jj THEN GO TO X83;
       FOR jp:=1 STEP 1 UNTIL jj DO y[i,jp]:=yy[i,jp];
       GO TO X83;
X81:   IF nnn=4 THEN GO TO X78 ELSE GO TO X83;
X82:   IF nnn≠4 THEN GO TO X80
X83:   END END;
       nnn:=nnn+1;  GO TO X54;
X84:   FOR j:=1 STEP 1 UNTIL jj DO
       BEGIN
          IF n>jc THEN GO TO X89
          ELSE IF n<jc THEN GO TO X85;
          IF L≤5 THEN
          BEGIN
             devsL[j]:=sL[j];  GO TO X86END;
          deveq:=eq; deaic:=aic; GO TO X86;
X85:   IF L<6 THEN
       BEGIN
```

```
            aaa:=devsL[j];  devsL[j]:=sL[j];
            sL[j]:=aaa;  GO TO X88END
       ELSE IF L=6 THEN
       BEGIN
            aaa:=deveq;  bbb:=devic−ai1;
            deaic:=−sL[1]Xbbb↑2;
            deveq:=(−sL[jj]+sL[1]/aaa)Xaaa↑2Xbbb;
            aic:=bbb+ai1;  eq:=aaa;  GO TO X88END;
       aaa:=deveq;  bbb:=deaic−ai1;
       deaic:=−sL[jj]Xbbb↑2;
       deveq:=(−sL[1]+sL[jj]/aaa)Xaaa↑2Xbbb;
       aic:=bbb+ai1;  eq:=aaa;  GO TO X88;
X86:   FOR i:=1 STEP 1 UNTIL ji DO
       BEGIN
            IF y[i,jj]=0 THEN GO TO X88;
            y[i,jj]:=0;
            IF jj<j THEN GO TO X89
            ELSE IF jj=j THEN GO TO X87;
            jk:=jj−1;
            FOR jq:=1 STEP 1 UNTIL jk DO
            BEGIN
                 yer[i,jq]:=−abs(yer[i,jq]);
                 y[i,jj]:=y[i,jj]+sL[jq]Xyer[i,jq]
            END;
X87:        y[i,jj]:=yer[i,jj]−y[i,jj]
       END
X88:   END;
       IF n<jc THEN GO TO X75
       ELSE IF n=jc THEN GO TO X53
X89:END YAAAA;
       READ ji;  ij:=4;
X90:YAAAA(ji,ij);
       GO TO X90;
```

CHAPTER III

SELF-JUDGMENT PROGRAMS WITH VARIABLE DIMENSIONS

In Programs 1–4, 9–15, 22–24, 301–304, 309–315, 322–324, and 410–415 *Cramer's method* is used to solve the linear equations for their slopes and intercept. As the delta determinant for the N-dimension equation

$$x_N = a_1x_1 + a_2x_2 + a_3x_3 + \cdots + a_{N-1}x_{N-1} + a_{N+1} \tag{1}$$

will vanish if one or more of the slopes is zero, *Cramer's method* can be used to solve equation (1) only if its exact dimensions are known. With the modified *Crout reduction method*, equation (1) can be solved for all values of the slopes. In Programs 25–29 and 325–329 the modified *Crout reduction method* is used.

Although Program 26 (*call word* ZAAAA) has been designed for use with large computers to solve any variation of equation (1) in which the functions $x_N, x_1, x_2 \cdots x_{N-1}$ are known, it can also be used with medium storage computers to replace Programs 1 (*call word* AAAAA), 2 (*call word* BAAAA), 3 (*call word* CAAAA), and 4 (*call word* DAAAA). The storage required will be determined by the values chosen for JQ, JD, and JR (defined under *input commands* for Programs 26 and 326) and by the compiler available. With the IBM 1620 60K computer at the University of Mississippi, values used for JQ, JD, and JR are 20, 15, and 16 respectively. Thus an equation with fifteen dimensions can be solved with twenty sets of conjugate data on this computer. JJ and JI determine the actual dimensions and the number of sets of conjugate data to be processed (see *input commands* for Programs 26 and 326).

Input information for Programs 1–4 and 301–304 is compatible with Programs 26 and 326 if JI = 20. Information generated by the feeder programs (8, 16–21, 32, 33, 35, and 36) can be processed with Program 26. Although information generated by Programs 32, 33, 35 and 36 is

179

compatible with Program 26, the first card in the output from Programs 8 and 16–21 must be replaced by two cards, as described for each feeder program in the first volume. (Further details are given under *input format* for Programs 26 and 326.)

In Program 26 (*call word* ZAAAA) the *fail–safe procedure* is not applied. A special normalization procedure (see *Crout reduction method*) replaces the *normalization* and *transposition mechanisms* used in Programs 1–4, 9–15, 22–24, 301–304, 309–315, 322–324, and 410–415. The steps taken by the computer are as follows:

1. The *reject–restore* commands are executed.

2. The *accepted sets of conjugate data* are normalized as described in the section on the *Crout reduction method*.

3. The parameters are calculated by the *Crout reduction method*. The *self-judgment principle* is not applied at the end of the first cycle.

4. After step 3 in the second cycle the following steps are taken.

(a) The *actual errors* for each value of each ordinate are calculated. If the *actual error* in any item of a set of conjugate information is greater than the corresponding maximum permitted error, all items of the set are set equal to zero.

(b) Sets of conjugate information not rejected in step (a) are used to recalculate the parameters and the *actual errors*. Next, the rejected information is reviewed and restored if the *actual error* for each item of information in the rejected sets is less than or equal to the associated *maximum permitted error*. The rejection procedure described in step (a) is not applied.

(c) Step (b) is repeated.

5. Steps (a), (b), and (c) are repeated for the third, fourth $\cdots$ JCth cycles.

6. In the (JC + 1)th cycle the *maximum permitted errors* for each parameter are computed with information obtained in the JCth cycle. The *self-judgment principle* is not applied in the *error analysis*.

SPECIAL MODIFICATIONS

In Program 326 (*call word* ZAAAS) the *self-judgment principle* is applied only to values of x_N (equation (1)). This one-dimensional *self-judgment* form of Program 26 is especially useful in analyzing curves with small slopes where a small error in a value for one ordinate may lead to the erroneous rejection of good data because the *actual error* in the corresponding value of another ordinate exceeds the *maximum permitted error*.

The input commands and the input and output formats are identical for Programs 26 and 326 except for obvious minor changes. Program 26 (*call word* ZAAAA) can be converted to Program 326 (*call word* ZAAAS) by replacing the FORTRAN statements as indicated below.

ORIGINAL *Program 26 (Call Word* ZAAAA)	REPLACEMENTS *Program 326 (Call Word* ZAAAS)
1 READ,ZAAAA,FEEDP	1 READ,ZAAAS,FEEDP
NUM = 26	NUM = 326
PUNCH,ZAAAA,NUM,JJ,FEEDP	PUNCH,ZAAAS,NUM,JJ,FEEDP
JRK = 0	IF(YY(I,JJ))127,130,127
DO 126 J = 1,JJ	127 AA = SQR(YER(I,JJ)*YER(I,JJ))
IF(YY(I,1))127,130,127	BB = SQR(DEV(I,JJ)*DEV(I,JJ))
127 AA = SQR(YER(I,J)*YER(I,J))	IF(AA − BB)129,128,128
BB = SQR(DEV(I,J)*DEV(I,J))	129 IF(NNN − 1)1,130,132
IF(AA − BB)129,128,128	130 DO 9003 J = 1,JJ
129 IF(NNN − 1)1,130,132	Y(I,J) = 0.0
130 Y(I,J) = 0.0	9003 DEV(I,J) = 0.0
DEV(I,J) = 0.0	GO TO 126
GO TO 126	128 IF(NNN − 1)1,126,133
128 IF(NNN − 1)1,126,133	131 DO 9001 J = 1,JJ
131 JRK = JRK + 1	9001 Y(I,J) = YY(I,J)
IF(JRK − JJ)126,43,1	GO TO 126
43 DO 9001 JP = 1,JJ	
9001 Y(I,JP) = YY(I,JP)	
GO TO 126	

CROUT REDUCTION METHOD

Descriptions of the *Crout reduction method* and its limitations can be found in many elementary texts dealing with numerical analyses. The actual mechanism for solving the N-dimensional equation (1) will not be discussed here.

For the general system of equations

$$a_1 x_{11} + a_2 x_{12} + \cdots + a_r x_{1r} + \cdots + a_{N+1} x_{1(N+1)} = x_{1N}$$

$$\vdots \qquad\qquad \vdots$$

$$a_1 x_{r1} + a_2 x_{r2} + \cdots + a_r x_{rr} + \cdots + a_{N+1} x_{r(N+1)} = x_{rN}$$

$$\vdots \qquad\qquad \vdots$$

$$a_1 x_{N1} + a_2 x_{N2} + \cdots + a_r x_{Nr} + \cdots + a_{N+1} x_{N(N+1)} = x_{NN}$$

the parameters $(a_1, a_2 \cdot a_r \cdot a_{N+1})$ can be calculated by Crout's method if the functional form of each variable in equation (1) is known. The method of least squares relates the matrix elements (x_{ij}) to the variable quantities in equation (1) thus:

First row elements:

$$x_{1r} = \sum_{i=1}^{G} x_i \qquad \text{with } x_{1(N+1)} = G$$

Here G is the number of data points to be processed.
All other elements:

$$x_{ij} = \sum_{i=1}^{G} x_i x_j \quad \text{with } x_{i(N+1)} = x_{1r}$$

One step in the *Crout reduction method* involves dividing by the diagonal elements of the matrix (x_{ii}). Thus, if the original data are normalized and then transposed symmetrically about the origin, infinities will occur and the method breaks down. Even if the diagonal elements (x_{ii}) are not quite zero, small variations in the raw data can result in gross errors in the parameters. Thus the Crout reduction method is extremely sensitive to small variations in the data.

To reduce the sensitivity of Crout's method the following fully automatic three-step normalization procedure has been incorporated in Programs 25–29 and 325–329.

(a) The maximum (XM) and minimum (XN) values for each ordinate are determined by a search method. Next, YA for each ordinate is computed as follows:

$$\text{If XN is negative:} \quad \text{YA} = 2.0 * \text{XN}$$
$$\text{If XN is zero:} \quad \text{YA} = -\text{XM}/10.0$$
$$\text{If XN is positive:} \quad \text{YA} = -\text{XN}/10.0$$

YA is then subtracted from each value of the associated ordinate.

(b) The maximum value for each transposed ordinate is divided into each ordinate value.

(c) After all elements of the *Crout reduction matrix* are computed they are divided by the element of maximum value.

After the parameters at the end of each programmed cycle are calculated, the ordinates are converted to their original values and the parameters are corrected automatically. Output and input information are therefore scaled in the same units.

With this fully automatic three-step normalization procedure it is almost impossible to induce round-off errors. For example, the linear three-dimensional equation:

$$y = m_1 x_1 + m_2 x_2 + c$$

with $m_1 = 1$, 10, 100, 10000, or 100000, $m_2 = 0$, and $c = 1.0$ can be solved exactly for a millionfold variation between corresponding values of x_1 or x_2 and y, or for a range of several thousand in the values of one ordinate. However, even with the three-step normalization procedure, the *Crout reduction method* remains extremely sensitive to small variations in the data points themselves. In processing twenty data points in the range $y = 1$ to 20 and $x = 0.01$ to 0.20 with the equation $y = mx + c$, we have found that a 5 percent error in the y value which defines the highest terminal data point (20, 0.20) leads to round-off error in the *Crout reduction matrix* if the *maximum permitted error* is 1 percent. In other words, if good data points are discarded and a bad point is retained, round-off error occurs and the appropriate *numerical code* (99999999.0) is punched and printed. An increase of the *maximum permitted error* from 1.0 to 1.1 percent allows the computer to discard the "wrong point" and the correct analysis is given. This remarkable ability to discern a wrong analysis can be reduced by increasing the parameter YA, calculated to step (a), or by increasing the word size in the computer. However, in our laboratories we have felt that the "discipline" imposed on the operator in his choice of *maximum permitted errors* is desirable.

INPUT COMMANDS FOR PROGRAMS 26 AND 326

The input commands K, L, and M, which appear in both the input and output formats for Programs 26 and 326, are not executed. Values of K, L, and M, which originate in the *feeder programs*, are not significant.

The executable commands can be classified in two groups.

Dimension Commands

JQ, JD, and JR appear in the *dimension* statements of the FORTRAN programs and must be selected before compilation. Their meanings are as follows.

JQ—The maximum number of sets of conjugate data that can be processed with the program. JQ should be a multiple of four

JD—The maximum dimensioned equation which can be solved with the program. Although JD cannot be less than two, the upper limits for both JD and JQ will be determined by the storage capacity of the computer

JR—The dimension of the *Crout reduction matrix*. This equals JD + 1.

Two commands which are selected after compilation and which appear in the input and output formats for Programs 26 and 326 are:

JI—The actual number of sets of conjugate data to be processed. JI *must be a multiple of four.*

JJ—The dimension of the equation to be processed. This information is not required if input information for Programs 1–4 and 301–304 is processed. Feeder Programs 32, 33, 35, and 36 generate this information automatically.

Reject–Restore and Cycle Commands

JC equals the number of cycles to be completed before the error analysis. In the second, third, ··· JCth cycles, the reject mechanism is applied once and the restore mechanism is applied twice.

The semiautomatic *reject–restore mechanism* is activated by the values selected for KA, KB, KC, and KD, if input information for Programs 1–4 and 301–304 is being processed, or for KA, KB, KC, KD, KE, and KF, if the input information is generated by Feeder Programs 32, 33, 35, or 36. The value chosen for KA determines which sets of conjugate information are to be "ignored" or "killed." "Ignored" sets are not used to calculate the parameters during the first cycle, but they are reviewed in the second cycle and restored to memory if they lie within the *error zone* of the computed curve. "Killed" sets are removed from memory and are not considered in the calculations.

In the processing of information for Programs 1–4 and 301–304, KA can have values of -1, 0, 1, 2, or 3. In the input formats values must be entered for all KA, KB, KC, KD (Programs 1–4 and 301–304), or for all KA, KB, KC, KD, KE, and KF (Programs 26 and 326). Thus for Program 1 (*call word* AAAAA) a card with KA $= -1$, KB $= 9$, KC $= 999$, KD $= 0$, means that no sets of conjugate data are to be "ignored or killed" during the first cycle.

The abbreviations used below are as follows

Kill(KB–KC)	The KBth to KCth *Sets of conjugate information* are to be removed from memory
Kill(KB,KC,KF)	The KBth, KCth, and KFth sets are to be removed from memory
Ignore(KB–KC; KD–KE)	The KBth to the KCth and the KDth to the KEth sets are to be ignored during the first application of the *self-judgment principle*
Ignore(KB,KC)	The KBth and KCth sets are to be ignored during the first cycle

REJECT–RESTORE COMMANDS

KA	Command	KA	Command
-1	No sets are ignored or killed	11	Kill(KB,KC,KD)
0	Ignore(KB–KC)	12	Kill(KB,KC,KD,KE)
1	Ignore(KB)	13	Kill(KB,KC,KD,KE,KF)
2	Ignore(KB,KC)	14	Kill(KB–KC; KD–KE)
3	Ignore(KB,KC,KD)	15	No sets are ignored or killed
4	Ignore(KB,KC,KD,KE)	16	Kill(KB–KC)
5	Ignore(KB,KC,KD,KE,KF)	17	Kill(KB)
6	Ignore(KB–KC; KD–KE)	18	Kill(KB); ignore(KC)
7	No sets are ignored or killed	19	Kill(KB,KD); ignore(KC)
8	Kill(KB–KC)	20	Kill(KB,KD); ignore(KC,KE)
9	Kill(KB)	21	Kill(KB,KD,KF); ignore(KC,KE)
10	Kill(KB,KC)	22	Kill(KB–KC); ignore(KD–KE)

INPUT FORMAT FOR PROGRAMS 26 AND 326

In the following, READ, JJ (26 or 326) means the information is entered only for ZAAAA $= 26$ or ZAAAS $= 326$. If JI $= 20$, Programs

26 and 326 will accept without change the input information for Programs 1–4 and 301–304. JI, which must be a multiple of four, is entered only once for each series of data decks with a given JI value. If JI is changed, the read-file of the computer must be "zeroed" (procedure for the IBM 1620 60K is RESET–INSERT–4907500RS) and a new JI value "read in." Input information for Programs 26 and 326 can be processed with *Autoplotter Program* 501 (*call word* AEEEE) if JJ = 4. Instructions have been given in Chapter I.

STATEMENT	COMMENT
READ,JI	JI($= 4 \times$ N, N $= 1, 2, 3, \cdots$) is the number of sets of conjugate data
READ,ZAAAA or ZAAAS,FEEDP	
READ,KA,KB,KC,KD,KE,KF }(26 or 326) READ,JJ	*Reject–restore commands*
or	
READ,KA,KB,KC,KD (1–4 or 301–304)	*Reject–restore commands*
READ,JC	Number of cycles before *error analysis*
READ,K,L,M	
READ,DEVF(J),RLM(J),WL(J),WU(J)	*Instrument reliability factors, entered* JJ times
READ,Y(I,J),Y(I+1,J),Y(I+2,J),Y(I+3,J) READ,YER(I,J),YER(I+1,J),YER(I+2,J),YER(I+3,J)	Entered JJ times for I $= 1, 5, \cdots$JI

Note: In this program the output information for the ordinates is rearranged (see Output Format for Programs 26 and 326). In the Input Format Y(I, 1) and YER(I, 1) refer to values for x_N in equation (1). Y(I, 2) and YER(I, 2) refer to values of x_1 and so on.

STATEMENT	COMMENT
READ,G	Number of sets of conjugate information
READ,OPER,INSTR READ,RUN,TEMP,WAVEL }	Identification

OPTIONAL EXTERNAL COMMANDS FOR PROGRAMS 26 AND 326

The choice of *program switch* setting determines the output generated by Programs 26 and 326.

SWITCH POSITIONS				COMMANDS EXECUTED AND COMMENTS
1	2	3	4	

| ON | | | | PUNCH,SL(J),SQRMS(J)   (J = 1, 2$\cdots$JJ) |

This command is executed at the end of each cycle. The SL(J)'s are the values for the parameters calculated in the preceding cycle, defined thus in equation (A)

(Y(I,J) have been rearranged to their output form.)
$$Y(I,JJ) = SL(1) \cdot Y(I, 1) + SL(2) \cdot Y(I, 2) + \cdots + SL(JJ)$$
SQRMS(J) is the standard deviation in the accepted value for the designated ordinate

ON ON

PUNCH,YY(I,JJ),YY(I+1,JJ),YY(I+2,JJ),
YY(I+3,JJ)
PUNCH,Y(I,JJ),Y(I+1,JJ),Y(I+2,JJ),Y(I+3,JJ) $\Big\}(I = 1, 5, \cdots JI)$

This command is executed at the end of each cycle. YY(I,JJ) is the Ith value of Y(I,JJ) in equation (A). Y(I,JJ) is the value used in the preceding cycle to calculate SL(1),SL(2)$\cdots$SL(JJ) and the standard deviations (SQRMS(1),$\cdots$)

ON OFF ON

PUNCH,YY(I,J),YY(I+1,J),YY(I+2,J),YY(I+3,J)
PUNCH,Y(I,J),Y(I+1,J),Y(I+2,J),Y(I+3,J)   For I = 1, 5,$\cdots$JI
PUNCH,YER(I,J),YER(I+1,J),YER(I+2,J),YER(I+3,J)
PUNCH,DEV(I,J),DEV(I+1,J),DEV(I+2,J),DEV(I+3,J)

This command is executed at the end of each cycle. YY(I,J) is the original information. Y(I,J) is the information actually used in the preceding cycle. YER(I,J) and DEV(I,J) are the *maximum permitted error* and the *actual error*, respectively, in YY(I,J). These data tables have been rearranged. Y(I,1) is the Y(I,2) in equation (A). Y(I,JJ) is the Y(I,JJ) in equation (A) but is equal to Y(I,1) in the input format

OFF   The commands given for both *switches* 1 and 2 ON are executed at the end of the N(= JC)th cycle if G1 $\neq$ G2 regardless of the settings for *switches* 1 and 2

ON   The commands given for *switches* 1, 2, and 3 ON, OFF, and ON respectively, are executed at the end of the N(= JC)th cycle regardless of the other *switch* settings if G1 $\neq$ G2

OUTPUT FORMAT FOR PROGRAMS 26 AND 326

STATEMENT*	COMMENT
PUNCH,ZAAAA or ZAAAS,NUM,JJ,FEEDP	NUM is the program number; JJ is the dimension of equation
PUNCH,JC	Number of cycles before the error analysis
PUNCH,K.L.M	
PUNCH,DEVF(J),RLM(J),WL(J),WU(J)	Punched JJ times
PRINT,CODE,WAVEL,RUN ⎫	Executed only for *code* = 99999999.0
PUNCH,CODE ⎬	or 88888888.0. If G1 < JJ + 2,
PUNCH,OPER,INSTR ⎪	the calculation is terminated.
PUNCH,RUN,TEMP,WAVEL ⎭	

PUNCH,JC,G,G1,G2
PUNCH,SL(J),SQRMS(J)   (J = 1, 2,···JJ)   If *switch* 1 is ON
PUNCH,YY(I,JJ),YY(I+1,JJ),YY(I+2,JJ),YY(I+3,JJ)   ⎧ If *switches* 1 and 2 are ON
PUNCH,Y(I,JJ),Y(I+1,JJ),Y(I+2,JJ),Y(I+3,JJ)   ⎪ for N = 1, 2,··· (JC − 1)
   (I = 1, 5,···JI)   ⎨ or for N = JC if *switch* 4
                                                   ⎩ is OFF and G1 ≠ G2

PUNCH,YY(I,J),YY(I+1,J),YY(I+2,J),YY(I+3,J)   ⎧ Executed if *switches* 1, 2
PUNCH,Y(I,J),Y(I+1,J),Y(I+2,J),Y(I+3,J)   ⎪ and 3 are ON, OFF, and
PUNCH,YER(I,J),YER(I+1,J),YER(I+2,J),YER(I+3,J) ⎬ ON respectively, for N
PUNCH,DEV(I,J),DEV(I+1,J),DEV(I+2,J),DEV(I+3,J) ⎪ = 1, 2,···(JC − 1), or
   (J = 1, 2···JJ; I = 1, 5,···JI)   ⎪ for N = JC if *switch* 4 is
                                                ⎩ ON and G1 ≠ G2

═══

* The commands between the double-lines are repeated N(= JC) times.

In the N + 1 cycle the *error analysis* is performed and the following operations are executed.

                   PUNCH,JC,G,G1,G2
                   PUNCH,SL(J),DEVSL(J),SQRMS(J)   (J = 1, 2,···JJ)
                   PUNCH,OPER,INSTR   ⎫
                   PUNCH,RUN,TEMP,WAVEL   ⎬ Identification
                                                  ⎭

DEFINITIONS

JJ	Dimension of equation being processed
JC	Number of cycles to be completed before the *error analysis*. Below the double line, JC becomes the cycle number
G	The number of sets of conjugate information entered in the input format
G1	The number of sets of conjugate information remaining after application of the *reject–restore command*
G2	The number of sets of conjugate information actually used to calculate SL(1), SL(2),··· DEVSL(1),···, etc., in the JCth cycles
DEVSL(J)	The *maximum permitted error* in SL(J). SL(J) and SQRMS(J) were calculated in the N(= JC)th cycle
K,L,M	Input commands originating in the *feeder programs*
DEVF(J),RLM(J), WL(J),WU(J)	*Instrument reliability factors* originating in the *feeder program*
SL(J)	The value of the Jth parameter calculated in the JCth cycle. Note that the input information is rearranged and that the equation (for the Ith set) is: $Y(I,JJ) = SL(1)*Y(I,1) + SL(2)*Y(I,2) + \cdots + SL(N)$
SQRMS(J)	The standard deviation in the *accepted values* for the Jth ordinate
YY(I,JJ)	The Ith value for the JJth ordinate available for calculation
Y(I,JJ)	The Ith value for the JJth ordinate actually used in the calculation
YY(I,J) and Y(I,J)	The Ith values for the Jth ordinate
DEV(I,J) and YER(I,J)	The actual error and the *maximum permitted error* respectively in YY(I,J)

Note: Values for the ordinates in the output format are rearranged from the input format. Thus Y(I,JJ) and YER(I,JJ) in the output format are identical with Y(I,1) and YER(I,1) in the input format. The actual rearrangement is as follows: The first ordinate becomes the last; for all other ordinates J is decreased by one.

RELIABILITY LIMITS FOR PROGRAMS 26 AND 326

The reliability limits for Programs 26 and 326 have been discussed in the section on the *Crout reduction method* in this chapter. There it is noted that, although it is virtually impossible to induce round-off errors in exact problems, round-off errors do occur if the data are not compatible with the question being tested. This ability to discern a "wrong analysis" has been retained. However, as noted, the sensitivity of the *Crout reduction matrix* to variations in the data can be reduced by making minor changes in the FORTRAN programs.

FORTRAN FOR PROGRAM NUMBER 26

CALL WORD ZAAAA

```
DIMENSION Y(JQ,JD),YY(JQ,JD),YER(JQ,JD),DEV(JQ,JD)
DIMENSION A(JR,JR),DEVF(JD),RLM(JD),WL(JD),WU(JD)
DIMENSION YM(JD),YN(JD),YA(JD),SL(JD),YB(JD)
DIMENSION SQRMS(JD),DEVSL(JD),FUSL(JD),FUNY(JD)
READ,JI
IJ=4
1 READ,ZAAAA,FEEDP
DO 18 I=1,JI
DO 18 J=1,JJ
Y(I,J)=0.0
YY(I,J)=0.0
YER(I,J)=0.0
18 DEV(I,J)=0.0
NPR=ZAAAA
IF(NPR-300)2,1,3
3 NPR=NPR-300
2 IF(NPR-26)4,5,1
5 READ,KA,KB,KC,KD,KE,KF
READ,JJ
GO TO 6
4 JJ=NPR+1
READ,KA,KB,KC,KD
6 READ,JC
READ,K,L,M
DO 7 J=1,JJ
7 READ,DEVF(J),RLM(J),WL(J),WU(J)
DO 8 I=1,JI,4
DO 8 J=1,JJ
READ,Y(I,J),Y(I+1,J),Y(I+2,J),Y(I+3,J)
8 READ,YER(I,J),YER(I+1,J),YER(I+2,J),YER(I+3,J)
READ,G
G1=0.0
READ,OPER,INSTR
READ,RUN,TEMP,WAVEL
NUM=26
PUNCH,ZAAAA,NUM,JJ,FEEDP
PUNCH,JC
N=JC
JC=0
PUNCH,K,L,M
DO 9 J=1,JJ
9 PUNCH,DEVF(J),RLM(J),WL(J),WU(J)
KQ=KA+2
IF(KQ-8)10,10,11
11 KQ=KQ-8
MK=2
IF(KQ-8)12,12,13
13 KQ=KQ-8
MK=3
IF(KQ-8)12,12,1
10 MK=1
12 DO 14 J=1,JJ
DO 15 I=1,JI
YY(I,J)=Y(I,J)
15 CONTINUE
IF(MK-3)30,20,1
20 GO TO (14,21,22,23,24,25,26,27),KQ
27 DO 28 I=KD,KE
28 Y(I,J)=0.0
```

```
21 DO 29 I=KB,KC
29 YY(I,J)=0.0
GO TO 14
26 YY(KF,J)=0.0
25 Y(KE,J)=0.0
24 YY(KD,J)=0.0
23 Y(KC,J)=0.0
22 YY(KB,J)=0.0
GO TO 14
30 GO TO (31,32,33,34,35,36,37,38),KQ
38 DO 39 I=KD,KE
39 Y(I,J)=0.0
32 DO 40 I=KB,KC
40 Y(I,J)=0.0
GO TO 31
37 Y(KF,J)=0.0
36 Y(KE,J)=0.0
35 Y(KD,J)=0.0
34 Y(KC,J)=0.0
33 Y(KB,J)=0.0
31 IF(MK-2)14,41,1
41 DO 16 I=1,JI
16 YY(I,J)=Y(I,J)
14 CONTINUE
DO 48 I=1,JI
IF(YY(I,1))44,45,44
44 G1=G1+1.0
GO TO 48
45 DO 42 J=1,JJ
YER(I,J)=0.0
DEV(I,J)=0.0
YY(I,J)=0.0
42 Y(I,J)=0.0
48 CONTINUE
DO 47 I=1,JI
AA=Y(I,1)
BB=YY(I,1)
CC=YER(I,1)
JB=0
DO 49 J=2,JJ
JB=JB+1
YER(I,JB)=YER(I,J)
Y(I,JB)=Y(I,J)
49 YY(I,JB)=YY(I,J)
Y(I,JJ)=AA
YY(I,JJ)=BB
YER(I,JJ)=CC
47 CONTINUE
50 JC=JC+1
NNN=1
51 DO 52 J=1,JJ
YM(J)=-10000000.0
YN(J)=10000000.0
999 FUNY(J)=1.0
DO 53 I=1,JI
Y(I,J)=Y(I,J)*FUNY(J)
IF(Y(I,J))54,53,54
54 IF(YM(J)-Y(I,J))55,56,56
55 YM(J)=Y(I,J)
56 IF(YN(J)-Y(I,J))53,53,57
57 YN(J)=Y(I,J)
53 CONTINUE
```

```
IF(YN(J))6666,8892,8893
8892 YA(J)=-YM(J)/10.0
GO TO 8891
8893 YA(J)=-YN(J)/10.0
GO TO 8891
6666 YA(J)=2.0*YN(J)
8891 AA=YM(J)-YA(J)
BB=YN(J)-YA(J)
AA=SQR(AA*AA)
BB=SQR(BB*BB)
IF(AA-BB)58,60,59
60 IF(AA)61,61,59
61 CODE=88888888.0
62 PRINT,CODE,WAVEL,RUN
PUNCH,CODE
PUNCH,OPER,INSTR
PUNCH,RUN,TEMP,WAVEL
GO TO 1
58 YB(J)=BB
GO TO 63
59 YB(J)=AA
63 DO 52 I=1,JI
IF(Y(I,J))64,52,64
64 Y(I,J)=Y(I,J)-YA(J)
IF(Y(I,J))65,66,65
66 Y(I,J)=(YN(J)-YA(J))/(10.0**6.0)
65 Y(I,J)=Y(I,J)/YB(J)
52 CONTINUE
JR=JJ+1
DO 46 J=1,JR
DO 46 I=1,JR
46 A(I,J)=0.0
DO 67 J=1,JJ
DO 67 JB=1,JJ
DO 67 I=1,JI
IF(Y(I,J))68,67,68
68 IF(JB-1)1,70,69
69 JP=JB-1
A(JB,J)=A(JB,J)+Y(I,J)*Y(I,JP)
GO TO 67
70 A(JB,J)=A(JB,J)+Y(I,J)
67 CONTINUE
G2=0.0
YAA=0.0
DO 71 J=1,JJ
71 A(J,JR)=A(J,JJ)
DO 72 I=1,JI
IF(Y(I,1))73,72,73
73 G2=G2+1.0
72 CONTINUE
A(1,JJ)=G2
G9=JJ+2
IF(G2-G9)74,75,75
74 CODE=99999999.0
GO TO 62
75 DO 76 J=2,JJ
JB=J-1
76 A(J,JJ)=A(1,JB)
DO 77 J=1,JR
DO 77 I=1,JJ
AA=SQR(A(I,J)*A(I,J))
IF(YAA-AA)78,77,77
```

```
78 YAA=AA
77 CONTINUE
DO 79 J=1,JR
DO 79 I=1,JJ
79 A(I,J)=A(I,J)/YAA
DO 80 J=1,JR
DO 80 I=1,JJ
IF(J-1)80,80,82
82 IF(J-1)83,83,84
83 JA=J-1
GO TO 85
84 JA=I-1
85 SET=0.0
SUM=0.0
IF(JA)86,86,87
87 DO 88 JK=1,JA
88 SUM=SUM+A(I,JK)*A(JK,J)
86 SET=A(I,J)-SUM
IF(J-1)89,89,90
89 A(I,J)=SET
GO TO 80
90 SOB=A(I,I)
IF(SOB)94,8889,94
8889 SOB=10.0**(-18.0)
94 A(I,J)=SET/SOB
80 CONTINUE
DO 81 I=1,JJ
JAN=JR-I
SUM2=0.0
IA=I-1
IF(IA)81,81,91
91 DO 93 JK=1,IA
JOB=JR-JK
93 SUM2=SUM2+A(JAN,JOB)*SL(JOB)
81 SL(JAN)=A(JAN,JR)-SUM2
DO 95 I=1,JI
DO 95 J=1,JJ
IF(Y(I,1))96,95,96
96 Y(I,J)=YB(J)*Y(I,J)
Y(I,J)=Y(I,J)+YA(J)
Y(I,J)=Y(I,J)/FUNY(J)
95 CONTINUE
SL(JJ)=SL(JJ)*YB(JJ)
AXYZ=0.0
JK=JJ-1
DO 205 J=1,JK
SL(J)=SL(J)*YB(JJ)/YB(J)
205 AXYZ=AXYZ+SL(J)*YA(J)
SL(JJ)=SL(JJ)-AXYZ+YA(JJ)
DO 206 J=1,JJ
1110 FUSL(J)=1.0
206 SL(J)=SL(J)*FUSL(J)
G3=G2-1.0
IF(N-JC)123,124,124
124 DO 8894 J=1,JJ
SQRMS(J)=0.0
DO 8894 I=1,JI
8894 DEV(I,J)=0.0
JK=JJ-1
DO 97 I=1,JI
RR=0.0
IF(YY(I,1))99,97,99
```

```
99 DO 98 J=1,JJ
IF(JJ-J)1,101,100
100 RR=RR+SL(J)*YY(I,J)
98 CONTINUE
101 QQ=RR+SL(JJ)
DEV(I,JJ)=YY(I,JJ)-QQ
DO 102 JP=1,JK
IF(SL(JP))103,104,103
104 DEV(I,JP)=0.0
GO TO 102
103 DEV(I,JP)=YY(I,JP)-(YY(I,JJ)-QQ+SL(JP)*YY(I,JP))/SL(JP)
102 CONTINUE
97 CONTINUE
DO 105 J=1,JJ
DO 105 I=1,JI
105 SQRMS(J)=SQRMS(J)+DEV(I,J)*DEV(I,J)
DO 8895 J=1,JJ
8895 SQRMS(J)=SQR(SQRMS(J)/G3)
123 IF(JC-1)1,107,122
107 PUNCH,JC,G,G1,G2
IF(N-JC)119,109,109
109 IF(SENSE SWITCH 1 )110,142
110 DO 111 J=1,JJ
111 PUNCH,SL(J),SQRMS(J)
142 IF(N-JC)1,118,112
112 IF(SENSE SWITCH 2)113,115
113 DO 114 I=1,JI,4
PUNCH,YY(I,JJ),YY(I+1,JJ),YY(I+2,JJ),YY(I+3,JJ)
114 PUNCH,Y(I,JJ),Y(I+1,JJ),Y(I+2,JJ),Y(I+3,JJ)
IF(N-JC)1,119,50
115 IF(SENSE SWITCH 3)116,50
116 DO 117 I=1,JI,4
DO 117 J=1,JJ
PUNCH,YY(I,J),YY(I+1,J),YY(I+2,J),YY(I+3,J)
PUNCH,Y(I,J),Y(I+1,J),Y(I+2,J),Y(I+3,J)
PUNCH,YER(I,J),YER(I+1,J),YER(I+2,J),YER(I+3,J)
117 PUNCH,DEV(I,J),DEV(I+1,J),DEV(I+2,J),DEV(I+3,J)
IF(N-JC)1,119,50
118 IF(G1-G2)9002,119,9002
9002 IF(SENSE SWITCH 4)116,113
120 DO 121 J=1,JJ
121 PUNCH,SL(J),DEVSL(J),SQRMS(J)
PUNCH,OPER,INSTR
PUNCH,RUN,TEMP,WAVEL
GO TO 1
122 IF(N-JC)107,9999,9999
9999 IF(NNN-IJ)125,107,1
125 DO 126 I=1,JI
JRK=0
DO 126 J=1,JJ
IF(YY(I,1))127,130,127
127 AA=SQR(YER(I,J)*YER(I,J))
BB=SQR(DEV(I,J)*DEV(I,J))
IF(AA-BB)129,128,128
129 IF(NNN-1)1,130,132
130 Y(I,J)=0.0
DEV(I,J)=0.0
GO TO 126
128 IF(NNN-1)1,126,133
131 JRK=JRK+1
IF(JRK-JJ)126,43,1
43 DO 9001 JP=1,JJ
```

```
9001 Y(I,JP)=YY(I,JP)
GO TO 126
132 IF(NNN-4)126,130,126
133 IF(NNN-4)131,126,131
126 CONTINUE
NNN=NNN+1
GO TO 51
119 DO 134 J=1,JJ
IF(N-JC)136,135,1
135 DEVSL(J)=SL(J)
GO TO 137
136 AAA=DEVSL(J)
DEVSL(J)=SL(J)
SL(J)=AAA
GO TO 134
137 DO 134 I=1,JI
IF(Y(I,J))138,134,138
138 Y(I,JJ)=0.0
IF(JJ-J)1,139,140
140 JK=JJ-1
DO 141 JQ=1,JK
141 Y(I,JJ)=Y(I,JJ)+SL(JQ)*YER(I,JQ)
139 YER(I,JJ)=SQR(YER(I,JJ)*YER(I,JJ))
Y(I,JJ)=-SQR(Y(I,JJ)*Y(I,JJ))
Y(I,JJ)=YER(I,JJ)-Y(I,JJ)
134 CONTINUE
IF(N-JC)120,50,1
END
```

ALGOL 60 FOR PROGRAM NUMBER 26

```
PROCEDURE  ZAAAA(ji,ij); ARRAY y,yy,yer,dev[1:jq,1:jd],a[1:jr,1:jr], devf,
rLm,wL,wu,ym,yn,ya,sL,yb,sqrms,devsL,fusL,funy[1:jd]; INTEGER ji,ij;
SWITCH  sw1:=x20,x5,x10,x9,x8,x7,x6,x4; SWITCH  sw2:=x19,x13,x18,x17,x16,x15,
x14,x12;
COMMENT: SELF-JUDGMENT PROGRAMS WITH VARIABLE DIMENSIONS;
    BEGIN INTEGER i,ia,j,jj,jb,jc,ja,jr,jp,jk,jan,job,jrk,jq,ka,kb,kc,kd,ke,kf,kq,
    k,L,m,mk,npr,num,n,num,feedp,run,oper,instr,g,g1,g2,g3,g9,code;
    REAL aa,aaa,axyz,bb,cc,qq,rr,run,set,sob,sum,sum2,temp,waveL,yaa;
        READ feedp;
        FOR i:=1 STEP 1 UNTIL ji DO
        FOR j:=1 STEP 1 UNTIL jj DO
        y[i,j]:=yy[i,j]:=yer[i,j]:=dev[i,j]:=0;
        npr:=26;
        IF npr=300 THEN GO TO X53
        ELSE IF npr>300 THEN npr:=npr−300;
        IF npr>26 THEN GO TO X53
        ELSE IF npr=26 THEN
        BEGIN
            READ ka,kb,kc,kd,ke,kf;
            READ jj; GO TO X1 END;
        jj:=npr+1; READ ka,kb,kc,kd;
X1:     READ jc; READ k,L,m;
        FOR j:=1 STEP 1 UNTIL jj DO READ devf[j],rLm[j],wL[j],wu[j];
        FOR i:=1 STEP 1 UNTIL ji DO
        FOR j:=1 STEP 1 UNTIL jj DO
        BEGIN
            READ y[i,j]; READ yer[i,j]
        END;
        READ g; g1:=0;
        READ oper,instr;
        READ run,temp,waveL; num:=26;
        PUNCH num,jj,feedp;
        PUNCH jc; n:=jc; jc:=0;
        PUNCH k,l,m;
        FOR j:=1 STEP 1 UNTIL jj DO PUNCH devf[j],rLm[j],wL[j],wu[j];
        kq:=ka+2;
        IF kq≤ 8 THEN GO TO X2;
        kq:=kq−8; mk:=2;
        IF kq≤8 THEN GO TO X3;
        mk:=3; kq:=kq− 8;
        IF kq>8 THEN GO TO X53;
X2:     mk:=1;
X3:     FOR j:=1 STEP 1 UNTIL jj DO
        BEGIN
            FOR i:=1 STEP 1 UNTIL ji DO yy[i,j]:=y[i,j];
            IF mk> 3 THEN GO TO X53
            ELSE IF mk<3 THEN GO TO X11;
            GO TO sw1[kq];
X4:         FOR i:=kd STEP 1 UNTIL ke DO y[i,j]:=0;
X5:         FOR i:=kb STEP 1 UNTIL kc DO yy[i,j]:=0;
            GO TO X14;
X6:         yy[kf,j]:=0;
X7:         y[ke,j]:=0;
```

```
X8:      yy[kd,j]:=0;
X9:      y[kc,j]:=0;
X10:     yy[kb,j]:=0; GO TO X20;
X11:     GO TO sw2[kq];
X12:     FOR i:=kd STEP 1 UNTIL ke DO y[i,j]:=0;
X13:     FOR i:=kb STEP 1 UNTIL kc DO y[i,j]:=0;
         GO TO X19;
X14:     y[kf,j]:=0;
X15:     y[ke,j]:=0;
X16:     y[kd,j]:=0;
X17:     y[kc,j]:=0;
X18:     y[kb,j]:=0;
X19:     IF mk>2 THEN GO TO X53
         ELSE IF mk=2 THEN
         FOR i:=1 STEP 1 UNTIL ji DO yy[i,j]:=y[i,j]
X20:     END
         FOR i:=1 STEP 1 UNTIL ji DO
         BEGIN
         IF yy[i,1]≠0 THEN
         BEGIN
         g1:=g1+1; GO TO X2X END;
         FOR j:=1 STEP 1 UNTIL jj DO
         yer[i,j]:=dev[i,j]:=yy[i,j[:=y[i,j]:=0
X2X:     END;
         FOR i:=1 STEP 1 UNTIL ji DO
         BEGIN
         aa:=y[i,1]; bb:=yy[i,1]; cc:=yer[i,1]; jb:=0;
         FOR j:=2 STEP 1 UNTIL jj DO
         BEGIN
         jb:=jb+1; yer[i,jb]:=yer[i,j];
         y[i,jb]:=y[i,j]; yy[i,jb]:=y[i,j]
         END;
         y[i,jj]:=aa; yy[i,jj]:=bb;
         yer[i,jj]:=cc
         END;
X21:     jc:=jc+1; nnn:=1;
X22:     FOR j:=1 STEP 1 UNTIL jj DO
         BEGIN
         ym[j]:=-10000000; yn[j]:=10000000; funy[j]:=1;
         FOR i:=1 STEP 1 UNTIL ji DO
         BEGIN
         y[i,j]:=y[i,j]Xfuny[j];
         IF y[i,j]=0 THEN GO TO X23;
         IF ym[j]<y[i,j] THEN ym[j]:=y[i,j];
         IF yn[j]>y[i,j] THEN yn[j]:=y[i,j]
X23:     END;
         IF yn[j]=0 THEN
         BEGIN
         ya[j]:=-ym[j]/10; GO TO X24END
         ELSE IF yn[j]>0 THEN
         BEGIN
         ya[j]:=-yn[j]/10; GO TO X24END;
         ya[j]:=2Xyn[j];
```

```
X24:    aa:=ym[j]-ya[j]; bb:=yn[j]-ya[j];
        aa:=abs(aa); bb:=abs(bb);
        IF aa<bb THEN GO TO X26
        ELSE IF aa>bbV(aa=bbVaa>0) THEN GO TO X27;
        code:=88888888;
X25:    PUNCH code; PUNCH oper,instr;
        PUNCH run,temp,waveL; GO TO X53;
X26:    yb[j]:=bb; GO TO X28;
X27:    yb[j]:=aa;
X28:    FOR i:=1 STEP 1 UNTIL ji DO
        IF y[i,j]≠0 THEN
        BEGIN
            y[i,j]:=y[i,j]-ya[j];
            IF y[i,j]=0 THEN y[i,j]:=(yn[j]-ya[j])/₁₀6;
            y[i,j]:=y[i,j]/yb[j]END END
        END;
        jr:=jj+1;
        FOR j:=1 STEP 1 UNTIL jr DO
        FOR i:=1 STEP 1 UNTIL jr DO a[i,j]:=0;
        FOR j:=1 STEP 1 UNTIL jj DO
        FOR jb:=1 STEP 1 UNTIL jj DO
        FOR i:=1 STEP 1 UNTIL ji DO
        BEGIN
            IF y[i,j]=0 THEN GO TO X29;
            IF jb<1 THEN GO TO X53
            ELSE IF jb>1 THEN
            BEGIN
                jp:=jb-1; a[jb,j]:=a[jb,j]+y[i,j]Xy[i,jp];
                GO TO X29END;
            a[jb,j]:=a[jb,j]+y[j,j]
X29:    END,
        g2:=yaa:=0
        FOR j:=1 STEP 1 UNTIL jj DO a[j,jr]:=a[j,jj];
        FOR i:=1 STEP 1 UNTIL ji DO
        IF y[i,1]≠0 THEN g2:=g2+1;
        a[1,jj]:=g2; g9:=jj+2;
        IF g2<g9 THEN
        BEGIN
            code:=99999999; GO TO X25END;
        FOR j:=2 STEP 1 UNTIL jj DO
        BEGIN
            jb:=j-1; a[j,jj]:=a[1,jb]
        END;
        FOR j:=1 STEP 1 UNTIL jr DO
        FOR i:=1 STEP 1 UNTIL jj DO
        BEGIN
            aa:=abs(a[i,j]);
            IF yaa<aa THEN yaa:=aa
        END;
        FOR j:=1 STEP 1 UNTIL jr DO
        FOR i:=1 STEP 1 UNTIL jj DO a[i,j]:=a[i,j]/yaa;
        FOR j:=1 STEP 1 UNTIL jr DO
        FOR i:=1 STEP 1 UNTIL jj DO
```

```
        BEGIN
          IF j≤1 THEN GO TO X31;
          IF j≤i THEN
          BEGIN
            ja:=j–1; GO TO X30END;
          ja:=i–1;
X30:      set:=sum:=0;
          IF ja>0 THEN
          FOR jk:=1 STEP 1 UNTIL ja DO sum:=sum+a[i,k]Xa[jk,j];
          set:=a[i,j]-sum;
          IF j≤i THEN
          BEGIN
            a[i,j]:=set; GO TO X31END;
          sob:=a[i,i];
          IF sob=0 THEN sob:=₁₀(–18);
          a[i,j]:=set/sob
X31:    END;
        FOR i:=1 STEP 1 UNTIL jj DO
        BEGIN
          jan:=jr–i; sum2:=0; ia:=i–1;
          IF ai>0 THEN
          FOR jk:=1 STEP 1 UNTIL ia DO
          BEGIN
            job:=jr–jk;
            sum2:=sum2+a[jan,job]XsL[job]
          END;
          sL[jan]:=a[jan,jr]–sum2
        END;
        FOR i:=1 STEP 1 UNTIL ji DO
        FOR j:=1 STEP 1 UNTIL jj DO
        IF y[i,1]≠0 THEN y[i,j]:=(yb[j]Xy[i,j]+ya[j])/funy[j];
        sL[jj]:=sL[jj]Xyb[jj]; axyz:=0; jk:=jj–1;
        FOR j:=1 STEP 1 UNTIL jk DO
        BEGIN
          sL[j]:=sL[j]Xyb[jj]/yb[j];
          axyz:=axyz+sL[j]Xya[j]
        END;
        sL[jj]:=sL[jj]–axyz+ya[jj];
        FOR j:=1 STEP 1 UNTIL jj DO
        BEGIN
          fusL[j]:=1; sL[j]:=sL[j]XfusL[j]
        END;
        g3:=g2–1;
        IF n<jc THEN GO TO X34;
        FOR j:=1 STEP 1 UNTIL jj DO
        FOR i:=1 STEP 1 UNTIL ji DO sqrms[j]:=dev[i,j]:=0;
        jk:=jj–1;
        FOR i:=1 STEP 1 UNTIL ji DO
        BEGIN
          rr:=0;
          IF yy[i,1]=0 THEN GO TO X33;
          FOR j:=1 STEP 1 UNTIL jj DO
```

```
        BEGIN
          IF jj<j THEN GO TO X53
          ELSE IF jj=j THEN GO TO X32;
          rr:=rr+sL[j]Xyy[i,j]
        END;
X32:    qq:=rr+sL[jj]; dev[i,jj]:=yy[i,jj]-qq;
        FOR jp:=1 STEP 1 UNTIL jk DO
        BEGIN
          IF sL[jp]=0 THEN
          BEGIN
            dev[i]:=0; GO TO X33END
          dev[i,jp]:=yy[i,jp]-(yy[i,jp]-qq+sL[jp]Xyy[i,jp])/sL[jp]
X33:    END END;
        FOR j:=1 STEP 1 UNTIL jj DO
        FOR i:=1 STEP 1 UNTIL ji DO sqrms[j]:=sqrms[j]+dev[i,j]↑2;
        FOR j:=1 STEP 1 UNTIL jj DO sqrms[j]:=sqrt(sqrms[jj]/g3);
X34:    IF jc<1 THEN GO TO X53
        ELSE IF jc>1 THEN GO TO X42;
X35:    PUNCH jc,g,g1,g2;
        IF n<jc THEN GO TO X49;
        COMMENT: At this point control either proceeds serially or is trans-
        ferred to Label X36 (see Optional External Commands for Program 26);
        FOR j:=1 STEP 1 UNTIL jj DO PUNCH sL[j],sqrms[j];
X36:    IF n<jc THEN GO TO X53
        ELSE IF n=jc THEN GO TO X40;
        COMMENT: At this point control either proceeds serially or is trans-
        ferred to Label X38 (see Optional External Commands for Program 26);
X37:    FOR i:=1 STEP 1 UNTIL ji DO PUNCH yy[i,jj];
        FOR i:=1 STEP 1 UNTIL ji DO PUNCH y[i,jj];
        IF n<jc THEN GO TO X53
        ELSE IF n=jc THEN GO TO X49 ELSE GO TO X21;
X38:    COMMENT: At this point control either proceeds serially or is trans-
        ferred to Label X21 (see Optional External Commands for Program 26);
X39:    FOR i:=1 STEP 1 UNTIL ji DO
        FOR j:=1 STEP 1 UNTIL jj DO
        BEGIN
          PUNCH yy[i,j]; PUNCH y[i,j];
          PUNCH yer[i,j]; PUNCH dev[i,j]
        END;
        IF n<jc THEN GO TO X53
        ELSE IF n=jc THEN GO TO X49 ELSE GO TO X21;
X40:    IF g1=g2 THEN GO TO X49;
        COMMENT: At this point control is either transferred to Label X39 or to
        Label X37 (see Optional External Commands for Program 26);
X41:    FOR j:=1 STEP 1 UNTIL jj DO PUNCH sL[j],devsL[j],sqrms[j];
        PUNCH oper,instr;
        PUNCH run,temp,waveL; GO TO X53;
X42:    IF n<jc∨nnn=ji THEN GO TO X35
        ELSE IF nnn>ji THEN GO TO X53;
        FOR i:=1 STEP 1 UNTIL ji DO
        BEGIN
          jrk:=0;
          FOR j:=1 STEP 1 UNTIL jj DO
```

```
        BEGIN
          IF yy[i,1]=0 THEN GO TO X43;
          aa:=abs(yer[i,j]); bb:=abs(dev[i,j]);
          IF aa≥bb THEN GO TO X44;
          IF nnn<1 THEN GO TO X53
          ELSE IF nnn>1 THEN GO TO X46;
X43:      y[i,j]:=dev[i,j]:=0; GO TO X48;
X44:      IF nnn<1 THEN GO TO X53
          ELSE IF nnn=1 THEN GO TO X48 ELSE GO TO X47;
X45:      jrk:=jrk+1;
          IF jrk>jj THEN GO TO X53
          ELSE IF jrk<jj THEN GO TO X48;
          FOR jp:=1 STEP 1 UNTIL jj DO y[i,jp]:=yy[i,jp];
          GO TO X48;
X46:      IF nnn=4 THEN GO TO X43 ELSE GO TO X48;
X47:      IF nnn≠4 THEN GO TO X45
        END
X48:    END;
        nnn:=nnn+1; GO TO X22;
X49:    FOR j:=1 STEP 1 UNTIL jj DO
        BEGIN
          IF n>jc THEN GO TO X53
          ELSE IF n=jc THEN
          BEGIN
            devsL[j]:=sL[j]; GO TO X50END;
          aaa:=devsL[j]; devsL[j]:=sL[j];
          sL[j]:=aaa; GO TO X52;
X50:      FOR i:=1 STEP 1 UNTIL ji DO
          BEGIN
            IF y[i,j]=0 THEN GO TO X52;
            y[i,jj]:=0;
            IF jj<j THEN GO TO X53
            ELSE IF jj>j THEN
            BEGIN
              jk:=jj-1;
              FOR jq:=1 STEP 1 UNTIL jk DO
                y[i,jj]:=y[i,jj]+sL[jq]Xyer[i,jq]END;
X51:        yer[i,jj]:=abs(yer[i,jj]);
            y[i,jj]:=-abs(y[i,jj]);
            y[i,jj]:=yer[i,jj]-y[i,jj]
          END
X52:    END;
        IF n<jc THEN GO TO X41
        ELSE IF n=jc THEN GO TO X21
X53:END ZAAAA;
    READ ji; ij:=4;
X54:ZAAAA(ji,ij);
    GO TO X54;
```

CHAPTER IV

MATHEMATICAL FRENCH CURVE

The "illustrative diagrams," descriptions, and tables of "selected information" used to describe numerical data in reports of experimental investigations are often of limited value to researchers interested in quantitative aspects of the phenomena. Obviously every "ideal report" should contain a section in which each observation and its reliability are given, but even if publication of such a report were possible it would be unreadable.

In this chapter there is described a method for reducing a set of raw data to equations whose limits of reliability are precisely defined by the *maximum permitted deviations* for each member of the set. These equations and the associated information, which can be given in a single short paragraph, may be used to regenerate the raw data and the associated *maximum permitted deviations*. Here the equations which describe a given set of raw data will be called the *functional form*.

Program 27 (*call word* ABAAA) can be used to compute this *functional form* for any set of raw data. An almost fully automatic version of this program, which will be described elsewhere,[1] is the mathematical equivalent of the French curve used by draftsmen. Thus the method used to obtain the *functional form* will be called the *mathematical French Curve*. Program 27 has been designed for use with medium storage computers, but it can easily be changed for use with larger or smaller computers. To illustrate the use of the *mathematical French curve*, hereafter designated as MFC, reduction of the raw data collected for two different types of investigation is considered below. Basic to the MFC is the assumption that one of the observables, or measured quantities, can always be expanded in terms of an arbitrarily chosen continuous function of all the other observables for a selected spectrum of raw data. *Thus the collected data alone determine the functional form.*

[1] P. A. D. de Maine, *Mathematical French Curves* (in preparation).

Case I. If there are two observables, or measured variables, O_1 and O_2, the MFC procedure is as follows: (1) Select the arbitrary function, $f(O_2)$; (2) expand the first observable in terms of $f(O_2)$ for a range of O_1 and O_2 values, thus:

$$O_1 = \alpha_0(\Delta\alpha_0) + \alpha_1(\Delta\alpha_1)f(O_2) + \alpha_2(\Delta\alpha_2)(f(O_2))^2 + \cdots \tag{1}$$

for $LL_1 \leq O_1 \leq UL_1$; $LL_2 \leq O_2 \leq UL_2$; G2/G1 given and $f(O_2)$ defined. Here $\Delta\alpha_0, \Delta\alpha_1, \Delta\alpha_2, \cdots$ are the *maximum permitted errors* for the designated expansion coefficients (α_0, α_1, $\alpha_2, \cdots$). LL and UL are the lowest and highest values respectively for the indicated observables used in equation (1). G2 is the number of sets of conjugate data actually used to compute α_0, $\alpha_1, \cdots$ and $\Delta\alpha_0$, $\Delta\alpha_1, \cdots$, whereas G1 is the number of sets of conjugate data remaining after application of the *fail–safe procedure*.

Concise statements like equation (1) can be obtained with programs that have the *self-judgment principle* incorporated. The *functional form* of the raw data can consist of one or more statements, similar to equation (1), for which the ranges of the observables overlap. Values for O_1 and its *maximum permitted deviation* can be generated from equation (1) and its associated information. Guides for selecting the arbitrary function $f(O_2)$ and the procedure for using the MFC are discussed later.

Case II. If three or more observables (O_1, O_2, $O_3, \cdots$) are investigated, the *functional form* of the raw data will consist of one or more statements like equation (2) below.

$$O_1 = \alpha_0(\Delta\alpha_0) + \alpha_1(\Delta\alpha_1)f(O_3, O_2) + \alpha_2(\Delta\alpha_2)(f(O_3, O_2))^2 + \cdots \tag{2}$$

for $LL_1 \leq O_1 \leq UL_1$; $LL_2 \leq O_2 \leq UL_2$; $LL_3 \leq O_3 \leq UL_3$; G2/G1 given and $f(O_3, O_2)$ defined. The significance of the symbols used here is the same as for equation (1).

Values for each observable and the associated *maximum permitted deviations* can be regenerated from equation (2) and its associated information.

Instructions are incorporated in Programs 27 and 327 for selecting 22 different arbitrary functions, and there are also provisions for the easy incorporation of three new functions (see *input commands* for Programs 27 and 327). The *upper* and *lower limits of reliability* for the two variable quantities in the input format, designated by Y(I, JJ) and FR(I), and the *reject–restore commands* determine the ranges for O_1 and O_2 in Case I. In Case II the information entered for FR(I) must be computed separately from values for O_2, O_3, etc. In Programs 27 and 327 the dimensions of equations (1) and (2) are entered in the input format. Some guides for selecting the arbitrary functions and further discussion of the computer procedure are given in the section on Method of Solution.

SPECIAL MODIFICATIONS

In Program 327 (*call word* ABAAS) the *self-judgment principle* is applied only to values of the first variable (Y(I, JJ)). However, if unrealistically large *maximum permitted deviations* for the second variable (FR(I)) are entered in Program 327 the values for $\Delta\alpha_0$, $\Delta\alpha_1$, $\cdots$ will be too large, and this would mean that the researcher will report his data to be more unreliable than it really is. If the slopes for plots of Y(I, JJ) versus FR(I) are small, Program 327 should be used in place of Program 27 to avoid the rejection of good data in the second, third, fourth, etc., dimensions.

Program 327 (*call word* ABAAS) is obtained from Program 27 (*call word* ABAAA) by changing the statements indicated here. The input and output formats are identical for both programs.

ORIGINAL	REPLACEMENTS
Program 27 (Call Word ABAAA)	*Program 327 (Call Word* ABAAS)

1 READ,ABAAA,FEEDP	1 READ,ABAAS,FEEDP
NUM=27	NUM=327
PUNCH,ABAAA,NUM,FEEDP	PUNCH,ABAAS,NUM,FEEDP
JRK=0	IF(YY(I,JJ))127,130,127
DO 126 J=1,JJ	127 AA=SQR(YER(I,JJ)*YER(I,JJ))
IF(YY(I,JJ))127,130,127	BB=SQR(DEV(I,JJ)*DEV(I,JJ))
127 AA=SQR(YER(I,J)YE*R(I,J))	IF(AA−BB)129,128,128
BB=SQR(DEV(I,J)*DEV(I,J))	129 IF(NNN−1)1,130,132
IF(AA−BB)129,128,128	130 DO 9003 J=1,JJ
129 IF(NNN−1)1,130,132	Y(I,J)=0.0
130 Y(I,J)=0.0	9003 DEV(I,J)=0.0
DEV(I,J)=0.0	GO TO 126
GO TO 126	128 IF(NNN−1)1,126,133
128 IF(NNN−1)1,126,133	131 DO 9001 J=1,JJ
131 JRK=JRK+1	9001 Y(I,J)=YY(I,J)
IF(JRK−JJ)126,43,1	GO TO 126
43 DO 9001 JP=1,JJ	
9001 Y(I,JP)=YY(I,JP)	
GO TO 126	

METHOD OF SOLUTION

With Programs 27 and 327 the input commands determine the dimension of the expansion and designate the arbitrary function of the second variable (FR(I)). If there are more than two observables, they must be combined so as to yield two variables and the associated *maximum permitted deviations*. The range of values allowed for the two variables

(Y(I, JJ) and FR(I)) in a particular expansion is defined by the values selected for the two sets of reliability limits (WL(1) and WU(1); WL(2) and WU(2)), which are described in the section on *instrument reliability factors*. The *reject–restore commands* should not be used to define the ranges.

The computer first calculates the values for the arbitrary function from values for FR(I) in the designated range, and then fits these values and the corresponding Y(I, JJ) to the expansion equation ((1) or (2)) whose dimension has been selected in advance. Next the *maximum permitted deviations* for each Y(I, JJ) and FR(I) are used to compute the *error zone* for the expansion equation. The *self-judgment principle* is applied to reject in the normal way sets of conjugate information lying outside the *error zone*. The procedure is then repeated for the programmed number of cycles (JC). In the *error analysis* the accepted sets of conjugate information are used in the usual way to compute the *maximum permitted error* for each expansion coefficient. If the expansion is successful, the operator selects a new range of Y(I, JJ) and FR(I) values and the procedure just described is repeated. If the expansion is unsuccessful, one of the following five changes must be made.

1. The *maximum permitted deviations* for each Y(I, JJ) and FR(I) are too small and should be increased.

2. The dimension of the expansion is too small and should be increased.

3. The arbitrarily selected function for FR(I) must be changed.

4. The ranges of Y(I, JJ) and FR(I) should be increased as there are insufficient sets of conjugate data.

5. There are erroneous data which must be discarded.

If there are fewer than five accepted sets of conjugate data for Program 27 or 327 the computer terminates the calculation, as indicated by *code* = 99999999.0 or 88888888.0 (see Output Format for Programs 27 and 327).

In *self-judgment programs* with the *Crout reduction method* (e.g., Programs 27 and 327) a wrong analysis frequently leads to the rejection of all sets of conjugate data (see Chapter III). However, the presence of the *Crout reduction method* helps to eliminate fault 2 and to reduce the need for change 3 through the choice of a dimension much larger than that normally required. Unlike Cramer's method the Crout reduction method can be used to compute zero slopes.

Here some guides for selection of the functions are given.

Viscosity or Conductance Data

For the viscosity coefficient or the conductance (Y(I, JJ)) of a solution with solute concentration FR(I), at a fixed temperature, a single six-dimension expansion with the arbitrary function equal to $(FR(I))^{1/2}$ is usually sufficient, even for a 10,000-fold range of concentrations.

If there are two or more solutes which determine the values of $Y(I, JJ)$, the arbitrary function can be set equal to the square root of their sum or product.

Absorbancies of Solutions

At a fixed wavelength and temperature the absorbancies ($Y(I, JJ)$) of solutions with a single solute whose concentration is $FR(I)$ are described by a single two-, three-, or four-dimension expansion with the arbitrary function equal to $FR(I)$. With two solutes the function chosen equals either the ratio or product of their concentrations.

If the temperature and solution composition are fixed, and the wavelength ($FR(I)$) is varied, the most useful functions are $FR(I)^{QQ1}$, $\exp(QQ1 \cdot FR(I))$, and $(FR(I))^{QQ1} \exp(QQ2 \cdot FR(I))$, with $QQ1$ and $QQ2$ nonzero rational numbers.

pH of Solutions

At a constant temperature the pH ($Y(I, JJ)$) of solutions with varied solute concentrations ($FR(I)$) are best expanded in terms of the log (solute concentration) or in terms of log (product of solute concentrations) if more than one solute is present.

Time or Temperature Variables

In experiments where a kinetic or thermodynamic parameter ($Y(I, JJ)$) varies with the time or temperature, ($FR(I)$), $Y(I, JJ)$ can be expanded in terms of $\exp(QQ1 \cdot FR(I))$ or $FR(I)^{QQ1}$.

COMPUTER PROCEDURE OF SOLUTION

If Program 27 or 327 is used to compute the *functional form* of raw data, the mathematical statements of equations (1) and (2) are written thus:

$$Y(I, JJ) = SL(JJ)(DEVSL(JJ)) + SL(1)(DEVSL(1))F(FR(I)) + \cdots \quad (3)$$

for $WL(1) \leq Y(I, JJ) \leq WU(1)$, $WL(2) \leq FR(I) \leq WU(2)$, $G2/G1$ given, and $F(FR(I))$ defined by the input commands L and M. $F(FR(I))$ is the arbitrarily selected function of the second variable ($FR(I)$). WL and WU are the lower and upper *limits of reliability* for the designated variables. DEVSL is the *maximum permitted error* for the expansion coefficient (SL). G1 is the number of sets of conjugate data remaining after application of the *fail–safe procedure*. G2 is the number of sets used to calculate the expansion coefficients and the associated *maximum permitted errors*.

The procedure for obtaining the information for equation (3) is as follows:

1. The *fail–safe procedure* is applied twice to reject values of $Y(I, JJ)$ and $FR(I)$ lying outside the selected ranges.

2. Accepted values of $FR(I)$ are used to compute $F(FR(I))$. The *instrument reliability factors* are used to calculate the *maximum permitted deviation* for each $Y(I, JJ)$ and each $F(FR(I))$. Next the ordinates for equation (3), designated by $Y(I, JJ)$, $Y(I, 1), \cdots Y(I, J - 1)$, are calculated and the *reject–restore commands* are executed.

3. All ordinate values are normalized by a special three-step procedure described in Chapter III. The modified *Crout reduction method* is then used to solve equation (3) for the expansion coefficients, [$SL(JJ)$, $SL(1)$, etc.]. Next, the coefficients are stored in memory ($SLX(J) = SL(J)$). The coefficient which has the lowest absolute value ($SL(N)$), and its associated ordinate ($Y(I, N)$), are determined. All ordinates are divided by $Y(I, N)$; then $Y(I, N)$ is replaced by $1.0/Y(I, N)$ and a new set of coefficients, $SL(J)$, is computed. $SLX(JJ)$ is set equal to $SL(N)$, each $SL(J)$ is set equal to the corresponding $SLX(J)$, and the ordinates are transformed to their original forms. The procedure just described is omitted if N is equal to JJ. This double-slope method is used to compute the expansion coefficients as it has been found (see Volume I) that the slopes are insensitive and the intercept is very sensitive to the normal fluctuations in experimental data.

4. If JC cycles are programmed, the *self-judgment principle* is applied in the normal way during the second to JCth cycles. Sets of conjugate information outside the *error zone* for equation (3) are rejected, and those inside the *error zone* are restored. Data rejected in step (1) are not considered.

5. After the JC cycle the *error analysis* is made with the sets of conjugate information (designated G2) accepted in the JC cycle.

If there are *fewer than five* accepted sets of conjugate information when the *self-judgment principle* is applied, the calculation will be terminated and *code* = 99999999.0 will be printed and punched. If all sets of conjugate information are rejected, *code* = 88888888.0.

INSTRUMENT RELIABILITY FACTORS

Two sets of *instrument reliability factors* must be entered in the input information for Program 27 or 327. $RLM(1)$, $WL(1)$, $WU(1)$, and $DEVF(1)$ or $DEV1(I)$ are associated exclusively with $Y(I, JJ)$. $RLM(2)$, $WL(2)$, $WU(2)$, and $DEVF(2)$ or $DEV2(I)$ refer to $FR(I)$.

The highest ($WU(1)$ or $WU(2)$) and lowest ($WL(1)$ or $WL(2)$) *limits of reliability* define the range of values to be used in the expansion for the designated variable.

RLM(1) and RLM(2) are estimated values of the *measured limits of reliability* (or *reproducibility*) for the designated variable. Although these values are not used in the actual calculations they must be entered.

The *maximum permitted deviation* for each value of each variable can be entered as a fixed fraction (DEVF(1), DEVF(2)) or in the same units (DEV1(I), DEV2(I)). The form used is determined by the value for K (see *input commands* for Programs 27 and 327, later in this chapter).

FAIL–SAFE PROCEDURE

The two applications of the *fail–safe procedure* serve to eliminate values of Y(I, JJ) and FR(I) outside the selected ranges, as described in the section on Computer Procedure of Solution. In both volume I and this volume it is assumed that a zero value for any observable (or variable) means that no measurement was taken. Thus in the selected ranges for Y(I, JJ) and FR(I) only those conjugate pairs for which Y(I, JJ) and FR(I) are nonzero will be used to solve equation (3). Infinities are avoided if WL(1) and WL(2) are not set equal to zero.

STATISTICAL BIAS

The fully automatic three-step normalization procedure described in Chapter III is incorporated in both Programs 27 and 327. Even with this procedure the *Crout reduction method* is very sensitive. Rejection of a good set of conjugate data with retention of even a single wrong set of conjugate data invariably leads to the rejection of all sets of conjugate data in a subsequent application of the *self-judgment principle*. This means that, in most cases where there are sets of conjugate data in gross error or where the arbitrary function is unsuitable or where the *maximum permitted deviations* are unrealistically low, the calculation will be terminated in the second cycle and *code* = 88888888.0 will be printed and punched. These three faults can be detected easily in autoplots of the input information for Programs 27 and 327. With JI equal to 20 the input information can be processed with *autoplotter Program 502* (*call word* BEEEE) as described in Chapter I.

Special weighting functions and the companion correction function can be introduced into Programs 27 and 327 by replacing the statements with numbers beginning at 999 and 1110 respectively.

INPUT COMMANDS FOR PROGRAMS 27 AND 327

Commands Executed During Compilation

JQ, JD, and JR which appear in the *dimension* statements, together with the compiler determine the storage capacity which is required for the machine language program.

JQ—The maximum number of sets of conjugate data that can be processed. It is conveniently chosen as a multiple of 4 (see JI).

JD—The maximum dimension equation that can be processed.

JR—Equal to or greater than (JD + 1).

IJ—Appears in the second FORTRAN statement for Program 27. It determines the number of times the reject and restore parts of the *self-judgment principle* are applied in each programmed cycle. IJ has been set equal to 4 in all *self-judgment programs*, and this value should not be altered without a thorough consideration of the entire program.

Commands Executed after Compilation

DIMENSION COMMANDS

JI—is the number of sets of conjugate data which are to be processed for each value of M6. JI *must be a multiple of 4 and it cannot exceed* JQ. If, for example, 10 sets are to be processed, JI = 12 and two zero sets are entered.

JJ—the dimension for the expansion of Y(I, JJ) against the arbitrary function of FR(I). JJ *cannot exceed* JD.

OPERATIONAL COMMANDS

In this section the commands: KA, JC, M6, K, L, and M will be discussed. L and M together define the arbitrary function of the second variable (FR(I)) which will be used in the expansion equation.

JC—the number of cycles which must be completed before the *error analysis*. In the second through the JCth cycles the *self-judgment principle* is applied. It is not applied in the first cycle and in the *error analysis* (or JC + 1) cycle.

The values entered for KA, KB, KC, KD, KE, and KF determine which sets of conjugate data are to be ignored or killed. "Ignore (KB–KC)" means that the KBth to KCth sets are not used during the first cycle but that they are reviewed for compatibility in the second cycle and restored if they are compatible. "Kill (KB, KC)" means that the KBth and KCth sets are to be removed from the memory.

REJECT–RESTORE COMMANDS

KA	Command	KA	Command
−1	No sets are ignored or killed	11	Kill(KB,KC,KD)
0	Ignore (KB−KC)	12	Kill(KB,KC,KD,KE)
1	Ignore(KB)	13	Kill(KB,KC,KD,KE,KF)
2	Ignore(KB,KC)	14	Kill(KB–KC; KD–KE)
3	Ignore(KB,KC,KD)	15	No sets are ignored or killed
4	Ignore(KB,KC,KD,KE)	16	Kill(KB–KC)
5	Ignore(KB,KC,KD,KE,KF)	17	Kill(KB)
6	Ignore(KB–KC; KD–KE)	18	Kill(KB); ignore (KC)
7	No sets are ignored or killed	19	Kill(KB,KD); ignore(KC)
8	Kill(KB–KC)	20	Kill(KB,KD); ignore(KC,KE)
9	Kill(KB)	21	Kill(KB,KD,KF); ignore(KC,KE)
10	Kill(KB,KC)	22	Kill(KB–KC); ignore(KD–KE)

The *reject–restore commands* should not be used to define the ranges for the two variables but should be reserved for their proper role within the ranges defined by the *lower* and *upper reliability limits* (see *instrument reliability factors*).

K—defines the forms in which the *maximum permitted deviations* for the two variables are entered.

$$K = 1 \qquad DEVF(1); DEVF(2)$$
$$K = 2 \qquad DEVF(1); DEV2(I)$$
$$K = 3 \qquad DEV1(I); DEVF(2)$$
$$K = 4 \qquad DEV1(I); DEV2(I)$$

M6—the number of wavelengths for which data are processed. If values other than spectral data are being processed, M6 is set equal to 1.

L and M values together determine the arbitrary function of FR(I) that is used in the expansion of the first variable, Y(I, JJ). For M = 23, 24, and 25, the statements numbered 322, 323, and 49 and the companion statements can be replaced by any function of the input information. For L = 1 to 4 the values for QQ1 and QQ2 are fixed by the computer. If $L \geq 5$, values for QQ1 and QQ2 must be entered.

L   *Commands**

L = 1	QQ1 = 1.0 = QQ2	L = 3	QQ1 = 0.50; QQ2 = 1.0
L = 2	QQ1 = 0.75; QQ2 = 1.0	L = 4	QQ1 = 0.25; QQ2 = 1.0

---

* For $L \geq 5$ any nonzero rational numbers can be entered for QQ1 and QQ2.

M   *Commands**

M	Selected Arbitrary Function	M	Selected Arbitrary Function
1	x^{mn}	15	$e^{mx} \cdot \arctan(nx)$
2	e^{mnx}	16	$\ln(mx) \cdot \sin(nx)$
3	$(\ln(mx))^n$	17	$\ln(mx) \cdot \cos(nx)$
4	$(\sin(mx))^n$	18	$\ln(mx) \cdot \arctan(nx)$
5	$(\cos(mx))^n$	19	$\sin(mx) \cdot \cos(nx)$
6	$(\arctan(mx))^n$	20	$\sin(mx) \cdot \arctan(nx)$
7	$x^m \cdot e^{nx}$	21	$\cos(mx) \cdot \arctan(nx)$
8	$x^m \cdot \ln(nx)$	22	$e^{m(x-n)^2}$
9	$x^m \cdot \sin(nx)$	23	Provided for inclusion of new
10	$x^m \cdot \cos(nx)$	24	arbitrary functions
11	$x^m \cdot \arctan(nx)$	25	
12	$e^{mx} \cdot \ln(nx)$		
13	$e^{mx} \cdot \sin(nx)$		
14	$e^{mx} \cdot \cos(nx)$		

---

* In this section x, m, and n refer to FR(I), QQ1, and QQ2 respectively. $\ln(x)$ is the natural logarithm of x.

INPUT FORMAT FOR PROGRAMS 27 AND 327

Here READ, QQ1, QQ2 (if $L \geq 5$) means that values for QQ1 and QQ2 are entered only if $L \geq 5$.

STATEMENT	COMMENT
READ,JI	The number of sets of conjugate data as a multiple of 4

> *Note:* JI is entered only with the first deck of input information. If subsequent decks have different JI values, the computer memory must be zeroed before each deck is read. Input information for Programs 27 and 327 can be processed with *autoplotter Program* 502 (*call word* BEEEE) only if $JI = 20$, and if the first card is removed.

STATEMENT	COMMENT
READ,ABAAA or ABAAS,FEEDP	Program number; source
READ,KA,KB,KC,KD,KE,KF	*Reject–restore commands*
READ,JJ	The dimension of the expansion
READ,JC	Cycle command
READ,M6	The number of wavelengths for which data are processed
READ,K,L,M	*Input commands*
READ,RLM(1),WL(1),WU(1) ⎱	*Instrument reliability factors*
READ,RLM(2),WL(2),WU(2) ⎰	for Y(I,JJ) and FR(I)
READ,DEVF(1)	*Maximum permitted deviations*
or	for Y(I,JJ) and FR(I). The
READ,DEV1(I),DEV1(I+1),DEV1(I+2),DEV1(I+3)	value entered for K determines the form
READ,DEVF(2)	
or	
READ,DEV2(I),DEV2(I+1),DEV2(I+2),DEV2(I+3)	
READ,Y(I,JJ),Y(I+1,JJ),Y(I+2,JJ),Y(I+3,JJ)	The first variable
READ,QQ1,QQ2 (if $L \geq 5$)	See Input Commands for L and M
READ,FR(I),FR(I+1),FR(I+2),FR(I+3)	The second variable
READ,OPER,INSTR ⎱	Identification
READ,RUN,TEMP,WAVEL ⎰	

The following information appears $(M6 - 1)$ times in the input format:

READ,Y(I,JJ),Y(I+1,JJ),Y(I+2,JJ),Y(I+3,JJ)
READ,QQ1,QQ2   (if $L \geq 5$)

> *Note:* M6 = 1 if nonspectral data are processed.

OPTIONAL EXTERNAL COMMANDS FOR PROGRAMS 27 AND 327

The switch positions selected for the four *program switches*, numbered 1 through 4, on the console of the IBM 1620 computer determine the amount of output information generated during each. cycle. In the following table the positions for each of the control switches are given.

SWITCH POSITIONS

1	2	3	4	Command Executed and Comments
ON				PUNCH,SL(J),SQRMS(J) (J = 1, 2···JJ) This command is executed at the end of each cycle. The SL(J)'s are values for the expansion coefficients defined in equation (A): $$Y(I, JJ) = SL(1) \cdot Y(I, 1) + SL(2) \cdot Y(I, 2) + \cdots + SL(JJ)$$ $$\cdots(A)$$ SQRMS(J) is the standard deviation in the accepted values for the designated ordinate.
ON	ON			$\left.\begin{array}{l}\text{PUNCH,YY(I,JJ),YY(I+1,JJ),YY(I+2,JJ),}\\ \text{YY(I+3,JJ)}\\ \text{PUNCH,Y(I,JJ),Y(I+1,JJ),Y(I+2,JJ)}\\ \text{Y(I+3,JJ)}\end{array}\right\}$ (I = 1, 5, ···) This command is executed at the end of each cycle. YY(I,JJ) is the Ith value of Y(I,JJ) in equation (A) and Y(I,JJ) is the value used in the preceding cycle to compute SL(1),SL(2),···SL(JJ), and the standard deviations (SQRMS(1),···)
ON	OFF	ON		PUNCH,YY(I,J),YY(I+1,J),YY(I+2,J),YY(I+3,J) PUNCH,Y(I,J),Y(I+1,J),Y(I+2,J),Y(I+3,J) PUNCH,YER(I,J),YER(I+1,J),YER(I+2,J),YER(I+3,J) PUNCH,DEV(I,J),DEV(I+1,J),DEV(I+2,J),DEV(I+3,J) This command is executed for I = 1, 5,···JI − 3 and J = 1,···JJ at the end of each cycle. YY(I, J) is the original information. Y(I, J) is the information actually used in the preceding cycle. YER(I, J) and DEV(I, J) are the *maximum permitted error* and the *actual error* in the YY(I,J). Note that the first variable (Y(I,JJ)) appears at the end of these data tables
			OFF	The commands listed for "*Switches* 1 and 2 ON" are executed at the end of the JCth cycle if G1 $\neq$ G2, regardless of the position for *switches* 1 and 2
			ON	The commands given for "*switches* 1, 2, and 3 ON, OFF, ON" respectively are executed at the end of the JCth cycle if G1 $\neq$ G2, regardless of the other switch positions

OUTPUT FORMAT FOR PROGRAMS 27 AND 327

STATEMENT	COMMENT
PUNCH,ABAAA or ABAAS,NUM,FEEDP	NUM is the number of the program
PUNCH,JJ,JI,JC,M4	M4 denotes the wavelength for the data. Other symbols are defined in input commands
PUNCH,M6	The number of wavelengths for which data are processed
PUNCH,K,L,M	*Input commands*
PUNCH,QQ1,QQ2	Defined by *input commands* L and M
PUNCH,DEVF(1),RLM(1),WL(1),WU(1) ⎫ PUNCH,DEVF(2),RLM(2),WL(2),WU(2) ⎬	*Instrument reliability factors* associated with the input information
PRINT,CODE,M4,RUN ⎫ PUNCH,CODE,M4 ⎪ PUNCH,OPER,INSTR ⎬ PUNCH,RUN,TEMP,WAVEL ⎭	Executed only for *code* = 99999999.0 or 88888888.0 if G1 ≤5.0. The calculation is terminated

PUNCH,JC,G,G1,G2 PUNCH,SL(J),SQRMS(J) (J = 1, 2···JJ) PUNCH,YY(I,JJ),YY(I+1,JJ),YY(I+2,JJ),YY(I+3,JJ) PUNCH,Y(I,JJ),Y(I+1,JJ),Y(I+2,JJ),Y(I+3,JJ)	If *switch* 1 is ON ⎛For I = 1, 5,···JI − 3. ⎜ Executed for N = 1, 2 ⎜ ···JC − 1 if *switches* 1 ⎬ and 2 are ON, and for ⎜ N = JC if *switch* 4 is ⎝ OFF and G1 ≠ G2
PUNCH,YY(I,J),YY(I+1,J),YY(I+2,J),YY(I+3,J) PUNCH,Y(I,J),Y(I+1,J),Y(I+2,J),Y(I+3,J) PUNCH,YER(I,J),YER(I+1,J),YER(I+2,J),YER(I+3,J) PUNCH,DEV(I,J),DEV(I+1,J),DEV(I+2,J),DEV(I+3,J) (for J = 1,···JJ; I = 1, 5···(JI − 3))	⎛Executed if *switches* 1, 2, ⎜ and 3 are ON, OFF, ON ⎬ for N = 1, 2,···(JC − 1) ⎜ or for N = JC if *switch* 4 ⎝ is ON and G1 ≠ G2

DEFINITIONS	
JC	The number of the cycles
G	The number of sets of conjugate data remaining after application of the *fail–safe procedure*
G1	Equals G in this program
G2	The number of accepted sets used in the preceding cycle to compute SL(J) and SQRMS(J)
SL(J)	The Jth expansion coefficient
SQRMS(J)	The standard deviation for all values of YY(I,J)
YY(I,J)	The original information for the Jth ordinate which remained after application of the *fail–safe procedure*
Y(I,J)	Values for the designated ordinate actually used to compute SL(J)
YER(I,J)	The *maximum permitted deviation* for YY(I,J)
DEV(I,J)	The *actual error* for YY(I,J). If DEV(I,J) is positive, the set of conjugate data has a value lower than it should be

The information between the double lines is generated at the end of each of the programmed JC cycles. In the (JC + 1) cycle the *error analysis* is made and the following operations are executed.

PUNCH,JC,G,G1,G2   JC here is (JC + 1). Values refer to (JC + 1)
                                     cycle

PUNCH,SL(J),DEVSL(J),SQRMS(J) $\left\{\begin{array}{l}\text{DEVSL(J) is the }maximum\ permitted\ error\text{ for}\\ \text{SL(J). SL(J) and SQRMS(J) are information}\\ \text{calculated in the preceding cycle}\end{array}\right.$

PUNCH,OPER,INSTR   }   Identification
PUNCH,RUN,TEMP,WAVEL }

The entire output format is repeated (M6 − 1) times with new data taken at different wavelengths.

RELIABILITY LIMITS FOR PROGRAMS 27 AND 327

It is virtually impossible to induce normal round-off errors in Programs 27 and 327. However, the very sensitive form of the *Crout reduction method* can lead to rejection of all good sets of conjugate data if one or more bad sets is retained and a single good set is rejected. This feature has been deliberately retained and is discussed in the section on *statistical bias*.

FORTRAN FOR PROGRAM NUMBER 27

CALL WORD ABAAA

```
DIMENSION Y(JQ,JD),DEV(JQ,JD),YER(JQ,JD),YY(JQ,JD)
DIMENSION A(JR,JR),RLM(JD),WL(JD),DEVF(JD),WU(JD)
DIMENSION YM(JD),YA(JD),SL(JD),C2(JQ),YN(JD),YB(JD)
DIMENSION DEV1(JQ),SQRMS(JD),DEV2(JQ),DEVSL(JD),FR(JQ)
DIMENSION FUNY(JD),FUSL(JD),SLX(JD)
READ,JI
IJ=4
1 READ,ABAAA,FEEDP
READ,KA,KB,KC,KD,KE,KF
READ,JJ
READ,JC
N=JC
READ,M6
READ,K,L,M
READ,RLM(1),WL(1),WU(1)
READ,RLM(2),WL(2),WU(2)
IF(K-2)2,2,3
2 READ,DEVF(1)
GO TO 5
3 DO 4 I=1,JI,4
4 READ,DEV1(I),DEV1(I+1),DEV1(I+2),DEV1(I+3)
DEVF(1)=5555.0
5 GO TO (6,7,6,7),K
6 READ,DEVF(2)
GO TO 9
7 DO 8 I=1,JI,4
8 READ,DEV2(I),DEV2(I+1),DEV2(I+2),DEV2(I+3)
DEVF(2)=5555.0
9 M5=M6
M4=0
10 DO 11 I=1,JI,4
11 READ,Y(I,JJ),Y(I+1,JJ),Y(I+2,JJ),Y(I+3,JJ)
QQ1=0.0
QQ2=1.0
IF(L-5)326,13,13
326 GO TO (327,328,329,330),L
327 QQ1=QQ1+0.25
328 QQ1=QQ1+0.25
329 QQ1=QQ1+0.25
330 QQ1=QQ1+0.25
GO TO 12
13 READ,QQ1,QQ2
12 G=0.0
JK=JJ-1
DO 4337 I=1,JI
DO 4337 J=1,JK
4337 Y(I,J)=YY(I,J)
G1=0.0
G2=0.0
IF(M4)1,14,153
14 DO 15 I=1,JI,4
15 READ,FR(I),FR(I+1),FR(I+2),FR(I+3)
DO 20 I=1,JI
20 C2(I)=FR(I)
GO TO (23,24,23,24),K
23 DO 25 I=1,JI
25 DEV2(I)=C2(I)*DEVF(2)
24 KQ=KA+2
IF(KQ-8)26,26,27
```

```
27 IF(KQ-16)28,28,29
28 KQ=KQ-8
GO TO (26,30,31,32,33,34,35,36),KQ
36 DO 37 I=KD,KE
37 C2(I)=0.0
30 DO 38 I=KB,KC
38 C2(I)=0.0
GO TO 26
35 C2(KF)=0.0
34 C2(KE)=0.0
33 C2(KD)=0.0
32 C2(KC)=0.0
31 C2(KB)=0.0
GO TO 26
29 IF(KQ-24)39,39,40
40 KA=-1
GO TO 26
39 KQ=KQ-16
GO TO (26,41,42,42,4333,4333,44,41),KQ
41 DO 45 I=KB,KC
45 C2(I)=0.0
GO TO 26
44 C2(KF)=0.0
4333 C2(KD)=0.0
42 C2(KB)=0.0
26 DO 46 I=1,JI
IF(C2(I)-WL(2))47,48,48
48 IF(C2(I)-WU(2))49,49,47
47 C2(I)=0.0
DO 143 J=1,JJ
YER(I,J)=0.0
Y(I,J)=0.0
143 YY(I,J)=0.0
GO TO 46
49 Z=C2(I)
ZER=C2(I)+DEV2(I)
IF(M-8)16,16,17
16 KQQ=M
GO TO 18
17 KQQ=M-8
IF(KQQ-8)19,19,21
21 KQQ=M-16
GO TO 147
148 GO TO (316,317,318,319,320,321,322,323),KQQ
19 GO TO (308,309,310,311,312,313,314,315),KQQ
18 GO TO (300,301,302,303,304,305,306,307),KQQ
300 Z=Z**QQ1
ZER=ZER**QQ1
GO TO 22
301 Z=EXP(Z*QQ1)
ZER=EXP(ZER*QQ1)
GO TO 22
302 Z=LOG(Z*QQ1)
ZER=LOG(ZER*QQ1)
GO TO 22
303 Z=SIN(Z*QQ1)
ZER=SIN(ZER*QQ1)
GO TO 22
304 Z=COS(QQ1*Z)
ZER=COS(QQ1*ZER)
GO TO 22
305 Z=ATN(Z*QQ1)
```

```
ZER=ATN(ZER*QQ1)
GO TO 22
306 Z=(Z**QQ1)*(EXP(QQ2*Z))
ZER=(ZER**QQ1)*(EXP(ZER*QQ2))
GO TO 146
307 Z=(Z**QQ1)*(LOG(QQ2*Z))
ZER=(ZER**QQ1)*(LOG(QQ2*ZER))
GO TO 146
308 Z=(Z**QQ1)*(SIN(QQ2*Z))
ZER=(ZER**QQ1)*(SIN(QQ2*ZER))
GO TO 146
309 Z=(Z**QQ1)*(COS(QQ2*Z))
ZER=(ZER**QQ1)* (COS(ZER*QQ2))
GO TO 146
310 Z=(Z**QQ1)*(ATN(QQ2*Z))
ZER=(ZER**QQ1)*(ATN(ZER*QQ2))
GO TO 146
311 Z=(EXP(QQ1*Z))*(LOG(QQ2*Z))
ZER=(EXP(QQ1*ZER))*(LOG(ZER*QQ2))
GO TO 146
312 Z=(EXP(Z*QQ1))*(SIN(QQ2*Z))
ZER=(EXP(ZER*QQ1))*(SIN(QQ2*ZER))
GO TO 146
313 Z=(EXP(Z*QQ1))*(COS(QQ2*Z))
ZER=(EXP(QQ1*ZER))*(COS(QQ2*ZER))
GO TO 146
314 Z=(EXP(QQ1*Z))*(ATN(QQ2*Z))
ZER=(EXP(ZER*QQ1))*(ATN(ZER*QQ2))
GO TO 146
315 Z=(LOG(QQ1*Z))*(SIN(QQ2*Z))
ZER=(LOG(QQ1*ZER))*(SIN(QQ2*ZER))
GO TO 146
316 Z=(LOG(QQ1*Z))*(COS(QQ2*Z))
ZER=(LOG(QQ1*ZER))*(COS(ZER*QQ2))
GO TO 146
317 Z=(LOG(Z*QQ1))*(ATN(QQ2*Z))
ZER=(LOG(ZER*QQ1))*(ATN(ZER*QQ2))
GO TO 146
318 Z=(SIN(QQ1*Z))*(COS(QQ2*Z))
ZER=(SIN(QQ1*ZER))*(COS(ZER*QQ2))
GO TO 146
319 Z=(SIN(Z*QQ1))*(ATN(Z*QQ2))
ZER=(SIN(ZER*QQ1))*(ATN(ZER*QQ2))
GO TO 146
320 Z=(COS(Z*QQ1))*(ATN(Z*QQ2))
ZER=(COS(ZER*QQ1))*(ATN(QQ2*ZER))
GO TO 146
321 Z=EXP(QQ1*((Z-QQ2)**2.0))
ZER=EXP(QQ1*((ZER-QQ2)**2.0))
GO TO 146
322 Z=1.0
ZER=1.0
GO TO 146
323 Z=1.0
ZER=1.0
GO TO 146
147 IF(KQQ-9)148,149,1
149 Z=1.0
ZER=1.0
GO TO 146
22 Z=Z**QQ2
ZER=ZER**QQ2
```

```
146 IF(Z)150,47,150
150 DO 151 J=1,JK
P=J
Y(I,J)=Z**P
YER(I,J)=ZER**P-Y(I,J)
151 YY(I,J)=Y(I,J)
46 CONTINUE
READ,OPER,INSTR
READ,RUN,TEMP,WAVEL
NUM=27
153 M4=M4+1
M5=M5+1
JC=N
PUNCH,ABAAA,NUM,FEEDP
PUNCH,JJ,JI,JC,M4
PUNCH,M6
PUNCH,K,L,M
PUNCH,QQ1,QQ2
PUNCH,DEVF(1),RLM(1),WL(1),WU(1)
PUNCH,DEVF(2),RLM(2),WL(2),WU(2)
JC=0
DO 154 I=1,JI
IF(C2(I))4335,155,4335
4335 IF(Y(I,JJ)-WL(1))155,156,156
156 IF(Y(I,JJ)-WU(1))157,157,155
155 Y(I,JJ)=0.0
YY(I,JJ)=0.0
YER(I,JJ)=0.0
DEV(I,JJ)=0.0
GO TO 154
157 G=G+1.0
YY(I,JJ)=Y(I,JJ)
IF(K-2)158,158,175
158 DEV1(I)=DEVF(1)*Y(I,JJ)
175 YER(I,JJ)=DEV1(I)
154 CONTINUE
G1=G
KQ=KA+2
IF(KQ-8)159,159,160
159 GO TO (161,162,163,164,165,166,167,168),KQ
168 DO 169 I=KD,KE
169 Y(I,JJ)=0.0
162 DO 170 I=KB,KC
170 Y(I,JJ)=0.0
GO TO 161
167 Y(KF,JJ)=0.0
166 Y(KE,JJ)=0.0
165 Y(KD,JJ)=0.0
164 Y(KC,JJ)=0.0
163 Y(KB,JJ)=0.0
GO TO 161
160 KQ=KQ-16
IF(KQ)161,161,207
207 GO TO (161,161,161,171,171,172,172,173),KQ
173 DO 174 I=KD,KE
174 Y(I,JJ)=0.0
GO TO161
172 Y(KE,JJ)=0.0
171 Y(KC,JJ)=0.0
161 CONTINUE
50 JC=JC+1
KKK=0
```

```
NNN=1
51 DO 52 J=1,JJ
YM(J)=-10000000.0
YN(J)=10000000.0
999 FUNY(J)=1.0
DO 53 I=1,JI
Y(I,J)=Y(I,J)*FUNY(J)
IF(Y(I,JJ))54,53,54
54 IF(YM(J)-Y(I,J))55,56,56
55 YM(J)=Y(I,J)
56 IF(YN(J)-Y(I,J))53,53,57
57 YN(J)=Y(I,J)
53 CONTINUE
IF(YN(J))6666,8892,8893
8892 YA(J)=-YM(J)/10.0
GO TO 8891
8893 YA(J)=-YN(J)/10.0
GO TO 8891
6666 YA(J)=2.0*YN(J)
8891 AA=YM(J)-YA(J)
BB=YN(J)-YA(J)
AA=SQR(AA*AA)
BB=SQR(BB*BB)
IF(AA-BB)58,60,59
60 IF(AA)61,61,59
61 CODE=88888888.0
62 PRINT,CODE,M4,RUN
PUNCH,CODE,M4
PUNCH,OPER,INSTR
PUNCH,RUN,TEMP,WAVEL
IF(M6-M4)1,1,10
58 YB(J)=BB
GO TO 63
59 YB(J)=AA
63 DO 52 I=1,JI
IF(Y(I,JJ))64,52,64
64 Y(I,J)=Y(I,J)-YA(J)
IF(Y(I,J))65,66,65
66 Y(I,J)=(YN(J)-YA(J))/(10.0**6.0)
65 Y(I,J)=Y(I,J)/YB(J)
52 CONTINUE
JR=JJ+1
DO 208 J=1,JR
DO 208I=1,JR
208 A(I,J)=0.0
DO 67 J=1,JJ
DO 67 JB=1,JJ
DO 67 I=1,JI
IF(Y(I,JJ))68,67,68
68 IF(JB-1)1,70,69
69 JP=JB-1
A(JB,J)=A(JB,J)+Y(I,J)*Y(I,JP)
GO TO 67
70 A(JB,J)=A(JB,J)+Y(I,J)
67 CONTINUE
G2=0.0
YAA=0.0
DO 71 J=1,JJ
71 A(J,JR)=A(J,JJ)
DO 72 I=1,JI
IF(Y(I,JJ))73,72,73
73 G2=G2+1.0
```

```
72 CONTINUE
A(1,JJ)=G2
G9=6.0
IF(G2-G9)74,75,75
74 CODE=99999999.0
GO TO 62
75 DO 76 J=2,JJ
JB=J-1
76 A(J,JJ)=A(1,JB)
DO 77 J=1,JR
DO 77 I=1,JJ
AA=SQR(A(I,J)*A(I,J))
IF(YAA-AA)78,77,77
78 YAA=AA
77 CONTINUE
DO 79 J=1,JR
DO 79 I=1,JJ
79 A(I,J)=A(I,J)/YAA
DO 80 J=1,JR
DO 80 I=1,JJ
IF(J-1)80,80,82
82 IF(J-I)83,83,84
83 JA=J-1
GO TO 85
84 JA=I-1
85 SET=0.0
SUM=0.0
IF(JA)86,86,87
87 DO 88 JK=1,JA
88 SUM=SUM+A(I,JK)*A(JK,J)
86 SET=A(I,J)-SUM
IF(J-1)89,89,90
89 A(I,J)=SET
GO TO 80
90 SOB=A(I,I)
IF(SOB)94,8889,94
8889 SOB=10.0**(-18.0)
94 A(I,J)=SET/SOB
80 CONTINUE
DO 81 I=1,JJ
JAN=JR-I
SUM2=0.0
IA=I-1
IF(IA)81,81,91
91 DO 93 JK=1,IA
JOB=JR-JK
93 SUM2=SUM2+A(JAN,JOB)*SL(JOB)
81 SL(JAN)=A(JAN,JR)-SUM2
DO 95 I=1,JI
DO 95 J=1,JJ
IF(Y(I,JJ))96,95,96
96 Y(I,J)=YB(J)*Y(I,J)
Y(I,J)=Y(I,J)+YA(J)
Y(I,J)=Y(I,J)/FUNY(J)
95 CONTINUE
SL(JJ)=SL(JJ)*YB(JJ)
AXYZ=0.0
JK=JJ-1
DO 205J=1,JK
SL(J)=SL(J)*YB(JJ)/YB(J)
205 AXYZ=AXYZ+SL(J)*YA(J)
SL(JJ)=SL(JJ)-AXYZ+YA(JJ)
```

```
DO 206 J=1,JJ
1110 FUSL(J)=1.0
206 SL(J)=SL(J)*FUSL(J)
N77=0
JK=JJ-1
IF(KKK)1,177,186
177 Z1=SQR(SL(JJ)*SL(JJ))
DO 178J=1,JK
SLX(J)=SL(J)
Z2=SQR(SL(J)*SL(J))
IF(Z1-Z2)178,178,179
179 N77=J
178 CONTINUE
IF(N77)1,181,182
182 DO 183 I=1,JI
QRO=Y(I,N77)
IF(Y(I,N77))184,183,184
184 DO 185 J=1,JJ
185 Y(I,J)=Y(I,J)/QRO
Y(I,N77)=1.0/QRO
183 CONTINUE
N99=N77
KKK=1
GO TO 51
186 SL(JJ)=SL(N99)
N77=N99
DO 187 J=1,JK
187 SL(J)=SLX(J)
SLX(JJ)=SL(N77)
DO 188 I=1,JI
QRO=Y(I,N77)
IF(Y(I,N77))189,188,189
189 DO 331 J=1,JJ
331 Y(I,J)=Y(I,J)/QRO
Y(I,N77)=1.0/QRO
188 CONTINUE
KKK=0
181 G3=G2-1.0
IF(N-JC)123,124,124
124 DO 8894 J=1,JJ
SQRMS(J)=0.0
DO 8894 I=1,JI
8894 DEV(I,J)=0.0
JK=JJ-1
DO 97 I=1,JI
RR=0.0
IF(YY(I,JJ))99,97,99
99 DO 98 J=1,JJ
IF(JJ-J)1,101,100
100 RR=RR+SL(J)*YY(I,J)
98 CONTINUE
101 QQ=RR+SL(JJ)
DEV(I,JJ)=YY(I,JJ)-QQ
DO 102 JP=1,JK
IF(SL(JP))103,104,103
104 DEV(I,JP)=0.0
GO TO 102
103 DEV(I,JP)=YY(I,JP)-(YY(I,JJ)-QQ+SL(JP)*YY(I,JP))/SL(JP)
102 CONTINUE
97 CONTINUE
DO 105 J=1,JJ
DO 105I=1,JI
```

```
105 SQRMS(J)=SQRMS(J)+DEV(I,J)*DEV(I,J)
DO 8895 J=1,JJ
8895 SQRMS(J)=SQR(SQRMS(J)/G3)
123 IF(JC-1)1,107,122
107 PUNCH,JC,G,G1,G2
IF(N-JC)119,109,109
109 IF(SENSE SWITCH 1)110,142
110 DO 111 J=1,JJ
111 PUNCH,SL(J),SQRMS(J)
142 IF(N-JC)1,118,112
112 IF(SENSE SWITCH 2)113,115
113 DO 114 I=1,JI,4
PUNCH,YY(I,JJ),YY(I+1,JJ),YY(I+2,JJ),YY(I+3,JJ)
114 PUNCH,Y(I,JJ),Y(I+1,JJ),Y(I+2,JJ),Y(I+3,JJ)
IF(N-JC)1,119,50
115 IF(SENSE SWITCH 3)116,50
116 DO 117 I=1,JI,4
DO 117 J=1,JJ
PUNCH,YY(I,J),YY(I+1,J),YY(I+2,J),YY(I+3,J)
PUNCH,Y(I,J),Y(I+1,J),Y(I+2,J),Y(I+3,J)
PUNCH,YER(I,J),YER(I+1,J),YER(I+2,J),YER(I+3,J)
117 PUNCH,DEV(I,J),DEV(I+1,J),DEV(I+2,J),DEV(I+3,J)
IF(N-JC)1,119,50
118 IF(G1-G2)9002,119,9002
9002 IF(SENSE SWITCH 4)116,113
120 DO 121 J=1,JJ
121 PUNCH,SL(J),DEVSL(J),SQRMS(J)
196 PUNCH,OPER,INSTR
PUNCH,RUN,TEMP,WAVEL
IF(M6-M4)1,1,10
122 IF(N-JC)107,9999,9999
9999 IF(NNN-IJ)125,107,1
125 DO 126 I=1,JI
JRK=0
DO 126 J=1,JJ
IF(YY(I,JJ))127,130,127
127 AA=SQR(YER(I,J)*YER(I,J))
BB=SQR(DEV(I,J)*DEV(I,J))
IF(AA-BB)129,128,128
129 IF(NNN-1)1,130,132
130 Y(I,J)=0.0
DEV(I,J)=0.0
GO TO 126
128 IF(NNN-1)1,126,133
131 JRK=JRK+1
IF(JRK-JJ)126,43,1
43 DO 9001 JP=1,JJ
9001 Y(I,JP)=YY(I,JP)
GO TO 126
132 IF(NNN-4)126,130,126
133 IF(NNN-4)131,126,131
126 CONTINUE
NNN=NNN+1
GO TO 51
119 DO 134 J=1,JJ
IF(N-JC)136,135,1
135 DEVSL(J)=SL(J)
GO TO 137
136 AAA=DEVSL(J)
DEVSL(J)=SL(J)
SL(J)=AAA
GO TO 134
```

```
137 DO 134 I=1,JI
IF(Y(I,JJ))138,134,138
138 Y(I,JJ)=0.0
IF(JJ-J)1,139,140
140 JK=JJ-1
DO 141 JQ=1,JK
YER(I,JQ)=-SQR(YER(I,JQ)*YER(I,JQ))
141 Y(I,JJ)=Y(I,JJ)+SL(JQ)*YER(I,JQ)
139 Y(I,JJ)=YER(I,JJ)-Y(I,JJ)
134 CONTINUE
IF(N-JC)120,50,1
END
```

ALGOL 60 FOR PROGRAM NUMBER 27

PROCEDURE ABAAA(ji,ij); ARRAY y,dev,yer,yy[1:jq,1:jd],a[1:jr,1:jr],rLm,wL,
devf,wu,ym,ya,sL,yn,yb,sqrms,devsL,funy,fusL,sLx[1:jd],c2,dev1,dev2,fr[1,jq];
INTEGER ji,ij; SWITCH sw1:=x2,x3,x2,x3; SWITCH sw2:=x6,x7,x8,x9; SWITCH
sw3:=x11,x12,x11,x12; SWITCH sw4:=x25,x14,x19,x18,x17,x16,x15,x13; SWITCH
sw5:=x25,x21,x24,x24,x23,x23,x22,x21; SWITCH sw6:=45,x46,x47,x48,x49,x50,x51,
x52; SWITCH sw7:=x37,x38,x39,x40,x41,x42,x43,x44; SWITCH sw8:=x29,x30,x31,
x32,x33,x34,x35,x36; SWITCH sw9:=x71,x61,x66,x65,x64,x63,x62,x60; SWITCH
sw10:=x71,x71,x71,x70,x70,x69,x69,x68;
COMMENT: MATHEMATICAL FRENCH CURVES;
   BEGIN INTEGER i,ia,j,jj,ja,jc,jk,jp,jr,jan,job,jrk,k,ka,kb,kc,kd,ke,kf,kq,
   kqq,kkk,L,m,m4,m5,m6,m9,n,num,nnn,n77,n99,feedp,oper,run,instr,g,g1,
   g2,g3,code;
   REAL aa,aaa,axyz,bb,qq,qq1,qq2,qro,rr,sob,sum,sum2,set,temp,waveL,
   yaa,z,zer;
      READ feedp;
      READ ka,kb,kc,kd,ke,kf;
      READ jj; READ jc; n:=jc;
      READ m6; READ k,L,m;
      READ rLm[1],wL[1],wu[1];
      READ rLm[2],wL[2],wu[2];
      IF k≤2 THEN
      BEGIN
         READ devf[1]; GO TO X1END;
      FOR i:= 1 STEP 1 UNTIL ji DO READ dev1[i];
      devf[1]:=5555;
X1:   GO TO sw1[k];
X2:   READ devf[2]; GO TO X4;
X3:   FOR i:=1 STEP 1 UNTIL ji DO READ dev2[i];
      devf[2]:=5555;
X4:   m5:=m6; m4:=0;
X5:   FOR i:=1 STEP 1 UNTIL ji DO READ y[i,jj];
      qq1:=0; qq2:=1;
      IF L<5 THEN
      BEGIN
         GO TO sw2[L];
X6:   qq1:=qq1+0.25;
X7:   qq1:=qq1+0.25;
X8:   qq1:=qq1+0.25;
X9:   qq1:=qq1+0.25; GO TO X10END;
      READ qq1,qq2
X10:   g:=0; jk:=jj−1;
      FOR i:=1 STEP 1 UNTIL ji DO
      FOR j:=1 STEP 1 UNTIL jk DO y[i,j]:=yy[i,j];
      g1:=g2:=0;
      IF m4<0 THEN GO TO w5
      ELSE IF m4>0 THEN GO TO X57;
      FOR i:=1 STEP 1 UNTIL ji DO READ fr[i];
      FOR i:=1 STEP 1 UNTIL ji DO c[i]:=fr[i];
      GO TO sw3[k];
X11:   FOR i:=1 STEP 1 UNTIL ji DO dev2[i]:=c2[i]Xdevf[2];

```
X12:    kq:=ka+2;
        IF kq≤8 THEN GO TO X25;
        ELSE IF kq>16 THEN GO TO X20;
        kq:=kq-8; GO TO sw4[kq];
X13:    FOR i:=kd STEP 1 UNTIL ke DO c2[i]:=0;
X14:    FOR i:=kb STEP 1 UNTIL kc DO c2[i]:=0;
        GO TO X25;
X15:    c2[kf]:=0;
X16:    c2[ke]:=0;
X17:    c2[kd]:=0;
X18:    c2[kc]:=0;
X19:    c2[kb]:=0; GO TO X25;
X20:    IF kq>24 THEN
        BEGIN
            ka:=-1; GO TO X25END;
        kq:=kq-16; GO TO sw5[kq];
X21:    FOR i:=kb STEP 1 UNTIL kc DO c2[i]:=0;
        GO TO X25;
X22:    c2[kf]:=0;
X23:    c2[kd]:=0;
X24:    c2[kb]:=0;
X25:    FOR i:=1 STEP 1 UNTIL ji DO
        BEGIN
            IF c2[i]<wL[2]∨c2[i]>wu[2]THEN
            BEGIN
X2X:            c2[i]:=0;
                FOR j:=1 STEP 1 UNTIL jj DO yer[i,j]:=y[i,j]:=yy[i,j]:=0;
                GO TO X56END;
            z:=c2[i]; zer:=c2[i]+dev2[i];
            IF m≤8 THEN
            BEGIN
                kqq:=m; GO TO X28 END;
            kqq:=m-8;
            IF kqq≤8 THEN GO TO X27;
            kqq:=m-16; GO TO X53;
X26:        GO TO sw6[kqq];
X27:        GO TO sw7[kqq];
X28:        GO TO sw8[kqq];
X29:        z:=z↑qq1; zer:=zer↑qq1; GO TO X54;
X30:        z:=exp(zXqq1); zer:=exp(zerXqq1); GO TO X54;
X31:        z:=Ln(zXqq1); zer:=exp(zerXqq1); GO TO X54;
X32:        z:=sin(zXqq1); zer:=sin(zerXqq1); GO TO X54;
X33:        z:=cos(zXqq1); zer:=cos(zerXqq1); GO TO X54;
X34:        z:=arctan(zXqq1); zer:=arctan(zerXqq1); GO TO X54;
X35:        z:=z↑qq1Xexp(zXqq2);
            zer:=zer↑qq1Xexp(zerXqq2); GO TO X55;
X36:        z:=z↑qq1XLn(zXqq2);
            zer:=zer↑qq1XLn(zerXqq2); GO TO X55;
X37:        z:=z↑qq1Xsin(zXqq2);
            zer:=zer↑qq1Xsin(zerXqq2); GO TO X55;
X38:        z:=z↑qq1Xcos(zXqq2);
            zer:=zer↑qq1Xcos(zerXqq2); GO TO X55;
```

```
X39:    z:=z↑qq1Xarctan(zXqq2);
        zer:=zer↑qq1Xarctan(zerXqq2); GO TO X55;
X40:    z:=exp(zXqq1)XLn(zXqq2);
        zer:=exp(zerXqq1)XLn(zerXqq2); GO TO X55;
X41:    z:=exp(zXqq1)Xsin(zXqq2);
        zer:=exp(zerXqq1)Xsin(zerXqq2); GO TO X55;
X42:    z:=exp(zXqq1)Xcos(zXqq2);
        zer:=exp(zerXqq1)Xcos(zerXqq2); GO TO X55;
X43:    z:=exp(zXqq1)Xarctan(zXqq2);
        zer:=exp(zerXqq1)Xarctan(zerXqq2); GO TO X55;
X44:    z:=Ln(zXqq1)Xsin(zXqq2);
        zer:=Ln(zerXqq1)Xsin(zerXqq2); GO TO X55;
X45:    z:=Ln(zXqq1)Xcos(zXqq2);
        zer:=Ln(zerXqq1)Xcos(zerXqq2); GO TO X55;
X46:    z:=Ln(zXqq1)Xarctan(zXqq2);
        zer:=Ln(zerXqq1)Xarctan(zerXqq2); GO TO X55;
X47:    z:=sin(zXqq1)Xcos(zXqq2);
        zer:=sin(zerXqq1)Xcos(zerXqq2); GO TO X55;
X48:    z:=sin(zXqq1)Xarctan(zXqq2);
        zer:=sin(zerXqq1)Xarctan(zerXqq2); GO TO X55;
X49:    z:=cos(zXqq1)Xarctan(zXqq2);
        zer:=cos(zerXqq1)Xarctan(zerXqq2); GO TO X55;
X50:    z:=exp(qq1X(z-qq2)↑2);
        zer:=exp(qq1X(zer-qq2)↑2); GO TO X55;
X51:    z:=zer:=1; GO TO X55;
X52:    z:=zer:=1; GO TO X55;
X53:    IF kqq>9 THEN GO TO w5
        ELSE GO TO X26;
        z:=zer:=1; GO TO X55;
X54:    z:=z↑qq2; zer:=zer↑qq2;
X55:    IF z=0 THEN GO TO X2X;
        FOR j:=1 STEP 1 UNTIL jk DO
        BEGIN
            p:=j; y[i,j]:=z↑p;
            yer[i,j]:=zer↑p-y[i,j]; yy[i,j]:=y[i,j]
        END
X56:    END;
        READ oper,instr;
        READ run,temp,waveL; num:=27;
X57:    m4:=m4+1;m5:=m5+1; jc:=n;
        PUNCH num,feedp;
        PUNCH jj,ji,jc,m4;
        PUNCH m6; PUNCH k,L,m;
        PUNCH qq1,qq2;
        PUNCH devf[1],rLm[1],wL[1],wu[1];
        PUNCH devf[2],rLm[2],wL[2],wu[2];
        jc:=0;
        FOR i:=1 STEP 1 UNTIL ji DO
        BEGIN
            IF c2[i]∨(y[i,jj]<wL[1])∨(y[i,jj]>wu[1])THEN
            BEGIN
X58:        y[i,jj]:=yer[i,jj]:=yy[i,jj]:=dev[i,jj]:=0;
```

```
             GO TO X59END;
             g:=g+1; yy[i,jj]=y[i,jj];
             IF k≤2 THEN dev1[i]:=devf[1]Xy[i,jj];
             yer[i,jj]:=dev1[i]
X59:    END;
             g1:=g; kq:=ka+2;
             IF kq>8 THEN GO TO X67;
             GO TO sw9[ kq];
X60:    FOR i:=kd STEP 1 UNTIL ke DO y[i,jj]:=0;
X61:    FOR i:=kb STEP 1 UNTIL kc DO y[i,jj]:=0;
             GO TO X71;
X62:    y[kf,jj]:=0;
X63:    y[ke,jj]:=0;
X64:    y[kd,jj]:=0;
X65:    y[kc,jj]:=0;
X66:    y[kb,jj]:=0;  GO TO X71;
X67:    kq:=kq-16;
             IF kq≤0 THEN GO TO X71;
             GO TO sw10[kq];
X68:    FOR i:=kd STEP 1 UNTIL ke DO y[i,jj]:=0;
             GO TO X71;
X69:    y[ke,jj]:=0;
X70:    y[kc,jj]:=0;
X71:    jc:=jc+1; kkk:=0; nnn:=1;
X72:    FOR j:=1 STEP 1 UNTIL jj DO
             BEGIN
               ym[j]:=-10000000.0; yn[j]:=10000000.0;
               funy[j]:=1;
               FOR i:=1 STEP 1 UNTIL ji DO
               BEGIN
                 y[i,j]:=y[i,j]Xfuny[j];
                 IF y[i,jj]=0 THEN GO TO X7X;
                 IF ym[j]<y[i,j] THEN ym[j]:=y[i,j];
                 IF yn[j]>y[i,j] THEN yn[j]:=y[i,j]
X7X:    END;
             IF yn[j]=0 THEN
             BEGIN
               ya[j]:=-ym[j]/10; GO TO X73END
             ELSE IF yn[j]>0 THEN
             BEGIN
               ya[j]:=-yn[j]/10; GO TO X73END
               ya[j]:=2Xyn[j];
X73:    aa:=abs(ym[j]-ya[j]);
             bb:=abs(yn[j]-ya[j]);
             IF aa<bb THEN GO TO X75
             ELSE IF aa>bbVaa>0 THEN GO TO X76;
             code:=88888888;
X74:    PUNCH code,m4;
             PUNCH oper,instr;
             PUNCH run,temp,waveL;
             IF m6≤m4 THEN GO TO w5 ELSE GO TO X5;
X75:    yb[j]:=bb; GO TO X77;
```

```
X76:      yb[j]:=aa;
X77:      FOR i:=1 STEP 1 UNTIL ji DO
          BEGIN
              IF y[i,jj]=0 THEN GO TO X78;
              y[i,j]:=y[i,j]-ya[j];
              IF y[i,jj]=0 THEN y[i,j]:=(yn[j]-ya[j])/₁₀6;
              y[i,j]:=y[i,j]/yb[j]
X78:      END END;
          jr:=jj+1;
          FOR j:=1 STEP 1 UNTIL jr DO
          FOR i:=1 STEP 1 UNTIL jr DO a[i,j]:=0;
          FOR j:=1 STEP 1 UNTIL jj DO
          FOR jb:=1 STEP 1 UNTIL jj DO
          FOR i:=1 STEP 1 UNTIL ji DO
          BEGIN
              IF y[i,jj]=0 THEN GO TO X79;
              IF jb<1 THEN GO TO w5
              ELSE IF jb>1 THEN
              BEGIN
                  jp:=jb-1;
                  a[jb,j]:=a[jb,j]+y[i,j]Xy[i,jp];
                  GO TO X79END;
              a[jb,j]:=a[jb,j]+y[i,j]
X79:      END;
          g2:=yaa:=0;
          FOR j:=1 STEP 1 UNTIL jj DO a[j,jr]:=a[j,jj];
          FOR i:=1 STEP 1 UNTIL ji DO
          IF y[i,jj]≠0 THEN g2:=g2+1;
          a[1,jj]:=g2; g9:=6;
          IF g2<g9 THEN
          BEGIN
              code:=99999999; GO TO X74END;
          FOR j:=2 STEP 1 UNTIL jj DO
          BEGIN
              jb:=j-1; a[j,jj]:=a[1,jb]END;
          FOR j:=1 STEP 1 UNTIL jr DO
          FOR i:=1 STEP 1 UNTIL jj DO
          BEGIN
              aa:=abs(a[i,j]);
              IF yaa<aa THEN yaa:=aa
          END;
          FOR j:=1 STEP 1 UNTIL jr DO
          FOR i:=1 STEP 1 UNTIL jj DO a[i,j]:=a[i,j]/yaa;
          FOR j:=1 STEP 1 UNTIL jr DO
          FOR i:=1 STEP 1 UNTIL jj DO
          BEGIN
              IF j≤1 THEN GO TO X81;
              IF j≤i THEN
              BEGIN
                  ja:=j-1; GO TO X80END;
              ja:=i-1;
X80:      set:=sum:=0;
```

```
         IF ja>0 THEN
         FOR jk:=1 STEP 1 UNTIL ja DO sum:=sum+a[i,jk]Xa[jk,j];
         set:=a[i,j]-sum;
         IF j≤i THEN
         BEGIN
            a[i,j]:=set; GO TO X81END;
         sob:=a[i,i];
         IF sob=0 THEN sob:=10(-18);
         a[i,j]:=set/sob
X81:     END;
         FOR i:=1 STEP 1 UNTIL jj DO
         BEGIN
            jan:=jr-i; sum2:=0; ia:=i-1;
            IF ia>0 THEN
            FOR jk:=1 STEP 1 UNTIL ia DO
            BEGIN
               job:=jr-jk;
               sum2:=sum2+a[jan,job]XsL[job]
            END;
            sL[jan]:=a[jan,jr]-sum2
         END;
         FOR i:=1 STEP 1 UNTIL ji DO
         FOR j:=1 STEP 1 UNTIL jj DO
         IF y[i,jj]≠0 THEN
         y[i,j]:=(yb[j]Xy[i,j]+ya[j])/funy[j];
         sL[jj]:=sL[jj]Xyb[jj]; axyz:=0; jk:=jj-1;
         FOR j:=1 STEP 1 UNTIL jk DO
         BEGIN
            sL[j]:=sL[j]Xyb[jj]/yb[j];
            axyz:=axyz+sL[j]Xya[j]
         END;
         sL[jj]:=sL[jj]-axyz+ya[jj];
         FOR j:=1 STEP 1 UNTIL jj DO
         BEGIN
            fusL[j]:=0; sL[j]:=sL[j]XfusL[j]
         END;
         n77:=0; jk:=jj-1;
         IF kkk<0 THEN GO TO w5
         ELSE IF kkk=0 THEN
         BEGIN
            z1:=abs(sL[jj]);
            FOR j:=1 STEP 1 UNTIL jk DO
            BEGIN
               sLX[j]:=sL[j]; z2:=abs(sL[j]);
               IF z1>z2 THEN n77:=j
            END;
            IF n77<0 THEN GO TO w5
            ELSE IF n77=0 THEN GO TO X82;
            FOR i:=1 STEP 1 UNTIL ji DO
            BEGIN
               qro:=y[i,n77];
```

```
        IF y[i,n77]≠0 THEN
        BEGIN
            FOR j:=1 STEP 1 UNTIL jj DO y[i,j]:=y[i,j]/qro;
            y[i,n77]:=1/qroEND
        END;
        n99:=n77; kkk:=1; GO TO X72END;
        n77:=n99;
        FOR j:=1 STEP 1 UNTIL jk DO sL[j]:=sLX[j];
        sLX[jj]:=jL[n77];
        FOR i:=1 STEP 1 UNTIL ji DO
        BEGIN
            qro:=y[i,n77];
            IF y[i,n77]≠0 THEN
            BEGIN
                FOR j:=1 STEP 1 UNTIL jj DO y[i,j]:=y[i,j]/qro;
                y[i,n77]:=1/qroEND
        END;
        kkk:=0;
X82:    g3:=g2-1;
        IF n<jc THEN GO TO X85;
        FOR j:=1 STEP 1 UNTIL jj DO
        FOR i:=1 STEP 1 UNTIL ji DO sqrms[j]:=dev[i,j]:=0;
        jk:=jj-1;
        FOR i:=1 STEP 1 UNTIL ji DO
        BEGIN
            rr:=0;
            IF yy[i,jj]=0 THEN GO TO X84;
            FOR j:=1 STEP 1 UNTIL jj DO
            BEGIN
                IF jj<j THEN GO TO w5
                ELSE IF jj=j THEN GO TO X83;
                rr:=rr+sL[j]Xyy[i,j]
            END;
X83:        qq:=rr+sL[jj]; dev[i,jj]:=yy[i,jj]-qq;
            FOR jp:=1 STEP 1 UNTIL jk DO
            BEGIN
                IF sL[jp]=0 THEN
                BEGIN
                    dev[i,jp]:=0; GO TO X84END;
                dev[i,p]:=yy[i,jp]-(yy[i,jj]-qq+sL[jp]Xyy[i,jp])/sL[jp]
X84:        END END;
        FOR j:=1 STEP 1 UNTIL jj DO
        FOR i:=1 STEP 1 UNTIL ji DO sqrms[j]:=sqrms[j]+dev[i,j]↑2;
        FOR j:=1 STEP 1 UNTIL jj DO sqrms[j]:=sqrt(sqrms[jj]/g3);
X85:    IF jc<1 THEN GO TO w5
        ELSE IF jc>1 THEN GO TO X93;
X86:    PUNCH jc,g,g1,g2;
        IF n<jc THEN GO TO w1;
        COMMENT: At this point control either proceeds serially or is trans-
        ferred to Label X87 (see Optional External Commands for Program 27);
        FOR j:=1 STEP 1 UNTIL jj DO PUNCH sL[j],sqrms[j];
X87:    IF n<jc THEN GO TO w5
        ELSE IF n=jc THEN GO TO X91;
```

COMMENT: At this point control either proceeds serially or is trans-
ferred to Label X89 (see Optional External Commands for Program 27);
X88:   FOR i:=1 STEP 1 UNTIL ji DO PUNCH yy[i,jj];
        FOR i:=1 STEP 1 UNTIL ji DO PUNCH y[i,jj];
        IF n<jc THEN GO TO w5
        ELSE IF n=jc THEN GO TO w1 ELSE GO TO X71;
X89:   COMMENT: At this point control either proceeds serially or is trans-
        ferred to Label X71 (see Optional External Commands for Program 27);
X90:   FOR i:=1 STEP 1 UNTIL ji DO
        FOR j:=1 STEP 1 UNTIL jj DO
        BEGIN
            PUNCH yy[i,j]; PUNCH y[i,j];
            PUNCH yer[i,j]; PUNCH dev[i,j]
        END;
        IF n<jc THEN GO TO w5
        ELSE IF n=jc THEN GO TO w1 ELSE GO TO X71;
X91:   IF g1=g2 THEN GO TO w1;
        COMMENT: At this point control is either transferred to Label X90 or
        to Label X88 (see Optional External Commands for Program 27);
X92:   FOR j:=1 STEP 1 UNTIL jj DO PUNCH sL[j],devsL[j],sqrms[j];
        PUNCH oper,instr;
        PUNCH run,temp,waveL;
        IF m6≤m4 THEN GO TO w5 ELSE GO TO X5;
X93:   IF n<jcVnnn=ji THEN GO TO X86
        ELSE IF nnn>ji THEN GO TO w5;
        FOR i:=1 STEP 1 UNTIL ji DO
        BEGIN
            jrk:=0;
            FOR j:=1 STEP 1 UNTIL jj DO
            BEGIN
                IF yy[i,1]=0 THEN GO TO X94;
                aa:=abs(yer[i,j]); bb:=abs(dev[i,j]);
                IF aa≥bb THEN GO TO X95;
                IF nnn<1 THEN GO TO w5
                ELSE IF nnn>1 THEN GO TO X97;
X94:   y[i,j]:=dev[i,j]:=0; GO TO X99;
X95:   IF nnn<1 THEN GO TO w5
                ELSE IF nnn=1 THEN GO TO X99 ELSE GO TO X98;
X96:   jrk:=jrk+1;
                IF jrk>jj THEN GO TO w5
                ELSE IF jrk<jj THEN GO TO X99;
                FOR jp:=1 STEP 1 UNTIL jj DO y[i,jp]:=yy[i,jp];
                GO TO X99;
X97:   IF nnn=4 THEN GO TO X94 ELSE GO TO X99;
X98:   IF nnn≠4 THEN GO TO X96
            END
X99:   END;
        nnn:=nnn+1; GO TO X72
w1:   FOR j:=1 STEP 1 UNTIL jj DO
        BEGIN
            IF n>jc THEN GO TO w5
            ELSE IF n=jc THEN
            BEGIN

```
          devsL[j]:=sL[j]; GO TO w2 END;
          aaa:=devsL[j]; devsL[j]:=sL[j];
          sL[j]:=aaa; GO TO w4;
w2:     FOR i:=1 STEP 1 UNTIL ji DO
        BEGIN
          IF y[i,j]=0 THEN GO TO w4;
          y[i,jj]:=0;
          IF jj<j THEN GO TO w5
          ELSE IF jj>j THEN
          BEGIN
              jk:=jj−1;
              FOR jq:=1 STEP 1 UNTIL jk DO
              BEGIN
                 yer[i,jq]:=-abs(yer[i,jq]);
                 y[i,jj]:=y[i,jj]+sL[jq]Xyer[i,jq]
              END END;
w3:          y[i,jj]:=yer[i,jj]−y[i,jj]
          END
w4:     END;
        IF n<jc THEN GO TO X92
        ELSE IF n=jc THEN GO TO X71
w5:  END ABAAA;
     READ ji; ij:=4;
w6:  ABAAA(ji,ij);
     GO TO w6;
```

CHAPTER V

JOB'S METHOD EQUATION

For systems with two active components, A and B, the net change in a variable (ΔV) frequently is plotted against a second variable (R) to obtain maxima and/or minima. R' is the value of R for which $\partial V / \partial R$ vanishes. The same mathematical treatment applies for several types of data.

1. In Job's Method of Continuous Variations,[1] or in one of its many different forms,[2] ΔV is the net increase in an additive physical property (usually absorbance) and R' is the mole ratio of A to B in the complex.

2. In cryoscopic studies of solutions, molten salts, or metals, ΔV is either the relative or absolute freezing point and R' is the mole ratio of A to B in the compound, complex, or eutectic mixture.

3. For plots of the boiling point (ΔV) versus the mole ratio of A to B in the liquid, R' is the mole ratio of A to B in the azeotrope.

4. In potentiometric titrations ΔV is either the change in EMF (ΔE), or it is $\Delta E / E$ where E equals the EMF of the solution. R' is the volume of titer solution required to reach the equivalence point in the redox reaction.

5. In conductometric titrations ΔV is either the change in conductance (ΔC), or it is $\Delta C / C$, with C equal to the conductance of the solution. R' is the volume of titer solution required to achieve the isoconductance point. In precipitation studies R' is the volume of titer solution required to complete precipitation.

In these examples ΔV has the general mathematical form

$$\Delta V = f(R) + C \qquad (1)$$

Here C is a constant and $f(R)$ is a continuous function of R whose first

[1] P. Job, *Ann. chim. Paris*, **9** (1928), 113.

[2] F. J. C. Rossotti and H. Rossotti, *The Determination of Stability Constants* (New York: McGraw-Hill Book Co., 1961), pp. 47–57.

derivative $(f'(R))$ satisfies the equation:

$$f'(R') = 0 \qquad\qquad (2)$$

The number of positive real roots for equation (2) is determined by the number of complexes, compounds, eutectic compounds, azeotropes, equivalence points, etc., for the system.

In this chapter equation (1) is called the Job's Method equation.

In Program 28 (call word BBAAA) ΔV and R are calculated from the measured absorbance ($Y(I, JJ)$), the absorbancy indices, and the concentrations or mole fractions of A and B according to the method of continuous variations. Next the functional form of ΔV is determined. Then its derivative is taken, and equation (2) is solved for R'. The *instrument reliability factors* for $Y(I,JJ)$ and for the concentration of B are used to compute the *error zones* for equation (1). The *self-judgment principle* is applied in the normal way to discard sets of conjugate information lying outside the *error zones* and to compute the *maximum permitted error* in R'. Input information for Programs 28 or 328 (see next section) can be processed with *autoplotter Program 503 (call word CEEEE)*, as described in Chapter I. In the normal procedure the autoplot would be inspected for terminal values of ΔV, and the *reject–restore commands* (see *input commands* for Programs 28 and 328) would be selected so that only sets of conjugate data near the terminal value are processed during the first cycle. Mathematical details of the procedure are noted in the section entitled "Method of Solution," later in this chapter. With a knowledge of the chemistry involved in examples 1 through 5 (see above) one can use Program 28 to obtain solutions for equation (2) from the data for these other types of measurements.

SPECIAL MODIFICATIONS

In Program 328 (*call word* BBAAS) the *self-judgment principle* is applied only in the ΔV dimension for the determination of the expansion coefficients of ΔV expanded in terms of R. In Program 28 the *self-judgment principle* is applied in each dimension of the expansion. Both programs have identical input and output formats. Program 328 should be used if sets of conjugate information are being rejected because the expansion coefficients are small. With *Switches* 1 to 4 in the designated positions (see "Optional External Commands for Programs 28 and 328" later in this chapter), sufficient output information is given to enable the operator to decide if this is occurring.

Here are the replacement statements for converting Program 28 to Program 328.

ORIGINAL	REPLACEMENT
Program 28 (*Call Word* BBAAA)	*Program* 328 (*Call Word* BBAAS)

1 READ,BBAAA,FEEDP	1 READ,BBAAS,FEEDP
NUM = 28	NUM = 328
PUNCH,BBAAA,NUM,FEEDP	PUNCH,BBAAS,NUM,FEEDP
JRK = 0	IF(YY(I,JJ))127,130,127
DO 126 J = 1,JJ	127 AA = SQR(YER(I,JJ)*YER(I,JJ))
IF(YY(I,JJ))127,130,127	BB = SQR(DEV(I,JJ)*DEV(I,JJ))
127 AA = SQR(YER(I,J)*YER(I,J))	IF(AA − BB)129,128,128
BB = SQR(DEV(I,J)*DEV(I,J))	129 IF(NNN − 1)1,130,132
IF(AA − BB)129,128,128	130 DO 9003 J = 1,JJ
129 IF(NNN − 1)1,130,132	Y(I,J) = 0·0
130 Y(I,J) = 0.0	9003 DEV(I,J) = 0.0
DEV(I,J) = 0.0	GO TO 126
GO TO 126	128 IF(NNN − 1)1,126,133
128 IF(NNN − 1)1,126,133	131 DO 9001 J = 1,JJ
131 JRK = JRK + 1	9001 Y(I,J) = YY(I,J)
IF (JRK − JJ)126,43,1	GO TO 126
43 DO 9001 JP = 1,JJ	
9001 Y(I,JP) = YY(I,JP)	
GO TO 126	

METHOD OF SOLUTION

The procedure in Programs 28 or 328 for the calculation of R' (see equations (1) and (2)) and the associated *maximum permitted error* (R'ER) is as follows: (a) The input information for these programs is processed with *Autoplotter Program* 503 (*call word* CEEEE), as described in Chapter I. (b) *Reject–restore commands* (see *input commands* for Programs 28 and 328) are selected so that six to ten sets of conjugate data, spread over the terminal value for ΔV, are used in calculating the expansion coefficients (see below).

In Programs 28 and 328, ΔV and R, defined for equation (1), are computed from the measured absorbance (A_0), the absorbancy indices of A and B (a_A and a_B), and the concentrations or mole fractions of A and B (C_A and C_B), thus:

$$\Delta V = A_0 - a_A \cdot C_A - a_B \cdot C_B \tag{3}$$

$$R = C_A / C_B \tag{4}$$

The absorbancy indices of both A and B can be entered in the following form:

$$a_A = {_A}a_0 + {_A}a_1 \cdot C_A + {_A}a_2 \cdot C_A^2 + {_A}a_3 \cdot C_A^3 + {_A}a_4 \cdot C_A^4 \tag{5}$$

Expansion coefficients ($_Aa_0$, $_Aa_1$, $\cdots$) in equation (5) can be computed from data for the separate solutions with one of the *expansion programs* in Chapter II.

The functional form of ΔV is computed by expanding the values for ΔV in terms of R, thus:

$$\Delta V = \alpha_0 + \alpha_1 R^n + \alpha_2 R^{2n} + \alpha_3 R^{3n} + \cdots \tag{6}$$

The value for n and the dimension of equation (6) are determined by the values entered for M and WAC(2) (see *input commands* for Programs 28 and 328). Next equation (6) is solved for R', the R value for which ΔV is a maximum or minimum. Finally the *maximum permitted error* in R', denoted by R'ER, is computed from the *instrument reliability factors*.

The values entered for A_0, a_A, a_B, C_A, and C_B are determined by the kind of data being processed. For example, if $A_0 = \Delta E/E$, $a_A = 0 = a_B$, $C_A = 1.0$, and C_B = volume of titer solution, R' and R'ER will refer to the volume of titer solution required to reach the equivalence point (see example 4).

Throughout the remainder of this chapter the discussion will be in terms of Job's Method of Continuous Variations (see example 1), with ΔV equal to the net increase in the absorbance at a fixed wavelength and temperature.

COMPUTER PROCEDURE OF SOLUTION

In computing R'(RAM) and R'ER(RAMER) the following instructions are executed by the computer.

1. *Read in* the input information, and apply the *fail–safe procedure* to the measured absorbance (Y(I, JJ)) and the concentration (or mole fraction) (C2(I)) of the second component to reject sets of conjugate data with unreliable information.

2. The ordinates for equation (6) are computed from nonzero sets of conjugate data and the absorbancy indices for A and B. Here Y(I, JJ) = ΔV, Y(I, 1) = R^n, Y(I, 2) = R^{2n}, etc. Next the *maximum permitted deviations* for the measured absorbance and C2(I) are used to calculate the *maximum permitted errors* in each value of each ordinate. YER(I, J) is the *maximum permitted error* for Y(I, J).

3. The *reject–restore commands* (see *input commands* for Programs 28 and 328), which activate the semiautomatic *reject–restore mechanism*, are executed. These commands should be selected only after inspection of the autoplot, as described in the preceding section.

4. The *double slope* and *Crout reduction methods* are used to compute the expansion coefficients (see equation (6)) from accepted sets of conjugate information for the selected dimension expansion. At the end of the first cycle the next step (step 5) is omitted.

5. During the second, third, $\cdots$ JCth cycles, the *self-judgment Principle* is applied in the normal way. During its application, sets of conjugate information lying outside or inside the error zone are rejected or restored, respectively. If there are fewer than six accepted sets of conjugate information (G2) the computer prints and punches *code*, and the calculation is terminated. Here $code = 99999999.0$ means $0 < G2 \leq 5$. $Code = 88888888.0$ means $G2 = 0$.

6. At the end of each cycle the standard deviations in each ordinate are calculated from all sets of conjugate information in the memory, even if they were not used in the preceding cycle. (See *input commands* for Programs 28 and 328.)

7. Next, equation (6) is solved by a search method for the maximum or minimum value of ΔV, ($Y(I, JJ)$), designated by the value entered for RLM(2) (see *input commands* for Programs 28 and 328). The computer is instructed to find the value for RAM to within 0.01.

8. After the JCth cycle, the *maximum permitted error* for each of the expansion coefficients is computed from the information obtained during the JCth cycle. Next, equation (6), with each expansion coefficient replaced by the sum of its original value plus its *maximum permitted error*, is solved for RAM + RAMER, where RAMER is the *maximum permitted error* in RAM.

9. Steps 1 through 8 are repeated for each of the other $M6 - 1$ wavelengths.

INSTRUMENT RELIABILITY FACTORS

In Programs 28 and 328 RLM(1), WAC(1), WL(1), WU(1), and DEVF(1) (or DEV1(I)) are associated exclusively with $Y(I, JJ)$, the measured absorbance. WL(2), WU(2), and DEVF(2) (or DEV2(I)) are associated with the concentration (or mole fraction) of the second component. It should be noted that RLM(2) and WAC(2) are *input commands* in Programs 28 and 328.

WL and WU denote the lowest and highest reliable values, respectively, for the designated observable. The form in which the *maximum permitted deviations* (i.e., DEVF(1) or DEV1(I)) are entered for each observable is determined by K (see *input commands* for Programs 28 and 328). DEVF(1) denotes a deviation entered as a fixed fraction of all $Y(I, JJ)$. DEV1(I) is the *maximum permitted deviation* in the Ith value of the measured absorbance ($Y(I, JJ)$). A net increase in the absorbance of less than $WAC(1) * Y(I, JJ)$ is regarded as unreliable. RLM(1), the *measured limit of reliability (or reproducibility)* for the measured absorbance is not used in the calculation but it must be entered.

FAIL-SAFE PROCEDURE

All sets of conjugate data with concentrations $(C2(I))$ or measured absorbancies $(Y(I, JJ))$ less than the lowest reliable values $(WL(2), WL(1))$ or greater than the highest reliable values $(WU(2), WU(1))$ are rejected. Also, all net increases in the absorbance less than $WAC(1) * Y(I, JJ)$ are rejected.

STATISTICAL BIAS

The fully automatic three-step normalization procedure described in Chapter III has been incorporated into Programs 28 and 328. It is virtually impossible to induce round-off error in these programs. However, infinities can occur if $WL(1)$ and/or $WL(2)$ are set equal to zero. This fault is avoided by setting $WL(1)$ and $WL(2)$ equal to the lowest acceptable values for the designated observables.

The extreme sensitivity of the *Crout reduction method* to gross errors in input information, discussed in both Chapters III and IV, has been retained in Programs 28 and 328.

Activity coefficients can be introduced into both programs by replacing the statements numbered 999 and 1110 by the desired weighting and correction functions. The sensitivity of the *Crout reduction method* is not altered significantly by the special weighting functions used to reduce *statistical bias*.

INPUT COMMANDS FOR PROGRAMS 28 AND 328

Dimension Commands

Values for JQ, JD, JR, and IJ, *selected before compilation*, determine the storage capacity required.

JQ The maximum number of sets of conjugate data that can be processed with the program. JQ should be a multiple of 4

JD The maximum dimension equation which can be solved with the program

JR The number of columns in the *Crout reduction matrix*, equals JD + 1

IJ In Programs 28 and 328 IJ = 4 (see the second FORTRAN statement). For IJ = 4, the reject mechanism (RJM) is applied once, followed by two successive applications of the restore part (RSM) of the *self-judgment principle* in the second, third $\cdots$ JCth cycles. The reader is advised to study the programs very carefully before changing the value for IJ. If one sets IJ = 7 the pattern of application for the second, third $\cdots$ JCth cycles is: RJM, RSM, RSM, RJM, RSM, RSM

JQ, JD, and JR appear in the *dimension* statements for the FORTRAN programs. Other *dimension commands* are entered after compilation with the input information. These are:

JI   The number of sets of conjugate data to be processed with the program. JI must be a multiple of 4, and it cannot exceed JQ. If there are 22 sets to be processed, JI = 24 and 2 zero sets must be entered

WAC(2)   Used here in place of the JJ in Programs 25–27 and 325–327. WAC(2) is the dimension of the functional form of ΔV, (Y(I, JJ)) (i.e., WAC(2) is the dimension of the expansion in equation (6)). WAC(2) cannot exceed JD

With the IBM 1620–60K computer at the University of Mississippi, JQ = 20, JD = 5, JR = 6, and IJ = 4 were used.

Expansion Commands

RLM(2)   Denotes the curvature of the plot of ΔV, (Y(I, JJ)), versus R, (Y(I,1))

RLM(2) = 0.0   Denotes a plot with a maximum

RLM(2) ≥ 1.0   Denotes a plot with a minimum

M   Determines the value of QQ (= n in equation 6) to be used in the expansion

M	QQ	M	QQ
1	1.0	6	0.5
2	0.9	7	0.4
3	0.8	8	0.3
4	0.7	9	0.2
5	0.6	10	0.1

Our usual values are WAC(2) = 5.0 and QQ = 1.0 or 0.5.

Other Commands

In this section there are discussed the *reject–restore commands* (KA, KB, KC, KD, KE, and KF), the *cycle command* (JC), *wavelength command* (M6), the *maximum permitted deviation command* (K), and the *absorbancy index command* (L).

JC   The number of cycles that will be completed before the *error analysis* (see Computer Procedure of Solution). The *self-judgment principle* is not applied in the first cycle or in the *error analysis* (JC + 1) cycle

M6   The number of wavelengths at which data are processed

K   Determines the forms of the *maximum permitted deviations* for the measured absorbance (DEVF(1) or DEV1(I) and the concentration or the mole fraction of the second component (DEVF(2) or DEV2(I))

K = 1	DEVF(1); DEVF(2)	K = 3	DEV1(I); DEVF(2)
K = 2	DEVF(1); DEV2(I)	K = 4	DEV1(I); DEV2(I)

KA,KB,KC,KD,KE, and KF determine which sets of conjugate information are to be killed or ignored. A killed set is completely removed from the memory and is not considered in applications of the *self-judgment principle*. Ignored sets are not considered in the first cycle or in the reject part of the *self-judgment principle*. However, in the two restore parts of the *self-judgment principle* ignored sets are considered. In the following table "Kill (KB–KC)" means that the KBth to KCth sets are to be removed from memory. "Ignore (KB, KC, KD)" means that the KBth, KCth, and KDth sets are to be ignored until the restore parts of the *self-judgment principle* are applied in the second cycle

KA	Command	KA	Command
−1	No sets are killed or ignored	11	Kill(KB,KC,KD)
0	Ignore(KB–KC)	12	Kill(KB,KC,KD,KE)
1	Ignore(KB)	13	Kill(KB,KC,KD,KE,KF)
2	Ignore(KB,KC)	14	Kill(KB–KC; KD–KE)
3	Ignore(KB,KC,KD)	15	No sets are killed or ignored
4	Ignore(KB,KC,KD,KE)	16	Kill(KB–KC)
5	Ignore(KB,KC,KD,KE,KF)	17	Kill(KB)
6	Ignore(KB–KC; KD–KE)	18	Kill(KB); ignore(KC)
7	No sets are ignored or killed	19	Kill(KB,KD); ignore(KC)
8	Kill(KB–KC)	20	Kill(KB,KD); ignore(KC,KE)
9	Kill(KB)	21	Kill(KB,KD,KF); ignore (KC,KE)
10	Kill(KB,KC)	22	Kill(KB–KC); ignore(KD–KE)

L   Determines the forms in which the absorbancy indices (a_A and a_B) of the separate components (A and B) are entered. $a_B = 0$ means that no value for the absorbancy index of B is to be entered. When a_B is dependent on the concentration of B, a_B will be entered in its *functional form* thus:

$$a_B = {}_0a_B + {}_Ba_1 \cdot C_B + {}_Ba_2 \cdot C_B^2 + {}_Ba_3 \cdot C_B^3 + {}_Ba_4 \cdot C_B^4$$

$20 < L \leq 30$	a_A is constant; $a_B = 0$
$30 < L \leq 40$	a_A is dependent; $a_B = 0$
$40 < L \leq 50$	a_A and a_B are constant
$50 < L \leq 60$	a_A is dependent; a_B is constant
$60 < L \leq 70$	a_A is constant; a_B is dependent
$70 < L \leq 80$	a_A and a_B are dependent

INPUT FORMAT FOR PROGRAMS 28 AND 328

Autoplots of the input information for Programs 28 and 328 can be obtained with *Autoplotter Program* 503 (*call word* CEEEE) if JI = 20 and the first card is removed (see Chapter I).

STATEMENT	COMMENT
READ,JI	Dimension command

> *Note.* JI, the number of sets of conjugate information to be processed as a multiple of 4, is entered only with the first deck of input information if subsequent decks have the same number of sets.

STATEMENT	COMMENT
READ,BBAAA or BBAAS,FEEDP	BBAAA = 28.0; BBAAS = 328.0; FEEDP = source
READ,JC	*Cycle command*
READ,M6	*Wavelength command*
READ,KA,KB,KC,KD,KE,KF	*Reject–restore commands*
READ,K,L,M	*Input commands*

STATEMENT	COMMENT
READ,RLM(1),WAC(1),WL(1),WU(1)	*Instrument reliability factors for* Y(I,JJ)
READ,RLM(2)WAC(2),WL(2),WU(2)	RLM(2) and WAC(2) are *input commands.* WL(2) and WU(2) are *instrument reliability factors* for C2(I)
READ,Y(I,JJ),Y(I+1,JJ),Y(I+2,JJ), Y(I+3,JJ)	Measured absorbance
READ,AI1X (20 < L < 40) or	
READ,AI1X,AI2X (40 < L ≤ 80)	
READ,A1(1),A1(2),A1(3),A1(4) $\Big\}$ READ,A2(1),A2(2),A2(3),A2(4)	Entered only for certain L values (see Input Commands)

DEFINITION

AI1X and AI2X are the concentration independent parts of the absorbancy indices for the first and second components respectively. A1(1), A1(2), A1(3), and A1(4) are the expansion coefficients describing the concentration dependent part of the absorbancy index for the first component.

READ,C1,(I),C1(I+1),C1(I+2),C1(I+3)	Concentration or mole fraction of first component
READ,C2(I),C2(I+1),C2(I+2),C2(I+3)	Concentration or mole fraction of second component
READ,DEVF(1) or READ,DEV1(I),DEV1(I+1), DEV1(I+2),DEV1(I+3) $\Big\}$	
READ,DEVF(2) or READ,DEV2(I),DEV2(I+1), DEV2(I+2),DEV2(I+3) $\Big\}$	Format of *Maximum permitted deviation* is determined by the value entered for **K** (see Input Commands)
READ,OPER,INSTR READ,RUN,TEMP,WAVEL $\Big\}$	Identification

The following information is entered for each of the other M6 − 1 wavelengths.
READ,Y(I,JJ),Y(I+1,JJ),Y(I+2,JJ),Y(I+3,JJ)
READ,AI1X   (20 < L ≤ 40)
    or
READ,AI1X,AI2X   (40 < L ≤ 80)
READ,A1(1),A1(2),A1(3),A1(4)
READ,A2(1),A2(2),A2(3),A2(4)

These symbols are defined above.

OPTIONAL EXTERNAL COMMANDS FOR PROGRAMS 28 AND 328

In the following table if no position is given for a switch this means the commands will be executed regardless of their positions.

SWITCH POSITIONS				COMMANDS EXECUTED AND COMMENTS
1	2	3	4	

1	2	3	4	
ON				PUNCH,SL(J),SQRMS(J) J=1,2,···WAC(2) This command is executed at the end of each cycle. The SL(J) are expansion coefficients calculated in the preceding cycles, defined in equation (A): $\quad$ Y = SL(1) . X^n + SL(2) . X^{2n} + ... + SL(JJ) (A) SQRMS(1), SQRMS(2),...SQRMS(JJ) are standard deviations for X^n, X^{2n}, ... Y, respectively. Y = ΔV; X = C1(I)/C2(I).
ON	ON			PUNCH,YY(I,JJ),YY(I+1,JJ),YY(I+2,JJ),YY(I+3,JJ) PUNCH,Y(I,JJ),Y(I+1,JJ),Y(I+2,JJ),Y(I+3,JJ) This command is executed at the end of each cycle. YY(I,JJ) is the Ith value of Y originally entered. Y(I,JJ) is the Ith value of Y used in the preceding cycle.
ON	OFF	ON		PUNCH,YY(I,J),YY(I+1,J),YY(I+2,J)YY(I+3,J) PUNCH,Y(I,J),Y(I+1,J),Y(I+2,J),Y(I+3,J) PUNCH,YER(I,J),YER(I+1,J),YER(I+2,J),YER(I+3,J) PUNCH,DEV(I,J),DEV(I+1,J),DEV(I+2,J),DEV(I+3,J) This command is executed at the end of each cycle for all I(= 1 to JI) and J(=1 to WAC(2)). YY(I,J) is the original information. Y(I,J) is the information used in the preceding cycle. YER(I,J) and DEV(I,J) are the *maximum permitted error* and the *actual error* in YY(I,J). Y(I,1) and Y(I,JJ) refer to X^n and Y in equation (A).
			OFF	The commands given for *switches* 1 and 2 ON are executed at the end of the JCth cycle if G2 $\neq$ G1 regardless of their positions. G2 and G1 are defined in the Output Format.
			ON	The commands for *switches* 1, 2, and 3, ON, OFF, and ON, are executed at the end of the JCth cycle if G2 $\neq$ G1 regardless of their positions.

OUTPUT FORMAT FOR PROGRAMS 28 AND 328

Symbols not specifically defined in this section have been defined in the preceding sections.

STATEMENT	COMMENT
PUNCH,BBAAA or BBAAS,NUM,FEEDP PUNCH,JJ,JI,JC,M4 PUNCH,M6	NUM = program number

DEFINITIONS

JJ = WAC(2)		The dimension of the expansion
JI		The number of sets of conjugate data, as a multiple of four
JC		Cycle command (see *input commands*)
M4		Designation of the wavelength at which data are processed
M6		The number of wavelengths at which data are processed

Input commands

PUNCH,K,L,M

$\left.\begin{array}{l}\text{PUNCH,RLM(1),WAC(1),WL(1),WU(1)}\\\text{PUNCH,RLM(2),WAC(2),WL(2),WU(2)}\end{array}\right\}$ Defined for the *input format*

$\left.\begin{array}{l}\text{PRINT,CODE,M4,RUN}\\\text{PUNCH,OPER,INSTR}\\\text{PUNCH,RUN,TEMP,WAVEL}\end{array}\right\}$ Executed only if code = 88888888.0 or 99999999.0 (see Computer Procedure of Solution). If G2 < 6, the calculation is terminated

PUNCH,JC,G,G1,G2
PUNCH,RAM
PUNCH,SL(J),SQRMS(J)   J = 1, 2, $\cdots$ JJ

$\left.\begin{array}{l}\text{PUNCH,YY(I,JJ),YY(I+1,JJ),YY(I+2,JJ),YY(I+3,JJ)}\\\text{PUNCH,Y(I,JJ),Y(I+1,JJ),Y(I+2,JJ),Y(I+3,JJ)}\\\text{(for I = 1,5, }\cdots\text{,(JI}-3))\end{array}\right\}$

If *switch* 1 is ON
For *switches* 1 and 2 ON, or for G2 $\neq$ G1 in the JCth cycle with *switch* 4 OFF

or

$\left.\begin{array}{l}\text{PUNCH,YY(I,J),YY(I+1,J),YY(I+2,J),YY(I+3,J)}\\\text{PUNCH,Y(I,J),Y(I+1,J),Y(I+2,J),Y(I+3,J)}\\\text{PUNCH,YER(I,J),YER(I+1,J),YER(I+2,J),YER(I+3,J)}\\\text{(for all J, and for I = 1,5, }\cdots\text{,(JI}-3))\end{array}\right\}$

For *switches* 1, 2, and 3 ON, OFF and ON, or for G2 $\neq$ G1 in the JCth cycle if *switch* 4 is ON

DEFINITIONS

JC		The number of the cycle
G		The number of sets of conjugate data remaining after the first application (i.e., WL(1), WL(2), WU(1), and WU(2)) of the *fail–safe procedure*
G1		The number of accepted sets after the second application (i.e., WAC(1)) of the *fail–safe procedure*
G2		The number of sets of conjugate information used to compute the SL(J) in the JCth cycle
RAM		The ratio of concentrations or mole fractions (i.e., C1(I)/C2(I)) at the terminal value for Y(I,JJ), which is the net increase in absorbance
SL(J)		The Jth expansion coefficient calculated in the JCth cycle
SQRMS(J)		The standard deviation for the Jth ordinate calculated from the original information (YY(I,J))
YY(I,J)		The original information for the Jth ordinate of the expansion equation (see equation (A) in table of "Optional External Commands for Programs 28 and 328")
Y(I,J)		The values for the Jth ordinate actually used to compute SL(J) and RAM
YER(I,J)		The *maximum permitted Error* in YY(I,J)
DEV(I,J)		The *actual error* in YY(I,J)

The information between the double lines is generated for each of the programmed (JC) cycles.

In the JC + 1 cycle, the computer performs the *error analysis* and executes the following commands.

PUNCH,JC,G,G1,G2   ⎫
PUNCH,RAM,RAMER   ⎬   G, G1, G2, and RAM are obtained in the preceding cycle. RAMER is the maximum permitted error in RAM
                          ⎭

PUNCH,OPER, INSTR   ⎫
PUNCH,RUN,TEMP,WAVEL ⎬   Identification

The entire output format is generated for each of the M6 wavelengths for which data are processed.

RELIABILITY LIMITS FOR PROGRAMS 28 AND 328

The reliability limits for Programs 28 and 328 are identical with those for Programs 27 and 327 (Chapter IV), 26 and 326 (Chapter III), and 25 and 325 (Chapter II). It is virtually impossible to induce normal round-off errors in these programs. The extreme sensitivity of the *Crout reduction method* should be noted if *code* = 88888888.0 appears in the output format.

FORTRAN FOR PROGRAM NUMBER 28
CALL WORD BBAAA

```
DIMENSION Y(JQ,JD),DEV(JQ,JD),YER(JQ,JD),YY(JQ,JD)
DIMENSION A(JR,JR),RLM(JD),WL(JD),DEVF(JD),WU(JD)
DIMENSION YM(JD),YA(JD),SL(JD),SLX(JD),C1(JQ),YN(JD)
DIMENSION YB(JD),DEV1(JQ),DEV2(JQ),SQRMS(JD),DEVSL(JD)
DIMENSION C2(JQ),WAC(JD),FUNY(JD),FUSL(JD),A1(4),A2(4)
DIMENSION R2(3),R4(3)
READ,JI
IJ=4
1 READ,BBAAA,FEEDP
READ,JC
N=JC
READ,M6
M5=M6
M4=0
READ,K,L,M
READ,KA,KB,KC,KD,KE,KF
Q=L
Q=Q/10.0
DO 2 I=1,8
P=I
IF(Q-P)3,3,2
3 LL=P
GO TO 4
2 CONTINUE
LL=9
4 READ,RLM(1),WAC(1),WL(1),WU(1)
READ,RLM(2),WAC(2),WL(2),WU(2)
QQ=0.0
DO 5 J=1,4
A1(J)=0.0
5 A2(J)=0.0
AI1X=0.0
AI2X=0.0
JJ=WAC(2)
GO TO (300,301,302,303,304,305,306,307,308,309),M
300 QQ=QQ+0.1
301 QQ=QQ+0.1
302 QQ=QQ+0.1
303 QQ=QQ+0.1
304 QQ=QQ+0.1
305 QQ=QQ+0.1
306 QQ=QQ+0.1
307 QQ=QQ+0.1
308 QQ=QQ+0.1
309 QQ=QQ+0.1
IF(LL-2)1,1,10
10 DO 6 I=1,JI,4
6 READ,Y(I,JJ),Y(I+1,JJ),Y(I+2,JJ),Y(I+3,JJ)
IF(LL-4)7,7,8
7 READ,AI1X
GO TO 9
8 READ,AI1X,AI2X
9 GO TO (1,1,20,11,20,11,20,11),LL
11 READ,A1(1),A1(2),A1(3),A1(4)
20 IF(LL-6)12,12,13
13 READ,A2(1),A2(2),A2(3),A2(4)
12 G=0.0
JK=JJ-1
DO 4337 J=1,JK
```

```
      DO 4337 I=1,JI
4337  Y(I,J)=YY(I,J)
      G1=0.0
      G2=0.0
      IF(M4)1,14,153
14    DO 15 I=1,JI,4
15    READ,C1(I),C1(I+1),C1(I+2),C1(I+3)
      DO 16 I=1,JI,4
16    READ,C2(I),C2(I+1),C2(I+2),C2(I+3)
      IF(K-2)17,17,19
17    READ,DEVF(1)
      GO TO 18
19    DO 21 I=1,JI,4
21    READ,DEV1(I),DEV1(I+1),DEV1(I+2),DEV1(I+3)
      DEVF(1)=5555.0
18    GO TO (22,23,22,23),K
22    READ,DEVF(2)
      GO TO 24
23    DO 25 I=1,JI,4
25    READ,DEV2(I),DEV2(I+1),DEV2(I+2),DEV2(I+3)
      DEVF(2)=5555.0
24    READ,OPER,INSTR
      READ,RUN,TEMP,WAVEL
      KQ=KA+2
      IF(KQ-8)26,26,27
27    IF(KQ-16)28,28,29
28    KQ=KQ-8
      GO TO (26,30,31,32,33,34,35,36),KQ
36    DO 37 I=KD,KE
37    C2(I)=0.0
30    DO 38 I=KB,KC
38    C2(I)=0.0
      GO TO 26
35    C2(KF)=0.0
34    C2(KE)=0.0
33    C2(KD)=0.0
32    C2(KC)=0.0
31    C2(KB)=0.0
      GO TO 26
29    IF(KQ-24)39,39,40
40    KA=-1
      GO TO 26
39    KQ=KQ-16
      GO TO (26,41,42,42,4333,4333,44,41),KQ
41    DO 45 I=KB,KC
45    C2(I)=0.0
      GO TO 26
44    C2(KF)=0.0
4333  C2(KD)=0.0
42    C2(KB)=0.0
26    DO 46 I=1,JI
      IF(C2(I)-WL(2))47,48,48
48    IF(C2(I)-WU(2))49,49,47
47    C2(I)=0.0
      C1(I)=0.0
      DO 143 J=1,JJ
      YER(I,J)=0.0
      Y(I,J)=0.0
143   YY(I,J)=0.0
      GO TO 46
49    GO TO (310,311,310,311),K
310   DEV2(I)=DEVF(2)*C2(I)
```

```
311 Y(I,1)=(C1(I)/C2(I))**QQ
YER(I,1)=(C1(I)/(C2(I)+DEV2(I)))**QQ
DO 312 J=2,JK
JP=J-1
Y(I,J)=Y(I,1)*Y(I,JP)
312 YER(I,J)=YER(I,1)*YER(I,JP)
DO 313J=1,JK
YY(I,J)=Y(I,J)
313 YER(I,J)=Y(I,J)-YER(I,J)
IF(C1(I))47,47,46
46 CONTINUE
NUM=28
153 M4=M4+1
M5=M5-1
JC=N
PUNCH,BBAAA,NUM,FEEDP
PUNCH,JJ,JI,JC,M4
PUNCH,M6
PUNCH,K,L,M
PUNCH,DEVF(1),RLM(1),WAC(1),WL(1),WU(1)
PUNCH,DEVF(2),RLM(2),WAC(2),WL(2),WU(2)
JC=0.0
DO 154 I=1,JI
IF(C2(I))155,155,4335
4335 IF(Y(I,JJ)-WL(1))155,156,156
156 IF(Y(I,JJ)-WU(1))157,157,155
155 YER(I,JJ)=0.0
Y(I,JJ)=0.0
YY(I,JJ)=0.0
DEV(I,JJ)=0.0
GO TO 154
157 G=G+1.0
Z1=C1(I)*C1(I)
Z2=Z1*C1(I)
Z3=Z2*C1(I)
Z4=Z3*C1(I)
Z5=A11X*C1(I)+Z1*A1(1)+Z2*A1(2)+A1(3)*Z3+Z4*A1(4)
Z1=C2(I)*C2(I)
Z2=Z1*C2(I)
Z3=Z2*C2(I)
Z4=Z3*C2(I)
Z6=A12X*C2(I)+A2(1)*Z1+A2(2)*Z2+A2(3)*Z3+A2(4)*Z4
XYZ=Y(I,JJ)-Z5-Z6
XYZ=SQR(XYZ*XYZ)
Z1=Y(I,JJ)*WAC(1)
Z1=SQR(Z1*Z1)
IF(XYZ-Z1)155,158,158
158 G1=G1+1.0
Y(I,JJ)=Y(I,JJ)-Z5-Z6
YY(I,JJ)=Y(I,JJ)
IF(K-2)175,175,176
175 DEV(I,JJ)=DEVF(1)*(Y(I,JJ)+Z5+Z6)
176 YER(I,JJ)=DEV(I,JJ)
154 CONTINUE
KQ=KA+2
IF(KQ-8)159,159,160
159 GO TO (161,162,163,164,165,166,167,168),KQ
168 DO 169 I=KD,KE
169 Y(I,JJ)=0.0
162 DO 170 I=KB,KC
170 Y(I,JJ)=0.0
GO TO 161
```

```
167 Y(KF,JJ)=0.0
166 Y(KE,JJ)=0.0
165 Y(KD,JJ)=0.0
164 Y(KC,JJ)=0.0
163 Y(KB,JJ)=0.0
GO TO 161
160 KQ=KQ-16
IF(KQ)161,161,207
207 GO TO (161,161,161,171,171,172,172,173),KQ
173 DO 174 I=KD,KE
174 Y(I,JJ)=0.0
GO TO 161
172 Y(KE,JJ)=0.0
171 Y(KC,JJ)=0.0
161 CONTINUE
50 JC=JC+1
NNN=1
KKK=0
51 DO 52 J=1,JJ
YM(J)=-10000000.0
YN(J)=10000000.0
999 FUNY(J)=1.0
DO 53 I=1,JI
Y(I,J)=Y(I,J)*FUNY(J)
IF(Y(I,JJ))54,53,54
54 IF(YM(J)-Y(I,J))55,56,56
55 YM(J)=Y(I,J)
56 IF(YN(J)-Y(I,J))53,53,57
57 YN(J)=Y(I,J)
53 CONTINUE
IF(YN(J))6666,8892,8893
8892 YA(J)=-YM(J)/10.0
GO TO 8891
8893 YA(J)=-YN(J)/10.0
GO TO 8891
6666 YA(J)=2.0*YN(J)
8891 AA=YM(J)-YA(J)
BB=YN(J)-YA(J)
AA=SQR(AA*AA)
BB=SQR(BB*BB)
IF(AA-BB)58,60,59
60 IF(AA)61,61,59
61 CODE=88888888.0
62 PRINT,CODE,M4,RUN
PUNCH,CODE,M4
PUNCH,OPER,INSTR
PUNCH,RUN,TEMP,WAVEL
IF(M6-M4)1,1,10
58 YB(J)=BB
GO TO 63
59 YB(J)=AA
63 DO 52 I=1,JI
IF(Y(I,JJ))64,52,64
64 Y(I,J)=Y(I,J)-YA(J)
IF(Y(I,J))65,66,65
66 Y(I,J)=(YN(J)-YA(J))/(10.0**6.0)
65 Y(I,J)=Y(I,J)/YB(J)
52 CONTINUE
JR=JJ+1
DO 208J=1,JR
DO 208 I=1,JR
208 A(I,J)=0.0
```

```
      DO 67 J=1,JJ
      DO 67 JB=1,JJ
      DO 67 I=1,JI
      IF(Y(I,JJ))68,67,68
68    IF(JB-1)1,70,69
69    JP=JB-1
      A(JB,J)=A(JB,J)+Y(I,J)*Y(I,JP)
      GO TO 67
70    A(JB,J)=A(JB,J)+Y(I,J)
67    CONTINUE
      G2=0.0
      YAA=0.0
      DO 71 J=1,JJ
71    A(J,JR)=A(J,JJ)
      DO 72 I=1,JI
      IF(Y(I,JJ))73,72,73
73    G2=G2+1.0
72    CONTINUE
      A(1,JJ)=G2
      G9=6.0
      IF(G2-G9)74,75,75
74    CODE=99999999.0
      GO TO 62
75    DO 76 J=2,JJ
      JB=J-1
76    A(J,JJ)=A(1,JB)
      DO 77 J=1,JR
      DO 77 I=1,JJ
      AA=SQR(A(I,J)*A(I,J))
      IF(YAA-AA)78,77,77
78    YAA=AA
77    CONTINUE
      DO 79 J=1,JR
      DO 79 I=1,JJ
79    A(I,J)=A(I,J)/YAA
      DO 80 J=1,JR
      DO 80 I=1,JJ
      IF(J-1)80,80,82
82    IF(J-I)83,83,84
83    JA=J-1
      GO TO 85
84    JA=I-1
85    SET=0.0
      SUM=0.0
      IF(JA)86,86,87
87    DO 88 JK=1,JA
88    SUM=SUM+A(I,JK)*A(JK,J)
86    SET=A(I,J)-SUM
      IF(J-I)89,89,90
89    A(I,J)=SET
      GO TO 80
90    SOB=A(I,I)
      IF(SOB)94,8889,94
8889  SOB=10.0**(-18.0)
94    A(I,J)=SET/SOB
80    CONTINUE
      DO 81 I=1,JJ
      JAN=JR-I
      SUM2=0.0
      IA=I-1
      IF(IA)81,81,91
91    DO 93 JK=1,IA
```

```
      JOB=JR-JK
   93 SUM2=SUM2+A(JAN,JOB)*SL(JOB)
   81 SL(JAN)=A(JAN,JR)-SUM2
      DO 95 I=1,JI
      DO 95 J=1,JJ
      IF(Y(I,JJ))96,95,96
   96 Y(I,J)=YB(J)*Y(I,J)
      Y(I,J)=Y(I,J)+YA(J)
      Y(I,J)=Y(I,J)/FUNY(J)
   95 CONTINUE
      SL(JJ)=SL(JJ)*YB(JJ)
      AXYZ=0.0
      JK=JJ-1
      DO 205 J=1,JK
      SL(J)=SL(J)*YB(JJ)/YB(J)
  205 AXYZ=AXYZ+SL(J)*YA(J)
      SL(JJ)=SL(JJ)-AXYZ+YA(JJ)
      DO 206 J=1,JJ
 1110 FUSL(J)=1.0
  206 SL(J)=SL(J)*FUSL(J)
      N77=0
      JK=JJ-1
      IF(KKK)1,177,186
  177 Z1=SQR(SL(JJ)*SL(JJ))
      DO 178 J=1,JK
      SLX(J)=SL(J)
      Z2=SQR(SL(J)*SL(J))
      IF(Z1-Z2)178,178,179
  179 N77=J
  178 CONTINUE
      IF(N77)1,181,182
  182 DO 183 I=1,JI
      QRO=Y(I,N77)
      IF(Y(I,N77))184,183,184
  184 DO 185 J=1,JJ
  185 Y(I,J)=Y(I,J)/QRO
      Y(I,N77)=1.0/QRO
  183 CONTINUE
      N99=N77
      KKK=1
      GO TO 51
  186 SL(JJ)=SL(N99)
      N77=N99
      DO 187J=1,JK
  187 SL(J)=SLX(J)
      SLX(JJ)=SL(N77)
      DO 188 I=1,JI
      QRO=Y(I,N77)
      IF(Y(I,N77))189,188,189
  189 DO 331 J=1,JJ
  331 Y(I,J)=Y(I,J)/QRO
      Y(I,N77)=1.0/QRO
  188 CONTINUE
      KKK=0
  181 G3=G2-1.0
      IF(N-JC)123,124,124
  124 DO 8894 J=1,JJ
      SQRMS(J)=0.0
      DO 8894 I=1,JI
 8894 DEV(I,J)=0.0
      JK=JJ-1
      DO 97 I=1,JI
```

```
      RR=0.0
      IF(YY(I,JJ))99,97,99
   99 DO 98 J=1,JJ
      IF(JJ-J)1,101,100
  100 RR=RR+SL(J)*YY(I,J)
   98 CONTINUE
  101 QX=RR+SL(JJ)
      DEV(I,JJ)=YY(I,JJ)-QX
      DO 102 JP=1,JK
      IF(SL(JP))103,104,103
  104 DEV(I,JP)=0.0
      GO TO 102
  103 DEV(I,JP)=YY(I,JP)-(YY(I,JJ)-QX+SL(JP)*YY(I,JP))/SL(JP)
  102 CONTINUE
   97 CONTINUE
      DO 105 J=1,JJ
      DO 105 I=1,JI
  105 SQRMS(J)=SQRMS(J)+DEV(I,J)*DEV(I,J)
      DO 8895 J=1,JJ
 8895 SQRMS(J)=SQR(SQRMS(J)/G3)
  123 IF(JC-1)1,107,122
  107 PUNCH,JC,G,G1,G2
      IF(N-JC)326,109,109
  109 R1=0.0
      R2(1)=1.0
  324 R1=R1+1.0
      R3=1.0/(2.0**R1)
  321 R2(2)=R2(1)-R3
      R2(3)=R2(1)+R3
      JQ1=1
      JK=JJ-1
      DO 315 I=1,3
      R4(I)=0.0
      DO 316 J=1,JK
      R5=J
  316 R4(I)=R4(I)+SL(J)*(R2(I)**(R5*QQ))
      R4(I)=R4(I)+SL(JJ)
      IF(I-1)1,315,317
  317 IF(RLM(2))1,318,320
  318 IF(R4(I)-R4(1))315,315,319
  319 JQ1=I
      R2(1)=R2(I)
      GO TO 315
  320 IF(R4(I)-R4(1))319,315,315
  315 CONTINUE
      GO TO (322,321,321),JQ1
  322 IF(R3-0.01)323,323,324
  323 IF(N-JC)325,328,328
  328 RAM=R2(1)
      PUNCH,RAM
      IF(SENSE SWITCH 1)203,142
  325 RAMER=RAM-R2(1)
      PUNCH,RAM,RAMER
      PUNCH,OPER,INSTR
      PUNCH,RUN,TEMP,WAVEL
      IF(M6-M4)1,1,10
  326 DO 327 J=1,JJ
  327 SL(J)=SQR(SL(J)*SL(J))+DEVSL(J)
      GO TO 109
  203 DO 111 J=1,JJ
  111 PUNCH,SL(J),SQRMS(J)
  142 IF(N-JC)1,118,112
```

```
112 IF(SENSE SWITCH 2)113,115
113 DO 114 I=1,JI,4
PUNCH,YY(I,JJ),YY(I+1,JJ),YY(I+2,JJ),YY(I+3,JJ)
114 PUNCH,Y(I,JJ),Y(I+1,JJ),Y(I+2,JJ),Y(I+3,JJ)
IF(N-JC)1,119,50
115 IF(SENSE SWITCH 3)116,50
116 DO 117 I=1,JI,4
DO 117 J=1,JJ
PUNCH,YY(I,J),YY(I+1,J),YY(I+2,J),YY(I+3,J)
PUNCH,Y(I,J),Y(I+1,J),Y(I+2,J),Y(I+3,J)
PUNCH,YER(I,J),YER(I+1,J),YER(I+2,J),YER(I+3,J)
117 PUNCH,DEV(I,J),DEV(I+1,J),DEV(I+2,J),DEV(I+3,J)
IF(N-JC)1,119,50
118 IF(G1-G2)9002,119,9002
9002 IF(SENSE SWITCH 4)116,113
122 IF(N-JC)107,9999,9999
9999 IF(NNN-IJ)125,107,1
125 DO 126 I=1,JI
JRK=0
DO 126 J=1,JJ
IF(YY(I,JJ))127,130,127
127 AA=SQR(YER(I,J)*YER(I,J))
BB=SQR(DEV(I,J)*DEV(I,J))
IF(AA-BB)129,128,128
129 IF(NNN-1)1,130,132
130 Y(I,J)=0.0
DEV(I,J)=0.0
GO TO 126
128 IF(NNN-1)1,126,133
131 JRK=JRK+1
IF(JRK-JJ)126,43,1
43 DO 9001 JP=1,JJ
9001 Y(I,JP)=YY(I,JP)
GO TO 126
132 IF(NNN-4)126,130,126
133 IF(NNN-4)131,126,131
126 CONTINUE
NNN=NNN+1
GO TO 51
119 DO 134 J=1,JJ
IF(N-JC)134,135,1
135 DEVSL(J)=SL(J)
DO 134 I=1,JI
IF(Y(I,JJ))138,134,138
138 Y(I,JJ)=0.0
IF(JJ-J)1,139,140
140 JK=JJ-1
DO 141 JQ=1,JK
YER(I,JQ)=-SQR(YER(I,JQ)*YER(I,JQ))
141 Y(I,JJ)=Y(I,JJ)+SL(JQ)*YER(I,JQ)
139 Y(I,JJ)=YER(I,JJ)-Y(I,JJ)
134 CONTINUE
IF(N-JC)1,50,1
END
```

ALGOL 60 FOR PROGRAM NUMBER 28

```
PROCEDURE BBAAA(ji,ij); ARRAY y,dev,yer,yy[1:jq,1:jd],a[1:jr,1:jr],rLm,wL,
devf,wu,ym,ya,sL,sLx,yn,yb,sqrms,devsL,wac,funy,fusL[1:jd],c1,dev1,dev2,
c2[1:jq],r2,r4[1:3],a1,a2[1:4]; INTEGER ji,ij; SWITCH sw1:=x2,x3,x4,x5,x6,x7,
x8,x9,x10,x11; SWITCH sw2:=x93,x93,x15,x14,x15,x14,x15,x14; SWITCH
sw3:=x17,x18,x17,x18; SWITCH sw4:=x32,x21,x26,x25,x24,x23,x22,x20; SWITCH
sw5:=x32,x28,x31,x31,x30,x30,x29,x32; SWITCH sw6:=x35,x36,x35,x36; SWITCH
sw7:=x54,x44,x49,x48,x47,x46,x45,x43,x43; SWITCH sw8:=X54,x54,x54,x53,x53,x52
x52,x51; SWITCH sw9:=x75,x72,x72;
COMMENT: JOB'S METHOD EQUATIONS;
    BEGIN INTEGER i,ia,j,jj,ja,jb,jc,jk,jp,jr,jan,job,jq1,jrk,k,ka,kb,kc,kd,ke,
    kf,kq,kkk,L,LL,m,m4,m5,m6,n,nnn,n77,n99,feedp,oper,run,instr,code,num,
    g,g1,g2,g3,g9;
    REAL ai1x,ai2x,axyz,aa,bb,oper,p,q,qq,qro,qx,rr,r1,r3,r5,ram,ramer,set,
    sum,sum2,sob,temp,waveL,xyz,yaa,z1,z2,z3,z4,z5,z6;
    READ feedp;
    READ jc; n:=jc;
    READ m6; m5:=m6; m4:=0;
    READ k,L,m;
    READ ka,kb,kc,kd,ke,kf;
    q:=L/10;
    FOR i:=1 STEP 1 UNTIL 8 DO
    BEGIN
        p:=i;
        IF q≤p THEN
        BEGIN
            LL:=p; GO TO X1END
        END;
        LL:=9;
X1:     READ rLm[1],wac[1],wL[1],wu[1];
        READ rLm[2],wac[2],wL[2],wu[2];
        qq:=0;
        FOR j:=1 STEP 1 UNTIL 4 DO a1[j]:=a2[j]:=0;
        ai1x:=ai2x:=0;
        jj:=wac[2];
        GO TO sw1[m];
X2:     qq:=qq+0.1;
X3:     qq:=qq+0.1;
X4:     qq:=qq+0.1;
X5:     qq:=qq+0.1;
X6:     qq:=qq+0.1;
X7:     qq:=qq+0.1;
X8:     qq:=qq+0.1;
X9:     qq:=qq+0.1;
X10:    qq:=qq+0.1;
X11:    qq:=qq+0.1;
        IF LL≤2 THEN GO TO X93;
X12:    FOR i:=1 STEP 1 UNTIL ji DO READ y[i,jj];
        IF LL≤4 THEN
        BEGIN
            READ ai1x; GO TO X13END;
            READ ai1x,ai2x;
```

```
X13:    GO TO sw2[LL];
X14:    READ a1[1],a1[2],a1[3],a1[4];
X15:    IF LL>6 THEN READ a2[1],a2[2],a2[3],a2[4];
        g:=0;  jk:=jj−1;
        FOR j:=1 STEP 1 UNTIL jk DO
        FOR i:=1 STEP 1 UNTIL ji DO y[i,j]:=yy[i,j];
        g1:=g2:=0;
        IF m4<0 THEN GO TO X93
        ELSE IF m4>0 THEN GO TO X38;
        FOR i:=1 STEP 1 UNTIL ji DO READ c1[i];
        FOR i:=1 STEP 1 UNTIL ji DO READ c2[i];
        IF k≤2 THEN
        BEGIN
           READ devf[1];  GO TO X16END;
        FOR i:=1 STEP 1 UNTIL ji DO READ dev1[i];
        devf[1]:=5555;
X16:    GO TO sw3[k];
X17:    READ devf[2];  GO TO X19;
X18:    FOR i:=1 STEP 1 UNTIL ji DO READ dev2[i];
        devf[2]:=5555;
X19:    READ oper,instr;
        READ run,temp,waveL;
        kq:=ka+2;
        IF kq≤8 THEN GO TO X32
        ELSE IF kq>16 THEN GO TO X27;
        kq:=kq−8;  GO TO sw4[kq];
X20:    FOR i:=kd STEP 1 UNTIL ke DO c2[i]:=0;
X21:    FOR i:=kb STEP 1 UNTIL kc DO c2[i]:=0;
        GO TO X32;
X22:    c2[kf]:=0;
X23:    c2[ke]:=0;
X24:    c2[kd]:=0;
X25:    c2[kc]:=0;
X26:    c2[kb]:=0;  GO TO X32;
X27:    IF kq>24 THEN
        BEGIN
           ka:=−1;  GO TO X32END;
        kq:=kq−16;
        GO TO sw5[kq];
X28:    FOR i:=kb STEP 1 UNTIL kc DO c2[i]:=0;
        GO TO X32;
X29:    c2[kf]:=0;
X30:    c2[kd]:=0;
X31:    c2[kb]:=0;
X32:    FOR i:=1 STEP 1 UNTIL ji DO
        BEGIN
           IF(c2[i]:<wL[2])∨(c2[i]>wu[2])THEN
           BEGIN
X33:          c2[i]:=c1[i]:=0;
              FOR j:=1 STEP 1 UNTIL jj DO yer[i,j]:=y[i,j]:=yy[i,j]:=0;
              GO TO X37END;
X34:       GO TO sw6[k];
X35:       dev2[i]:=devf[2]Xc2[i];
```

```
X36:     y[i,1]:=(c1[i]/c2[i])↑qq;
         yer[i,1]:=(c1[i]/(c2[i]+dev2[i]))↑qq;
         FOR j:=2 STEP 1 UNTIL jk DO
         BEGIN
             jp:=j-1;
             y[i,j]:=y[i,1]Xy[i,jp];
             yer[i,j]:=yer[i,1]xyer[i,jp]
         END;
         FOR j:=1 STEP 1 UNTIL jk DO
         BEGIN
             yy[i,j]:=y[i,j];
             yer[i,j]:=y[i,j]-yer[i,j]
         END;
         IF c1[i]≤0 THEN GO TO X33
X37:     END;
         num:=28;
X38:     m4:=m4+1;  m5:=m5-1;  jc:=n;
         PUNCH num,feedp;
         PUNCH jj,ji,jc,m4;
         PUNCH m6;  PUNCH k,L,m;
         PUNCH devf[1],rLm[1],wac[1],wL[1],wu[1];
         PUNCH devf[2],rLm[2],wac[2],wL[2],wu[2];
         jc:=0;
         FOR i:=1 STEP 1 UNTIL ji DO
         BEGIN
             IF c2[i]≤0V(y[i,jj]<wL[1])V(y[i,jj]>wu[1])THEN
             BEGIN
X39:             yer[i,jj]:=y[i,jj]:=yy[i,jj]:=dev[i,jj]:=0;
                 GO TO X42END;
X40:         g:=g+1;
             z1:=c1[i]↑2;
             z2:=c1[i]↑3;
             z3:=c1[i]↑4;
             z4:=c1[i]↑5;
             z5:=ai1xXc1[i]+z1Xa1[1]+z2Xa1[2]+z3Xa1[3]+z4Xa1[4];
             z1:=c2[i]↑2;
             z2:=c2[i]↑3;
             z3:=c2[i]↑4;
             z4:=c2[i]↑5;
             z6:=ai2xXc2[i]+z1Xa2[1]+z2Xa2[2]+z3Xa2[3]+z4Xa2[4];
             xyz:=abs(y[i,jj]-z5-z6);
             z1:=abs(y[i,jj]Xwac[1]);
             IF xyz<z1 THEN GO TO X39;
X41:         g1:=g1+1;
             y[i,jj]:=y[i,jj]-z5-z6;  yy[i,jj]:=y[i,jj];
             IF k≤2 THEN dev[i,jj]:=devf[1]X(y[i,jj]+z5+z6);
             yer[i,jj]:=dev[i,jj]
X42:     END;
         kq:=ka+2;
         IF kq≤8 THEN
         BEGIN
             GO TO sw7[kq];
X43:         FOR i:=kd STEP 1 UNTIL ke DO y[i,jj]:=0;
X44:         FOR i:=kb STEP 1 UNTIL kc DO y[i,jj]:=0;
```

```
            GO TO X54;
X45:   y[kf,jj]:=0;
X46:   y[ke,jj]:=0;
X47:   y[kd,jj]:=0;
X48:   y[kc,jj]:=0;
X49:   y[kb,jj]:=0;  GO TO X54;
X50:   kq:=kq-16;
       IF kq≤0 THEN GO TO X54;
       GO TO sw8[kq];
X51:   FOR i:=kd STEP 1 UNTIL ke DO y[i,jj]:=0;
       GO TO X54;
X52:   y[ke,jj]:=0;
X53:   y[kc,jj]:=0;
X54:   jc:=jc+1; kkk:=0; nnn:=1;
X55:   FOR j:=1 STEP 1 UNTIL jj DO
       BEGIN
          ym[j]:=-10000000.0; yn[j]:=10000000.0;
          funy[j]:=1;
          FOR i:=1 STEP 1 UNTIL ji DO
          BEGIN
             y[i,j]:=y[i,j]Xfuny[j];
             IF y[i,jj]=0 THEN GO TO X56;
             IF ym[j]<y[i,j] THEN ym[j]:=y[i,j];
             IF yn[j]>y[i,j] THEN yn[j]:=y[i,j]
X56:      END;
          IF yn[j]=0 THEN
          BEGIN
             ya[j]:=-ym[j]/10;  GO TO X57END
          ELSE IF yn[j]>0 THEN
          BEGIN
             ya[j]:=-yn[j]/10;  GO TO X57END;
          ya[j]:=2Xyn[j];
X57:      aa:=abs(ym[j]-ya[j]);
          bb:=abs(yn[j]-ya[j]);
          IF aa<bb THEN GO TO X59
          ELSE IF aa>bb∨aa>0 THEN GO TO X60;
          code:=88888888;
X58:      PUNCH code,m4;
          PUNCH oper,instr;
          PUNCH run,temp,waveL;
          IF m6≤m4 THEN GO TO X93 ELSE GO TO X12;
X59:      yb[j]:=bb;  GO TO X61;
X60:      yb[j]:=aa;
X61:      FOR i:=1 STEP 1 UNTIL ji DO
          BEGIN
             IF y[i,jj]=0 THEN GO TO X62;
             y[i,j]:=y[i,j]-ya[j];
             IF y[i,jj]=0 THEN y[i,j]:=(yn[j]-ya[j])/₁₀6;
             y[i,j]:=y[i,j]/yb[j]
X62:      END END;
          jr:=jj+1;
          FOR j:=1 STEP 1 UNTIL jr DO
          FOR i:=1 STEP 1 UNTIL jr DO a[i,j]:=0;
```

```
          FOR j:=1 STEP 1 UNTIL jj DO
          FOR jb:=1 STEP 1 UNTIL jj DO
          FOR i:=1 STEP 1 UNTIL ji DO
          BEGIN
            IF y[i,jj]=0 THEN GO TO X63;
            IF jb<1 THEN GO TO X93
            ELSE IF jb>1 THEN
            BEGIN
              jp:=jb−1;
              a[jb,j]:=a[jb,j]+y[i,j]Xy[i,jp];
              GO TO X63END;
            a[jb,j]:=a[jb,j]+y[i,j]
X63:      END;
          g2:=yaa:=0;
          FOR j:=1 STEP 1 UNTIL jj DO a[j,jr]:=a[j,jj];
          FOR i:=1 STEP 1 UNTIL ji DO
          IF y[i,jj]≠0 THEN g2:=g2+1;
          a[1,jj]:=g2;  g9:=6;
          IF g2<g9 THEN
          BEGIN
            code:=99999999; GO TO X58END;
          FOR j:=2 STEP 1 UNTIL jj DO
          BEGIN
            jb:=j−1;  a[j,jj]:=a[1,jb]END;
          FOR j:=1 STEP 1 UNTIL jr DO
          FOR i:=1 STEP 1 UNTIL jj DO
          BEGIN
            aa:=abs(a[i,j]);
            IF yaa<aa THEN yaa:=aa
          END;
          FOR j:=1 STEP 1 UNTIL jr DO
          FOR i:=1 STEP 1 UNTIL jj DO a[i,j]:=a[i,j]/yaa;
          FOR j:=1 STEP 1 UNTIL jr DO
          FOR i:=1 STEP 1 UNTIL jj DO
          BEGIN
            IF j≤1 THEN GO TO X65;
            IF j≤i THEN
            BEGIN
              ja:=j−1;  GO TO X64END;
            ja:=i−1;
X64:        set:=sum:=0;
            IF ja>0 THEN
            FOR jk:=1 STEP 1 UNTIL ja DO sum:=sum+a[i,jk]Xa[jk,j];
            set:=a[i,j]−sum;
            IF j≤i THEN
            BEGIN
              a[i,j]:=set;  GO TO X65END;
            sob:=a[i,i];
            IF sob=0 THEN sob:=₁₀(−18);
            a[i,j]:=set/sob
X65:      END;
          FOR i:=1 STEP 1 UNTIL jj DO
          BEGIN
```

```
jan:=jr−i;  sum2:=0;  ia:=i−1;
IF ia>0 THEN
FOR jk:=1 STEP 1 UNTIL ia DO
BEGIN
    job:=jr−jk;
    sum2:=sum2+a[jan,job]XsL[job]
END;
sL[jan]:=a[jan,jr]−sum2
END;
FOR i:=1 STEP 1 UNTIL ji DO
FOR j:=1 STEP 1 UNTIL jj DO
IF y[i,jj]≠0 THEN
y[i,j]:=(yb[j]Xy[i,j]+ya[j])/funy[j];
sL[jj]:=sL[jj]Xyb[jj];  axyz:=0;  jk:=jj−1;
FOR j:=1 STEP 1 UNTIL jk DO
BEGIN
    sL[j]:=sL[j]Xyb[jj]/yb[j];
    axyz:=axzy+sL[j]Xya[j]
END;
sL[jj]:=sL[jj]−axyz+ya[jj];
FOR j:=1 STEP 1 UNTIL jj DO
BEGIN
    fusL[j]:=0;  sL[j]:=sL[j]XfusL[j]
END;
n77:=0;  jk:=jj−1;
IF kkk<0 THEN GO TO X93
ELSE IF kkk=0 THEN
BEGIN
    z1:=abs(sL[jj]);
    FOR j:=1 STEP 1 UNTIL jk DO
    BEGIN
        sLX[j]:=sL[j];  z2:=abs(sL[j]);
        IF z1>z2 THEN n77:=j
    END;
    IF n77<0 THEN GO TO X93
    ELSE IF n77=0 THEN GO TO X66;
    FOR i:=1 STEP 1 UNTIL ji DO
    BEGIN
        qro:=y[i,n77];
        IF y[i,n77]≠0 THEN
        BEGIN
            FOR j:=1 STEP 1 UNTIL jj DO y[i,j]:=y[i,j]/qro;
            y[i,n77]:=1/qroEND
        END;
        n99:=n77;  kkk:=1;  GO TO X55END;
    n77:=n99;
    FOR j:=1 STEP 1 UNTIL jk DO sL[j]:=sLX[j];
    sLX[jj]:=jL[n77];
    FOR i:=1 STEP 1 UNTIL ji DO
    BEGIN
        qro:=y[i,n77];
        IF y[i,n77]≠0 THEN
        BEGIN
```

```
            FOR j:=1 STEP 1 UNTIL jj DO y[i,j]:=y[i,j]/qro;
            y[i,n77]:=1/qroEND
         END;
         kkk:=0;
X66:     g3:=g2-1;
         IF n<jc THEN GO TO X69;
         FOR j:=1 STEP 1 UNTIL jj DO
         FOR i:=1 STEP 1 UNTIL ji DO sqrms[j]:=dev[i,j]:=0;
         jk:=jj-1;
         FOR i:=1 STEP 1 UNTIL ji DO
         BEGIN
            rr:=0;
            IF yy[i,jj]=0 THEN GO TO X68;
            FOR j:=1 STEP 1 UNTIL jj DO
            BEGIN
               IF jj<j THEN GO TO X93
               ELSE IF jj=j THEN GO TO X67;
               rr:=rr+sL[j]Xyy[i,j]
            END;
X67:        qx:=rr+sL[jj]; dev[i,jj]:=yy[i,jj]-qx;
            FOR jr:=1 STEP 1 UNTIL jk DO
            BEGIN
               IF sL[jp]=0 THEN
               BEGIN
                  dev[i,jp]:=0; GO TO X68END;
               dev[i,p]:=yy[i,jp]-(yy[i,jj]-qx+sL[jp]Xyy[i,jp])/sL[jp]
X68:        END END;
         FOR j:=1 STEP 1 UNTIL jj DO
         FOR i:=1 STEP 1 UNTIL ji DO sqrms[j]:=sqrms[j]+dev[i,j]↑2;
         FOR j:=1 STEP 1 UNTIL jj DO  sqrms[j]:=sqrt(sqrms[jj]/g3);
X69:     IF jc<1 THEN GO TO X93
         ELSE IF jc>1 THEN GO TO X84;
X70:     PUNCH jc,g,g1,g2;
         IF n<jc THEN GO TO X77;
X7X:     r1:=0; r2[1]:=1;
X71:     r1:=r1+1; r3:=1/2↑r1;
X72:     r2[2]:=r2[1]-r3; r2[3]:=r2[1]+r3;
         jqj:=1; jk:=jj-1;
         FOR i:=1 STEP 1 UNTIL 3 DO
         BEGIN
            r4[i]:=0;
            FOR j:=1 STEP 1 UNTIL jk DO
            BEGIN
               r5:=j;
               r4[i]:=r4[i]+sL[j]X(r2[i]↑(r5Xqq))
            END;
            r4[i]:=r4[i]+sL[jj];
            IF i<1 THEN GO TO X93
            ELSE IF i=1 THEN GO TO X74;
            IF rLm[2]<0 THEN GO TO X93
            ELSE IF rLm[2]=0 THEN
            BEGIN
               IF r4[i]≤r4[1] THEN GO TO X74;
```

```
X73:     jq1:=i;  r2[1]:=r2[i];
         GO TO X74END;
       IF r4[i]<r4[1] THEN GO TO X73
X74:   END;
       GO TO sw9[jq1];
X75:   IF r3>0.01 THEN GO TO X71;
       IF n<jc THEN GO TO X76
       ram:=r2[1];  PUNCH ram;
       COMMENT: At this point control is either transferred to Label X78 or
       to Label X79 (see OPTIONAL EXTERNAL COMMANDS FOR PROGRAM
       28);
X76:   ramer:=ram−r2[1];  PUNCH ram,ramer;
       PUNCH oper,inster;  PUNCH run,temp,waveL;
       IF m6≤m4 THEN GO TO X93 ELSE GO TO X12;
X77:   FOR j:=1 STEP 1 UNTIL jj DO sL[j]:=devsL[j]+abs(sL[j]);
       GO TO X7X;
X78:   FOR j:=1 STEP 1 UNTIL jj DO PUNCH sL[j],sqrms[j];
X79:   IF n<jc THEN GO TO X93
       ELSE IF n=jc THEN GO TO X83;
       COMMENT: At this point control either proceeds serially or is trans-
       ferred to Label X81 (see OPTIONAL EXTERNAL COMMANDS FOR
       PROGRAM 28);
X80:   FOR i:=1 STEP 1 UNTIL ji DO PUNCH yy[i,jj];
       FOR i:=1 STEP 1 UNTIL ji DO PUNCH y[i,jj];
       IF n<jc THEN GO TO X93
       ELSE IF n=jc THEN GO TO X91 ELSE GO TO X54;
X81:   COMMENT: At this point control either proceeds serially or is trans-
       ferred to Label X54 (see OPTIONAL EXTERNAL COMMANDS FOR
       PROGRAM 28);
X82:   FOR i:=1 STEP 1 UNTIL ji DO
       FOR j:=1 STEP 1 UNTIL jj DO
       BEGIN
          PUNCH yy[i,j];  PUNCH y[i,j];
          PUNCH yer[i,j];  PUNCH dev[i,j]
       END;
       IF n<jc THEN GO TO X93
       ELSE IF n=jc THEN GO TO X91 ELSE GO TO X54
X83:   IF g1=g2 THEN GO TO X91;
       COMMENT: At this point control is either transferred to Label X82 or
       to Label X80 (see OPTIONAL EXTERNAL COMMANDS FOR PROGRAM
       28);
X84:   IF n<jc∨nnn=ij THEN GO TO X70;
       ELSE IF nnn>ij THEN GO TO X93;
       FOR i:=1 STEP 1 UNTIL ji DO
       BEGIN
          jrk:=0;
          FOR j:=1 STEP 1 UNTIL jj DO
          BEGIN
             IF yy[i,1]=0 THEN GO TO X85;
             aa:=abs(yer[i,j]);  bb:=abs(dev[i,j]);
             IF aa≥bb THEN GO TO X86;
             IF nnn<1 THEN GO TO X93
             ELSE IF nnn>1 THEN GO TO X88;
```

```
X85:      y[i,j]:=dev[i,j]:=0;  GO TO X90;
X86:      IF nnn<1 THEN GO TO X93
          ELSE IF nnn=1 THEN GO TO X90 ELSE GO TO X89;
X87:      jrk:=jrk+1;
          IF jrk>jj THEN GO TO X93
          ELSE IF jrk<jj THEN GO TO X90;
          FOR jp:=1 STEP 1 UNTIL jj DO y[i,jp]:=yy[i,jp];
          GO TO X90;
X88:      IF nnn=4 THEN GO TO X85 ELSE GO TO X90
X89:      IF nnn≠4 THEN GO TO X87
          END
X90:  END;
          nnn:=nnn+1;  GO TO X55;
X91:  FOR j:=1 STEP 1 UNTIL jj DO
      BEGIN
          IF n>jc THEN GO TO X93
          ELSE IF n<jc THEN GO TO X92;
          devsL[j]:=sL[j];
          FOR i:=1 STEP 1 UNTIL ji DO
          BEGIN
              IF y[i,jj]=0 THEN GO TO X92;
              y[i,jj]:=0;
              IF jj<j THEN GO TO X93
              ELSE IF jj>j THEN
              BEGIN
                  jk:=jj-1;
                  FOR jq:=1 STEP 1 UNTIL jk DO
                  BEGIN
                      yer[i,jq]:=-abs(yer[i,jq]);
                      y[i,jj]:=y[i,jj]+sL[jq]Xyer[i,jq]
                  END END;
                  y[i,jj]:=yer[i,jj]-y[i,jj]
              END
X92:  END;
          IF n=jc THEN GO TO X54
X93:END BBAAA;
      READ ji;  ij:=4;
X94:BBAAA(ji,ij);
      GO TO X94;
```

CHAPTER VI

TWIN-EQUILIBRIA

With Program 29 (*call word* CBAAA) the unknown parameters (K_1, K_2, absorbancy indices for A, B, C_1, and C_2) for each of the following four systems of equations can be calculated from absorbance data collected at several wavelengths for solutions of several different concentrations at a fixed temperature. The absorbancy indices for A, B, C_1, and C_2 can be either dependent or independent of their concentrations. Activity coefficients can be introduced as described in the sections "Statistical Bias" and "Input Commands" in this chapter.

$$\left. \begin{aligned} 2A &\overset{K_1}{\rightleftharpoons} C_1 \\ C_1 + A &\overset{K_2}{\rightleftharpoons} C_2 \end{aligned} \right\} \text{I} \qquad\qquad \left. \begin{aligned} A + B &\overset{K_1}{\rightleftharpoons} C_1 \\ C_1 + A &\overset{K_2}{\rightleftharpoons} C_2 \end{aligned} \right\} \text{III}$$

$$\left. \begin{aligned} 2A &\overset{K_1}{\rightleftharpoons} C_1 \\ 3A &\overset{K_2}{\rightleftharpoons} C_2 \end{aligned} \right\} \text{II} \qquad\qquad \left. \begin{aligned} A + B &\overset{K_1}{\rightleftharpoons} C_1 \\ 2A + B &\overset{K_2}{\rightleftharpoons} C_2 \end{aligned} \right\} \text{IV}$$

The principal equations will be discussed in the section entitled "Method of Solution," later in the chapter.

Programs 29 and 329 (see "Special Modifications," which follows) have been designed with variable dimensions which can be altered to fit the memory available. JQ must be selected before compilation. JI, the number of sets of conjugate data to be processed, is entered with the input information (see "Input Commands"). These programs can be used only with large computers.

SPECIAL MODIFICATIONS

In Program 329 (*call word* CBAAS) during the final iteration, the *self-judgment principle* is applied only to the principal ordinate, designated by y ($= A_M$), for the spectrophotometric equations (see Method of Solution). *Input* and *output formats* for Programs 29 (*call word* CBAAA) and 329 (*call word* CBAAS) are identical. Program 329 should be used if some of the products (formation constant times absorbancy index of complex), or the absorbancy indices of A or B, are small. In these situations some sets of conjugate data may be erroneously rejected if the *self-judgment principle* is applied in all dimensions.

Program 29 can be converted to Program 329 by making the following changes.

ORIGINAL	REPLACEMENT
Program 29 (*Call Word* CBAAA)	*Program* 329 (*Call Word* CBAAS)
1 READ,CBAAA,FEEDP	1 READ,CBAAS,FEEDP
NUM = 29	NUM = 329
PUNCH,CBAAA,NUM,FEEDP	PUNCH,CBAAS,NUM,FEEDP
JRK = 0	IF(YY(I,JJ))127,130,127
DO 126 J = 1,JJ	127 AA = SQR(YER(I,JJ)*YER(I,JJ))
IF(YY(I,JJ))127,130,127	BB = SQR(DEV(I,JJ)*DEV(I,JJ))
127 AA = SQR(YER(I,J)*YER(I,J))	IF(AA − BB)129,128,128
BB = SQR(DEV(I,J)*DEV(I,J))	129 IF(NNN − 1)1,130,132
IF(AA − BB)129,128,128	130 DO 9003 J = 1,JJ
129 IF(NNN − 1)1,130,132	Y(I,J) = 0.0
130 Y(I,J) = 0.0	9003 DEV(I,J) = 0.0
DEV(I,J) = 0.0	GO TO 126
GO TO 126	128 IF(NNN − 1)1,126,133
128 IF(NNN − 1)1,126,133	131 DO 9001 J = 1,JJ
131 JRK = JRK + 1	9001 Y(I,J) = YY(I,J)
IF(JRK − JJ)126,43,1	GO TO 126
43 DO 9001 JP = 1,JJ	
9001 Y(I,JP) = YY(I,JP)	
GO TO 126	

METHOD OF SOLUTION

The symbols and their FORTRAN equivalents used throughout this chapter are given next.

Text	FORTRAN	Comment
C_A	C1(I)	Concentration of A before equilibrium
C_B	C2(I)	Concentration of B before equilibrium
C_1	C3(I)	Concentration of C_1
C_2	C4(I)	Concentration of C_2
A_M	OAM(I)	Measured absorbance
a_A, a_B, a_{C_1}, a_{C_2}	See output format	Absorbancy indices of the designated species
$A^{\alpha 0}$, $A^{\alpha 1}$, $A^{\alpha 2}$, $A^{\alpha 3}$, $A^{\alpha 4}$	See output format	Expansion coefficients of designated species
K_1, K_2	RLM(1); RLM(2)	Formation constants (arbitrary values)

Principal Equations

For equation sets I to IV the following equations can be derived.[1] In deriving these equations it was assumed that the activities could be replaced by the concentrations. (See "Statistical Bias" in this chapter for instructions for introducing activity coefficients.) Throughout this section the following abbreviations are used.

a_A dependent: Means that the absorbancy index of A can be expressed in the form:

$$a_A = {}_A\alpha_0 + {}_A\alpha_1\bar{C}_A$$

with $\bar{C}_A$ the actual concentration of A. All other absorbancy indices are concentration independent.

a_A, a_B, a_{C_1} dependent: Means that only a_{C_2} is concentration independent. a_A, a_B, and a_{C_1} are assumed to have two-dimensional forms thus:

$$a_A = {}_A\alpha_0 + {}_A\alpha_1\bar{C}_A, \qquad a_B = {}_B\alpha_0 + {}_B\alpha_1\bar{C}_B,$$

$$\text{and} \qquad a_{C_1} = {}_{C_1}\alpha_0 + {}_{C_1}\alpha_1 C_1$$

EQUATION SET I

$$K_1 = C_1/\beta^2 \tag{1}$$

$$K_2 = C_2/C_1\beta \tag{2}$$

$$\beta = C_A - 2C_1 - 3C_2$$

In the following equations $\rho = K_1K_2$.

$$A_M = (a_{C_1})C_1 + (3a_{C_1}\rho)C_1\beta^2 + (a_{C_2}\rho)\beta^2(C_A - 2C_1) + (a_A)\beta$$
$$+ (3a_A\rho)\beta^3 - (3\rho)A_M\beta^2 \tag{3}$$

a_A dependent:

$$A_M = (a_{C_1})C_1 + (3a_{C_1}\rho)C_1\beta^2 + (a_{C_2}\rho)\beta^2(C_A - 2C_1) + ({}_A\alpha_0)\beta$$
$$+ (3_A\alpha_0\rho)\beta^3 - (3\rho)A_M\beta^2 + ({}_A\alpha_1)\beta^2 + (3_A\alpha_1\rho)\beta^4 \tag{4}$$

a_A, a_{C_1} dependent:

$$A_M = ({}_{C_1}\alpha_0)C_1 + (3_{C_1}\alpha_0\rho)C_1\beta^2 + (a_{C_2}\rho)\beta^2(C_A - 2C_1) + ({}_A\alpha_0)\beta$$
$$+ (3_A\alpha_0\rho)\beta^3 - (3\rho)A_M\beta^2 + ({}_A\alpha_1)\beta^2 + (3_A\alpha_1\rho)\beta^4$$
$$+ ({}_{C_1}\alpha_1)C_1^2 + (3_{C_1}\alpha_1\rho)C_1^2\beta^2 \tag{5}$$

a_A, a_{C_2} dependent:

$$A_M = (a_{C_1})C_1 + (3a_{C_1}\rho)C_1\beta^2 + ({}_{C_2}\alpha_0\rho)\beta^2(C_A - 2C_1) + ({}_A\alpha_0)\beta$$
$$+ (3_A\alpha_0\rho)\beta^3 - (3\rho)A_M\beta^2 + ({}_A\alpha_1)\beta^2 + (3_A\alpha_1\rho)\beta^4$$
$$+ ({}_{C_2}\alpha_1\rho)C_2\beta^2(C_A - 2C_1) \tag{6}$$

[1] P. A. D. de Maine, *J. Mississippi Acad. Sci.*, **9** (1963), 168.

a_A, a_{C_1}, a_{C_2} dependent:

$$A_M = (c_1\alpha_0)\,C_1 + (3c_1\alpha_0 P)C_1\beta^2 + (c_2\alpha_0 P)\beta^2(C_A - 2\,C_1) + (_A\alpha_0)\beta$$
$$+ (3_A\alpha_0 P)\beta^3 - (3P)A_M\beta^2 + (_A\alpha_1)\beta^2 + (3_A\alpha_1 P)\beta^4$$
$$+ (c_1\alpha_1)C_1^2 + (3c_1\alpha_1 P)C_1^2\beta^2 + (c_2\alpha_1 P)C_2\beta^2(C_A - 2C_1) \qquad (7)$$

a_{C_1} dependent:

$$A_M = (c_1\alpha_0)C_1 + (3c_1\alpha_0 P)C_1\beta^2 + (a_{C_2}P)\beta^2(C_A - 2C_1) + (a_A)\beta$$
$$+ (3a_A P)\beta^3 - (3P)A_M\beta^2 + (c_1\alpha_1)C_1^2 + (3c_1\alpha_1 P)C_1^2\beta^2 \qquad (8)$$

a_{C_1}, a_{C_2} dependent:

$$A_M = (c_1\alpha_0)C_1 + (3c_1\alpha_0 P)C_1\beta^2 + (c_2\alpha_0 P)\beta^2(C_A - 2C_1) + (a_A)\beta$$
$$+ (3a_A P)\beta^3 - (3P)A_M\beta^2 + (c_1\alpha_1)C_1^2 + (3c_1\alpha_1 P)C_1^2\beta^2$$
$$+ (c_2\alpha_1 P)\beta^2 C_2(C_A - 2C_1) \qquad (9)$$

a_{C_2} dependent:

$$A_M = (a_{C_1})C_1 + (3a_{C_1}P)C_1\beta^2 + (c_2\alpha_0 P)\beta^2(C_A - 2C_1) + (a_A)\beta$$
$$+ (3a_A P)\beta^3 - (3P)A_M\beta^2 + (c_2\alpha_1 P)\beta^2 C_2(C_A - 2C_1) \qquad (10)$$

EQUATION SET II

$$K_1 = C_1/\beta^2 \qquad (11)$$
$$K_2 = C_2/\beta^3 \qquad (12)$$
$$\beta = C_A - 2C_1 - 3C_2$$

Here $P = K_2/K_1$. The basic spectrophotometric equation is:

$$A_M = (a_{C_1})C_1 + (3a_{C_1}P)C_1^2 + (a_{C_2}P)C_1(C_A - 2C_1) + (a_A)\beta$$
$$+ (3a_A P)\beta C_1 - (3P)C_1 A_M \qquad (13)$$

a_A dependent:

$$A_M = (a_{C_1})C_1 + (3a_{C_1}P)C_1^2 + (a_{C_2}P)C_1(C_A - 2C_1) + (_A\alpha_0)\beta$$
$$+ (3_A\alpha_0 P)\beta C_1 - (3P)C_1 A_M + (_A\alpha_1)\beta^2 + (3_A\alpha_1 P)\beta^2 C_1 \qquad (14)$$

a_A, a_{C_1} dependent:

$$A_M = (c_1\alpha_0)C_1 + (3c_1\alpha_0 P + c_1\alpha_1)C_1^2 + (a_{C_2}P)C_1(C_A - C_1) + (_A\alpha_0)\beta$$
$$+ (3_A\alpha_0 P)\beta C_1 - (3P)C_1 A_M + (_A\alpha_1)\beta^2 + (3_A\alpha_1 P)\beta^2 C_1$$
$$+ (3c_1\alpha_1 P)C_1^3 \qquad (15)$$

a_A, a_{C_2} dependent:

$$A_M = (a_{C_1})C_1 + (3a_{C_1}P)C_1^2 + (c_2\alpha_0 P)C_1(C_A - 2C_1) + (_A\alpha_0)\beta$$
$$+ (3_A\alpha_0 P)\beta C_1 - (3P)C_1 A_M + (_A\alpha_1)\beta^2 + (3_A\alpha_1 P)\beta^2 C_1$$
$$+ (c_2\alpha_1 P)C_1 C_2(C_A - 2C_1) \qquad (16)$$

a_A, a_{C_1}, a_{C_2} dependent:

$$
\begin{aligned}
A_M = {}& (c_1\alpha_0)C_1 + (3c_1\alpha_0\rho + c_1\alpha_1)C_1^2 + (c_2\alpha_0\rho)C_1(C_A - 2C_1) \\
& + (_A\alpha_0)\beta + (3_A\alpha_0\rho)\beta C_1 - (3\rho)C_1 A_M + (_A\alpha_1)\beta^2 \\
& + (3_A\alpha_1\rho)\beta^2 C_1 + (3c_1\alpha_1\rho)C_1^3 \\
& + (c_2\alpha_1\rho)C_1 C_2(C_A - 2C_1)
\end{aligned}
\tag{17}
$$

a_{C_1} dependent:

$$
\begin{aligned}
A_M = {}& (c_1\alpha_0)C_1 + (3c_1\alpha_0\rho + c_1\alpha_1)C_1^2 + (a_{C_2}\rho)C_1(C_A - 2C_1) + (a_A)\beta \\
& + (3a_A\rho)\beta C_1 - (3\rho)C_1 A_M + (3c_1\alpha_1\rho)C_1^3
\end{aligned}
\tag{18}
$$

a_{C_1}, a_{C_2} dependent:

$$
\begin{aligned}
A_M = {}& (c_1\alpha_0)C_1 + (3c_1\alpha_0\rho + c_1\alpha_1)C_1^2 + (c_2\alpha_0\rho)C_1(C_A - 2C_1) + (a_A)\beta \\
& + (3a_A\rho)\beta C_1 - (3\rho)C_1 A_M + (3c_1\alpha_1\rho)C_1^3 \\
& + (c_2\alpha_1\rho)C_1 C_2(C_A - 2C_1)
\end{aligned}
\tag{19}
$$

a_{C_2} dependent:

$$
\begin{aligned}
A_M = {}& (a_{C_1})C_1 + (3a_{C_1}\rho)C_1^2 + (c_2\alpha_0\rho)C_1(C_A - 2C_1) + (a_A)\beta \\
& + (3a_A\rho)\beta C_1 - (3\rho)C_1 A_M + (c_2\alpha_1\rho)C_1 C_2(C_A - 2C_1)
\end{aligned}
\tag{20}
$$

EQUATION SET III

$$
K_1 = C_1/\beta\gamma
\tag{21}
$$

$$
K_2 = C_2/C_1\beta
\tag{22}
$$

$$
\beta = C_A - C_1 - 2C_2
$$

$$
\gamma = C_B - C_1 - C_2
$$

Here $\rho = K_1 K_2$. The possible equations are:

$$
\begin{aligned}
A_M = {}& (a_{C_1})C_1 + (2a_{C_1}\rho)C_1\gamma\beta + (a_{C_2}\rho)\gamma\beta(C_A - C_1) + (a_A)\beta \\
& + (2a_A\rho)\gamma\beta^2 + (a_B)\gamma + (2a_B\rho)\gamma^2\beta - (2\rho)A_M\gamma\beta
\end{aligned}
\tag{23}
$$

a_A dependent:

$$
\begin{aligned}
A_M = {}& (a_{C_1})C_1 + (2a_{C_1}\rho)C_1\gamma\beta + (a_{C_2}\rho)\gamma\beta(C_A - C_1) + (_A\alpha_0)\beta \\
& + (2_A\alpha_0\rho)\gamma\beta^2 + (a_B)\gamma + (2a_B\rho)\gamma^2\beta - (2\rho)A_M\gamma\beta \\
& + (_A\alpha_1)\beta^2 + (2_A\alpha_1\rho)\gamma\beta^3
\end{aligned}
\tag{24}
$$

a_A, a_B dependent:

$$
\begin{aligned}
A_M = {}& (a_{C_1})C_1 + (2a_{C_1}\rho)C_1\gamma\beta + (a_{C_2}\rho)\gamma\beta(C_A - C_1) + (_A\alpha_0)\beta \\
& + (2_A\alpha_0\rho)\gamma\beta^2 + (_B\alpha_0)\gamma + (2_B\alpha_0\rho)\gamma^2\beta - (2\rho)A_M\gamma\beta \\
& + (_A\alpha_1)\beta^2 + (2_A\alpha_1\rho)\gamma\beta^3 + (_B\alpha_1)\gamma^2 + (2_B\alpha_1)\rho\gamma^3\beta
\end{aligned}
\tag{25}
$$

a_A, a_{C_1} dependent:

$$
\begin{aligned}
A_M = {} & (_{C_1}\alpha_0)C_1 + (2_{C_1}\alpha_0\rho)C_1\gamma\beta + (a_{C_2}\rho)\gamma\beta(C_A - C_1) + (_A\alpha_0)\beta \\
& + (2_A\alpha_0\rho)\gamma\beta^2 + (a_B)\gamma + (2a_B\rho)\gamma^2\beta - (2\rho)A_M\gamma\beta \\
& + (_A\alpha_1)\beta^2 + (2_A\alpha_1\rho)\gamma\beta^3 + (_{C_1}\alpha_1)C_1^2 + (2_{C_1}\alpha_1\rho)C_1^2\gamma\beta
\end{aligned} \quad (26)
$$

a_A, a_{C_2} dependent:

$$
\begin{aligned}
A_M = {} & (a_{C_1})C_1 + (2a_{C_1}\rho)C_1\gamma\beta + (_{C_2}\alpha_0\rho)\gamma\beta(C_A - C_1) + (_A\alpha_0)\beta \\
& + (2_A\alpha_0\rho)\gamma\beta^2 + (a_B)\gamma + (2a_B\rho)\gamma^2\beta - (2\rho)A_M\gamma\beta \\
& + (_A\alpha_1)\beta^2 + (2_A\alpha_1\rho)\gamma\beta^3 + (_{C_2}\alpha_1\rho)\gamma\beta C_2(C_A - C_1)
\end{aligned} \quad (27)
$$

a_A, a_B, a_{C_1} dependent:

$$
\begin{aligned}
A_M = {} & (_{C_1}\alpha_0)C_1 + (2_{C_1}\alpha_0\rho)C_1\gamma\beta + (_{C_2}\alpha_0\rho)\gamma\beta(C_A - C_1) + (_A\alpha_0)\beta \\
& + (2_A\alpha_0\rho)\gamma\beta^2 + (_B\alpha_0)\gamma + (2_B\alpha_0\rho)\gamma^2\beta - (2\rho)A_M\gamma\beta \\
& + (_A\alpha_1)\beta^2 + (2_A\alpha_1\rho)\gamma\beta^3 + (_B\alpha_1)\gamma^2 + (2_B\alpha_1\rho)\gamma^3\beta \\
& + (_{C_1}\alpha_1)C_1^2 + (2_{C_1}\alpha_1\rho)C_1^2\gamma\beta
\end{aligned} \quad (28)
$$

a_A, a_B, a_{C_2} dependent:

$$
\begin{aligned}
A_M = {} & (a_{C_1})C_1 + (2a_{C_1}\rho)C_1\gamma\beta + (_{C_2}\alpha_0\rho)\gamma\beta(C_A - C_1) + (_A\alpha_0)\beta \\
& + (2_A\alpha_0\rho)\gamma\beta^2 + (_B\alpha_0)\gamma + (2_B\alpha_0\rho)\gamma^2\beta - (2\rho)A_M\gamma\beta \\
& + (_A\alpha_1)\beta^2 + (2_A\alpha_1\rho)\gamma\beta^3 + (_B\alpha_1)\gamma^2 + (2_B\alpha_1\rho)\gamma^3\beta \\
& + (_{C_2}\alpha_1\rho)C_2\gamma\beta(C_A - C_1)
\end{aligned} \quad (29)
$$

a_A, a_{C_1}, a_{C_2} dependent:

$$
\begin{aligned}
A_M = {} & (_{C_1}\alpha_0)C_1 + (2_{C_1}\alpha_0\rho)C_1\gamma\beta + (_{C_2}\alpha_0\rho)\gamma\beta(C_A - C_1) + (_A\alpha_0)\beta \\
& + (2_A\alpha_0\rho)\gamma\beta^2 + (a_B)\gamma + (2a_B\rho)\gamma^2\beta - (2\rho)A_M\gamma\beta \\
& + (_A\alpha_1)\beta^2 + (2_A\alpha_1\rho)\gamma\beta^3 + (_{C_1}\alpha_1)C_1^2 + (2_{C_1}\alpha_1\rho)C_1^2\gamma\beta \\
& + (_{C_2}\alpha_1\rho)C_2\gamma\beta(C_A - C_1)
\end{aligned} \quad (30)
$$

a_B dependent:

$$
\begin{aligned}
A_M = {} & (a_{C_1})C_1 + (2a_{C_1}\rho)\gamma\beta C_1 + (a_{C_2}\rho)\gamma\beta(C_A - C_1) + (a_A)\beta \\
& + (2a_A\rho)\gamma\beta^2 + (_B\alpha_0)\gamma + (2_B\alpha_0\rho)\gamma^2\beta - (2\rho)A_M\gamma\beta \\
& + (_B\alpha_1)\gamma^2 + (2_B\alpha_1\rho)\gamma^3\beta
\end{aligned} \quad (31)
$$

a_B, a_{C_1} dependent:

$$
\begin{aligned}
A_M = {} & (_{C_1}\alpha_0)C_1 + (2_{C_1}\alpha_0\rho)\gamma\beta C_1 + (a_{C_2}\rho)\gamma\beta(C_A - C_1) + (a_A)\beta \\
& + (2a_A\rho)\gamma\beta^2 + (_B\alpha_0)\gamma + (2_B\alpha_0\rho)\gamma^2\beta - (2\rho)A_M\gamma\beta \\
& + (_B\alpha_1)\gamma^2 + (2_B\alpha_1\rho)\gamma^3\beta + (_{C_1}\alpha_1)C_1^2 + (2_{C_1}\alpha_1\rho)C_1\gamma\beta
\end{aligned} \quad (32)
$$

a_B, a_{C_2} dependent:

$$
\begin{aligned}
A_M = {} & (a_{C_1})C_1 + (2a_{C_1}\rho)\gamma\beta C_1 + (_{C_2}\alpha_0\rho)\gamma\beta(C_A - C_1) + (a_A)\beta \\
& + (2a_A\rho)\gamma\beta^2 + (_B\alpha_0)\gamma + (2_B\alpha_0\rho)\gamma^2\beta - (2\rho)A_M\gamma\beta \\
& + (_B\alpha_1)\gamma^2 + (2_B\alpha_1\rho)\gamma^3\beta + (_{C_2}\alpha_1\rho)C_2\gamma\beta(C_A - C_1)
\end{aligned} \quad (33)
$$

a_B, a_{C_1}, a_{C_2} dependent:

$$A_M = (c_1\alpha_0)C_1 + (2c_1\alpha_0\rho)\gamma\beta C_1 + (c_2\alpha_0\rho)\gamma\beta(C_A - C_1) + (a_A)\beta + (2a_A\rho)\gamma\beta^2$$
$$+ (B\alpha_0)\gamma + (2B\alpha_0\rho)\gamma^2\beta - (2\rho)A_M\gamma\beta + (B\alpha_1)\gamma^2 + (2B\alpha_1\rho)\gamma^3\beta$$
$$+ (c_1\alpha_1)C_1^2 + (2c_1\alpha_1\rho)C_1^2\gamma\beta + (c_2\alpha_1\rho)C_2\gamma\beta(C_A - C_1) \quad (34)$$

a_{C_1} dependent:

$$A_M = (c_1\alpha_0)C_1 + (2c_1\alpha_0\rho)\gamma\beta C_1 + (a_{C_2})\gamma\beta(C_A - C_1) + (a_A)\beta$$
$$+ (2a_A\rho)\gamma\beta^2 + (a_B)\gamma + (2a_B)\gamma^2\beta - (2\rho)A_M\gamma\beta$$
$$+ (c_1\alpha_1)C_1^2 + (2c_1\alpha_1\rho)C_1^2\gamma\beta \quad (35)$$

a_{C_1}, a_{C_2} dependent:

$$A_M = (c_1\alpha_0)C_1 + (2c_1\alpha_0\rho)\gamma\beta C_1 + (c_2\alpha_0\rho)\gamma\beta(C_A - C_1) + (a_A)\beta$$
$$+ (2a_A\rho)\gamma\beta^2 + (a_B)\gamma + (2a_B)\gamma^2\beta - (2\rho)A_M\gamma\beta$$
$$+ (c_1\alpha_1)C_1^2 + (2c_1\alpha_1\rho)C_1^2\gamma\beta + (c_2\alpha_1\rho)C_2\gamma\beta(C_A - C_1) \quad (36)$$

a_{C_2} dependent:

$$A_M = (a_{C_1})C_1 + (2a_{C_1}\rho)C_1\gamma\beta + (c_2\alpha_0\rho)\gamma\beta(C_A - C_1) + (a_A)\beta$$
$$+ (2a_A\rho)\gamma\beta^2 + (a_B)\gamma + (2a_B\rho)\gamma^2\beta - (2\rho)A_M\gamma\beta$$
$$+ (c_2\alpha_1\rho)\gamma\beta C_2(C_A - C_1) \quad (37)$$

a_A, a_B, a_{C_1}, a_{C_2} dependent:

$$A_M = (c_1\alpha_0)C_1 + (2c_1\alpha_0\rho)C_1\gamma\beta + (c_2\alpha_0\rho)\gamma\beta(C_A - C_1) + (A\alpha_0)\beta$$
$$+ (2A\alpha_0\rho)\gamma\beta^2 + (B\alpha_0)\gamma + (2B\alpha_0\rho)\gamma^2\beta - (2\rho)A_M\gamma\beta$$
$$+ (A\alpha_1)\beta^2 + (2A\alpha_1\rho)\gamma\beta^3 + (B\alpha_1)\gamma^2 + (2B\alpha_1\rho)\gamma^3\beta$$
$$+ (c_1\alpha_1)C_1^2 + (2c_1\alpha_1\rho)C_1^2\gamma\beta + (c_2\alpha_1\rho)C_2\gamma\beta(C_A - C_1) \quad (38)$$

EQUATION SET IV

$$K_1 = C_1/\gamma\beta \quad (39)$$
$$K_2 = C_2/\beta^2\gamma \quad (40)$$
$$\beta = C_A - C_1 - 2C_2$$
$$\gamma = C_A - C_1 - C_2$$

Here $\rho = K_2/K_1$. Possible spectrophotometric equations are given next.

$$A_M = (a_{C_1})C_1 + (2a_{C_1}\rho)C_1^2 + (a_{C_2}\rho)C_1(C_A - C_1) + (a_A)\beta + (2a_A\rho)C_1\beta$$
$$+ (a_B)\gamma + (2a_B\rho)C_1\gamma - (2\rho)C_1A_M \quad (41)$$

a_A dependent:

$$A_M = (a_{C_1})C_1 + (2a_{C_1}\rho)C_1^2 + (a_{C_2}\rho)C_1(C_A - C_1) + (A\alpha_0)\beta + (2A\alpha_0\rho)C_1\beta$$
$$+ (a_B)\gamma + (2a_B\rho)C_1\gamma - (2\rho)C_1A_M + (A\alpha_1)\beta^2$$
$$+ (2A\alpha_1\rho)C_1\beta^2 \quad (42)$$

a_A, a_B dependent:

$$A_M = (a_{C_1})C_1 + (2a_{C_1}P)C_1^2 + (a_{C_2}P)C_1(C_A - C_1) + (_A\alpha_0)\beta$$
$$+ (2_A\alpha_0P)C_1\beta + (_B\alpha_0)\gamma + (2_B\alpha_0P)C_1\gamma - (2P)C_1A_M$$
$$+ (_A\alpha_1)\beta^2 + (2_A\alpha_1P)C_1\beta^2 + (_B\alpha_1)\gamma^2 + (2_B\alpha_1P)C_1\gamma^2 \tag{43}$$

a_A, a_{C_1} dependent:

$$A_M = (c_1\alpha_0)C_1 + (2c_1\alpha_0P + c_1\alpha_1)C_1^2 + (a_{C_2}P)C_1(C_A - C_1) + (_A\alpha_0)\beta$$
$$+ (2_A\alpha_0P)C_1\beta + (a_B)\gamma + (2a_BP)C_1\gamma - (2P)C_1A_M$$
$$+ (_A\alpha_1)\beta^2 + (2_A\alpha_1P)C_1\beta^2 + (2c_1\alpha_1P)C_1^3 \tag{44}$$

a_A, a_{C_2} dependent:

$$A_M = (a_{C_1})C_1 + (2a_{C_1}P)C_1^2 + (c_2\alpha_0P)C_1(C_A - C_1) + (_A\alpha_0)\beta + (2_A\alpha_0P)C_1\beta$$
$$+ (a_B)\gamma + (2a_BP)C_1\gamma - (2P)C_1A_M + (_A\alpha_1)\beta^2$$
$$+ (2_A\alpha_1P)C_1\beta^2 + (c_2\alpha_1P)C_1C_2(C_A - C_1) \tag{45}$$

a_A, a_B, a_{C_1} dependent:

$$A_M = (c_1\alpha_0)C_1 + (2c_1\alpha_0P + c_1\alpha_1)C_1^2 + (a_{C_2}P)C_1(C_A - C_1) + (_A\alpha_0)\beta$$
$$+ (2_A\alpha_0P)C_1\beta + (_B\alpha_0)\gamma + (2_B\alpha_0P)C_1\gamma - (2P)C_1A_M$$
$$+ (_A\alpha_1)\beta^2 + (2_A\alpha_1P)C_1\beta^2 + (_B\alpha_1)\gamma^2 + (2_B\alpha_1P)C_1\gamma^2$$
$$+ (2c_1\alpha_1P)C_1^3 \tag{46}$$

a_A, a_B, a_{C_2} dependent:

$$A_M = (a_{C_1})C_1 + (2a_{C_1}P)C_1^2 + (c_2\alpha_0P)C_1(C_A - C_1) + (_A\alpha_0)\beta$$
$$+ (2_A\alpha_0P)C_1\beta + (_B\alpha_0)\gamma + (2_B\alpha_0P)C_1\gamma - (2P)C_1A_M$$
$$+ (_A\alpha_1)\beta^2 + (2_A\alpha_1P)C_1\beta^2 + (_B\alpha_1)\gamma^2 + (2_B\alpha_1P)C_1\gamma^2$$
$$+ (c_2\alpha_1P)C_1C_2(C_A - C_1) \tag{47}$$

a_A, a_{C_1}, a_{C_2} dependent:

$$A_M = (c_1\alpha_0)C_1 + (2c_1\alpha_0P + c_1\alpha_1)C_1^2 + (c_2\alpha_0P)C_1(C_A - C_1) + (_A\alpha_0)\beta$$
$$+ (2_A\alpha_0P)C_1\beta + (a_B)\gamma + (2a_BP)C_1\gamma - (2P)C_1A_M$$
$$+ (_A\alpha_1)\beta^2 + (2_A\alpha_1P)C_1\beta^2 + (2c_1\alpha_1P)C_1^3$$
$$+ (c_2\alpha_1P)C_1C_2(C_A - C_1) \tag{48}$$

a_B dependent:

$$A_M = (a_{C_1})C_1 + (2a_{C_1}P)C_1^2 + (a_{C_2}P)C_1(C_A - C_1) + (a_A)\beta$$
$$+ (2a_AP)C_1\beta + (_B\alpha_0)\gamma + (2_B\alpha_0P)C_1\gamma - (2P)C_1A_M$$
$$+ (_B\alpha_1)\gamma^2 + (2_B\alpha_1P)C_1\gamma^2 \tag{49}$$

a_B, a_{C_1} dependent:

$$A_M = (_{C_1}\alpha_0)C_1 + (2_{C_1}\alpha_0\rho + _{C_1}\alpha_1)C_1^2 + (a_{C_2}\rho)C_1(C_A - C_1) + (a_A)\beta$$
$$+ (2a_A\rho)C_1\beta + (_B\alpha_0)\gamma + (2_B\alpha_0\rho)C_1\gamma - (2\rho)C_1A_M$$
$$+ (_B\alpha_1)\gamma^2 + (2_B\alpha_1\rho)C_1\gamma^2 + (2_{C_1}\alpha_1\rho)C_1^3 \tag{50}$$

a_B, a_{C_2} dependent:

$$A_M = (a_{C_1})C_1 + (2a_{C_1}\rho)C_1^2 + (_{C_2}\alpha_0\rho)C_1(C_A - C_1) + (a_A)\beta$$
$$+ (2a_A\rho)C_1\beta + (_B\alpha_0)\gamma + (2_B\alpha_0\rho)C_1\gamma - (2\rho)C_1A_M$$
$$+ (_B\alpha_1)\gamma^2 + (2_B\alpha_1\rho)C_1\gamma^2 + (_{C_2}\alpha_1\rho)C_1C_2(C_A - C_1) \tag{51}$$

a_B, a_{C_1}, a_{C_2} dependent:

$$A_M = (_{C_1}\alpha_0)C_1 + (2_{C_1}\alpha_0\rho + _{C_1}\alpha_1)C_1^2 + (_{C_2}\alpha_0\rho)C_1(C_A - C_1) + (a_A)\beta$$
$$+ (2a_A\rho)C_1\beta + (_B\alpha_0)\gamma + (2_B\alpha_0\rho)C_1\gamma - (2\rho)C_1A_M$$
$$+ (_B\alpha_1)\gamma^2 + (2_B\alpha_1\rho)C_1\gamma^2 + (2_{C_1}\alpha_1\rho)C_1^3$$
$$+ (_{C_2}\alpha_1\rho)C_1C_2(C_A - C_1) \tag{52}$$

a_{C_1} dependent:

$$A_M = (_{C_1}\alpha_0)C_1 + (2_{C_1}\alpha_0\rho + _{C_1}\alpha_1)C_1^2 + (a_{C_2}\rho)C_1(C_A - C_1) + (a_A)\beta$$
$$+ (2a_A\rho)C_1\beta + (a_B)\gamma + (2a_B\rho)C_1\gamma - (2\rho)C_1A_M$$
$$+ (2_{C_1}\alpha_1\rho)C_1^3 \tag{53}$$

a_{C_1}, a_{C_2} dependent:

$$A_M = (_{C_1}\alpha_0)C_1 + (2_{C_1}\alpha_0\rho + _{C_1}\alpha_1)C_1^2 + (_{C_2}\alpha_0\rho)C_1(C_A - C_1) + (a_A)\beta$$
$$+ (2a_A\rho)C_1\beta + (a_B)\gamma + (2a_B\rho)C_1\gamma - (2\rho)C_1A_M$$
$$+ (2_{C_1}\alpha_1\rho)C_1^3 + (_{C_2}\alpha_1\rho)C_1C_2(C_A - C_1) \tag{54}$$

a_{C_2} dependent:

$$A_M = (a_{C_1})C_1 + (2a_{C_1}\rho)C_1^2 + (_{C_2}\alpha_0\rho)C_1(C_A - C_1) + (a_A)\beta + (2a_A\rho)C_1\beta$$
$$+ (a_B)\gamma + (2a_B\rho)C_1\gamma - (2\rho)C_1A_M$$
$$+ (_{C_2}\alpha_1\rho)C_1C_2(C_A - C_1) \tag{55}$$

a_A, a_B, a_{C_1}, a_{C_2} dependent:

$$A_M = (_{C_1}\alpha_0)C_1 + (2_{C_1}\alpha_0\rho + _{C_1}\alpha_1)C_1^2 + (_{C_2}\alpha_0\rho)C_1(C_A - C_1) + (_A\alpha_0)\beta$$
$$+ (2_A\alpha_0\rho)C_1\beta + (_B\alpha_0)\gamma + (2_B\alpha_0\rho)C_1\gamma - (2\rho)C_1A_M$$
$$+ (_A\alpha_1)\beta^2 + (2_A\alpha_1\rho)C_1\beta^2 + (_B\alpha_1)\gamma^2 + (2_B\alpha_1\rho)C_1\gamma^2$$
$$+ (2_{C_1}\alpha_1\rho)C_1^3 + (_{C_2}\alpha_1\rho)C_1C_2(C_A - C_1) \tag{56}$$

Solution of Principal Equations for K_1, K_2, a_A, a_B, a_{C_1} and a_{C_2}

The method used to solve each equation set for all the unknown parameters is illustrated here for *equation set I*. If all species obey Beer's

Law this set is described by equations (A), (B) and (C).

$$K_1 = C_1/\beta^2 \tag{A}$$

$$K_2 = C_2/C_1\beta \tag{B}$$

$$\beta = C_A - 2C_1 - 3C_2$$

$$A_M = (a_{C_1})C_1 + (3a_{C_1}\rho)C_1\beta^2 + (a_{C_2}\rho)\beta^2(C_A - 2C_1) + (a_A)\beta$$
$$+ (3a_A\rho)\beta^3 - (3\rho)A_M\beta^2 \tag{C}$$

Absorbancies (A_M), measured at several wavelengths at a fixed temperature, for solutions with several different concentrations of A are processed as follows.

Step 1. Choose arbitrary values for the two formation constants $(K_1^0$ and $K_2^0)$.

Step 2. Use a double-search method to compute the concentrations of the two complexes in each solution from equations (A) and (B) with K_1^0 and K_2^0. The actual method used is described in the next section.

Step 3. Calculate the ordinates for equation (C).

Step 4. Solve Equation (C) for ρ then calculate a new value for K_2, denoted by K_2^I, using $K_1 = K_1^0$.

Step 5. Steps 2 (with K_2^0 replaced by K_2^I) to 4 are repeated until successive iterations yield the same value for K_2. Then a_A, a_{C_1} and a_{C_2} are computed.

Step 6. Steps 1 to 5 are repeated with data collected at the other wavelengths. The same value for K_1 is used at each wavelength.

Step 7. Steps 1 to 6 are repeated with several different values of K_1, denoted by K_1^0, K_1^I, K_1^{II}, K_1^{III}, $\cdots$

Step 8. The values of K_1, denoted by K_1^0, K_1^I, K_1^{II}, K_1^{III}, $\cdots$ and the computed values for K_2, denoted by K_2^0, K_2^I, K_2^{II} $\cdots$ at each wavelength $(\lambda_1, \lambda_2 \lambda_3, \cdots)$ are tabulated thus:

	λ_1	λ_2	λ_3	λ_4	λ_5	Mean K_2	ΔK_2*
K_1^0	K_2^I	K_2^I	K_2^I	K_2^I	K_2^I	K_{2M}^I	ΔK_2^I
K_1^I	K_2^{II}	K_2^{II}	K_2^{II}	K_2^{II}	K_2^{II}	K_{2M}^{II}	ΔK_2^{II}
K_1^{II}	K_2^{III}	K_2^{III}	K_2^{III}	K_2^{III}	K_2^{III}	K_{2M}^{III}	ΔK_2^{III}
K_1^{III}	K_2^{IV}	K_2^{IV}	K_2^{IV}	K_2^{IV}	K_2^{IV}	K_{2M}^{IV}	ΔK_2^{IV}
K_1^{IV}	K_2^{V}	K_2^{V}	K_2^{V}	K_2^{V}	K_2^{V}	K_{2M}^{V}	ΔK_2^{V}
K_1^{V}	K_2^{VI}	K_2^{VI}	K_2^{VI}	K_2^{VI}	K_2^{VI}	K_{2M}^{VI}	ΔK_2^{VI}

* Standard deviation in K_2.

The mean value for K_2 with the lowest standard deviation and the associated values for K_1, a_A, a_{C_1} and a_C completely define *Equation Set I*.

The above procedure is used to solve each equation set for all unknown parameters, even when one or more of the absorbing species does not obey Beer's Law. Moreover, activity coefficients can be introduced as described in the section on "Statistical Bias."

In Programs 29 and 329 steps 1 to 6 are carried out for any number of different wavelengths. With these programs the rows in the table at the top of this page are computed independently (step 7). Step 8 must be carried out separately.

Programs 29 and 329 could be tested only in parts at the University of Mississippi due to the limited size of the IBM 1620 60K computer. The first part (ending with the statement: 515 CONTINUE) in which the ordinates for the equations are computed has been thoroughly tested. However, the second part could be partially tested only in the branch $M = 1$, $L = 1$. Every effort has been made to spot errors but it is possible that there are undetected errors in some branches.

The first part can readily be changed to become a feeder program for Program 26 or 326 (see below). With output information from the feeder program the slopes in the selected spectrophotometric equation can be computed. From these slopes the operator next calculates a new value for K, reprocesses his information with the Feeder Program, and recalculates the slopes. This procedure is repeated until a fixed value for K is obtained.

CONVERSION OF PART I OF PROGRAM 29 TO FEEDER PROGRAM 37

The following statements are to be removed from Part I

```
JC=N
PUNCH,CBAAA,NUM,FEEDP
PUNCH,JJ,JI,JC,M4
PUNCH,M6
PUNCH,K,L,M
PUNCH,DEVF(1),RLM(1),WAC(1),WL(1),WU(1
PUNCH,DEVF(2),RLM(2),WAC(2),WL(2),WU(2)
JC=1
```

The last seven statements in Part I are replaced by the following.

ORIGINAL	REPLACEMENT
JK = JJ − 1	IF(M4 − 1)1,600,601
DO 515 I = 1,JI	600 PUNCH,JI
DO 515 J = 1,JJ	601 ZAAAS = 326.0
YY(I,J) = Y(I,J)	PUNCH,ZAAAS,FEEDP
IF(Y(I,JJ))515,516,515	PUNCH,KA,KB,KC,KD,KE,KF
516 Y(I,J) = 0.0	PUNCH,JJ

ORIGINAL	REPLACEMENT
515 CONTINUE	PUNCH,JC
	PUNCH,K,L,M
	PUNCH, DEV(1),RLM(1),WL(1),WU(1)
	PUNCH,DEVF(2),RLM(2),WL(2),WU(2)
	DO 515 I=1,JI,4
	DO 515 J=1,JJ
	PUNCH,Y(I,J),Y(I+1,J),Y(I+2,J)Y(I+3,J)
	515 PUNCH,YER(I,J),YER(I+1,J),YER(I+2,J),YER(I+3,J)
	PUNCH,G
	PUNCH,OPER,INSTR
	WAVEL=M4
	PUNCH,RUN,TEMP,WAVEL
	IF(M6−M5)1,1,10
	END

The output information generated by Feeder Program 37 (*call word* KBAAA) is compatible with Program 326 (*call word* ZAAAS). The wavelength for which data are processed is indicated by WAVEL.

COMPUTER PROCEDURE OF SOLUTION

FORTRAN symbols used in this section have been defined at the beginning of the Method of Solution section. EQX(JC, 1) and EQX(JC, 2) are the values for K_1 and K_2 at the end of the JCth cycle. For all JC EQX(JC, 1) equals RLM(1), the arbitrary value for K_1. In Programs 29 and 329 JC denotes the cycle number (output) and the programmed number of iterations (input). Instructions to the computer include the following.

Step 1. Read the information for the first wavelength. Apply the *fail–safe procedure* to two observables (OAM(I) and C1(I) or C2(I)) to reject unreliable information (see *fail–safe procedure*). Then execute the *Kill* commands (see Input Commands).

Step 2. With the arbitrary values for K_1 and K_2, and the initial concentrations of A and B, denoted by EQX(1,1), EQX(1,2), C1(I) and C2(I) respectively, compute the concentrations of $A(= CA)$, $B(= CB)$, $C_1(= CA1)$ and $C_2(= CA2)$ at equilibrium in each solution. The first two equations in each set are used in these calculations. The method of solving for CA1 and CA2 is illustrated next for equation set I. The two Mass Law equations, expressed in FORTRAN, are:

EQX(JC,1)=CA1/((C1(I)−2.0*CA1−3.0*CA2)**2.0)   (D)

EQX(JC,2)=CA2/(CA1*(C1(I)−2.0*CA1−3.0*CA2))   (E)

(a) With CA2 = 0.0 solve equation (D) for CA1 by a direct method.

(b) With the CA1 obtained in step (a) solve equation (E) for CA2 by a direct method.

(c) Repeat steps (a) and (b) with the new value for CA2 until CX1/CA1 and CX2/CA2 both lie in the range, 0.999 to 1.001. CX1 and CX2 are the values for CA1 and CA2 computed in the preceding iteration for $I = 2, 3 \cdots JI$. For each repetition of step (a) CA2 is set equal to its value in the preceding solution.

(d) Steps (a) to (c) are repeated with C1(I) replaced by C1(I) + DEV2(I). Here DEV2(I) is the *maximum permitted error* in C1(I). For equation sets II and IV C2(I) is replaced by C2(I) + DEV2(I), and CA2 (step b) is calculated by a binary search method similar to the search method described in Chapter IV of Volume I. Here PP = 0.0001.

Step 3. The ordinates (Y(I, J)) and the associated *maximum permitted errors* (YER(I, J)) are computed for the spectrophotometric equation from information obtained in step 2 and the measured absorbance (OAM(I)). The values for L and M together determine which equation is solved (see Input Commands for Programs 29 and 329).

Step 4. The spectrophotometric equation is solved by the double slope version of the *Crout reduction method* for ρ ($= K_1K_2$ or K_2/K_1) and a new value for K_2(EQX(JC,2)) is obtained. To reduce the chance of rejection of good data when the *self-judgment principle* is applied in the JC + 1 cycle, EQX(JC,2) is computed from two independent slopes. If both values are negative, EQX(JC,2) is set equal to one quarter of the absolute value of the smallest numerical EQX(JC,2). If one value of EQX(JC,2) is positive, the selected value is positive.

Step 5. Step 2, with K_2 replaced by EQX(JC,2), Step 3 and Step 4 are repeated for the cycles numbered 3, 4, $\cdots$ JC.

Step 6. In the JC + 1 cycle steps 4 and 5 are omitted. After the ordinates for the spectrophotometric equation are computed (Step 3) it is solved for the slopes and intercept by the double-slope method. The *self-judgment principle* is then applied in the normal way.

Step 7. With the sets of conjugate information accepted in step 6 the *maximum permitted error* for each slope and for the intercept is computed in the JC + 2 cycle.

Step 8. From the information obtained in steps 6 and 7, values for each of the parameters (K_1 (known), K_2, a_A, a_B, a_{C_1} and a_{C_2}') and their *maximum permitted errors* are computed.

With Feeder Program 37 (*call word* KBAAA) and Program 326 (*call word* ZAAAS) step 4 is done separately. Steps 1 to 3 are effected with the feeder program.

INSTRUMENT RELIABILITY FACTORS

In Programs 29 and 329 there are two sets of *instrument reliability factors*. DEVF(1) or DEV1(I), WL(1) and WU(1) are associated exclusively with the measured absorbance, OAM(I). DEVF(2) (or DEV2(I)), WAC(1), WAC(2), WL(2), and WU(2) refer to concentrations thus:

DEVF(2) (or DEV2(I)), WL(2) and WU(2) are associated with C1(I) if M = 1 or 2 or with C2(I) if M = 3 or 4.

WAC(1) and WAC(2) refer to the concentrations of the first (CA1) and second (CA2) complexes respectively.

Note: Here RLM(1) and RLM(2), normally defined as the measured limits of reliability, are the arbitrary values for the first (K_1) and second (K_2) formation constants. (See Input Format for Programs 29 and 329.)

WL and WU are the lowest and highest reliable values for the designated observable. WAC(1) and WAC(2) are defined thus:

If CA1 < WAC(1) * CX and/or CA2 < WAC(2) * CX (where CX = C1 (I) if C1(I) < C2(I), and CX = C2(I) if C2(I) < C1(I)) the values for CA1 and CA2 are to be set equal to zero. Thus these values will not be used to compute the ordinates for the spectrophotometric equations.

The *maximum permitted deviations* can be entered as DEVF or as DEV___(I) for each of the designated observables (see Input Commands for Programs 29 and 329). DEVF is a fixed fraction while DEV___(I) is the *maximum permitted deviation* for the Ith value of the indicated observable.

FAIL–SAFE PROCEDURE

The *fail–safe procedure* is applied in turn to the measured absorbance (OAM(I)) and to the concentration (C1(I) or C2(I)). After CA1 and CA2, the concentrations of the complexes, are calculated as described in the section on Computer Procedure of Solution, the *fail–safe procedure* is applied again, with use of WAC(1) and WAC(2).

STATISTICAL BIAS

The special three-step normalization procedure described in Chapter III is incorporated in both Programs 29 and 329. It is virtually impossible to induce round-off errors in these programs. However, if the lower limits of reliability (WL(1) and WL(2)) are set equal to zero, infinities can occur. The extreme sensitivity of the *Crout reduction method* to gross error in the raw data, discussed in Chapters III and IV, has been retained in Programs 29 and 329.

Activity coefficients can be introduced into both programs by replacing the statement numbered 999 with the desired weighting function. The procedure is as follows:

(a) Examine the ordinates given in the section on "Method of Solution."

(b) For each ordinate select the function of activity coefficients (FUNY(J)) and replace the statement 999 thus:

GO TO (701,702,703,704, $\cdots$,999), J
701 FUNY(1) = selected function
GO TO 999
702 FUNY(2) = selected function
GO TO 999
703

$$\vdots$$

999 FUNY(JJ) = 1.0

The dimensions of the computed "GO TO" statement will equal the dimension (JJ) of the equation being tested.

INPUT COMMANDS FOR PROGRAMS 29 AND 329

For Programs 29 and 329 the commands are classed in three groups.

Dimension Commands

The values selected for JQ, JP, and IJ *before* compilation determine the storage required.

JQ is the maximum number of sets of conjugate data that can be processed with the program. JQ should be a multiple of four.

JP equals two plus the maximum number of cycles that will be programmed (see cycle command). JP is often set equal to twelve.

IJ is set equal to four in programs 29 and 329 (see second FORTRAN statement). IJ determines the number of times the reject parts and the restore parts will be applied in each application of the *self-judgment principle*. IJ can be changed only with careful consideration of the entire program.

JI is selected *after compilation*. It is the number of sets of conjugate data, in multiples of four, to be processed. For example, if the actual number of sets is ten, JI is set equal to 12 and two zero sets are entered.

(*Note: Programs 29 and 329 cannot be used with small or medium storage computers.*)

Equation Commands

The values entered for L and M together determine the spectrophotometric equation to be used.

M = 1	Equation Set I	L must equal 1 to 8
M = 2	Equation Set II	
M = 3	Equation Set III	L must equal 9 to 24
M = 4	Equation Set IV	

"a_A dependent" means that the absorbancy index for A is assumed to have the form: $a_A = {}_A\alpha_0 + {}_A\alpha_1[A]$ and that the absorbancy indices for all other species are independent of their concentrations. The ordinates computed can be ascertained by reference to the equation number given under "method of solution." For example if $M = 1$, $L = 1$ then the ordinates are: $Y(I,1)=CA1$; $Y(I,2)=CA1*CA*CA$; $Y(I,3)=CA*CA*(C1(I)-2.0* CA1)$; $Y(I,4)=CA$; $Y(I,5)=CA**3.0$; $Y(I,6)=OAM(I)*CA*CA$; $Y(I,7)=OAM(I)$. (Here CA1 is the concentration of the first complex (C_1) and CA is the concentration of A at equilibrium.) The equation parameters (see output format for Programs 29 and 329) would be: $SL(1)=a_{C_1}$; $SL(2)=3a_{C_1}\rho$; $SL(3)=a_{C_2}\rho$; $SL(4)=a_A$; $SL(5)=3a_A\rho$; $SL(6)=-3\rho$; $SL(7)=$zero. (Here $\rho = K_1K_2$; a_A, a_{C_1} and a_{C_2} are the absorbancy indices of A, C_1 and C_2 respectively.

L	Dependent	Equations		L	Dependent	Equations	
		M = 1	M = 2			M = 3	M = 4
1	—	3	13	12	a_A, a_{C_1}	26	44
2	a_A	4	14	13	a_A, a_{C_2}	27	45
3	a_A, a_{C_1}	5	15	14	a_A, a_B, a_{C_1}	28	46
4	a_A, a_{C_2}	6	16	15	a_A, a_B, a_{C_2}	29	47
5	a_A, a_{C_1}, a_C	7	17	16	a_A, a_{C_1}, a_{C_2}	30	48
6	a_{C_1}	8	18	17	a_B	31	49
7	a_{C_1}, a_{C_2}	9	19	18	a_B, a_{C_1}	32	50
8	a_{C_2}	10	20	19	a_B, a_{C_2}	33	51
				20	a_B, a_{C_1}, a_{C_2}	34	52
		M = 3	M = 4	21	a_{C_1}	35	53
				22	a_{C_1}, a_{C_2}	36	54
				23	a_{C_2}	37	55
9	—	23	41	24	$a_A, a_B, a_{C_1}, a_{C_2}$	38	56
10	a_A	24	42				
11	a_A, a_B	25	43				

Other Commands

JC is the number of iterations that must be completed before the *self-judgment principle* is applied. In Programs 29 and 329 the *self-judgment principle* is applied in the $(JC + 1)$th cycle and the *error analysis* is made in the $(JC + 2)$th cycle.

M6 is the number of wavelengths for which data are to be processed.

K denotes the forms in which the two *maximum permitted deviations* will appear in the input format.

K = 1	DEVF(1); DEVF(2)
K = 2	DEVF(1); DEV2(I)
K = 3	DEV1(I); DEVF(2)
K = 4	DEV1(I); DEV2(I)

The values entered for KA, KB, KC, KD, KE, and KF determine which sets of conjugate data are to be "ignored" or "killed." "Ignored" sets are not used in the calculations during the first JC cycles, but they are considered in the two restore parts of the *self-judgment principle* which is applied in the (JC + 1)th cycle. "Killed" sets are removed from the memory.

Ignore (KB–KC). This means that the KBth to the KCth sets are to be ignored.
Kill (KB,KC). This means that the KBth and KCth sets are to be removed from the memory.

KA	Comment	KA	Comment
−1	No sets are killed or ignored	11	Kill(KB,KC,KD)
0	Ignore(KB–KC)	12	Kill(KB,KC,KD,KE)
1	Ignore(KB)	13	Kill(KB,KC,KD,KE,KF)
2	Ignore(KB,KC)	14	Kill(KB–KC; KD–KE)
3	Ignore(KB,KC,KD)	15	No sets are killed or ignored
4	Ignore(KB,KC,KD,KE)	16	Kill(KB–KC)
5	Ignore(KB,KC,KD,KE,KF)	17	Kill(KB)
6	Ignore(KB–KC; KD–KE)	18	Kill(KB),Ignore(KC)
7	No sets are killed or ignored	19	Kill(KB,KD),Ignore(KC)
8	Kill(KB–KC)	20	Kill(KB,KD),Ignore(KC,KE)
9	Kill(KB)	21	Kill(KB,KD,KF),Ignore(KC,KE)
10	Kill(KB,KC)	22	Kill(KB–KC);Ignore(KD–KE)

INPUT FORMAT FOR PROGRAMS 29 AND 329

"M = 3 or 4, L = 9 − 24" beside a statement means that the information is to be entered only if M = 3 or 4 and L = 9 to 24.

STATEMENT	COMMENT
READ,JI	

Note: JI is entered only with the first set of input information if subsequent sets have the same number of sets of conjugate data. If a subsequent set has a different JI the read-file of the computer must be zeroed and the new value for JI inserted. Input information for Programs 29 and 329 can be processed with *Autoplotter Program* 503 (*call word* CEEEE) if JI = 20 and the first card of this input information is removed.

READ,CBAAA or CBAAS,FEEDP	{ Program number and source of information
READ,JC	Cycle command
READ,M6	Wavelength command
READ,K,L,M	Input commands
READ,KA,KB,KC,KD,KF	Reject–restore commands

READ,RLM(1),WAC(1),WL(1),WU(1)
READ,RLM(2),WAC(2),WL(2),WU(2)

> RLM(1) and RLM(2) are arbitrary values for K_1 and K_2 respectively. WL(1), WU(1) are *Instrument Reliability Factors* for the measured absorbance. WAC(1),WAC(2),WL(2), WU(2) are *Instrument Reliability Factors* for the concentration terms.

READ,OAM(I),OAM(I+1),OAM(I+2),OAM(I+3)

{ Measured absorbance at the first wavelength.

READ,C1(I),C1(I+1),C1(I+2),C1(I+3)

Concentration of A.

READ,C2(I),C2(I+1),C2(I+2),C2(I+3)

(M = 3 or 4; L = 9 to 16)
(Concentration of B).

READ,DEVF(1)
or
READ,DEV1(I),DEV1(I+1),DEV1(I+2),DEV1(I+3)
READ,DEVF(2)
or
READ,DEV2(I),DEV2(I+1),DEV2(I+2),DEV2(I+3)

> Format for the *maximum permitted deviations* is determined by the value of K.

READ,OPER,INSTR
READ,RUN,TEMP,WAVEL

} Identification

The following information is entered for each of the other M6 − 1 wavelengths.
READ,OAM(I),OAM(I+1),OAM(I+2),OAM(I+3)   Measured Absorbance.

OPTIONAL EXTERNAL COMMANDS FOR PROGRAMS 29 AND 329

The positions of the four optional program switches on the console of the IBM 1620 60K determine the quantity of information obtained.

SWITCH POSITIONS

1	2	3	4	COMMANDS EXECUTED AND COMMENTS
ON				PUNCH,SL(J),SQRMS(J) J=1,2, ⋯ JJ This command is executed at the end of each cycle. SL(1),SL(2), ⋯ SL(JJ−1) are the slopes for the spectrophotometric equation. SL(JJ) is the intercept, which should equal zero. SQRMS(1), SQRMS(2), ⋯ are the standard deviations in Y(I,1),⋯ Y(I,JJ) respectively. Y(I,JJ) = OAM(I),Y(I,1)=CA1 etc.
ON	ON			PUNCH,YY(I,JJ),YY(I+1,JJ),YY(I+2,JJ),YY(I+3,JJ) PUNCH,Y(I,JJ),Y(I+1,JJ),Y(I+2,JJ),Y(I+3,JJ) This command is executed at the end of each cycle YY(I,JJ) is the Ith value of the measured absorbance (OAM(I)) originally entered. Y(I,JJ) is the value for OAM(I) used in the preceding cycle.

SWITCH POSITIONS

1	2	3	4	COMMANDS EXECUTED AND COMMENTS
ON	OFF	ON		PUNCH,YY(I,J),YY(I+1,J),YY(I+2,J),YY(I+3,J) PUNCH,Y(I,J),Y(I+1,J),Y(I+2,J),Y(I+3,J) PUNCH,YER(I,J),YER(I+1,J),YER(I+2,J),YER(I+3,J) PUNCH,DEV(I,J),DEV(I+1,J),DEV(I+2,J),DEV(I+3,J) This command is executed at the end of each cycle for all I(1 to JI) and J(1 to JJ). YY(I,J) is the original information. Y(I,J) is the information used in the preceding cycle. YER(I,J) and DEV(I,J) are the Maximum Permitted Error and the Actual Error in YY(I,J). Y(I,1) and Y(I,JJ) refer to C_1 and A_M in the spectrophotometric equations.
			OFF	The commands given for *switches* 1 and 2 ON are executed at the end of the (JC+1) cycle if G2≠G1. G2 and G1 are defined in the Output Format.
			ON	The commands for *switches* 1, 2 and 3 ON, OFF, and ON are executed at the end of the (JC + 1)th cycle if G2 ≠G1.

OUTPUT FORMAT FOR PROGRAMS 29 AND 329

Symbols not specifically defined in this section have been defined in the preceding sections.

STATEMENT	COMMENT
PUNCH,CBAAA or CBAAS,NUM,FEEDP PUNCH,JJ,JI,JC,M4	NUM is the program number

---

DEFINITIONS

JJ—the dimension of the spectrophotometric equation
JI—the number of sets of conjugate data entered originally
JC—the number of iterations before the Self-Judgment Principle is applied
M4—the number designating the wavelength for which data are processed

---

PUNCH,M6	*Wavelength command*
PUNCH,K,L,M	*Input commands*
PUNCH,DEVF(1),RLM(1),WAC(1),WL(1),WU(1)	⎫ Defined for the *Input*
PUNCH,DEVF(2),RLM(2),WAC(2),WL(2),WU(2)	⎬ *Format*

PRINT,CODE,M4,RUN	⎫ Executed only for CODE
PUNCH,CODE,M4	⎪ = 99999999.0 or 88888888.0 if
PUNCH,OPER,INSTR	⎬ G1 ≤ 5.0. The calculation is
PUNCH,RUN,TEMP,WAVEL	⎭ terminated.
PUNCH,JC,G,G1,G2	
PUNCH,EQX(J,1),EQX(J,2)	(J = 1, 2, ⋯ JC)
⋮ ⋮ ⋮	
PUNCH,SL(J),SQRMS(J)	(J = 1,2,⋯JJ) (If Switch 1 is ON)

DEFINITIONS

JC—the number designating the iteration just completed

G—the number of sets of conjugate information remaining after the first two applications of the *Fail–Safe Procedure*

G1—the number of sets of conjugate information remaining after the third application of the *Fail–Safe Procedure*

G2—the number of accepted sets used in the preceding cycle to compute EQX(J,1),EQX(J,2)

EQX(J,1)—the arbitrary value for the first formation constant (K_1 or RLM(1))

EQX(J,2)—the value for the second formation constant (K_2) calculated in the JCth cycle.

SL(J),SQRMS(J) are defined under *optional external commands for Programs* 29 and 329.

PUNCH,YY(I,JJ),YY(I+1,JJ),YY(I+2,JJ),YY(I+3,JJ)
PUNCH,Y(I,JJ),Y(I+1,JJ),Y(I+2,JJ),Y(I+3,JJ)

(For I = 1,5, $\cdots$ JI − 3) Executed if *switches* 1 and 2 are ON for N = 1, 2, $\cdots$ JC, and for N = JC + 1 if *switch* 4 is OFF and G1 ≠ G2.

PUNCH,YY(I,J),YY(I+1,J),YY(I+2,J),YY(I+3,J)
PUNCH,Y(I,J),Y(I+1,J),Y(I+2,J),Y(I+3,J)
PUNCH,YER(I,J),YER(I+1,J),YER(I+2,J),YER(I+3,J)
PUNCH,DEV(I,J),DEV(I+1,J),DEV(I+2,J),DEV(I+3,J)
(for J = 1, $\cdots$ JJ; I = 1,5, $\cdots$ JI − 3)

Executed if *switches* 1, 2 and 3 are ON, OFF, ON for N = 1, 2, $\cdots$ JC or for N = JC if *switch* 4 is ON and G1 ≠ G2.

Note: YY(I,JJ),Y(I,JJ),YY(I,J),Y(I,J),YER(I,J) and DEV(I,J) are defined under *optional external commands for Programs* 29 and 329. If DEV (I,J) is positive, the set of conjugate data has a value lower than it should be.

===

The information between the double lines is generated at the end of the 2, 3, $\cdots$ (JC + 1)th cycles. In the (JC + 2)th cycle the *error analysis* is performed and the following commands are executed.

PUNCH,JC,G,G1,G2
PUNCH,EQX(JP,1),DEEQ1,EQX(JP,2),DEEQ2
PUNCH,AC1(1),AC1ER(1),AC1(2),AC1ER(2)
PUNCH,AC2(1),AC2ER(1),AC2(2),AC2ER(2)
PUNCH,AIA(1),AIAER(1),AIA(2),AIAER(2)
PUNCH,AIB(1),AIBER(1),AIB(2),AIBER(2)
PUNCH,OPER,INSTR   } Identification
PUNCH,RUN,TEMP,WAVEL

DEFINITIONS

EQX(JP,1)—Arbitrary value for the first formation constant (K_1)
DEEQ1—*Maximum permitted error* in EQX(JP,1)
EQX(JP,2)—Final value for the second formation constant (K_2)
DEEQ2—*Maximum permitted error* in EQX(JP,2)
AC1(1),AC1(2)—Parameters defining the absorbancy index of C_1
AC1ER(1), AC1ER(2)—*Maximum permitted errors* in AC1(1) and AC1(2)
AC2(1), AC2(2)—Parameters defining the absorbancy index of C_2
AC2ER(1), AC2ER(2)—*Maximum permitted errors* in AC2(1) and AC2(2)
AIA(1), AIA(2)—Parameters defining the absorbancy index of A
AIAER(1), AIAER(2)—*Maximum permitted errors* in AIA(1) and AIA(2)
AIB(1), AIB(2)—Parameters defining the absorbancy index of B
AIBER(1), AIBER(2)—*Maximum permitted errors* in AIB(1) and AIB(2)

The entire output format is repeated M6 − 1 times with new data at different wavelengths.

RELIABILITY LIMITS FOR PROGRAMS 29 AND 329

In Programs 29 and 329 it is virtually impossible to induce normal round-off error. However, the extremely sensitive form of the *Crout reduction method*, discussed in Chapter III, can lead to round-off error in evaluation of the Crout matrix if the arbitrary value for K_1 greatly differs from its true value.

FORTRAN FOR PROGRAM NUMBER 29
CALL WORD CBAAA

```
DIMENSION Y(JQ,15),DEV(JQ,15),YER(JQ,15),YY(JQ,15),AC2ER(2)
DIMENSION A(16,16),RLM(2),WL(2),DEVF(2),WU(2),AIBER(2)
DIMENSION DEV1(JQ),SQRMS(15),DEVSL(15),DEV2(JQ),C2(JQ)
DIMENSION WAC(2),FUNY(15),FUSL(15),OAM(JQ),C1(JQ),EQX(JP,2))
DIMENSION SLX(15),AC1(2),AC2(2),AIB(2),AIA(2),AC1ER(2)
DIMENSION YN(15),YA(15),YB(15),YM(15),SL(15),AIAER(2)
READ,JI
IJ=4
1 READ,CBAAA,FEEDP
DEEQ1=0.0
CQ1=100.0
CQ2=100.0
PPT=0.0
PP=0.0
CB=0.0
CA2=0.0
CA1=0.0
READ,JC
N=JC
READ,M6
M5=M6
M4=0
READ,K,L,M
READ,KA,KB,KC,KD,KE,KF
READ,RLM(1),WAC(1),WL(1),WU(1)
READ,RLM(2),WAC(2),WL(2),WU(2)
N=N+1
DO 315 J=1,N
315 EQX(J,1)=RLM(1)
EQX(1,2)=RLM(2)
N=N-1
10 DO 2 I=1,JI,4
2 READ,OAM(I),OAM(I+1),OAM(I+2),OAM(I+3)
G1=0.0
G2=0.0
IF(M4)1,3,153
3 DO 4 I=1,JI,4
4 READ,C1(I),C1(I+1),C1(I+2),C1(I+3)
IF(L-9)5,6,6
5 DO 7 I=1,JI
7 C2(I)=C1(I)
GO TO 9
6 DO 8 I=1,JI,4
8 READ,C2(I),C2(I+1),C2(I+2),C2(I+3)
9 IF(K-2)11,11,12
11 READ,DEVF(1)
GO TO 13
12 DO 14 I=1,JI,4
14 READ,DEV1(I),DEV1(I+1),DEV1(I+2),DEV1(I+3)
DEVF(1)=5555.0
13 GO TO (15,16,15,16),K
15 READ,DEVF(2)
GO TO 17
16 DO 18 I=1,JI,4
18 READ,DEV2(I),DEV2(I+1),DEV2(I+2),DEV2(I+3)
DEVF(2)=5555.0
17 READ,OPER,INSTR
READ,RUN,TEMP,WAVEL
JJ=0
```

```
   IF(L-12)19,19,20
19 LL=L
   GO TO 21
20 LL=L-12
21 GO TO (22,23,24,25),M
22 GO TO (309,307,305,306,304,307,306,308,1,1,1,1),LL
23 GO TO (309,307,306,306,305,308,307,308,1,1,1,1),LL
24 IF(L-12)310,310,311
310 GO TO (1,1,1,1,1,1,1,1,307,305,303,303),LL
311 GO TO (304,301,302,302,305,303,304,302,305,304,306,300),LL
25 IF(L-12)312,312,313
312 GO TO (1,1,1,1,1,1,1,1,307,305,303,304),LL
313 GO TO (304,302,302,303,305,304,304,303,306,305,306,301),LL
300 JJ=JJ+1
301 JJ=JJ+1
302 JJ=JJ+1
303 JJ=JJ+1
304 JJ=JJ+1
305 JJ=JJ+1
306 JJ=JJ+1
307 JJ=JJ+1
308 JJ=JJ+1
309 JJ=JJ+7
   KQ=KA+2
   IF(KQ-8)26,26,27
27 IF(KQ-16)28,28,29
28 KQ=KQ-8
   GO TO (26,30,31,32,33,34,35,36),KQ
36 DO 37 I=KD,KE
37 C2(I)=0.0
30 DO 38 I=KB,KC
38 C2(I)=0.0
   GO TO 26
35 C2(KF)=0.0
34 C2(KE)=0.0
33 C2(KD)=0.0
32 C2(KC)=0.0
31 C2(KB)=0.0
   GO TO 26
29 IF(KQ-24)39,39,40
40 KA=-1
   GO TO 26
39 KQ=KQ-16
   GO TO (26,41,42,42,4333,4333,44,41),KQ
41 DO 45 I=KB,KC
45 C2(I)=0.0
   GO TO 26
44 C2(KF)=0.0
4333 C2(KD)=0.0
42 C2(KB)=0.0
26 DO 46 I=1,JI
   IF(C2(I)-WL(2))47,48,48
48 IF(C2(I)-WU(2))49,49,47
47 C2(I)=0.0
   C1(I)=0.0
   DO 143 J=1,JJ
   YER(I,J)=0.0
   Y(I,J)=0.0
143 YY(I,J)=0.0
   GO TO 46
49 GO TO (314,46,314,46),K
314 DEV2(I)=DEVF(2)*C2(I)
```

```
46 CONTINUE
NUM=29
153 M4=M4+1
M5=M5-1
JC=N
G=0.0
PUNCH,CBAAA,NUM,FEEDP
PUNCH,JJ,JI,JC,M4
PUNCH,M6
PUNCH,K,L,M
PUNCH,DEVF(1),RLM(1),WAC(1),WL(1),WU(1)
PUNCH,DEVF(2),RLM(2),WAC(2),WL(2),WU(2)
JC=1
DO 154I=1,JI
Y(I,JJ)=OAM(I)
IF(C1(I))155,155,4336
4336 IF(C2(I))155,155,4335
4335 IF(Y(I,JJ)-WL(1))155,156,156
156 IF(Y(I,JJ)-WU(1))157,157,155
155 YER(I,JJ)=0.0
Y(I,JJ)=0.0
YY(I,JJ)=0.0
DEV(I,JJ)=0.0
GO TO 154
157 G=G+1.0
IF(K-2)158,158,496
158 DEV1(I)=DEVF(1)*Y(I,JJ)
496 YY(I,JJ)=Y(I,JJ)
YER(I,JJ)=DEV1(I)
154 CONTINUE
IF(KQ-8)159,159,160
159 GO TO (161,162,163,164,165,166,167,168),KQ
168 DO 169 I=KD,KE
169 Y(I,JJ)=0.0
162 DO 170 I=KB,KC
170 Y(I,JJ)=0.0
GO TO 161
167 Y(KF,JJ)=0.0
166 Y(KE,JJ)=0.0
165 Y(KD,JJ)=0.0
164 Y(KC,JJ)=0.0
163 Y(KB,JJ)=0.0
GO TO 161
160 KQ=KA-14
IF(KQ)161,161,207
207 GO TO (161,161,161,171,171,172,172,173),KQ
173 DO 174 I=KD,KE
174 Y(I,JJ)=0.0
GO TO 161
172 Y(KE,JJ)=0.0
171 Y(KC,JJ)=0.0
161 CONTINUE
427 DO 316 I=1,JI
AXY=SQR(YY(I,JJ)*YY(I,JJ))
IF(AXY)317,317,318
317 DO319 J=1,JJ
Y(I,J)=0.0
YER(I,J)=0.0
DEV(I,J)=0.0
319 YY(I,J)=0.0
GO TO 316
318 CAY=1.0
```

```
IF(C1(I)-CQ1)607,608,608
607 CA1=0.0
CA2=0.0
GO TO610
608 IF(C2(I)-CQ2)607,610,610
610 CQ1=C1(I)
CQ2=C2(I)
321 CX2=CA2
CX1=CA1
IF(M-2)322,322,324
322 CXX=C1(I)-3.0*CA2
CYY=4.0*EQX(JC,1)*(CXX)+1.0
CZZ=EQX(JC,1)*(CXX**2.0)
CA1=(CYY-SQR((CYY**2.0)-4.0*CZZ*4.0*EQX(JC,1)))/(8.0*EQX(JC,1))
IF(M-1)1,323,326
323 CXX=C1(I)-2.0*CA1
CA2=(EQX(JC,2)*CA1*CXX)/(1.0+3.0*EQX(JC,2)*CA1)
CA=C1(I)-2.0*CA1-3.0*CA2
GO TO 339
324 CXX=1.0+EQX(JC,1)*((C2(I)-CA2)+(C1(I)-2.0*CA2))
CYY=EQX(JC,1)*(C1(I)-2.0*CA2)*(C2(I)-CA2)
CZZ=2.0*EQX(JC,1)
CA1=(CXX-SQR((CXX**2.0)-4.0*CYY*EQX(JC,1)))/CZZ
IF(M-3)1,325,326
325 CXX=C1(I)-CA1
CA2=(EQX(JC,2)*CA1*CXX)/(1.0+2.0*EQX(JC,2)*CA1)
CA=C1(I)-CA1-2.0*CA2
CB=C2(I)-CA1-CA2
GO TO 339
326 PP=PP+1.0
RQ=1.0/(2.0**PP)
327 PPT=PPT+RQ
IF(C1(I)-C2(I))328,328,329
328 CA2=C1(I)*PPT
GO TO 330
329 CA2=C2(I)*PPT
330 IF(M-2)1,331,332
331 CA=C1(I)-2.0*CA1-3.0*CA2
IF(CA)333,333,334
333 PPT=PPT-RQ
GO TO 326
334 CBB=EQX(JC,2)*(CA**3.0)
GO TO 335
332 CA=C1(I)-CA1-2.0*CA2
IF(CA)333,333,336
336 CB=C2(I)-CA1-CA2
IF(CB)333,333,337
337 CBB=EQX(JC,2)*(CA**2.0)*CB
335 IF(CA2-CBB)327,339,338
338 IF(RQ-0.0001)339,339,333
339 PP=2.0
CY=CX2/CA2-1.0
CY=SQR(CY*CY)
CX=CX1/CA1-1.0
CX=SQR(CX*CX)
IF(CX-0.001)320,320,321
320 IF(CY-0.001)340,340,321
340 IF(CAY-1.0)1,341,345
341 CAER=CA
CBER=CB
CA1ER=CA1
CA2ER=CA2
```

```
CAY=2.0
IF(M-2)342,342,343
342 C1(I)=C1(I)+DEV2(I)
GO TO321
343 C2(I)=C2(I)+DEV2(I)
GO TO 321
345 A99=CA1ER
B99=CA2ER
IF(C1(I)-C2(I))503,503,505
503 C99=WAC(1)*C1(I)
D99=WAC(2)*C1(I)
GO TO 504
505 C99=WAC(1)*C2(I)
D99=WAC(2)*C2(I)
504 IF(A99-C99)506,507,507
506 DO 509 J=1,JJ
Y(I,J)=0.0
509 YER(I,J)=0.0
GO TO 316
507 IF(B99-D99)506,508,508
508 G1=G1+1.0
IF(M-2)346,346,367
346 C1(I)=C1(I)-DEV2(I)
Y(I,1)=CA1ER
YER(I,1)=CA1-Y(I,1)
Y(I,4)=CAER
YER(I,4)=CA-Y(I,4)
IF(M-2)347,348,1
347 GO TO (349,350,350,351,350,352,354,353),LL
350 J7=7
J8=8
J9=9
J10=10
J11=11
GO TO 357
351 J11=9
J7=7
J8=8
GO TO 357
352 J9=7
J10=8
GO TO 358
353 J11=7
GO TO 359
354 J9=7
J10=8
J11=9
GO TO 358
349 Y(I,2)=CA1ER*CAER*CAER
YER(I,2)=CA1*CA*CA-Y(I,2)
Y(I,3)=CAER*CAER*(C1(I)-2.0*CA1ER)
YER(I,3)=CA*CA*(C1(I)-2.0*CA1)-Y(I,3)
Y(I,5)=CAER*CAER*CAER
YER(I,5)=CA*CA*CA-Y(I,5)
Y(I,6)=CAER*CAER*YY(I,JJ)
YER(I,6)=CA*CA*(YY(I,JJ)+DEV1(I))-Y(I,6)
GO TO 316
357 Y(I,J7)=CAER*CAER
YER(I,J7)=CA*CA-Y(I,J7)
Y(I,J8)=CAER**4.0
YER(I,J8)=CA**4.0-Y(I,J8)
GO TO (316,349,358,359,358,316,316,316),LL
```

```
358 Y(I,J9)=CA1ER*CA1ER
YER(I,J9)=CA1*CA1-Y(I,J9)
Y(I,J10)=CA1ER*CA1ER*CAER*CAER
YER(I,J10)=CA1*CA1*CA*CA-Y(I,J10)
GO TO (316,316,349,316,359,349,359,316),LL
359 Y(I,J11)=CAER*CAER*(C1(I)-CA1ER)*CA2ER
YER(I,J11)=CA*CA*CA2*(C1(I)-CA1)-Y(I,J11)
GO TO 349
348 GO TO (355,356,356,360,356,361,361,363),LL
356 J7=7
J8=8
J9=9
J10=10
GO TO 364
360 J7=7
J8=8
J10=9
GO TO 364
361 J9=7
J10=8
GO TO 365
363 J10=7
GO TO 366
355 Y(I,2)=CA1ER*CA1ER
YER(I,2)=CA1*CA1-Y(I,2)
Y(I,3)=CA1ER*(C1(I)-2.0*CA1ER)
YER(I,3)=CA1*(C1(I)-2.0*CA1)-Y(I,3)
Y(I,5)=CA1ER*CAER
YER(I,5)=CA1*CA-Y(I,5)
Y(I,6)=CA1ER*YY(I,JJ)
YER(I,6)=CA1*(YY(I,JJ)+DEV1(I))-Y(I,6)
GO TO 316
364 Y(I,J7)=CAER*CAER
YER(I,J7)=CA*CA-YER(I,J7)
Y(I,J8)=CAER*CAER*CA1ER
YER(I,J8)=CA*CA*CA1-Y(I,J8)
GO TO (316,355,365,366,365,316,316,316),LL
365 Y(I,J9)=CA1ER*CA1ER*CA1ER
YER(I,J9)=CA1*CA1*CA1-Y(I,J9)
GO TO (316,316,355,316,366,355,366,316),LL
366 Y(I,J10)=CA1ER*CA2ER*(C1(I)-2.0*CA1ER)
YER(I,J10)=CA1*CA2*(C1(I)-2.0*CA1)-Y(I,J10)
GO TO (316,316,316,355,355,316,355,355),LL
367 C2(I)=C2(I)-DEV2(I)
LL=L-8
Y(I,1)=CA1ER
YER(I,1)=CA1-CA1ER
Y(I,4)=CAER
YER(I,4)=CA-CAER
Y(I,6)=CBER
YER(I,6)=CB-CBER
IF(M-3)1,381,391
381 IF(LL-12)368,368,382
368 GO TO (369,374,374,375,376,374,377,378,379,379,380,379),LL
374 J9=9
J10=10
J11=11
J12=12
J13=13
J14=14
J15=15
GO TO 370
```

```
375 J9=9
J10=10
J13=11
J14=12
GO TO 370
376 J9=9
J10=10
J15=11
GO TO 370
377 J9=9
J10=10
J11=11
J12=12
J15=13
GO TO 370
378 J10=10
J9=9
J13=11
J14=12
J15=13
GO TO 370
379 J11=9
J12=10
J13=11
J14=12
J15=13
GO TO 371
380 J11=9
J12=10
J15=11
GO TO 371
382 LLL=LL-12
GO TO (389,389,390,374),LLL
389 J13=9
J14=10
J15=11
GO TO 372
390 J15=9
GO TO 373
369 Y(I,2)=CA1ER*CBER*CAER
YER(I,2)=CA1*CB*CA-Y(I,2)
Y(I,3)=CBER*CAER*(C1(I)-CA1ER)
YER(I,3)=CB*CA*(C1(I)-CA1)-Y(I,3)
Y(I,5)=CBER*CAER*CAER
YER(I,5)=CB*CA*CA-Y(I,5)
Y(I,7)=CAER*CBER*CBER
YER(I,7)=CA*CB*CB-Y(I,7)
Y(I,8)=CAER*CBER*(YY(I,JJ))
YER(I,8)=CA*CB*(YY(I,JJ)+DEV1(I))-Y(I,8)
GO TO 316
370 Y(I,J9)=CAER*CAER
YER(I,J9)=CA*CA-Y(I,J9)
Y(I,J10)=CBER*CAER*CAER*CAER
YER(I,J10)=CB*CA*CA*CA-Y(I,J10)
IF(LL-12)383,383,384
384 GO TO (316,316,316,371),LLL
383 GO TO (316,369,371,372,373,371,371,372,316,316,316,316),LL
371 Y(I,J11)=CBER*CBER
YER(I,J11)=CB*CB-Y(I,J11)
Y(I,J12)=CBER*CBER*CBER*CAER
YER(I,J12)=CB*CB*CB*CA-Y(I,J12)
IF(LL-12)385,385,386
```

```
386 GO TO (316,316,316,372),LLL
385 GO TO (316,316,369,316,316,372,373,316,369,372,373,372),LL
372 Y(I,J13)=CA1ER*CA1ER
YER(I,J13)=CA1*CA1-Y(I,J13)
Y(I,J14)=CA1ER*CA1ER*CAER*CBER
YER(I,J14)=CA1*CA1*CA*CB-Y(I,J14)
IF(LL-12)387,387,388
388 GO TO (369,373,316,373),LLL
387 GO TO (316,316,316,369,316,369,316,373,316,369,316,373),LL
373 Y(I,J15)=CBER*CAER*CA2ER*(C1(I)-CA1ER)
YER(I,J15)=CB*CA*CA2*(C1(I)-CA1)-Y(I,J15)
GO TO 369
391 IF(LL-12)392,392,412
392 GO TO (394,405,405,406,407,405,408,409,410,410,411,410),LL
405 J9=9
J10=10
J11=11
J12=12
J13=13
J14=14
GO TO 395
406 J9=9
J10=10
J13=11
GO TO 395
407 J9=9
J10=10
J14=11
GO TO 395
408 J14=13
J9=9
J10=10
J11=11
J12=12
GO TO 395
409 J9=9
J10=10
J13=11
J14=12
GO TO 395
410 J11=9
J12=10
J13=11
J14=12
GO TO 398
411 J11=9
J12=10
J14=11
GO TO 398
412 LLL=LL-12
GO TO (413,413,414,405),LLL
413 J13=9
J14=10
GO TO 401
414 J14=9
GO TO 404
394 Y(I,2)=CA1ER*CA1ER
YER(I,2)=CA1*CA1-Y(I,2)
Y(I,3)=CA1ER*(C1(I)-CA1ER)
YER(I,3)=CA1*(C1(I)-CA1)-Y(I,3)
Y(I,5)=CA1ER*CAER
YER(I,5)=CA1*CA-Y(I,5)
```

```
Y(I,7)=CA1ER*CBER
YER(I,7)=CA1*CB-Y(I,7)
Y(I,8)=CA1ER*YY(I,JJ)
YER(I,8)=CA1*(YY(I,JJ)+DEV1(I))-Y(I,8)
GO TO 316
395 Y(I,J9)=CAER*CAER
YER(I,J9)=CA*CA-Y(I,J9)
Y(I,J10)=CA1ER*CAER*CAER
YER(I,J10)=CA1*CA*CA-Y(I,J10)
IF(LL-12)396,396,397
397 GO TO (316,316,316,398),LLL
396 GO TO (316,394,398,401,404,398,398,401,316,316,316,316),LL
398 Y(I,J12)=CA1ER*CBER*CBER
YER(I,J12)=CA1*CB*CB-Y(I,J12)
Y(I,J11)=CBER*CBER
YER(I,J11)=CB*CB-Y(I,J11)
IF(LL-12)399,399,400
400 GO TO (316,316,316,401),LLL
399 GO TO (316,316,394,316,316,401,404,316,394,401,404,401),LL
401 Y(I,J13)=CA1ER*CA1ER*CA1ER
YER(I,J13)=CA1*CA1*CA1-Y(I,J13)
IF(LL-12)402,402,403
403 GO TO (394,404,316,404),LLL
402 GO TO (316,316,316,394,316,394,316,404,316,394,316,404),LL
404 Y(I,J14)=CA1ER*CA2ER*(C1(I)-CA1ER)
YER(I,J14)=CA1*CA2*(C1(I)-CA1)-Y(I,J14)
GO TO 394
316 CONTINUE
JK=JJ-1
DO 515 I=1,JI
DO 515 J=1,JK
YY(I,J)=Y(I,J)
IF(Y(I,JJ))515,516,515
516 Y(I,J)=0.0
515 CONTINUE
```

THE FORTRAN IN THE NEXT SECTION HAS NOT BEEN THOROUGHLY TESTED
BECAUSE OF THE INADEQUATE STORAGE OF THE IBM 1620-60K AT THE
UNIVERSITY OF MISSISSIPPI.HOWEVER THE ENTIRE PROGRAM HAS
BEEN PROCESSED WITH THE PRECOMPILER.IN THE SECTION ON COMPUTER
PROCEDURE OF SOLUTION INSTRUCTIONS ARE GIVEN FOR THE CONVERSION
OF THE FIRST PART OF PROGRAM 29 (CALL WORD CBAAA) TO A FEEDER
PROGRAM (NUMBER 37,CALL WORD KBAAA)FOR THE VARIABLE DIMENSION
SELF-JUDGEMENT PROGRAM(CHAPTER III).FEEDER PROGRAM 37 (CALL
WORD KBAAA)HAS BEEN THOROUGHLY TESTED.

```
50 JC=JC+1
NNN=1
KKK=0
51 DO 52 J=1,JJ
YM(J)=-10000000.0
YN(J)=10000000.0
999 FUNY(J)=1.0
DO 53 I=1,JI
Y(I,J)=Y(I,J)*FUNY(J)
IF(Y(I,JJ))54,53,54
54 IF(YM(J)-Y(I,J))55,56,56
55 YM(J)=Y(I,J)
56 IF(YN(J)-Y(I,J))53,53,57
57 YN(J)=Y(I,J)
53 CONTINUE
IF(YN(J))6666,8892,8893
```

```
8892 YA(J)=-YM(J)/10.0
GO TO 8891
8893 YA(J)=-YN(J)/10.0
GO TO 8891
6666 YA(J)=2.0*YN(J)
8891 AA=YM(J)-YA(J)
BB=YN(J)-YA(J)
AA=SQR(AA*AA)
BB=SQR(BB*BB)
IF(AA-BB)58,60,59
60 IF(AA)61,61,59
61 CODE=88888888.0
62 PRINT,CODE,M4,RUN
PUNCH,CODE,M4
PUNCH,OPER,INSTR
PUNCH,RUN,TEMP,WAVEL
IF(M6-M4)1,1,10
58 YB(J)=BB
GO TO 63
59 YB(J)=AA
63 DO 52 I=1,JI
IF(Y(I,JJ))64,52,64
64 Y(I,J)=Y(I,J)-YA(J)
IF(Y(I,J))65,66,65
66 Y(I,J)=(YN(J)-YA(J))/(10.0**6.0)
65 Y(I,J)=Y(I,J)/YB(J)
52 CONTINUE
JR=JJ+1
DO 208J=1,JR
DO 208 I=1,JR
208 A(I,J)=0.0
DO 67 J=1,JJ
DO 67 JB=1,JJ
DO 67 I=1,JI
IF(Y(I,JJ))68,67,68
68 IF(JB-1)1,70,69
69 JP=JB-1
A(JB,J)=A(JB,J)+Y(I,J)*Y(I,JP)
GO TO 67
70 A(JB,J)=A(JB,J)+Y(I,J)
67 CONTINUE
G2=0.0
YAA=0.0
DO 71 J=1,JJ
71 A(J,JR)=A(J,JJ)
DO 72 I=1,JI
IF(Y(I,JJ))73,72,73
73 G2=G2+1.0
72 CONTINUE
A(1,JJ)=G2
G9=6.0
IF(G2-G9)74,75,75
74 CODE=99999999.0
GO TO 62
75 DO 76 J=2,JJ
JB=J-1
76 A(J,JJ)=A(1,JB)
DO 77 J=1,JR
DO 77 I=1,JJ
AA=SQR(A(I,J)*A(I,J))
IF(YAA-AA)78,77,77
78 YAA=AA
```

```
77 CONTINUE
DO 79 J=1,JR
DO 79 I=1,JJ
79 A(I,J)=A(I,J)/YAA
DO 80 J=1,JR
DO 80 I=1,JJ
IF(J-1)80,80,82
82 IF(J-I)83,83,84
83 JA=J-1
GO TO 85
84 JA=I-1
85 SET=0.0
SUM=0.0
IF(JA)86,86,87
87 DO 88 JK=1,JA
88 SUM=SUM+A(I,JK)*A(JK,J)
86 SET=A(I,J)-SUM
IF(J-1)89,89,90
89 A(I,J)=SET
GO TO 80
90 SOB=A(I,I)
IF(SOB)94,8889,94
8889 SOB=10.0**(-18.0)
94 A(I,J)=SET/SOB
80 CONTINUE
DO 81 I=1,JJ
JAN=JR-I
SUM2=0.0
IA=I-1
IF(IA)81,81,91
91 DO 93 JK=1,IA
JOB=JR-JK
93 SUM2=SUM2+A(JAN,JOB)*SL(JOB)
81 SL(JAN)=A(JAN,JR)-SUM2
DO 95 I=1,JI
DO 95 J=1,JJ
IF(Y(I,JJ))96,95,96
96 Y(I,J)=YB(J)*Y(I,J)
Y(I,J)=Y(I,J)+YA(J)
Y(I,J)=Y(I,J)/FUNY(J)
95 CONTINUE
SL(JJ)=SL(JJ)*YB(JJ)
AXYZ=0.0
JK=JJ-1
DO 205 J=1,JK
SL(J)=SL(J)*YB(JJ)/YB(J)
205 AXYZ=AXYZ+SL(J)*YA(J)
SL(JJ)=SL(JJ)-AXYZ+YA(JJ)
DO 206 J=1,JJ
1110 FUSL(J)=1.0
206 SL(J)=SL(J)*FUSL(J)
N77=0
JK=JJ-1
IF(KKK)1,177,186
177 Z1=SQR(SL(JJ)*SL(JJ))
DO 178 J=1,JK
SLX(J)=SL(J)
Z2=SQR(SL(J)*SL(J))
IF(Z1-Z2)178,178,179
179 N77=J
178 CONTINUE
IF(N77)1,181,182
```

```
182 DO 183 I=1,JI
QRO=Y(I,N77)
IF(Y(I,N77))184,183,184
184 DO185 J=1,JJ
185 Y(I,J)=Y(I,J)/QRO
Y(I,N77)=1.0/QRO
183 CONTINUE
N99=N77
KKK=1
GO TO 51
186 SL(JJ)=SL(N99)
N77=N99
DO 187 J=1,JK
187 SL(J)=SLX(J)
SLX(JJ)=SL(N77)
DO 188 I=1,JI
QRO=Y(I,N77)
IF(Y(I,N77))189,188,189
189 DO 498J=1,JJ
498 Y(I,J)=Y(I,J)/QRO
Y(I,N77)=1.0/QRO
188 CONTINUE
KKK=0
181 G3=G2-1.0
IF(N+1-JC)123,124,124
124 DO 8894 J=1,JJ
SQRMS(J)=0.0
DO 8894 I=1,JI
8894 DEV(I,J)=0.0
JK=JJ-1
DO 97 I=1,JI
RR=0.0
IF(YY(I,JJ))99,97,99
99 DO 98 J=1,JJ
IF(JJ-J)1,101,100
100 RR=RR+SL(J)*YY(I,J)
98 CONTINUE
101 QX=RR+SL(JJ)
DEV(I,JJ)=YY(I,JJ)-QX
DO 102 JP=1,JK
IF(SL(JP))103,104,103
104 DEV(I,JP)=0.0
GO TO 102
103 DEV(I,JP)=YY(I,JP)-(YY(I,JJ)-QX+SL(JP)*YY(I,JP))/SL(JP)
102 CONTINUE
97 CONTINUE
DO 105 J=1,JJ
DO105 I=1,JI
105 SQRMS(J)=SQRMS(J)+DEV(I,J)*DEV(I,J)
DO 8895 J=1,JJ
8895 SQRMS(J)=SQR(SQRMS(J)/G3)
123 IF(N-JC)122,107,107
107 PUNCH,JC,G,G1,G2
IF(N+1-JC)119,428,428
428 GO TO (511,511,512,512),M
511 ROW1=-SL(6)/3.0
IF(SL(4))513,514,513
514 ROW2=0.0
GO TO 415
513 ROW2=SL(5)/(3.0*SL(4))
GO TO 415
512 ROW1=-SL(8)/2.0
```

```
    IF(SL(4))416,417,416
417 ROW2=0.0
    GO TO 415
416 ROW2=SL(5)/(2.0*SL(4))
415 IF(ROW1)418,418,419
419 Z99=ROW1
    GO TO 422
418 IF(ROW2)420,420,421
420 ROW2=-ROW2/4.0
421 Z99=ROW2
422 JPP=JC
    GO TO (423,424,423,424),M
423 EQX(JPP,2)=Z99/EQX(JPP,1)
    GO TO 425
424 EQX(JPP,2)=Z99*EQX(JPP,1)
425 DO 426 J=1,JPP
426 PUNCH,EQX(J,1),EQX(J,2)
    IF(SENSE SWITCH 1)203,142
203 DO 111 J=1,JJ
111 PUNCH,SL(J),SQRMS(J)
142 IF(N+1-JC)1,118,112
112 IF(SENSE SWITCH 2)113,115
113 DO 114 I=1,JI,4
    PUNCH,YY(I,JJ),YY(I+1,JJ),YY(I+2,JJ),YY(I+3,JJ)
114 PUNCH,Y(I,JJ),Y(I+1,JJ),Y(I+2,JJ),Y(I+3,JJ)
    IF(N+1-JC)1,119,427
115 IF(SENSE SWITCH 3)116,427
116 DO 117 I=1,JI,4
    DO 117 J=1,JJ
    PUNCH,YY(I,J),YY(I+1,J),YY(I+2,J),YY(I+3,J)
    PUNCH,Y(I,J),Y(I+1,J),Y(I+2,J),Y(I+3,J)
    PUNCH,YER(I,J),YER(I+1,J),YER(I+2,J),YER(I+3,J)
117 PUNCH,DEV(I,J),DEV(I+1,J),DEV(I+2,J),DEV(I+3,J)
    IF(N+1-JC)1,119,427
118 IF(G1-G2)9002,119,9002
9002 IF(SENSE SWITCH 4)116,113
122 IF(N+1-JC)107,9999,9999
9999 IF(NNN-IJ)125,107,1
125 DO 126 I=1,JI
    JRK=0
    DO 126 J=1,JJ
    IF(YY(I,JJ))127,130,127
127 AA=SQR(YER(I,J)*YER(I,J))
    BB=SQR(DEV(I,J)*DEV(I,J))
    IF(AA-BB)129,128,128
129 IF(NNN-1)1,130,132
130 Y(I,J)=0.0
    DEV(I,J)=0.0
    GO TO 126
128 IF(NNN-1)1,126,133
131 JRK=JRK+1
    IF(JRK-JJ)126,43,1
43 DO 9001 JP=1,JJ
9001 Y(I,JP)=YY(I,JP)
    GO TO 126
132 IF(NNN-4)126,130,126
133 IF(NNN-4)131,126,131
126 CONTINUE
    NNN=NNN+1
    GO TO51
119 IF(N+1-JC)429,135,1
135 DO 134 J=1,JJ
```

```
DEVSL(J)=SL(J)
DO 134 I=1,JI
IF(Y(I,JJ))138,134,138
138 Y(I,JJ)=0.0
IF(JJ-J)1,139,140
140 JK=JJ-1
DO 141JQ=1,JK
YER(I,JQ)=-SQR(YER(I,JQ)*YER(I,JQ))
141 Y(I,JJ)=Y(I,JJ)+SL(JQ)*YER(I,JQ)
139 Y(I,JJ)=YER(I,JJ)-Y(I,JJ)
134 CONTINUE
GO TO 50
429 DO 430 J=1,2
AC1(J)=0.0
AC1ER(J)=0.0
AC2(J)=0.0
AC2ER(J)=0.0
AIA(J)=0.0
AIB(J)=0.0
AIAER(J)=0.0
430 AIBER(J)=0.0
JP=JC-1
GO TO (431,431,433,433),M
431 AC1(1)=DEVSL(1)
AC1ER(1)=SL(1)
AC2(1)=DEVSL(3)/(EQX(JP,1)*EQX(JP,2))
IF(M-1)1,451,452
451 DEEQ2=-SL(6)/(EQX(JP,1)*3.0)
GO TO 453
452 DEEQ2=-SL(6)*EQX(JP,1)/3.0
453 AC2ER(1)=-3.0*(SL(3)+AC2(1)*SL(6)/3.0)/DEVSL(6)
AIA(1)=DEVSL(4)
AIAER(1)=SL(4)
LL=L
IF(M-1)1,432,442
432 GO TO (434,435,436,437,438,439,440,441),LL
435 AIA(2)=DEVSL(7)
AIAER(2)=SL(7)
GO TO 434
436 AC1(2)=DEVSL(9)
AC1ER(2)=SL(9)
GO TO 435
437 AC2(2)=-DEVSL(9)/(DEVSL(6)/3.0)
AC2ER(2)=-3.0*(SL(9)+AC2(2)*SL(6)/3.0)/DEVSL(6)
GO TO 435
438 AC2(2)=-DEVSL(11)/(DEVSL(6)/3.0)
AC2ER(2)=(SL(11)+AC2(2)*SL(6)/3.0)/(-DEVSL(6)/3.0)
GO TO436
439 AC1(2)=DEVSL(7)
AC1ER(2)=SL(7)
GO TO 434
440 AC2(2)=-DEVSL(9)/(DEVSL(6)/3.0)
AC2ER(2)=-3.0*(SL(9)+AC2(2)*SL(6)/3.0)/DEVSL(6)
GO TO 439
441 AC2(2)=-DEVSL(7)/(DEVSL(6)/3.0)
AC2ER(2)=-3.0*(SL(7)+AC2(2)*SL(6)/3.0)/DEVSL(6)
GO TO 434
442 GO TO (434,444,445,446,447,448,449,450),LL
444 AIA(2)=DEVSL(7)
AIAER(2)=SL(7)
GO TO 434
445 AC1(2)=-DEVSL(9)/DEVSL(6)
```

```
      AC1ER(2)=-(SL(9)+AC1(1)*SL(6))/DEVSL(6)
      GO TO 444
  446 AC2(2)=-3.0*DEVSL(9)/DEVSL(6)
      AC2ER(2)=-3.0*(SL(9)+AC2(2)*SL(6)/3.0)/DEVSL(6)
      GO TO 444
  447 AC2(2)=-3.0*DEVSL(10)/DEVSL(6)
      AC2ER(2)=-3.0*(SL(9)+AC2(2)*SL(6)/3.0)/DEVSL(6)
      GO TO 445
  448 AC1(2)=-DEVSL(7)/DEVSL(6)
      AC1ER(2)=-(SL(7)+AC1(1)*SL(6))/DEVSL(6)
      GO TO 434
  449 AC2(2)=-3.0*DEVSL(8)/DEVSL(6)
      AC2ER(2)=-3.0*(SL(8)+AC2(2)*SL(6)/3.0)/DEVSL(6)
      GO TO448
  450 AC2(2)=-3.0*DEVSL(7)/DEVSL(6)
      AC2ER(2)=-3.0*(SL(7)+AC2(2)*SL(6)/3.0)/DEVSL(6)
      GO TO 434
  433 AC1(1)=DEVSL(1)
      AC1ER(1)=SL(1)
      AC2(1)=-2.0*DEVSL(3)/DEVSL(8)
      IF(M-3)1,454,456
  454 DEEQ2=-SL(8)/(2.0*EQX(JP,1))
      GO TO 455
  456 DEEQ2=-SL(8)*EQX(JP,1)/2.0
  455 AC2ER(1)=-2.0*(SL(3)+AC2(1)*SL(8)/2.0)/DEVSL(8)
      AIA(1)=DEVSL(4)
      AIAER(1)=SL(4)
      AIB(1)=DEVSL(6)
      AIBER(1)=SL(6)
      LL=L
      IF(M-3)1,457,475
  457 IF(L-12)458,458,462
  458 GO TO (1,1,1,1,1,1,1,1,434,459,460,461),LL
  459 AIA(2)=DEVSL(9)
      AIAER(2)=SL(9)
      GO TO 434
  460 AIB(2)=DEVSL(11)
      AIBER(2)=SL(11)
      GO TO 459
  461 AC1(2)=DEVSL(11)
      AC1ER(2)=SL(11)
      GO TO 459
  462 LL=L-12
      GO TO (463,464,465,466,467,468,469,470,471,472,473,474),LL
  463 AC2(2)=-DEVSL(11)*2.0/DEVSL(8)
      AC2ER(2)=-2.0*(SL(11)+AC2(2)*SL(8)/2.0)/DEVSL(8)
      GO TO459
  464 AC1(2)=DEVSL(13)
      AC1ER(2)=SL(13)
      GO TO 460
  465 AC2(2)=-2.0*DEVSL(13)/DEVSL(8)
      AC2ER(2)=-2.0*(SL(13)+AC2(2)*SL(2)/2.0)/DEVSL(8)
      GO TO460
  466 AC2(2)=-2.0*DEVSL(13)/DEVSL(8)
      AC2ER(2)=-2.0*(SL(10)+AC2(2)*SL(8)/2.0)/DEVSL(8)
      GO TO 461
  467 AIB(2)=DEVSL(9)
      AIBER(2)=SL(9)
      GO TO 434
  468 AC1(2)=DEVSL(11)
      AC1ER(2)=SL(11)
      GO TO 467
```

```
469 AC2(2)=-DEVSL(11)*2.0/DEVSL(8)
AC2ER(2)=-2.0*(SL(11)+AC2(2)*SL(8)/2.0)/DEVSL(8)
GO TO 467
470 AC2(2)=-2.0*DEVSL(13)/DEVSL(8)
AC2ER(2)=-2.0*(SL(13)+AC2(2)*SL(8)/2.0)/DEVSL(8)
GO TO 468
471 AC1(2)=DEVSL(9)
AC1ER(2)=SL(9)
GO TO 434
472 AC2(2)=-2.0*DEVSL(11)/DEVSL(8)
AC2ER(2)=-2.0*(SL(11)+AC2(2)*SL(8)/2.0)/DEVSL(8)
GO TO 471
473 AC2(2)=-2.0*DEVSL(9)/DEVSL(8)
AC2ER(2)=-2.0*(SL(9)+AC2(2)*SL(8)/2.0)/DEVSL(8)
GO TO 434
474 AC2(2)=-2.0*DEVSL(15)/DEVSL(8)
AC2ER(2)=-2.0*(SL(15)+AC2(2)*SL(8)/2.0)/DEVSL(8)
GO TO 464
475 IF(L-12)476,476,480
476 GO TO (1,1,1,1,1,1,1,1,434,477,478,479),LL
477 AIA(2)=DEVSL(9)
AIAER(2)=SL(9)
GO TO 434
478 AIB(2)=DEVSL(11)
AIBER(2)=SL(11)
GO TO 477
479 AC1(2)=-DEVSL(11)/DEVSL(8)
AC1ER(2)=-(SL(11)+AC1(2)*SL(8))/DEVSL(8)
GO TO 477
480 LL=L-12
GO TO (481,482,483,484,485,486,487,488,489,490,491,492),LL
481 AC2(2)=-2.0*DEVSL(11)/DEVSL(8)
AC2ER(2)=-2.0*(SL(11)+SL(8)*AC2(2)/2.0)/DEVSL(8)
GO TO 477
482 AC1(2)=-DEVSL(13)/DEVSL(8)
AC1ER(2)=-(SL(13)+AC1(2)*SL(8))/DEVSL(8)
GO TO 478
483 AC2(2)=-2.0*DEVSL(13)/DEVSL(8)
AC2ER(2)=-2.0*(SL(13)+SL(8)*AC2(2)/2.0)/DEVSL(8)
GO TO 478
484 AC2(2)=-2.0*DEVSL(12)/DEVSL(8)
AC2ER(2)=-2.0*(SL(12)+SL(8)*AC2(2)/2.0)/DEVSL(8)
GO TO 479
485 AIB(2)=DEVSL(9)
AIBER(2)=SL(9)
GO TO 434
486 AC1(2)=-DEVSL(11)/DEVSL(8)
AC1ER(2)=-(SL(11)+AC1(2)*SL(8))/DEVSL(8)
GO TO 485
487 AC2(2)=-2.0*DEVSL(11)/DEVSL(8)
AC2ER(2)=-2.0*(SL(11)+SL(8)*AC2(2)/2.0)/DEVSL(8)
GO TO 485
488 AC2(2)=-2.0*DEVSL(12)/DEVSL(8)
AC2ER(2)=-2.0*(SL(12)+SL(8)*AC2(2)/2.0)/DEVSL(8)
GO TO 486
489 AC1(2)=-DEVSL(9)/DEVSL(8)
AC1ER(2)=-(SL(9)+AC1(2)*SL(8))/DEVSL(8)
GO TO 434
490 AC2(2)=-2.0*DEVSL(10)/DEVSL(8)
AC2ER(2)=-2.0*(SL(10)+SL(8)*AC2(2)/2.0)/DEVSL(8)
GO TO 489
491 AC2(2)=-2.0*DEVSL(9)/DEVSL(8)
```

```
AC2ER(2)=-2.0*(SL(9)+SL(8)*AC2(2)/2.0)/DEVSL(8)
GO TO 434
492 AC2(2)=-2.0*DEVSL(14)/DEVSL(8)
AC2ER(2)=-2.0*(SL(14)+SL(8)*AC2(2)/2.0)/DEVSL(8)
GO TO 482
434 CONTINUE
PUNCH,EQX(JP,1),DEEQ1,EQX(JP,2),DEEQ2
PUNCH,AC1(1),AC1ER(1),AC1(2),AC1ER(2)
PUNCH,AC2(1),AC2ER(1),AC2(2),AC2ER(2)
PUNCH,AIA(1),AIAER(1),AIA(2),AIAER(2)
PUNCH,AIB(1),AIBER(1),AIB(2),AIBER(2)
PUNCH,OPER,INSTR
PUNCH,RUN,TEMP,WAVEL
RLM(2)=EQX(JP,2)
IF(M6-M4)1,1,10
END
```

ALGOL 60 FOR PROGRAM NUMBER 29

```
PROCEDURE CBAAA(ji,ij); ARRAY y,dev,yer,yy[1:jq,1:15],a[1:16,1:16],ac2er,
rLm,wL,devf,wu,aiber,wac,ac1,ac2,aib,aia,ac1er,aiaer[1:2],dev1,dev2,c1,c2,
oam[1:jq],sqrms,devsL,funy,fusL,sLx,yn,ym,ya,yb,sL[1:15],eqx[1:jp,1:2];
INTEGER ji,ij; SWITCH sw1:=x4,x5,x4,x5; SWITCH sw2:=x8,x9,x10,x12;
SWITCH sw3:=x23,x21,x19,x20,x18,x21,x20,x22,v31,v31,v31,v31; SWITCH sw4:
=x23,x21,x20,x20,x19,x22,x21,x22,v31,v31,v31,v31; SWITCH sw5:=v31,v31,v31,
v31,v31,v31,v31,v31,x21,x19,x17,x17; SWITCH sw6:=x18,x15,x16,x16,x19,x17,
x18,x16,x19,x18,x20,x14; SWITCH sw7:=v31,v31,v31,v31,v31,v31,v31,v31,x21,
x19,x17,x18; SWITCH sw8:=x18,x16,x16,x17,x19,x18,x18,x17,x20,x19,x20,x15;
SWITCH sw9:=x36,x25,x30,x29,x28,x27,x26,x24; SWITCH sw10:=x36,x32,x35,
x35,x34,x34,x33,x32; SWITCH sw11:=x38,x39,x38,x39; SWITCH sw12:=x54,x44,
x49,x48,x47,x46,x45,x43; SWITCH sw13:=x54,x54,x54,x53,x53,x52,x52,x51;
SWITCH sw14:=x74,x70,x70,x71,x70,x72,x74,x73; SWITCH sw15:=w34,x75,x77,
x78,x77,w34,w34,w34; SWITCH sw16:=w34,w34,x75,w34,x78,x75,x78,w34;
SWITCH sw17:=x84,x80,x80,x81,x80,x82,x82,x83; SWITCH sw18:=w34,x84,x86,
x87,x86,w34,w34,w34; SWITCH sw19:=w34,w34,x84,w34,x87,x84,x87,w34;
SWITCH sw20:=w34,w34,w34,x84,x84,w34,x84,x84; SWITCH sw21:=x99,x89,
x89,x90,x91,x89,x92,x93,x94,x94,x95,x94; SWITCH sw22:=x97,x97,x98,x89;
SWITCH sw23:=w34,w34,w34,w4; SWITCH sw24:=w34,x99,w4,w7,w10,w4,w4,w7,
w34,w34,w34,w34; SWITCH sw25:=w34,w34,w34,w7; SWITCH sw26:=w34,w34,
x99,w34,w34,w7,w10,w34,x99,w7,w10,w7; SWITCH sw27:=x99,w10,w34,w10;
SWITCH sw28:=w34,w34,w34,x99,w34,x99,w34,w10,w34,x99,w34,w10; SWITCH
sw29:=w23,w13,w13,w14,w15,w13,w16,w17,w18,w18,w19,w18; SWITCH sw30:
=w21,w21,w22,w13; SWITCH sw31:=w34,w34,w34,w27; SWITCH sw32:=w34,w23,
w27,w30,w33,w27,w27,w30,w34,w34,w34,w34; SWITCH sw33:=w34,w34,w34,w30;
SWITCH sw34:=w34,w34,w34,w34,w30,w33,w34,w23,w30,w33,w30; SWITCH
sw35:=w23,w33,w34,w33; SWITCH sw36:=w34,w34,w34,w23,w34,w23,w34,w33,
w34,w23,w34,w33; SWITCH sw37:=w55,w55,w56,w56; SWITCH sw38:=w59,w60,
w59,w60; SWITCH sw39:=w77,w77,w94,w94; SWITCH sw40:=v30,w79,w80,w81,
w82,w83,w84,w85; SWITCH sw41:=v30,w87,w88,w89,w90,w91,w92,w93; SWITCH
sw42:=v31,v31,v31,v31,v31,v31,v31,v31,v30,w96,w97,w98; SWITCH sw43:=v1,v2,
v3,v4,v5,v6,v7,v8,v9,v10,v11,v12; SWITCH sw44:=v31,v31,v31,v31,v31,v31,v31,
v31,v30,v14,v15,v16; SWITCH sw45:=v18,v19,v20,v21,v22,v23,v24,v25,v26,v27,
v28,v29;
COMMENT: TWIN-EQUILIBRIA;
     BEGIN INTEGER i,j,jj,jb,jc,jp,jr,jk,jrk,jpp,jan,job,j7,j8,j9,j10,j11,j12,j13,
     j14,j15,k,kkk,ka,kb,kc,kd,ke,kf,kq,L,LL,LLL,m,m4,m5,m6,n,num,nnn,n77,
     n99,oper,instr,run,code,g,g1,g2,g3,g9,feedp;
     REAL aa,a99,axy,axyz,bb,b99,cq1,cq2,ca,cb,ca1,ca2,cx1,cx2,cxx,cyy,czz,
     czy,cbb,cx,cy,caer,cber,ca1er,ca2er,c99,d99,deeq1,deeq2,pp,ppt,qx,qro,rr,
     rq,row1,row2,set,sob,sum,sum2,temp,waveL,yaa,z1,z2,z99;
       READ feedp;
       deeq1:=ppt:=pp:=cb:=ca2:=ca1:=0;
       cq1:=cq2:=100;
       READ jc; n:=jc;
       READ m6; m5:=m6; m4:=0;
       READ k,L,m;
       READ ka,kb,kc,kd,ke,kf;
       READ rLm[1],wac[1],wL[1],wu[1];
       READ rLm[2],wac[2],wL[2],wu[2];
       n:=n+1;
```

```
         FOR j:=1 STEP 1 UNTIL n DO eqx[j,1]:=rLm[1];
         eqx[1,2]:=rLm[2]; n:=n−1;
X1:      FOR i:=1 STEP 1 UNTIL ji DO READ oam[i];
         g1:=g2=0;
         IF m4<0 THEN GO TO v31
         ELSE IF m4>0 THEN GO TO X40;
         FOR i:=1 STEP 1 UNTIL ji DO READ c1[i];
         IF L<9 THEN
         BEGIN
            FOR i:=1 STEP 1 UNTIL ji DO c2[i]:=c1[i];
            GO TO X2END;
         FOR i:=1 STEP 1 UNTIL ji DO READ c2[i];
X2:      IF k≤2 THEN
         BEGIN
            READ devf[1]; GO TO X3END;
         FOR i:=1 STEP 1 UNTIL ji DO READ dev1[i];
         devf[1]:=5555;
X3:      GO TO sw1[k];
X4:      READ devf[2]; GO TO X6;
X5:      FOR i:=1 STEP 1 UNTIL ji DO READ dev2[i];
         devf[2]:=5555;
X6:      READ oper,instr;
         READ run,temp,waveL; jj:=0;
         IF L≤12 THEN
         BEGIN
            LL:=L; GO TO X7END;
         LL:=L−12;
X7:      GO TO sw2[m];
X8:      GO TO sw3[LL];
X9:      GO TO sw4[LL];
X10:     IF L≤12 THEN GO TO sw5[LL];
X11:     GO TO sw6[LL];
X12:     IF L≤12 THEN GO TO sw7[LL];
X13:     GO TO sw8[LL];
X14;     jj:=jj+1;
X15:     jj:=jj+1;
X16:     jj:=jj+1;
X17:     jj:=jj+1;
X18:     jj:=jj+1;
X19:     jj:=jj+1;
X20:     jj:=jj+1;
X21:     jj:=jj+1;
X22:     jj:=jj+1;
X23:     jj:=jj+7;
         kq:=ka+2;
         IF kq≤8 THEN GO TO X36;
         IF kq>16 THEN GO TO X31;
         kq:=kq−8; GO TO sw9[kq];
X24:     FOR i:=kd STEP 1 UNTIL ke DO c2[i]:=0;
X25:     FOR i:=kb STEP 1 UNTIL kc DO c2[i]:=0;
         GO TO X36;
X26:     c2[kf]:=0;
X27:     c2[ke]:=0;
```

```
X28:    c2[kd]:=0;
X29:    c2[kc]:=0;
X30:    c2[kb]:=0;  GO TO X36;
X31:    IF kq>24 THEN
        BEGIN
            ka:=-1;  GO TO X36END;
        kq:=kq-16;  GO TO sw10[kq];
X32:    FOR i:=kb STEP 1 UNTIL kc DO c2[i]:=0;
        GO TO X36;
X33:    c2[kf]:=0;
X34:    c2[kd]:=0;
X35:    c2[kb]:=0;
X36:    FOR i:=1 STEP 1 UNTIL ji DO
        BEGIN
            IF(c2[i]<wL[2])V(c2[i])>wu[2]THEN
            BEGIN
X37:            c2[i]:=c1[i]:=0;
                FOR j:=1 STEP 1 UNTIL jj DO yer[i,j]:=y[i,j]:=yy[i,j]:=0;
                GO TO X39END;
            GO TO sw11[k];
X38:        dev2[i]:=devf[2]Xc2[i]
X39:    END;
        num:=29;
X40:    m4:=m4+1; m5:=m5-1; jc:=n; g:=0;
        PUNCH num,feedp;
        PUNCH jj,ji,jc,m4;
        PUNCH m6;  PUNCH k,L,m;
        PUNCH devf[1],rLm[1],wac[1],wL[1],wu[1];
        PUNCH devf[2],rLm[2],wac[2],wL[2],wu[2];
        jc:=1;
        FOR i:=1 STEP 1 UNTIL ji DO
        BEGIN
            y[i,jj]:=oam[i];
            IF(c1[i]≤0)V(c2[i]≤0)V(y[i,jj]<wL[1])V(y[i,jj]>wu[1])THEN
            BEGIN
X41:            yer[i,jj]:=y[i,jj]:=yy[i,jj]:=dev[i,jj]:=0;
                GO TO X42END;
            g:=g+1;
            IF k≤2 THEN dev1[i]:=devf[1]Xy[i,jj];
            yy[i,jj]:=y[i,jj];  yer[i,jj]:=dev1[i]
X42:    END;
        IF kq>8 THEN GO TO X50;
        GO TO sw12[kq];
X43:    FOR i:=kd STEP 1 UNTIL ke DO y[i,jj]:=0;
X44:    FOR i:=kb STEP 1 UNTIL kc DO y[i,jj]:=0;
        GO TO X54;
X45:    y[kf,jj]:=0;
X46:    y[ke,jj]:=0;
X47:    y[kd,jj]:=0;
X48:    y[kc,jj]:=0;
X49:    y[kb,jj]:=0;  GO TO X54;
X50:    kq:=ka-14;
        IF kq≤0 THEN GO TO X54;
```

```
         GO TO sw13[kq];
X51:     FOR i:=kd STEP 1 UNTIL ke DO y[i,jj]:=0;
         GO TO X55;
X52:     y[ke,jj]:=0;
X53:     y[kc,jj]:=0;
X54:     FOR i:=1 STEP 1 UNTIL ji DO
         BEGIN
X55:       axy:=abs(yy[i,jj]);
           IF axy≤0 THEN
           BEGIN
X56:         FOR j:=1 STEP 1 UNTIL jj DO y[i,j]:=yer[i,j]:=dev[i,j]:=yy[i,j]:=0;
             GO TO w34END;
           cay:=1;
           IF c1[i]<cq1THEN
           BEGIN
X57:         ca1:=ca2:=0;  GO TO X58END;
           IF c2[i]<cq2 THEN GO TO X57;
X58:       cq1:=c1[i];  cq2:=c2[i];
X59:       cx2:=ca2;  cx1:=ca1;
           IF m≤2 THEN
           BEGIN
             cxx:=c1[i]−3Xca2;  cyy:=4Xeqx[jc,1]Xcxx+1;
             czz:=eqx[jc,1]Xcxx↑2;
             ca1:=(cyy−sqrt((cyy↑2)−4XczzX4Xeqx[jc,1]))/(8Xeqx[jc,1]);
             IF m<1 THEN GO TO V31
             ELSE IF m>1 THEN GO TO X61;
             cxx:=c[i]−2Xca1;
             ca2:=(eqx[jc,2]Xca1Xcxx)/(1+3Xeqx[jc,2]Xca1);
             ca:=c1[i]−2Xca1−3Xca2;  GO TO X6XEND;
X60:       cxx:=1+eqx[jc,1]X((c2[i]−ca2)+(c1[i]−2Xca2));
           cyy:=eqx[jc,1]X(c1[i]−2Xxa2)X(c2[i]−ca2);
           czz:=2Xeqx[jc,1];
           ca1:=(cxx−sqrt((cxx↑2)−4XcyyXeqx[jc,1]))/czz;
           IF m<3 THEN GO TO V31
           ELSE IF m=3 THEN
           BEGIN
             cxx:=c1[i]−ca1;
             ca2:=(eqx[jc,2]Xca1Xcxx)/(1+2Xeqx[jc,2]Xca1);
             ca:=c1[i]−ca1−2Xca2;
             cb:=c2[i]−ca1−ca2;  GO TO X6XEND;
X61:       pp:=pp+1;  rq:=1/2↑pp;
X62:       ppt:=ppt+rq;
           IF c1[i]≤c2[i]THEN
           BEGIN
             ca2:=c1[i]Xppt;  GO TO X63END;
           ca2:=c2[i]Xppt;
X63:       IF m<2 THEN GO TO V31
           ELSE IF m>2 THEN GO TO X65;
           ca:=c1[i]−2Xca1−3Xca2;
           IF ca≤0 THEN
           BEGIN
X64:         ppt:=ppt−rq;  GO TO X61END;
           cbb:=eqx[jc,2]X(ca↑3);  GO TO X66;
```

```
X65:    ca:=c1[i]−ca1−2Xca2;
        IF ca≤0 THEN GO TO X64;
        cb:=c2[i]−ca1−ca2;
        IF cb≤0 THEN GO TO X64;
        cbb:=eqx[jc,2]Xca↑2Xcb;
X66:    IF ca2<cbb THEN GO TO X62
        ELSE IF ca2>cbb∧rq>0.0001 THEN GO TO X64;
X6X:    pp:=2;
        cy:=cx2/ca2−1; cy:=abs(cy);
        cx:=cx1/ca1−1; cx:=abs(cx);
        IF(cx>0.001)∨(cy>0.001)THEN GO TO X59;
        IF cay<1 THEN GO TO V31
        ELSE IF cay=1 THEN
        BEGIN
            caer:=ca; cber:=cb;
            ca1er:=ca1; ca2er:=ca2; cay:=2;
            IF m≤2 THEN
            BEGIN
                c1[i]:=c1[i]+dev2[i]; GO TO X59END;
            c2[i]:=c2[i]+dev2[i]; GO TO X59END;
X67:    a99:=ca1er; b99:=ca2er;
        IF c1[i]≤c2[i]THEN
        BEGIN
            c99:=wac[i]Cc1[i]; d99:=wac[2]Xc1[i];
            GO TO X68END;
        c99:=wac[i]Xc2[i]; d99:=wac[2]Xc2[i];
X68:    IF a99<c99 THEN
        BEGIN
X69:        FOR j:=1 STEP 1 UNTIL jj DO y[i,j]:=yer[i,j]:=0;
            GO TO W34
        END;
        IF b99<d99 THEN GO TO X69;
        g1:=g1+1;
        IF m>2 THEN GO TO X88;
        c1[i]:=c1[i]−dev2[i]; y[i,1]:=ca1er;
        yer[i,1]:=ca1−y[i,1]; y[i,4]:=caer;
        yer[i,4]:=ca−y[i,4];
        IF m>2 THEN GO TO V31
        ELSE IF m=2 THEN GO TO X79;
        GO TO sw14[LL];
X70:    j7:=7; j8:=8; j9:=9; j10:=10; j11:=11; GO TO X76;
X71:    j11:=9; j7:=7; j8:=8; GO TO X76;
X72:    j9=7; j10:=8; GO TO X77;
X73:    j11:=7; GO TO X78;
X74:    j9:=7; j10:=8; j11:=9; GO TO X77;
X75:    y[i,2]:=ca1erXcaer↑2; yer[i,2]:=ca1Xca↑2−y[i,2];
        y[i,3]:=caer↑2X(c1[i]−2Xca1er);
        yer[i,3]:=ca↑2X(c1[i]−2Xca1)−y[i,3];
        y[i,5]:=caer↑3; yer[i,5]:=ca↑3−y[i,5];
        y[i,6]:=caer↑2Xyy[i,jj];
        yer[i,6]:=ca↑2X(yy[i,jj]+dev1[i])−y[i,6];
        GO TO W34;
X76:    y[i,j7]:=caer↑2; yer[i,j7]:=ca↑2−y[i,j7];
```

```
              y[i,j8]:=caer↑4;  yer[i,j8]:=ca↑4−y[i,j8];
              GO TO sw15[LL];
X77:          y[i,j9]:=ca1er↑2;  yer[i,j9]:=ca1↑2−y[i,j9];
              y[i,j10]:=ca1er↑2Xcaer↑2;
              yer[i,j10]:=ca1↑2Xca↑2−y[i,j10];  GO TO sw16[LL];
X78:          y[i,j11]:=caer↑2X(c1[i]−ca1er)Xca2er;
              yer[i,j11]:=ca↑2Xca2X(c1[i]−ca1)−y[i,j11];
              GO TO X75;
X79:          GO TO sw17[LL];
X80:          j7:=7;  j8:=8;  j9:=9;  j10:=10;  GO TO X85;
X81:          j7:=7;  j8:=8;  j10:=9;  GO TO X85;
X82:          j9:=7;  j10:=8;  GO TO X86;
X83:          j10:=7;  GO TO X87;
X84:          y[i,2]:=ca1er↑2;  yer[i,2]:=ca1↑2−y[i,2];
              y[i,3]:=ca1erX(c1[i]−2Xca1er);
              yer[i,3]:=ca1X(c1[i]−2Xca1)−y[i,3];
              y[i,5]:=ca1erXcaer;  yer[i,5]:=ca1Xca−y[i,5];
              y[i,6]:=ca1erXyy[i,jj];
              yer[i,6]:=ca1X(yy[i,jj]+dev1[i])−y[i,6];  GO TO W34;
X85:          y[i,j7]:=caer↑2;  yer[i,j7]:=ca↑2−yer[i,j7];
              y[i,j8]:=caer↑3;  yer[i,j8]:=ca↑2Xca1−y[i,j8];
              GO TO sw18[LL];
X86:          y[i,j9]:=ca1er↑3;  yer[i,j9]:=ca1↑3−y[i,j9];
              GO TO sw19[LL];
X87:          y[i,j10]:=ca1erXca2erX(c1[i]−2Xca1er);
              yer[i,j10]:=ca1Xca2X(c1[i]−2Xca1)−y[i,j10];
              GO TO sw20[LL];
X88:          c2[i]:=c2[i]−dev2[i];  LL:=L−8;
              y[i,1]:=ca1er;  yer[i,1]:=ca1−ca1er;
              y[i,4]:=caer;  yer[i,4]:=ca−caer;
              y[i,6]:=cber;  yer[i,6]:=cb−cber;
              IF m<3 THEN GO TO V31
              ELSE IF m>3 THEN GO TO W11;
              IF LL>12 THEN GO TO X96;
              GO TO sw21[LL];
X89:          j9:=9;  j10:=10;  j11:=11;  j12:=12;  j13:=13;
              j14:=14;  j15:=15;  GO TO W1;
X90;          j9:=9;  j10:=10;  j13:=11;  j14:=12;  GO TO W1;
X91:          j9:=9;  j10:=10;  j15:=11;  GO TO W1;
X92:          j9:=9;  j10:=10;  j11:=11;  j12:=12;  j15:=13;  GO TO W1;
X93:          j10:=10;  j9:=9;  j13:=11;  j14:=12;  j15:=13;  GO TO W1;
X94:          j11:=9;  j12:=10;  j13:=11;  j14:=12;  j15:=13;  GO TO W4;
X95:          j11:=9;  j12:=10;  j15:=11;  GO TO W4;
X96:          LLL:=LL−12;  GO TO sw22[LLL];
X97:          j13:=9;  j14:=10;  j15:=11;  GO TO W7;
X98:          j15:=9;  GO TO W10;
X99:          y[i,2]:=ca1erXcberXcaer;  yer[i,2]:=ca1XcbXca−y[i,2];
              y[i,3]:=cberXcaerX(c1[i]−ca1er);
              yer[i,3]:=cbXcaX(c1[i]− ca1)− y[i,3];
              y[i,5[:=cberXcaer↑2;
              yer[i,5]:=cbXca↑2−y[i,5];
              y[i,7]:=caerXcber↑2;
              yer[i,7]:=caXcb↑2−y[i,7];
```

```
        y[i,8]:=caerXcberXyy[i,jj];
        yer[i,8]:=caXcbX(yy[i,jj]+dev1[i]−y[i,8]; GO TO W34;
W1:     y[i,j9]:=caer↑2; yer[i,j9]:=ca↑2−y[i,j9];
        y[i,j10]:=cberXcaer↑3; yer[i,j10]:=cbXca↑3−y[i,j10];
W2:     IF LL>12 THEN GO TO sw23[LLL];
W3:     GO TO sw24[LL];
W4:     y[i,j11]:=cber↑2; yer[i,j11]:=cb↑2−y[i,j11];
        y[i,j12]:=cber↑3Xcaer; yer[i,j12]:=cb↑3Xca−y[i,j12];
W5:     IF LL>12 THEN GO TO sw25[LLL];
W6:     GO TO sw26[LL];
W7:     y[i,j13]:=caler↑2; yer[i,j13]:=ca1↑2−y[i,j13];
        y[i,j14]:=caler↑2XcaerXcber;
        yer[i,j14]:=ca1↑2XcaXcb−y[i,j14];
W8:     IF LL>12 THEN GO TO sw27[LLL];
W9:     GO TO sw28[LL];
W10:    y[i,j15]:=cberXcaerXca2erX(c1[i]−caler);
        yer[i,j15]:=cbXcaXca2X(c1[i]−y[i,j15];
        GO TO X99;
W11:    IF LL>12 THEN GO TO W20;
W12:    GO TO sw29[LL];
W13:    j9:=9; j10:=10; j11:=11; j12:=12; j13:=13; j14:=14;
        GO TO W24;
W14:    j9:=9; j10:=10; j13:=11; GO TO W24;
W15:    j9:=9; j10:=10; j14:=11; GO TO W24;
W16:    j14:=13; j9:=9; j10:=10; j11:=11; j12:=12; GO TO W24;
W17:    j9:=9; j10:=10; j13:=11; j14:=12; GO TO W24;
W18:    j11:=9; j12:=10; j13:=11; j14:=12; GO TO W27;
W19:    j11:=9; j12:=10; j14:=11; GO TO W27;
W20:    LLL:=LL−12; GO TO sw30[LLL];
W21:    j13:=9; j14:=10; GO TO W30;
W22:    j14:=9; GO TO W33;
W23:    y[i,2]:=caler↑2; yer[i,2]:=ca1↑2−y[i,2];
        y[i,3]:=calerX(c1[i]−caler);
        yer[i,3]:=ca1X(c1[i]−ca1)−y[i,3];
        y[i,5]:=calerXcaer; yer[i,5]:=ca1Xca−y[i,5];
        y[i,7]:=calerXcber; yer[i,7]:=ca1Xcb−y[i,7];
        y[i,8]:=calerXyy[i,jj];
        yer[i,8]:=ca1X(yy[i,jj]+dev1[i]−y[i,8];
        GO TO W34;
W24:    y[i,j9]:=caer↑2; yer[i,j9]:=ca↑2−y[i,j9];
        y[i,j10]:=calerXcaer↑2; yer[i,j10]:=ca1Xca↑2−y[i,j10];
W25:    IF LL>12 THEN GO TO sw31[LLL];
W26:    GO TO sw32[LL];
W27:    y[i,j12]:=calerXcber↑2; yer[i,j12]:=ca1Xcb↑2−y[i,j12];
        y[i,j11]:=cber↑2; yer[i,j11]:=cb↑2−y[i,j11];
W28:    IF LL>12 THEN GO TO sw33[LLL];
W29:    GO TO sw34[LL];
W30:    y[i,j13]:=caler↑3; yer[i,j13]:=−ca1↑3−y[i,j13];
W31:    IF LL>12 THEN GO TO sw35[LLL];
W32:    GO TO sw36[LL];
W33:    y[i,j14]:=calerXca2erX(c1[i]−caler);
        yer[i,j14]:=ca1Xca2X(c1[i]−ca1)−y[i,j14];
        GO TO W23
```

```
W34:    END;
        jk:=jj−1;
        FOR i:=1 STEP 1 UNTIL ji DO
        FOR j:=1 STEP 1 UNTIL jk DO
        BEGIN
            yy[i,j]:=y[i,j];
            IF y[i,jj]=0 THEN y[i,j]:=0
W35:    END;
W36:    jc:=jc+1;  nnn:=1;  kkk:=0;
W37:    FOR j:=1 STEP 1 UNTIL jj DO
        BEGIN
            ym[j]:= −10000000.0;  yn[j]:=10000000.0;
            funy[j]:=1;
            FOR i:=1 STEP 1 UNTIL ji DO
            BEGIN
                y[i,j]:=y[i,j]Xfuny[j];
                IF y[i,jj]=0 THEN GO TO W38;
                IF ym[j]<y[i,j] THEN ym[j]:=y[i,j];
                IF yn[j]>y[i,j] THEN yn[j]:=y[i,j]
W38:        END;
            IF yn[j]=0 THEN
            BEGIN
                ya[j]:= −ym[j]/10;  GO TO W39END;
            ELSE IF yn[j]>0 THEN
            BEGIN
                ya[j]:=−yn[j]/10;  GO TO W39END;
            ya[j]:=2Xyn[j];
W39:        aa:=ym[j]−ya[j];  bb:=yn[j]−ya[j];
            aa:=abs(aa);  bb:=abs(bb);
            IF aa<bb THEN
            BEGIN
                yb[j]:=bb;  GO TO W41END
            ELSE IF aa> bbVaa>0 THEN yb[j]:=aa
            ELSE BEGIN
                code:=88888888;
W40:            PUNCH code,W4;  PUNCH oper,instr;
                PUNCH run,temp,waveL;
                IF m6≤m4 THEN GO TO V31 ELSE GO TO X1END;
W41:        FOR i:=1 STEP 1 UNTIL ji DO
            BEGIN
                IF y[i,jj]=0 THEN GO TO W42;
                y[i,j]:=y[i,j]−ya[j];
                IF y[i,j]=0 THEN y[i,j]:=(yn[j]−ya[j]/₁₀6;
                y[i,j]:=y[i,j]/yb[j]
W42:        END
        END;
        jr:=jj+1;
        FOR j:=1 STEP 1 UNTIL jr DO
        FOR i:=1 STEP 1 UNTIL jr DO a[i,j]:=0;
        FOR j:=1 STEP 1 UNTIL jj DO
        FOR jb:=1 STEP 1 UNTIL jj DO
        FOR i:=1 STEP 1 UNTIL ji DO
        BEGIN
```

```
        IF y[i,jj]<0 THEN GO TO W43;
        IF jb<1 THEN GO TO V31
        ELSE IF jb>1 THEN
        BEGIN
           jp:=jb−1;
           a[jb,j]:=a[jb,j]+y[i,j]Xy[i,jp];
           GO TO W43END;
        a[jb,j]:=a[jb,j]+y[i,j]
W43:    END;
        g2:=yaa:=0;
        FOR j:=1 STEP 1 UNTIL jj DO a[j,jr]:=a[j,jj];
        FOR i:=1 STEP 1 UNTIL ji DO
        IF y[i,jj]≠0 THEN g2:=g2+1;
        a[1,jj]:=g2; g9:=g;
        IF g2<g9 THEN
        BEGIN
           code:=99999999; GO TO W40END;
        FOR j:=2 STEP 1 UNTIL jj DO
        BEGIN
           jb:=j−1; a[j,jj]:=a[1,jb]
        END;
        FOR j:=1 STEP 1 UNTIL jr DO
        FOR i:=1 STEP 1 UNTIL jj DO
        BEGIN
           aa:=abs(a[i,j]);
           IF yaa<aa THEN yaa:=aa
W44:    END
        FOR j:=1 STEP 1 UNTIL jr DO
        FOR i:=1 STEP 1 UNTIL jj DO a[i,j]:=a[i,j]/yaa;
        FOR j:=1 STEP 1 UNTIL jr DO
        FOR i:=1 STEP 1 UNTIL jj DO
        BEGIN
           IF j≤1 THEN GO TO W46;
           IF j≤i THEN
           BEGIN
              ja:=j−1; GO TO W45END;
           ja:=i−1;
W45:       set:=sum:=0
           IF ya>0 THEN
           FOR jk:=1 STEP 1 UNTIL ja DO sum:=sum+a[i,jk]Xa[jk,j];
           set:=a[i,j]−sum;
           IF j<i THEN
           BEGIN
              a[i,j]:=set; GO TO W46END;
           sob:=a[i,i];
           IF sob=0 THEN sob:=₁₀(−18);
           a[i,j]:=set/sob
W46:    END;
        FOR i:=1 STEP 1 UNTIL jj DO
        BEGIN
           jan:=jr−i; sum2;=0; ia:=i−1;
           IF ia>0 THEN
           FOR jk:=1 STEP 1 UNTIL ia DO
```

```
        BEGIN
          job:=jr−jk;
          sum2:=sum2+a[jan,job]Xs L[job]
        END;
        s L[jan]:=a[jan,jr]−sum2
      END;
      FOR i:=1 STEP 1 UNTIL ji DO
      FOR j:=1 STEP 1 UNTIL jj DO
      BEGIN
        IF y[i,jj]=0 THEN GO TO W47;
        y[i,j]:=yb[j]Xy[i,j];
        y[i,j]:=y[i,j]+ya[j];
        y[i,j]:=y[i,j]/funy[j]
W47:  END;
      s L[jj]:=s L[jj]Xyb[jj]; axyz:=0; jk:=jj−1;
      FOR j:=1 STEP 1 UNTIL jk DO
      BEGIN
        s L[j]:=s L[j]Xyb[jj]/yb[j];
        axyz:=axyz+s L[j]Xya[j]
      END;
      s L[jj]:=s L[jj]−axyz+ya[jj];
      FOR j:=1 STEP 1 UNTIL jj DO
      BEGIN
        fus L[j]:=1;  s L[j]:=s L[j]Xfus L[j]
      END;
      nn7:=0; jk:=jj−1;
      IF kkk<0 THEN GO TO V31
      ELSE IF kkk> 0 THEN GO TO W48;
      z1:=abs(s L[jj]);
      FOR j:=1 STEP 1 UNTIL jk DO
      BEGIN
        s Lx[j]:=s L[j]; z2:=abs(s L[j]);
        IF z1>z2 THEN a77:=j
      END;
      IF n77<0 THEN GO TO V31
      ELSE IF n77=0 THEN GO TO W49;
      FOR i:=1 STEP 1 UNTIL ji DO
      BEGIN
        qro:=y[i,n77];
        IF y[i,n77]≠0 THEN
        BEGIN
          FOR j:=1 STEP 1 UNTIL jj DO y[i,j]:=y[i,j]/qro;
          y[i,n77]:=1/qro END
      END;
      n99:=n77; kkk:=1; GO TO W37;
W48:  s L[jj]:=s L[n99]; n77:=n99;
      FOR j:=1 STEP 1 UNTIL jk DO s L[j]:=s Lx[j];
      s Lx[jj]:=s L[n77];
      FOR i:=1 STEP 1 UNTIL ji DO
      BEGIN
        qro:=y[i,n77];
        IF y[i,n77]≠0 THEN
        BEGIN
```

```
          FOR j:=1 STEP 1 UNTIL jj DO y[i,j]:=y[i,j]/qro;
          y[i,n77]:=1/qro END
      END;
      kkk:=0;
W49:  g3:=g2-1;
      IF n+1<jc THEN GO TO W53;
      FOR j:=1 STEP 1 UNTIL jj DO
      BEGIN
        sqrms[j]:=0;
        FOR i:=1 STEP 1 UNTIL ji DO dev[i,j]:=0
      END;
      jk:=jj-1;
      FOR i:=1 STEP 1 UNTIL ji DO
      BEGIN
        rr:=0;
        IF yy[i,jj]=0 THEN GO TO W53;
        FOR j:=1 STEP 1 UNTIL jj DO
        BEGIN
          IF jj<j THEN GO TO V31
          ELSE IF jj=j THEN GO TO W50;
          rr:=rr+sL[j]Xyy[i,j]
        END;
W50:    qx:=rr+sL[jj];  dev[i,jj]:=yy[i,jj]-qx;
        FOR jp:=1 STEP 1 UNTIL jk DO
        BEGIN
          IF sL[jp]=0 THEN
          BEGIN
            dev[i,jp]:=0;  GO TO W51END;
          dev[i,jp]:=yy[i,jp]-(yy[i,jj]-qx+sL[jp]Xyy[i,jp])/sL[jp]
W51:      END
W52:    END;
      FOR j:=1 STEP 1 UNTIL jj DO
      FOR i:=1 STEP 1 UNTIL ji DO sqrms[j]:=sqrms[j]+dev[i,j]+2;
      FOR j:=1 STEP 1 UNTIL jj DO sqrms[j]:=sqrt(sqrms[j]/g3);
W53:  IF n<jc THEN GO TO W67;
W54:  PUNCH jc,g,g1,g2;
      IF n+1<jc THEN GO TO W74;
      GO TO sw37[m];
W55:  row1:=-sL[6]/3;
      IF sL[4]=0 THEN
      BEGIN
        row2:=0;  GO TO W57END;
      row2:=sL[5]/(3XsL[4]);  GO TO W57;
W56:  row1:=-sL[8]/2;
      IF sL[4]=0 THEN
      BEGIN
        row2:=0;  GO TO W57END;
      row2:=sL[5]/(2XsL[4]);
W57:  IF row1>0 THEN
      BEGIN
        z99:=row1;  GO TO W58END;
      IF row2≤0 THEN row2:=-row2/4;  z99:=row2;
W58:  jpp:=jc;  GO TO sw38[m];
```

W59: eqx[jpp,2]:=z99/eqx[jpp,1]; GO TO W61;
W60: eqx[jpp,2]:=z99/eqx[jpp,1];
W61: FOR j:=1 STEP 1 UNTIL jpp DO PUNCH eqx[j,1],eqx[j,2];
      COMMENT: At this point control either proceeds serially or is
      transferred to label W62 (See Optional External Commands for
      Program 29);
      FOR j:=1 STEP 1 UNTIL jj DO PUNCH sL[j],sqrms[j];
W62: IF n+1<jc THEN GO TO V31
      ELSE IF n+1=jc THEN GO TO W66;
      COMMENT: At this point control either proceeds serially or is
      transferred to label W64 (See Optional External Commands for
      Program 29);
W63: FOR i:=1 STEP 1 UNTIL ji DO PUNCH yy[i,jj];
      FOR i:=1 STEP 1 UNTIL ji DO PUNCH y[i,jj];
      IF n+1<jc THEN GO TO V31
      ELSE IF n+1=jc THEN GO TO W74 ELSE GO TO X55
W64: COMMENT: At this point control either proceeds serially or is
      transferred to label X55 (See Optional External Commands for
      Program 29);
W65: FOR i:=1 STEP 1 UNTIL ji DO
      FOR j:=1 STEP 1 UNTIL jj DO
      BEGIN
          PUNCH yy[i,j]; PUNCH y[i,j];
          PUNCH yer[i,j]; PUNCH dev[i,j]
      END;
      IF n+1<jc THEN GO TO V31
      ELSE IF n+1=jc THEN GO TO W74 ELSE GO TO X55
W66: IF g1=g2 THEN GO TO W74;
      COMMENT: At this point control is either transferred to label W65 or to
      label W63 (See Optional External Commands for Program 29);
W67: IF n+1<jc THEN GO TO W54;
      IF nnn>ij THEN GO TO V31
      ELSE IF nnn=ij THEN GO TO W54;
      FOR i:=1 STEP 1 UNTIL ji DO
      BEGIN
          jrk:=0;
          FOR j:=1 STEP 1 UNTIL jj DO
          BEGIN
              IF yy[i,jj]=0 THEN GO TO W68;
              aa:=abs(yer[i,j]); bb:=abs(dev[i,j]);
              IF aa≥bb THEN GO TO W69;
              IF nnn<1 THEN GO TO V31
              ELSE IF nnn>1 THEN GO TO W71;
W68:   y[i,j]:=dev[i,j]:=0; GO TO W73;
W69:   IF nnn<1 THEN GO TO V31
              ELSE IF nnn>1 THEN GO TO W72 ELSE GO TO W73;
W70:   jrk:=jrk+1;
              IF jrk>jj THEN GO TO V31
              ELSE IF jrk=jj THEN
              BEGIN
                  FOR jp:=1 STEP 1 UNTIL jj DO y[i,jp]:=yy[i,jp];
                  GO TO W73;
W71:   IF nnn=4 THEN GO TO W68 ELSE GO TO W73

```
W72:        IF nnn≠4 THEN GO TO W70 END
           END
W73:  END;
      nnn:=nnn+1; GO TO W37;
W74:  IF n+1>jc THEN GO TO V31
      ELSE IF n+1<jc THEN GO TO W76;
      FOR j:=1 STEP 1 UNTIL jj DO
      BEGIN
        devsL[j]:=sL[j];
        FOR i:=1 STEP 1 UNTIL ji DO
        BEGIN
          IF y[i,jj]=0 THEN GO TO W75;
          y[i,jj]:=0;
          IF jj<j THEN GO TO V31
          ELSE IF jj>j THEN
          BEGIN
            jk:=jj−1;
            FOR jq:=1 STEP 1 UNTIL jk DO
            BEGIN
            yer[i,jq]:=−abs(yer[i,jq]);
            y[i,jj]:=y[i,jj]+sL[jq]Xyer[i,jq]
            END END;
          y[i,jj]:=yer[i,jj]−y[i,jj]
        END
W75:  END;
      GO TO W36;
W76:  FOR j:=1 STEP 1 UNTIL 2 DO ac1[j]:=ac1er[j]:=ac2[j]:=ac2er[j]:=aia[j]
          :=aib[j]:=aiaer[j]:=aiber[j]:=0;
      jp:=jc−1;  GO TO sw39[m];
W77:  ac1[1]:=devsL[1]; ac1er[1]:=sL[1];
      ac2[1]:=devsL[3]/(eqx[jp,1]Xeqx[jp,2]);
      IF m<1 THEN GO TO V31
      ELSE IF m=1 THEN
      BEGIN
        deeq2:=−sL[6]/eqx[jp,1]X3;  GO TO W78END;
      deeq2:=−sL[6]Xeqx[jp,1]/3;
W78:  ac2er[1]:=−3X(sL[3]+ac2[1]XsL[6]/3)/devsL[6];
      aia[1]:=devsL[4]; aiaer[1]:=sL[4]; LL:=L;
      IF m<1 THEN GO TO V31
      ELSE IF m>1 THEN GO TO W86;
      GO TO sw40[LL];
W79:  aia[2]:=devsL[7]; aiaer[2]:=sL[7];
      GO TO V30;
W80:  ac1[2]:=devsL[9]; ac1er[2]:=sL[9];  GO TO W79;
W81:  ac2[2]:=−devsL[9]/(devsL[6]/3);
      ac2er[2]:=−3X(sL[9]+ac2[2]XsL[6]/3)/devsL[6];
      GO TO W79;
W82:  ac2[2]:=−devsL[11]/(devsL[6]/3);
      ac2er[2]:=(sL[11]+ac2[2]XsL[6]/3)/(−devsL[6]/3);
      GO TO W80;
W83:  ac1[2]:=devsL[7]; ac1er[2]:=sL[7];  GO TO V30;
W84:  ac2[2]:=−devsL[9]/(devsL[6]/3):
      ac2er[2]:=−3X(sL[9]+ac2[2]XsL[6]/3)/devsL[6];
```

```
         GO TO W83;
W85:     ac2[2]:=−devsL[7]/(devsL[6]/3);
         ac2er[2]:=−3X(sL[7]+ac2[2]XsL[6]/3)/devsL[6];
         GO TO V30;
W86:     GO TO sw41[LL];
W87:     aia[2]:=devsL[7];  aiaer[2]:=sL[7];  GO TO V30;
W88:     ac1[2]:=−devsL[9]/devsL[6];
          ac1er[2]:=−(sL[9]+ac1[1]XsL[6])/devsL[6];
         GO TO W87;
W89:     ac2[2]:=−3XdevsL[9]/devsL[6];
         ac2er[2]:=−3X(sL[9]+ac2[2]XsL[6]/3)/devsL[6];
         GO TO W87;
W90:     ac2[2]:=−3XdevsL[10]/devsL[6];
         ac2er[2]:=−3X(sL[9]+ac2[2]XsL[6]/3)/devsL[6];
         GO TO W88;
W91:     ac1[2]:=−devsL[7]/devsL[6];
         ac1er[2]:=−(sL[7]+ac1[1]XsL[6])/devsL[6];
         GO TO V30;
W92:     ac2[2]:=−3XdevsL[8]/devsL[6];
         ac2er[2]:=−3X(sL[8]+ac2[2]XsL[6]/3)/devsL[6];
         GO TO W91;
W93:     ac2[2]:=−3XdevsL[7]/devsL[6];
         ac2er[2]:=−3X(sL[7]+ac2[2]XsL[6]/3)/devsL[6];
         GO TO V30;
W94:     ac1[1]:=devsL[1];  ac1er[1]:=sL[1];
         ac2[1]:=−2XdevsL[3]/devsL[8];
         IF m<3 THEN GO TO V31
         ELSE IF m=3 THEN
         BEGIN
            deeq2:=−sL[8]/(2Xeqx[jp,1]); GO TO W95END;
         deeq2:=−sL[8]Xeqx[jp,1]/2;
W95:     ac2er:=−2X(sL[3]+ac2[1]XsL[8]/2)/devsL[8];
         aia[1]:=devsL[4];  aiaer[1]:=sL[4];
         aib[1]:=devsL[6];  aiber[1]:=sL[6];  LL:=L;
         IF m<3 THEN GO TO V31
         ELSE IF m>3 THEN GO TO V13;
         IF L>12 THEN GO TO W99;
         GO TO sw42[LL];
W96:     aia[2]:=devsL[9];  aiaer[2]:=sL[9];  GO TO V30;
W97:     aib[2]:=devsL[11];  aiber[2]:=sL[11];  GO TO W96;
W98:     ac1[2]:=devsL[11];  ac1er[2]:=sL[11];  GO TO W96;
W99:     LL:=L−12;
         GO TO sw43[LL];
V1:      ac2[2]:=−devsL[11]X2/devsL[8];
         ac2er[2]:=−2X(sL[11]+ac2[2]XsL[8]/2)/devsL[8];
         GO TO W96;
V2:      ac1[2]:=devsL[13];  ac1er[2]:=sL[13];
         GO TO W97;
V3:      ac2[2]:=−2XdevsL[13]/devsL[8];
         ac2er[2]:=−2X(sL[13]+ac2[2]XsL[2]/2)devsL[8];
         GO TO W97;
V4:      ac2[2]:=−2XdevsL[13]/devsL[8];
         ac2er[2]:=−2X(sL[10]+ac2[2]XsL[8]/2)/devsL[8];
```

```
       GO TO W98;
V5:    aib[2]:=devsL[9]; aiber[2]:=sL[9]; GO TO V30;
V6:    ac1[2]:=devsL[11]; ac1er[2]:=sL[11]; GO TO V5;
V7:    ac2[2]:=−devsL[11]X2/devsL[8];
       ac2er[2]:=−2X(sL[11]+ac2[2]XsL[8]/devsL[8];
       GO TO V5;
V8:    ac2[2]:=−2XdevsL[13]/devsL[8];
       ac2er[2]:=−2X(sL[13]+ac2[2]XsL[8]/2)/devsL[8];
       GO TO V6;
V9:    ac1[2]:=devsL[9]; ac1er[2]:=sL[9]; GO TO V30;
V10:   ac2[2]:=−2XdevsL[11]/devsL[8];
       ac2er[2]:=−2X(sL[11]+ac2[2]XsL[8]/2)/devsL[8];
       GO TO V9;
V11:   ac2[2]:=−2XdevsL[9]/devsL[8];
       ac2er[2]:=−2X(sL[9]+ac2[2]XsL[8]/2)/devsL[8];
       GO TO V30;
V12:   ac2[2]:=−2XdevsL[15]/devsL[8];
       ac2er[2]:=−2X(sL[15]+ac2[2]XsL[8]/2)/devsL[8];
       GO TO V2;
V13:   IF L>12 THEN GO TO V17;
       GO TO sw44[LL];
V14:   aia[2]:=devsL[9]; aiaer[2]:=sL[9]; GO TO V30;
V15:   aib[2]:=devsL[11]; aiber[2]:=sL[11]; GO TO V14;
V16:   ac1[2]:=−devsL[11]/devsL[8];
       ac1er[2]:=−(sL[11]+ac1[2]XsL[8])/devsL[8];
       GO TO V14;
V17:   LL:=L−12; GO TO sw45[LL];
V18:   ac2[2]:=−2XdevsL[11]/devsL[8];
       ac2er[2]:=−2X(sL[11]+sL[8]Xac2[2]/2)/devsL[8];
       GO TO V14;
V19:   ac1[2]:=−devsL[13]/devsL[8];
       ac1er[2]:=−(sL[13]+ac1[2]XsL[8])/devsL[8];
       GO TO V15;
V20:   ac2[2]:=−2XdevsL[13]/devsL[8];
       ac2er[2]:=−2X(sL[13]+sL[8]Xac2[2]/2)/devsL[8];
       GO TO V15;
V21:   ac2[2]:=−2XdevsL[12]/devsL[8];
       ac2er[2]:=−2X(sL[12]+sL[8]Xac2[2]/2)/devsL[8];
       GO TO V16;
V22:   aib[2]:=devsL[9]; aiber[2]:=sL[9]; GO TO V30;
V23:   ac1[2]:=−devsL[11]/devsL[8];
       ac1er[2]:=−(sL[11]+ac1[2]XsL[8])/devsL[8];
       GO TO V22;
V24:   ac2[2]:=−2XdevsL[11]/devsL[8];
       ac2er[2]:=−2X(sL[11]+sL[8]Xac2[2]/2)/devsL[8];
       GO TO V22;
V25:   ac2[2]:=−2XdevsL[12]/devsL[8];
       ac2er[2]:=−2X(sL[12]+sL[8]Xac2[2]/2)/devsL[8];
       GO TO V23;
V26:   ac1[2]:=−devsL[9]/devsL[8];
       ac1er[2]:=−(sL[9]+ac1[2]XsL[8])/devsL[8];
       GO TO V30;
V27:   ac2[2]:=−2XdevsL[10]/devsL[8];
```

```
          ac2er[2]:=−2X(sL[10]+sL[8]Xac2[2]/2)/devsL[8];
          GO TO V26;
V28:      ac2[2]:=−2XdevsL[9]/devsL[8];
          ac2er[2]:=−2X(sL[9]+sL[8]Xac2[2]/2)/devsL[8];
          GO TO V30;
V29:      ac2[2]:=−2XdevsL[14]/devsL[8];
          ac2er[2]:=−2X(sL[14]+sL[8]Xac2[2]/2)/devsL[8];
          GO TO V19;
V30:      PUNCH eqx[jp,1],deeq1,eqx[jp,2],deeq2;
          PUNCH ac1[1],ac1er[1],ac1[2],ac1er[2];
          PUNCH ac2[1],ac2er[1],ac2[2],ac2er[2];
          PUNCH aia[1],aiaer[1],aia[2],aiaer[2];
          PUNCH aib[1];aiber[1],aib[2],aiber[2];
          PUNCH oper,instr;
          PUNCH run,temp,waveL;
          rLm[2]:=eqx[jp,2];
          IF m6>m4 THEN GO TO X1
V31:END CBAAA;
          READ ji; ij:=4;
V32:CBAAA(ji,ij);
          GO TO V32;
```

CHAPTER VII

MOLAR POLARIZATION EQUATIONS

Weak interactions which occur in non-polar solutions have been studied extensively by spectral methods, but there is little supporting quantitative non-spectrophotometric evidence. Several chemists have asserted or implied that spectrophotometric methods should not be used to determine formation constants and other parameters for weak complexes as the results are meaningless. In 1955 Scott[1] asserted that a minor rearrangement of the Ketelaar[2] spectrophotometric equation and the original form yield quite different results from a given set of data for a weak complex such as benzene-iodine. Scott attributed the differences he reported to the neglect of activity coefficients and artificial thermodynamic parameters. Mulliken, in his published comments[1] on Scott's paper, accepted Scott's views and, asserted that the absorbancy index for a complex can be assumed to be independent of its environment only near the band center. These remarks clearly imply that the parameters for the complex can be determined only with data collected at the absorption maximum for the complex.

Other arguments often used are that the weak complexes are not physically distinct chemical entities and that the spectrophotometric evidence for their existence is a misinterpretation of non-specific interactions which occur in solution. Hildebrand and his co-workers[3] apparently accepted the contact charge-transfer hypothesis of Orgel and Mulliken[4]. A variation of this hypothesis, proposed by Murrell[5], and the

[1] R. L. Scott, *Proc. Intl. Conf. on Coordination Compounds*, Amsterdam (1955), 265; and *Rec. trav. chim.*, **75** (1956), 787.

[2] J. A. A. Ketelaar, C. van de Stolpe, A. Goudsmit, and W. Dzcubas, *Rec. trav. chim.*, **71** (1952), 1104.

[3] K. Shinoda and J. H. Hildebrand, *J. Phys. Chem.*, **62** (1958), 295; and others by J. H. H.

[4] L. E. Orgel and R. S. Mulliken, *J. Am. Chem. Soc.*, **79** (1957), 4839.

[5] J. N. Murrell, *J. Am. Chem. Soc.*, **81** (1959), 5037. *Quart. Revs.* (London), **15** (1961), 191.

original version, as reviewed by McGlynn[6] and Mason[7], stress the importance of non-stereospecific interactions. Mulliken, in his first three papers on charge-transfer theory[8-10], repeatedly stressed the importance of secondary interactions such as van der Waals forces, London's Dispersion Forces, etc. However, in a recent review Mulliken and Person[11] have implied that contact charge-transfer contributions may not be as important as Mulliken has hitherto supposed.

Attempts to obtain quantitative nonspectrophotometric evidence for weak complexes have been frustrated by experimental difficulties and limitations of the methods used. While qualitative evidence of specific weak complexes has been obtained from solubility[12], calorimetric[13], cryoscopic[14,15], vapor pressure[16] and dielectric constant[17] studies, only the calorimetric[18,19] and cryoscopic[20] methods have yielded quantitative information which can be compared with results obtained by spectrophotometric methods. These isolated comparisons strongly suggest that "weak complexes" do result from the direct interaction of the component molecules, and not from vague statistical fluctuations biased by the weak non-specific forces in these solutions.

Clearly a general nonspectrophotometric method for studying a variety of systems, hitherto studied only by optical methods, is most urgently required. Polarization measurements seemed to offer the best possibility.

Earp and Glasstone[21], Hammick, Norris, and Sutton[22], Few and Smith[23], Maryott[24], Kortüm and Walz[25], and Maryott, Hobbs and Gross[26], have all applied the measurement of dielectric constant to the study of molecular interactions. In general, their results have been hard to interpret and the equations which they developed have only limited

[6] S. P. McGlynn, *Chem. Revs.*, **58** (1958), 1113.

[7] S. F. Mason, *Quart. Revs.* (London) **15** (1961), 287.

[8] R. S. Mulliken, *J. Am. Chem. Soc.*, **72** (1950), 600.

[9] R. S. Mulliken, *J. Am. Chem. Soc.* **74** (1952), 811.

[10] R. S. Mulliken, *J. Phys. Chem.* **56** (1952), 801.

[11] R. S. Mulliken and W. B. Person, *Ann. Rev. Phys. Chem.*, **13** (1962), 107.

[12] G. Kortüm and W. M. Vogel, *Z. Elektrochem.*, **59** (1955), 16.

[13] K. Hartley and H. A. Skinner, *Trans. Faraday Soc.*, **46** (1950), 621.

[14] P. A. D. de Maine and P. J. Santiago, *Can. J. Chem.*, **38** (1960), 157.

[15] P. A. D. de Maine and R. D. Srivastava, *J. Miss. Acad. Sci.*, **10** (1964), 67.

[16] W. C. Herndon, private communication.

[17] W. C. Herndon and H. W. Sanders, *J. Miss. Acad. Sci.*, **9** (1963), 55.

[18] C. Reid and R. S. Mulliken, *J. Am. Chem. Soc.*, **76** (1954), 3869.

[19] P. A. D. de Maine, *J. Chem. Phys.*, **26** (1957), 1199.

[20] R. D. Srivastava and P. A. D. de Maine, *J. Miss. Acad. Sci.*, **10** (1964), 51.

[21] D. P. Earp and S. Glasstone, *J. Chem. Soc.*, **1935**, 1709.

[22] D. L. Hammick, A. Norris and L. E. Sutton, *J. Chem. Soc.*, **1938**, 1755.

[23] A. V. Few and J. W. Smith, *J. Chem., Soc.*, **1949**, 2781.

[24] A. A. Maryott, *J. Research Natl. Bur. Standards*, **41** (1948), 1 and 7.

[25] G. Kortüm and H. Walz, *Z. Elektrochem.*, **57** (1953), 73.

[26] A. A. Maryott, M. E. Hobbs and P. M. Gross, *J. Chem. Phys.*, **9**, (1941) 415; and *J. Am. Chem. Soc.*, **71** (1949), 1671.

applicability. However, during the past year there has been developed a polarization method which can be used to study non-electrolyte systems. The results obtained by this method will be discussed in detail elsewhere[27,28]. The basic computer programs used in processing the data will be discussed in this chapter.

Definitions of the molar or volume polarization in terms of the static dielectric constant, density, and average molecular weight of the solution can be found in books such as *Dielectric Behavior and Structure*[29]. The three most frequently used definitions are:

$$P = \frac{\epsilon - 1}{\epsilon + 2} M/d = \rho_{CM} M/d \qquad \text{(Clausius–Mossotti)}[30]$$

$$P = \frac{(\epsilon - 1)(2\epsilon + 1)}{9\epsilon} M/d = \rho_{OK} M/d \qquad \text{(Onsager–Kirkwood)}[31,32]$$

$$P = \frac{(\epsilon - 1)(\epsilon + 4)}{(8\epsilon + 7)} M/d = \rho_H M/d \qquad \text{(Henriquez)}[33]$$

In these equations d is the solution density; M is the average molecular weight; and ϵ is the static dielectric constant of the solution. In this chapter ρ denotes the dielectric part of the polarization calculated by one of the three equations. Specific note is made whenever the dielectric constant is replaced with the square of the refractive index.

For the reversible reaction, $aA + bB \overset{K}{\rightleftarrows} C$, in an inert medium, S, the following equations can be derived.

$$\rho(n_A M_A + n_B M_B + n_S M_S)/d = (n_A - an_C)P_A + (n_B - bn_C)P_B + n_C P_C + n_S P_S \tag{1}$$

and

$$\rho V - C_S P_S = P_{AP} = (C_A - aC_C)P_A + (C_B - bC_C)P_B + C_C P_C \tag{2}$$

The symbols are defined as follows:

$(C_A - aC_C)$, $(C_B - bC_C)$ and C_C are the concentrations of A, B and C at equilibrium. C_S is the concentration of the inert medium. All concentrations are in moles per liter.

V is $(C_A M_A + C_B M_B + C_S M_S)/d$.

d is density of the solution.

[27] J. S. Menendez, M. S. Thesis University of Mississippi (in preparation).

[28] J. S. Menendez, P. A. D. de Maine and W. C. Herndon (in preparation).

[29] C. P. Smyth, *Dielectric Behavior and Structure*, (New York: McGraw-Hill, 1955).

[30] R. Clausius, *Die mechanische wärmetheorie*, vol. II (Braunschweig: Friedrich Vieweg, 1879), p. 62.

[31] L. Onsager, *J. Am. Chem. Soc.*, **58** (1936), 1486.

[32] J. G. Kirkwood, *Trans. Faraday Soc.* **42A**, (1946), 7.

[33] P. C. Henriquez, *Rec. trav. chim.*, **54**, (1935), 574.

$(n_A - an_C)$, $(n_B - bn_C)$, n_C and n_S are the mole fractions at equilibrium of A, B, C and the inert medium.

P_A, P_B and P_C are the molar polarizations of A, B and C.

P_{AP} is the apparent molar polarization.

In deriving equations (1) and (2) it has been assumed that the molar polarizations (or refractions) are additive at a fixed temperature. If "a" and "b" are known, equations (1) and (2) can be solved for P_C and C_C (or n_C) with values for ρ, M_S, M_A, M_B, C_S, C_A, C_B, P_S, P_A and P_B. P_S, P_A, P_B and P_C may be dependent on concentration or composition. We shall assume that P_S, P_A and P_B can be expanded in terms of their concentrations thus:

$$P_S = P_S^0 + S1.C_S + S2.C_S^2 + S3.C_S^3 + S4.C_S^4 \tag{3}$$

and that the molar polarization of the complex (P_C) is independent of the solution composition. In equation (3) C_S is the concentration of S, and P_S^0, $S1$, $S2$, $S3$ and $S4$ are constants for a fixed temperature.

Equation (2) has the form of the basic spectrophotometric equation and can be solved with one of the spectrophotometric programs (9–11, 25, 309–311, 325, 410, 411) for the formation constant (K) and the molar polarization of the complex (P_C), if values are known for "a" and "b" in the equilibrium equation. Information required includes ρ, M_S, M_A, M_B, P_S, P_A, P_B, C_S, C_A and C_B for several solutions with different concentrations of A and B at a fixed temperature. Thus dielectric constant (or refractive index) data can be used to study complex formation between A and B through the use of a combination of the expansion programs (9, 22–25, 309, 322–325) to compute the functional forms of P_A, P_B and P_S, and the spectrophotometric programs (9–11, 25, 309–311, 325, 410, 411).

Program 30 (call word DBAAA) is used to compute from the raw data the input information required for the expansion programs and the spectrophotometric programs. If one of the variable dimension programs (25 or 325) is used, JI, which appears in their input formats (see Chapter II of this volume), must be set equal to twenty. Thus Program 30 is designed for processing twenty sets of conjugate data. If fewer than twenty sets are processed, zeros must be entered for the missing values.

The spectrophotometric program selected for calculating K and P_C will be determined by the values of "a" and "b" and by the experimental conditions. Thus if $a = b = 1$, $C_A \ll C_B$, P_A is constant and $P_B = 0$, the Scott[1] or Ketelaar[2] methods (L = 6 and 7 in Programs 9, 25, 309 and 325) or one of the iterative methods (Programs 10, 11, 310, 311, 410, 411) is used. If $a = 2$ and $b = 0$, only the iterative methods (Programs 10, 11, 310, 311, 410, 411) can be used. The expansion program selected for computing the functional forms of P_S, P_A and P_B is determined by the dimension of the expansion. If in equation (3) $S2 = S3 = S4 = 0$, P_S^0 and $S1$ can be computed with the two-dimension expansion programs (L = 1 or 3, Programs 9 and 309) or with the variable dimension expansion programs (L = 1 or 3, Programs 25 and 325). In the expansion and spectrophotometric programs the measured absorbance (OAM(I)) and the absorbancy indices of A and B are mathematically equivalent to the apparent molar polarization (P_{AP} = P(I)) and the molar polarizations of A and B respectively.

The input information required for the spectrophotometric program is calculated by Feeder Program 30 (*call word* DBAA) from the following information for a series of solutions at a fixed temperature.

1. The dielectric constant (or square of the refractive index).

2. The molar polarizations for A, B and the solvent, S. Except for the reaction $aA \rightleftarrows C$, all molar polarizations can be expressed in their functional forms (see equation (3)). If $aA \rightleftarrows C$, P_A, calculated by the method of limiting intercepts, must be constant and P_S can be in its functional form or be a constant.

3. The density of the solution at the temperature (T2°C) of polarization measurement.

4. The initial concentrations in moles per liter of S, A and B at T2°C. These can be computed from the measured weights and volumes with Program 5, 6 or 7 (see Chapter II, Volume I).

5. The molecular weights of S, A and B if the formation constant is calculated in mole fraction units.

Calculation of the functional forms of P_S, P_A and P_B is achieved by the following steps.

(a) Data for binary solutions ((1), (3)–(5) above) are processed with Program 30 to obtain the input information for one of the *expansion programs* (9, 22–25, 309, 322–325). One component must be an inert solvent whose molar polarization is independent of concentration. In our laboratories carbon tetrachloride is used as the basic inert solvent. The functional form of the molar polarization of solute A,

$$P_A = P_A^0 + A1.C_A + A2.C_A^2 + A3.C_A^3 + A4.C_A^4 \tag{4}$$

is obtained with the *expansion programs* (see Chapter II). C_A is the concentration of A. The dimension of the expansion is selected by the operator before processing his raw data with Program 30. P_A^0, $A1$, $A2$, $A3$ and $A4$ are constants for each system at a fixed temperature.

(b) If the reaction studied is $aA \rightleftarrows C$, equation (4) is solved for the intercept (P_A^0) with the appropriate expansion program. The calculation of P_A^0 by a heterogeneous or a homogeneous expansion is called the *method of limiting intercepts* (see Chapter II)

To illustrate these points let us suppose that the one : one reversible reaction between naphthalene (Nap) and trinitrobenzene (TNB) in n-heptane is studied. For the reaction: Nap + TNB $\overset{K}{\rightleftarrows}$ C, it is assumed that all activity coefficients are unity and that P_C is independent of the composition of the solution. To calculate the formation constant (K) and molar polarization of the complex (P_C) at T2°C, data for the following five systems at room temperature (T1°C) and T2°C are required.

1. Carbon tetrachloride.

2. n-heptane-carbon tetrachloride. As the dipole moment of n-heptane is not zero, the functional form of P_S (S is n-heptane) must be computed. It is assumed that the molar polarization of carbon tetrachloride is independent of concentration.

3. n-heptane-TNB. The functional form of P_{TNB} is calculated with information for this system plus the functional form of P_S.

4. n-heptane-Nap. The functional form of P_{Nap} is computed from data for this system plus the functional form of P_S.

5. n-heptane-Nap-TNB. Data for this system plus the functional forms of P_S, P_{Nap} and P_{TNB}, are used to compute input information required for Program 10, 310 or 410 from which K and P_C are obtained.

The programs required to complete all calculations are:

(a) Program 5 (*call word* EAAAA) (see Chapter II, Volume I). This program is used to compute the concentrations of each component in each system at T2°C from data collected at T1°C.

(b) Program 30 (*call word* DBAAA) is used three times to generate the input information required for the calculation of the functional forms of P_S, P_{TNB} and P_{Nap} with an *expansion program*. It is used a fourth time to compute input information for Program 410 (*call word* JAASS; see Chapter XI).

(c) Program 325 (*call word* YAAAS) (see Chapter II) is used to calculate the functional forms of P_S, P_{Nap} and P_{TNB}. This variable dimension expansion program, in which the *self-judgment principle* is applied only to the one ordinate (y = Y(I,JJ)), is preferred to Programs 9, 22–25, 309, and 322–324 for if the slopes (A1, A2, A3 and A4) in equation (4) are small or even zero they will still be computed.

(d) Program 410 (*call word* JAASS). While Programs 10 (*call word* JAAAA) or 310 (*call word* JAAAS) could be used in place of Program 410 we have found that the almost fully automatic Program 410 is the most useful if the reliability of the data is good (see Chapter XI). Program 410 will be used to compute K and P_C from information generated with Program 30 (*call word* DBAAA).

The input commands for each program are selected on the basis of the output formats required. The *instrument reliability factors* used in Program 30 and generated in the input information for Programs 325 and 410, are selected on the basis of the experimental conditions. The computer time required to process all information depends on the number of non-zero sets of conjugate data and the values selected for J and EQ0 (see Input Commands for Program 30 (this chapter)). In general, with twenty non-zero sets of conjugate data and the IBM 1620 60K computer at the University of Mississippi, 20–30 minutes were required for the actual calculations.

SECONDARY CORRECTION FACTORS

Errors due to neglect of temperature-volume-density changes and the non-ideality of solutions can be eliminated by calculating the concentrations and densities, required as input information for Program 30 (*call word* DBAAA), with one of the programs (5, 6 or 7) given in Chapter II of Volume I. In these three programs there are instructions for both *additive* and *exact* calculations. In the *additive* calculations it is assumed that contributions for each component in each solution at each temperature may be summed. Our experiences are that the neglect of the temperature-volume-density corrections, usually not more than two or three percent, can lead to erroneous conclusions. Corrections for non-ideality can, in general, be ignored.

INSTRUMENT RELIABILITY FACTORS

There are two classes of *instrument reliability factors* which must be entered in the input format for Program 30 (*call word* DBAAA).

1. *Instrument reliability factors* associated exclusively with Program 30. These are the factors associated exclusively with the dielectric constant DE(I) (or square of the refractive index).

RLM1—The *measured limit of reliability* or *reproducibility*.

WL1—The *lowest reliable value* of DE(I).

WU1—The *highest reliable value* of DE(I).

Each DE(I) less than WL1 or greater than WU1 is rejected and all members of the corresponding set of conjugate information (P(I), C1(I), etc.) in Program 30 are set equal to zero. WL1 and WU1 in the output format for Program 30 are the lowest and highest calculated values for the apparent molar polarization (P(I)).

2. *Instrument reliability factors* not applied in Program 30. These factors appear in the output information and are applied in the expansion and spectrophotometric programs.

DEVF1 or DEV1(I)—The *maximum permitted deviation* in the apparent molar polarization (P(I)).

The following factors are associated exclusively with the concentration of A, C1(I)), if the reaction is $aA \rightleftarrows C$ or if a homogeneous expansion (L = 1) is performed; or with the concentration of B,(C2(I)), if the reaction is $aA + bB \rightleftarrows C$ or if a heterogeneous expansion (L = 3) is performed.

DEVF2 or DEV2(I)—The *maximum permitted deviation* in the concentration.

RLM2—The *measured limit of reliability* or *reproducibility*.

WL2—The *lowest reliable concentration*.

WU2—The *highest reliable concentration*.

The one (WAC1) and two (WAC1, WAC2) additional *instrument reliability factors* used in the *expansion* and *spectrophotometric programs* respectively, are not entered in the input for Program 30. They have been set equal to 0.10 in Program 30. This means that if the absolute value of $(P_{AP} - C_A P_A - C_B P_B)$ is less than WAC1 $* P_{AP}$, or if C_C is less than WAC2 $* C_A$, the entire set of conjugate information will be rejected in the *expansion* or *spectrophotometric program*.

The form in which the *maximum permitted deviations* are entered in the input for Program 30 and their form in the output format are determined by the value entered for K (see Input Commands for Program 30 (*call word* DBAAA)). DEVF1 and DEVF2 are fractions of the designated observables. DEV1(I) and DEV2(I) are the *maximum permitted deviations* for the Ith value of the indicated observable.

FAIL–SAFE PROCEDURE

In Program 30 the *fail-safe procedure* is applied only once for the first observable, DE(I). After unreliable values of the dielectric constant (or square of the refractive index) are discarded, WL1 and WU1 are set equal to the lowest and highest values respectively of the apparent molar polarization (or refraction), P(I). The other *instrument reliability factors* (DEVF1 or DEV1(I), DEVF2 or DEV2(I), RLM2, WL2, WU2, WAC1, WAC2) are applied in the expansion and spectrophotometric programs, as described in the relevant chapters in this and the preceding volumes.

It is most important to remember that while WL1 and WU1 must be in the same units as DE(I), the associated *maximum permitted deviation* (DEVF1 or DEV1(I)) must be expressed in terms of the apparent molar polarization (P(I)), which is computed in Program 30.

STATISTICAL BIAS

Devices for reducing *statistical bias* are incorporated in the *expansion* (9, 22–25, 309, 322–325) and *spectrophotometric* (9–11, 25, 309–311, 325, 410, 411) programs. *Round-off errors* can occur with Program 30 only if the distributor word size exceeds the limits given by the computer manufacturer, so for all practical purposes these errors need not be considered. Infinities occur if one of the two *lowest reliable values* (WL1 and WL2) is set equal to zero and there are partial sets of conjugate data. For instance, if WL1 $\neq$ 0 and WL2 = 0, an infinity will occur for the set with DE(I) $\neq$ 0, C1(I) $\neq$ 0 and C2(I) = 0.

Activity coefficients can be introduced by modifications to Program 30 before computation. We prefer to introduce activity coefficients, if they are desired, into the expansion or spectrophotometric programs.

INPUT COMMANDS FOR PROGRAM 30

In Program 30 the values entered for NQR, K, L and M define the *input* and *output formats*. The *reject–restore commands* (KA, KB, KC, KD, KE, KF) and the *cycle commands* (J), which appear in the *input* and *output formats*, are not executed in Program 30. They are executed in the subsequent program and should therefore be selected with consideration of the *input commands* for the *expansion* or *spectrophotometric* program. For our calculations the following values were selected: J = 3; KA = -1, KB = KC = KD = KE = KF = 0. Changes in these commands do not require reprocessing of the raw data with Program 30. For consistency other commands are M6 = 1 and JJ = 2 or 4. WACRR, entered for NQR = 410 or 411, is conveniently chosen equal to DEVF1 or, if the *maximum permitted deviation* is in the form DEV1(I), the largest permitted fractional error in the apparent molar polarization, P(I) (see Chapter XI for further details).

NQR—The number of the *expansion* (9, 22–25, 309, 322–325) or *spectrophotometric* (9–11, 25, 309–311, 325, 410, 411) *program* for which input information is to be generated.

K—Defines the forms in which the *maximum permitted deviations* are entered in both the Feeder Program (30) and subsequent programs.

    K = 1   DEVF1; DEVF2
    K = 2   DEVF1; DEV2(I)
    K = 3   DEV1(I); DEVF2
    K = 4   DEV1(I); DEV2(I)

M—Designates the number of components in the system and the concentration units (mole fraction or moles/liter) used in calculating the apparent molar polarization (P_{AP} = P(I)) and the formation constant (K).

    M = 1   Moles per liter; two component system.
    M = 2   Mole fractions; two component system.
    M = 3   Moles per liter; three component system.
    M = 4   Mole fractions; three component system.

The program requires that inert solvent always be counted as a component, although its concentration can be zero.

WAVEL—Defines ρ, used in computing the apparent molar polarization $(P(I))$, in terms of the dielectric constant $(\epsilon = DE(I))$. If the square of the refractive index is entered for $DE(I)$, ρ will be defined in terms of the refractive index.

WAVEL = 1.0 $\qquad \rho = (\epsilon - 1)/(\epsilon + 2)$ $\qquad$ (Clausius–Mossotti)

WAVEL = 2.0 $\qquad \rho = (\epsilon - 1)(2\epsilon + 1)/9\epsilon$ $\qquad$ (Onsager–Kirkwood)

WAVEL = 3.0 $\qquad \rho = (\epsilon - 1)(\epsilon + 4)/(8\epsilon + 7)$ $\qquad$ (Henriquez)

WAVEL = 4.0 ⎫
WAVEL = 5.0 ⎬ Statements 61, 62, and 63, which calculate ρ, can be
WAVEL = 6.0 ⎭ replaced by any function of the observables.

The values of L and NQR designate the forms in which the molar polarization (or refraction) of the components (S, A and B) are entered in Program 30, and the forms in which P_A and P_B will appear in the input format for the *expansion* or *spectrophotometric program*. In addition, L defines the dimension of the expansion, and the method used in calculating the formation constant (K) and molar polarization of the complex (P_C). The interpretation of each L value for each value of NQR is given below.

Expansion Programs

(NQR = 9, 22–25, 309, AND 322–325)

L = 1 $\qquad$ The *Sets of conjugate data* are expanded homogeneously with the designated *expansion program* thus:

$$P_{AP}/C_A = P_A^0 + A1 \cdot C_A + A2 \cdot C_A^2 + \cdots$$

Here P_{AP} is the apparent molar polarization of a solution with C_A moles per liter of A. The intercept (P_A^0) and slopes ($A1$, $A2$, $\cdots$), which define the *functional form* of the molar polarization of A, are computed with the designated *expansion program* from information generated by Program 30. For the *variable dimension expansion programs* (25 and 325) the dimension of the equation is arbitrarily set equal to 4 and JI (see Chapter II) = 20.

L = 3 $\qquad$ Sets of conjugate data for a system containing both A and B are expanded *heterogeneously* thus:

$$P_{AP}/C_A = P_A^0 + D1 \cdot C_B + D2 \cdot C_B^2 + \cdots$$

Here C_A and C_B are concentrations in moles per liter of A and B respectively. If Program 25 or 325 is used to compute P_A^0, D1, D2, $\cdots$, the dimension (JJ) is arbitrarily set equal to 4 and JI = 20. The intercept (P_A^0) and slopes (D1, D2, $\cdots$) define the *functional form* of solutions with A and B varied. This expansion is especially useful for studies of complex formation between two components in a system with three active components.

Spectrophotometric Programs

NQR = 9, 25, 309, AND 325

Five of the seven spectrophotometric equations discussed in Chapter III of Volume I (see also Chapter II, this volume) can be used for tests of data compatibility with the apparent molar polarization and the molar polarizations replacing the measured absorbance and absorbancy indices respectively. The other two spectrophotometric equations, Beer's Law equation (L = 1) and the Collision equation (L = 3), are two dimension expansions (see above).

L = 2   The Simple Collision equation
L = 4   de Maine–Koubek equation
L = 5   Multiple Collision equation
L = 6   Scott equation
L = 7   Ketelaar equation

If the experimental conditions are satisfactory the Scott[1] or Ketelaar[2] equations can be solved for the formation constant (K) and the molar polarization of the complex (P_C) with Programs 9, 25, 309 or 325 and information generated by Program 30.

NQR = 10, 11, 310, 311, 410 OR 411

"P_S-constant" means that the molar polarization of S does not depend on its concentration. "P_S-dependent" means that the molar polarization of S depends on its concentration (C_S) thus:

$$P_S = P_S^0 + a_1 C_S + a_2 C_S^2 + a_3 C_S^3 + a_4 C_S^4$$

For L greater than 80 the molar polarization of the inert medium (P_S) is a function of its concentration. For L less than or equal to 80, P_S is constant. QQ1 and QQ2 are coefficients in the reaction: $QQ1 \cdot A + QQ2 \cdot B \rightleftarrows C$

$\left.\begin{array}{l} 0 < L \le 20 \\ 80 < L \le 100 \end{array}\right\}$ QQ2 = 0.0 and $QQ1 \cdot A \rightleftarrows C$
                (for Programs 10, 310 and 410, QQ1 = 2.0)

$\left.\begin{array}{l} 0 < L \le 10 \\ 80 < L \le 90 \end{array}\right\} P_A$-constant

$\left.\begin{array}{l} 10 < L \le 20 \\ 90 < L \le 100 \end{array}\right\} P_A$-dependent

$\left.\begin{array}{l} 20 < L \le 80 \\ 100 < L \le 160 \end{array}\right\}$ $QQ1 \cdot A + QQ2 \cdot B \rightleftarrows C$
                (for Programs 10, 310 and 410, QQ1 = QQ2 = 1.0)

$\left.\begin{array}{l} 20 < L \le 30 \\ 100 < L \le 110 \end{array}\right\} P_A$-constant; $P_B = 0.0$

$\left.\begin{array}{l} 30<L\leq 40 \\ 110<L\leq 120 \end{array}\right\} P_A\text{--dependent; } P_B = 0.0$

$\left.\begin{array}{l} 40<L\leq 50 \\ 120<L\leq 130 \end{array}\right\} P_A \text{ and } P_B \text{ are constant}$

$\left.\begin{array}{l} 50<L\leq 60 \\ 130<L\leq 140 \end{array}\right\} P_A\text{--dependent; } P_B\text{--constant}$

$\left.\begin{array}{l} 60<L\leq 70 \\ 140<L\leq 150 \end{array}\right\} P_A\text{--constant; } P_B\text{--dependent}$

$\left.\begin{array}{l} 70<L\leq 80 \\ 150<L\leq 160 \end{array}\right\} P_A \text{ and } P_B \text{ are dependent.}$

INPUT FORMAT FOR PROGRAM 30 (Call Word DBAAA)

In the following "READ, QQ1, QQ2 (If NQR = 11, 311, or 411)" means the information is to be entered if spectrophotometric program 11, 311, or 411 is used. For a reaction $aA + bB = C$, M = 3 or 4 (a three component system; A, B and inert solvent). For solutions with no inert solvent CS(I) = 0.

STATEMENT	COMMENT
READ,NQR,FEEDP	{ NQR—The *expansion* or *spectrophotometric program* to be used in the next step.
READ,QQ1,QQ2	(If NQR = 11, 311 or 411) QQ1 · A + QQ2 · B $\overset{K}{\rightleftarrows}$ C
READ,J	(If NQR ≠ 410 or 411) } See Input Commands for indicated programs
or	
READ,J,WACRR	(If NQR = 410 or 411)
READ,EQ0	(If NQR = 10,11,310,311,410 or 411) { Arbitrary value for the formation constant
READ,PP	(If NQR = 11,311 or 411)

If the maximum percent difference between the calculated and actual concentrations of C that can be tolerated is Q, PP will have the following values:

PP	Q	PP	Q
0.01	1.0	0.00001	0.001
0.001	0.1	0.000001	0.0001
0.0001	0.01		

READ,K,L,M	*Input commands*
READ,RLM1,WL1,WU1	*Instrument reliability factors* for the dielectric constant (DE(I)) (subscript 1) and for the concentration of A or B
READ,RLM2,WL2,WU2	
READ,DE(I),DE(I+1),DE(I+2),DE(I+3)	} Dielectric constant or the square of the refractive index

READ,PS   (If NQR = 9,22–25,309,322–325; L = 1–4)

READ,PA,PS   (If NQR = 9,25,309 or 325; L = 5–7)

                         (If NQR = 10,11,310,311,410 or 411; $0 < L \leq 40$; $80 < L \leq 120$)

READ,PA,PB,PS   (If NQR = 10,11,310,311,410 or 411; $40 < L \leq 80$; $120 < L \leq 160$)

READ,S1,S2,S3,S4   (If NQR = 10,11,310,311,410 or 411; $80 < L \leq 160$)

READ,A1,A2,A3,A4   (If NQR = 10,11,310,311,410 or 441)   } Entered for certain L

READ,B1,B2,B3,B4   (If NQR = 10,11,310,311,410 or 411)   } values

---

PS, PA and PB are the concentration independent parts of the molar polarization of S, A and B respectively. The coefficients S1, S2, S3, S4 define PX, the concentration dependent part of the molar polarization of the inert medium thus: $PX = PS + S1*CS + S2*CS^2 + S3*CS^3 + S4*CS^4$ CS is the concentration of the inert medium.

READ,WMS,WM1   (If M = 1 or 2)   } WMS, WM1 and WM2 are the molecular weights of S, A and B respectively. A value for WMS is entered even if there is no S present.

READ,WMS,WM1,WM2   (If M = 3 or 4)

READ,DEN2(I),DEN2(I + 1),DEN2(I + 2),DEN2(I + 3)

DEN2(I) is the density of the Ith solution at the temperature of measurement (T2°C).

READ,CS(I),CS(I + 1),CS(I + 2),CS(I + 3)   Concentration (M/1) of S at T2°C (Must be entered even if all CS(I) = 0.0)

READ,C1(I),C1(I + 1),C1(I + 2),C1(I + 3)   Concentration (M/1) of A at T2°C.

READ,C2(I),C2(I + 1),C2(I + 2),C2(I + 3)   (If M = 3 or 4)   { Concentration (M/1) of B at T2°C.

READ,DEVF1   (If K = 1 or 2)   See *instrument reliability factors*. These *maximum permitted deviations* refer to information in the *output format* for Program 30. Thus DEVF1 is the *maximum permitted deviation* in the apparent molar polarization (P(I)).

     or

READ,DEV1(I),DEV1(I + 1),DEV1(I + 2),DEV1(I + 3)

                       (If K = 3 or 4)

READ,DEVF2   (If K = 1 or 3)

     or

READ,DEV2(I),DEV2(I + 1),DEV2(I + 2),DEV2(I + 3)

                       (If K = 2 or 4)

READ,OPER,INSTR   } Identification

READ,RUN,TEMP,WAVEL

READ,KA,KB,KC,KD,KE,KF   (If NQR = 25 or 325)   }

     or   } Reject–Restore Commands

READ,KA,KB,KC,KD   (If NQR $\neq$ 25 or 325)   }

OUTPUT FORMAT FOR PROGRAM 30 (*Call Word* DBAAA)

The output information generated by Program 30 (*call word* DBAAA) can be processed with the expansion (9, 22–25, 309, 322–325) or spectrophotometric (9–11, 25, 309–311, 325, 410, 411) program designated by

NQR. If Program 25 or 325 is used, one card with a single item of information ($JI = 20$) is put at the beginning of the first set of input information obtained from Program 30. This card is not needed for subsequent sets of input information for Programs 25 and 325. No such card is required for Programs 9–11, 301–311, 410 and 411.

The information generated by Program 30 (*call word* DBAAA) has the format described for the program with number NQR. Some symbols in the expansion and spectrophotometric programs are redefined thus:

OAM(I)—Apparent Molar Polarization
AIAX—PA
AIBX—PB

Usually the Input Information for the expansion and spectrophotometric programs would be autoplotted (see Chapter I) before use of the *self-judgment programs* to allow rejection of erroneous data.

RELIABILITY LIMITS FOR PROGRAM 30 (*Call Word* DBAAA)

If the lowest reliable value for one of the observables (WL1 or WL2) is chosen equal to zero, infinities can occur (see section, "Statistical Bias"). Otherwise it is impossible to induce (with data collected in this laboratory) *round-off* or *underflow errors* in Program 30 or in the expansion and spectrophotometric programs.

FORTRAN FOR PROGRAM NUMBER 30

CALL WORD DBAAA

```
DIMENSION VOL(20),DEN1(20),DEN2(20),DE(20),C1(20),C2(20),CS(20)
DIMENSION DEV1(20),DEV2(20),P(20)
1 READ,NQR,FEEDP
WAC1=0.10
WAC2=0.10
NPR=NQR
IF(NPR-300)2,1,3
3 NPR=NPR-300
IF(NPR-100)2,1,133
133 NPR=NPR-100
2 IF(NPR-12)4,1,5
5 NPR=NPR-10
4 NPR=NPR-8
DO 6 I=1,20
VOL(I)=0.0
DEN1(I)=0.0
DEN2(I)=0.0
DE(I)=0.0
C1(I)=0.0
C2(I)=0.0
6 CS(I)=0.0
WM1=0.0
WMS=0.0
WM2=0.0
A1=0.0
PS=0.0
PA=0.0
PB=0.0
A2=0.0
A3=0.0
A4=0.0
B1=0.0
B2=0.0
B3=0.0
B4=0.0
S1=0.0
S2=0.0
S3=0.0
S4=0.0
IF(NPR-3)7,8,7
8 READ,QQ1,QQ2
7 IF(NQR-400)130,1,132
130 READ,J
GO TO 131
132 READ,J,WACRR
131 GO TO (9,10,10,9,9,9,9),NPR
10 READ,EQO
IF(NPR-3)9,11,9
11 READ,PP
9 M6=1
READ,K,L,M
READ,RLM1,WL1,WU1
READ,RLM2,WL2,WU2
GO TO (12,13,13,12,12,12,12),NPR
13 Q=L
Q=Q/10.0
DO 14 I=1,20
PX=I
IF(Q-PX)15,15,14
```

```
15 LL=PX
GO TO 16
14 CONTINUE
12 LL=L
16 DO 17 I=1,20,4
17 READ,DE(I),DE(I+1),DE(I+2),DE(I+3)
GO TO (18,52,52,20,20,20,20),NPR
18 IF(LL-5)20,21,21
20 READ,PS
GO TO 27
21 READ,PA,PS
GO TO 27
52 IF(LL-4)53,53,54
53 READ,PA,PS
GO TO 19
54 IF(LL-8)55,55,56
55 READ,PA,PB,PS
GO TO 19
56 IF(LL-12)53,53,55
19 IF(LL-8)22,22,23
22 GO TO (24,25,24,25,24,25,24,25),LL
25 READ,A1,A2,A3,A4
24 IF(LL-6)27,27,26
26 READ,B1,B2,B3,B4
GO TO 27
23 READ,S1,S2,S3,S4
LL=LL-8
L=L-80
GO TO 22
27 GO TO (29,29,30,30),M
29 READ,WMS,WM1
GO TO 33
30 READ,WMS,WM1,WM2
33 DO 34 I=1,20,4
34 READ,DEN2(I),DEN2(I+1),DEN2(I+2),DEN2(I+3)
DO 35 I=1,20,4
35 READ,CS(I),CS(I+1),CS(I+2),CS(I+3)
DO 36 I=1,20,4
36 READ,C1(I),C1(I+1),C1(I+2),C1(I+3)
GO TO (37,37,38,38),M
38 DO 39 I=1,20,4
39 READ,C2(I),C2(I+1),C2(I+2),C2(I+3)
37 IF(K-2)40,40,41
40 READ,DEVF1
GO TO 43
41 DO 42 I=1,20,4
42 READ,DEV1(I),DEV1(I+1),DEV1(I+2),DEV1(I+3)
43 GO TO (44,45,44,45),K
44 READ,DEVF2
GO TO 47
45 DO 46 I=1,20,4
46 READ,DEV2(I),DEV2(I+1),DEV2(I+2),DEV2(I+3)
47 READ,OPER,INSTR
READ,RUN,TEMP,WAVEL
M9=WAVEL
DO 48 I=1,20
IF(DE(I)-WL1)111,112,112
112 IF(DE(I)-WU1)49,49,111
111 DE(I)=0.0
C1(I)=0.0
C2(I)=0.0
GO TO 48
```

```
49 IF(DEN2(I))48,48,50
50 IF(C1(I))48,48,51
51 GO TO (70,71,70,71),M
70 AA=CS(I)*CS(I)*CS(I)
PX=PS+S1*CS(I)*CS(I)+S2*CS(I)*CS(I)+S3*AA+S4*CS(I)*AA
PX=CS(I)*PX
71 GO TO (57,58,59,61,62,63),M9
57 P(I)=(DE(I)-1.0)/(DE(I)+2.0)
GO TO60
58 P(I)=(DE(I)-1.0)*(2.0*DE(I)+1.0)/(9.0*DE(I))
GO TO 60
59 P(I)=(DE(I)-1.0)*(DE(I)+4.0)/(8.0*DE(I)+7.0)
GO TO 60
61 P(I)=1111.1
GO TO 60
62 P(I)=2222.2
GO TO 60
63 P(I)=3333.3
60 GO TO (64,66,64,66),M
64 AA=CS(I)*WMS+C1(I)*WM1+C2(I)*WM2
P(I)=P(I)*AA/DEN2(I)-PX
GO TO 48
66 TM=C1(I)+C2(I)+CS(I)
CS(I)=CS(I)/TM
C1(I)=C1(I)/TM
C2(I)=C2(I)/TM
WMW=CS(I)*WMS+C1(I)*WM1+C2(I)*WM2
AA=CS(I)*CS(I)*CS(I)
AAA=AA*CS(I)
PX=PS*CS(I)+S1*CS(I)*CS(I)+S2*AA+S3*AAA+S4*AAA*CS(I)
P(I)=P(I)*WMW/DEN2(I)-PX
48 CONTINUE
DO 113 I=1,20
IF(P(I))114,113,114
114 WU1=P(I)
WL1=P(I)
GO TO 115
113 CONTINUE
115 DO 116 I=1,20
IF(P(I))117,116,117
117 IF(WU1-P(I))118,119,119
118 WU1=P(I)
119 IF(WL1-P(I))116,116,120
120 WL1=P(I)
116 CONTINUE
QNR=NQR
FEEDP=30.0
IF(NPR-7)122,121,1
121 READ,KA,KB,KC,KD,KE,KF
GO TO 123
122 READ,KA,KB,KC,KD
123 GO TO (72,75,75,73,73,73,73),NPR
72 PUNCH,NQR,FEEDP
GO TO 74
73 PUNCH,QNR,FEEDP
IF(NPR-7)74,125,1
125 PUNCH,KA,KB,KC,KD,KE,KF
GO TO (140,141,140,141,141,141,141),L
140 JJ=4
GO TO 124
141 JJ=2
GO TO 124
```

```
74 PUNCH,KA,KB,KC,KD
124 IF(NQR-400)134,1,136
134 PUNCH,J
GO TO 135
136 PUNCH,J,WACRR
135 PUNCH,M6
PUNCH,K,L,M
PUNCH,RLM1,WL1,WU1
PUNCH,RLM2,WL2,WU2
105 IF(K-2)76,76,77
76 PUNCH,DEVF1
GO TO 79
77 DO 78 I=1,20,4
78 PUNCH,DEV1(I),DEV1(I+1),DEV1(I+2),DEV1(I+3)
79 GO TO (80,81,80,81),K
80 PUNCH,DEVF2
GO TO 82
81 DO 83 I=1,20,4
83 PUNCH,DEV2(I),DEV2(I+1),DEV2(I+2),DEV2(I+3)
82 GO TO (84,85,85,84,84,84,84),NPR
84 DO 86 I=1,20,4
86 PUNCH,P(I),P(I+1),P(I+2),P(I+3)
GO TO (87,88,88,97,97,97,87),NPR
87 IF(L-5)97,90,90
90 PUNCH,PA,WAC1
GO TO 97
88 IF(LL-4)91,91,92
91 PUNCH,PA
GO TO 93
92 PUNCH,PA,PB
93 GO TO (94,95,94,95,94,95,94,95),LL
95 PUNCH,A1,A2,A3,A4
94 IF(LL-6)97,97,96
96 PUNCH,B1,B2,B3,B4
97 DO 98 I=1,20,4
98 PUNCH,C1(I),C1(I+1),C1(I+2),C1(I+3)
GO TO (99,100,100,99,99,99,99),NPR
99 IF(LL-3)101,102,102
100 IF(LL-2)101,101,102
102 DO 103 I=1,20,4
103 PUNCH,C2(I),C2(I+1),C2(I+2),C2(I+3)
101 GO TO (85,105,105,85,85,85,85),NPR
85 PUNCH,OPER,INSTR
PUNCH,RUN,TEMP,WAVEL
GO TO 110
75 PUNCH,NQR,FEEDP
IF(NPR-3)106,107,107
107 PUNCH,QQ1,QQ2
106 IF(NQR-400)138,1,137
137 PUNCH,J,WACRR
GO TO 139
138 PUNCH,J
139 PUNCH,EQO
IF(NPR-3)108,109,108
109 PUNCH,PP
108 PUNCH,M6
PUNCH,K,L,M
PUNCH,KA,KB,KC,KD
PUNCH,RLM1,WAC1,WL1,WU1
PUNCH,RLM2,WAC2,WL2,WU2
GO TO 84
110 GO TO 1
END
```

ALGOL 60 FOR PROGRAM NUMBER 30

PROCEDURE DBAAA; ARRAY voL,den1,den2,de,c1,c2,cs,dev1,dev2,p[1:20];
SWITCH sw1:=x3,x2,x2,x3,x3,x3,x3; SWITCH sw2:=x5,x4,x4,x5,x5,x5,x5; SWITCH
SWITCH sw3:=x7,x9,x9,x8,x8,x8,x8; SWITCH sw4:=x15,x14,x15,x14,x15,x14,x15,
x14; SWITCH sw5:=x18,x18,x19,x19; SWITCH sw6:=x22,x22,x21,x21; SWITCH
sw7:=x24,x25,x24,x25; SWITCH sw8:=s27,s28,s27,s28; SWITCH sw9:=x29,x30,
x31,x32,x33,x34; SWITCH sw10:=x36,x37,x36,x37; SWITCH sw11:=x41,x64,x64,
x42,x42,x42,x42; SWITCH sw12:=x43,x44,x43,x44,x44,x44,x44; SWITCH sw13:
=x49,x50,x49,x50; SWITCH sw14:=x52,x63,x63,x52,x52,x52,x52; SWITCH sw15:
=x53,x54,x54,x58,x58,x58,x53; SWITCH sw16:=x57,x56,x57,x56,x57,x56,x57,x56;
SWITCH sw17:=x59,x60,x60,x59,x59,x59,x59; SWITCH sw18:=x63,xzx,xzx,x63,
x63,x63,x63;
COMMENT: MOLAR POLARIZATION EQUATION;
 BEGIN INTEGER i,j,jj,k,ka,kb,kc,kd,ke,kf,L,LL,m,m6,m9,nqr,npr,feedp,
oper,instr,run;
 REAL a1,a2,a3,a4,aa,aaa,b1,b2,b3,b4,devf1,devf2,eqo,pa,pb,ps,pp,px,qq1,
qq2,q,qnr,rLm1,rLm2,s1,s2,s3,s4,temp,tm,wac1,wac2,wacrr,wm1,wm2,
wms,wL1,wL2,wu1,wu2,waveL,wmw;
 READ nqr;feedp;
 wac1:=wac2:=0;
 IF npr=300 THEN GO TO X66
 ELSE IF npr>300 THEN
 BEGIN
  npr:=npr−300;
  IF npr=100 THEN GO TO X66
  ELSE IF npr>100 THEN npr:=npr−100 END;
 IF npr=12 THEN GO TO X66
 ELSE IF npr>12 THEN npr:=npr−10;
 npr:=npr−8;
 FOR i:=1 STEP 1 UNTIL 20 DO voL[i]:=den1[i]:=den2[i]:=de[i]:=c1[i]
  :=c2[i]:=cs[i]:=0;
 wm1:=wms:=wm2:=ps:=pa:=pb:=a1:=a2:=a3:=a4:=b1:=b2:=b3:=b4:=s1:=s2
  :=s3:=s4:=0;
 IF npr=3 THEN READ qq1;qq2;
 IF nqr=400 THEN GO TO X66
 ELSE IF nqr<400 THEN
 BEGIN
  READ j; GO TO X1END;
 READ j,wacrr;
X1: GO TO sw1[npr];
X2: READ eqo;
 IF npr=3 THEN READ pp;
X3: m6:=1;
 READ k,L,M;
 READ rLm1,wL1,wu1;
 READ rLm2,wL2,wu2;
 GO TO sw2[npr];
X4: q:=L/10;
 FOR i:=1 STEP 1 UNTIL 20 DO
 BEGIN
  px:=i;
  IF q≤px THEN

```
              BEGIN
                  LL:=px;  GO TO X6END
              END;
X5:       LL:=L;
X6:       FOR i:=1 STEP 1 UNTIL 20 DO READ de[i];
          GO TO sw3[npr];
X7:       IF LL<5 THEN
          BEGIN
X8:           READ ps;  GO TO X17END;
          READ pa,ps;  GO TO X17;
X9:       IF LL≤4 THEN
          BEGIN
X10:          READ pa,ps;  GO TO X12END;
          IF LL≤8 THEN
          BEGIN
X11:          READ pa,pb,ps;  GO TO X12END;
          IF LL≤12 THEN GO TO X10 ELSE GO TO X11;
X12:      IF LL≤8 THEN
          BEGIN
X13:          GO TO sw4[LL];
X14:          READ a1,a2,a3,a4;
X15:          IF LL≤6 THEN GO TO X17;
              READ b1,b2,b3,b4;  GO TO X17END;
X16:      READ s1,s2,s3,s4;
          LL:=LL−8;  L:=L−80;  GO TO X13;
X17:      GO TO sw5[m];
X18:      READ wms,wm1;  GO TO X19;
X19:      READ wms,wm1,wm2;
X20:      FOR i:=1 STEP 1 UNTIL 20 DO READ den2[i];
          FOR i:=1 STEP 1 UNTIL 20 DO READ cs[i];
          FOR i:=1 STEP 1 UNTIL 20 DO READ c1[i];
          GO TO sw6[m];
X21:      FOR i:=1 STEP 1 UNTIL 20 DO READ c2[i];
X22:      IF k≤2 THEN
          BEGIN
              READ devf1;  GO TO X23END;
          FOR i:=1 STEP 1 UNTIL 20 DO READ dev1[i];
X23:      GO TO sw7[k];
X24:      READ devf2;  GO TO X26;
X25:      FOR i:=1 STEP 1 UNTIL 20 DO READ dev2[i];
X26:      READ oper,instr;
          READ run,temp,waveL;  m9:=waveL;
          FOR i:=1 STEP 1 UNTIL 20 DO
          BEGIN
              IF de[i]<wL1∨de[i]>wu1 THEN
              BEGIN
                  de[i]:=c1[i]:=c2[i]:=0;  GO TO X38END;
              IF den2[i]≤0∨c1[i]≤0 THEN GO TO X38;
              GO TO sw8[m];
X27:      aa:=cs[i]↑3;
          px:=pxX(ps+s1Xcs[i]+s2Xcs[i]↑2+s3Xaa+s4Xcs[i]Xaa);
X28:      GO TO sw9[m9];
X29:      p[i]:=(de[i]−1)/(de[i]+2);  GO TO X35;
```

```
X30:    p[i]:=(de[i]−1)X(2Xde[i]+1)/(9Xde[i]); GO TO X35;
X31:    p[i]:=(de[i]−1)X(de[i]+4)/(8Xde[i]+7); GO TO X35;
X32:    p[i]:=1111.1; GO TO X35;
X33:    p[i]:=2222.2; GO TO X35;
X34:    p[i]:=3333.3;
X35:    GO TO sw10[m];
X36:    aa:=cs[i]Xwms+c1[i]Xwm1+c2[i]Xwm2;
        p[i]:=p[i]Xaa/den2[i]−px; GO TO X38;
X37:    tm:=c1[i]+c2[i]+cs[i]; cs[i]:=cs[i]/tm;
        c1[i]:=c1[i]/tm; c2[i]:=c2[i]/tm;
        wmw:=cs[i]Xwms+c1[i]Xwm1+c2[i]Xwm2;
        aa:=cs[i]↑3; aaa:=aaXcs[i];
        px:=psXcs[i]+s1Xcs[i]↑2+s2Xaa+s3Xaaa+s4XaaaXcs[i];
        p[i]:=p[i]Xwmw/den2[i]−px
X38:    END;
        FOR i:=1 STEP 1 UNTIL 20 DO
        IF p[i]≠0 THEN
        BEGIN
            wu1:=wL1:=p[i]END;
        FOR i:=1 STEP 1 UNTIL 20 DO
        BEGIN
            IF p[i]=0 THEN GO TO X39;
            IF wu1<p[i] THEN wu1:=p[i];
            IF wL1>p[i] THEN wL1:=p[i]
X39:    END;
        qnr:=nqr; feedp:=30;
        IF npr>7 THEN GO TO X66
        ELSE IF npr=7 THEN
        BEGIN
            READ ka,kb,kc,kd,ke,kf; GO TO X40END;
        READ ka,kb,kc,kd;
X40:    GO TO sw11[npr];
X41:    PUNCH nqr,feedp; GO TO X45;
X42:    PUNCH nqr,feedp;
        IF npr>7 THEN GO TO X66
        ELSE IF npr=7 THEN
        BEGIN
            GO TO sw12[L];
X43:    jj:=4; GO TO X46;
X44:    jj:=2; GO TO X46END;
X45:    PUNCH ka,kb,kc,kd;
X46:    IF nqr=400 THEN GO TO X66
        ELSE IF nqr<400 THEN
        BEGIN
            PUNCH j; GO TO X47END;
        PUNCH j,wacrr;
X47:    PUNCH m6; PUNCH k,L,m;
        PUNCH rLm1,wL1,wu1;
        PUNCH rLm2,wL2,wu2;
XZX:    IF k≤2 THEN
        BEGIN
            PUNCH devf1; GO TO X48END;
        FOR i:=1 STEP 1 UNTIL 20 DO PUNCH dev1[i];
```

```
X48:   GO TO sw13[k];
X49:   PUNCH devf2;  GO TO X51;
X50:   FOR i:=1 STEP 1 UNTIL 20 DO PUNCH dev2[i];
X51:   GO TO sw14[npr];
X52:   FOR i:=1 STEP 1 UNTIL 20 DO PUNCH p[i];
       GO TO sw15[npr];
X53:   IF L<5 THEN GO TO X58;
       PUNCH pa,wac1;  GO TO X58;
X54:   IF LL≤4 THEN
       BEGIN
          PUNCH pa;  GO TO X55END;
       PUNCH pa,pb;
X55:   GO TO sw16[LL];
X56:   PUNCH a1,a2,a3,a4;
X57:   IF LL>6 THEN PUNCH b1,b2,b3,b4;
X58:   FOR i:=1 STEP 1 UNTIL 20 DO PUNCH c1[i];
       GO TO sw17[npr];
X59:   IF LL<3 THEN GO TO X62 ELSE GO TO X61;
X60:   IF LL≤2 THEN GO TO X62;
X61:   FOR i:=1 STEP 1 UNTIL 20 DO PUNCH c2[i];
X62:   GO TO sw18[npr];
X63:   PUNCH oper,instr;
       PUNCH run,temp,waveL;  GO TO X66;
X64:   PUNCH nqr,feedp;
       IF npr≥3 THEN PUNCH qq1,qq2;
       IF nqr=400 THEN GO TO X66
       ELSE IF nqr>400 THEN
       BEGIN
          PUNCH j,wacrr;  GO TO X65END;
       PUNCH j;
X65:   PUNCH eqo;
       IF npr=3 THEN PUNCH pp;
       PUNCH m6;  PUNCH k,L,m;  PUNCH ka,kb,kc,kd;
       PUNCH rLm1,wac1,wL1,wu1;
       PUNCH rLm2,wac2,wL2,wu2;
       GO TO X52
X66:END DBAAA;
X67:DBAAA;
       GO TO X67;
```

CHAPTER VIII

RESOLUTION OF SPECTRA

Program 31 (*call word* EBAAA) is a feeder program to be used in calculating the true absorbancy index of a complex from the true formation constant and the input information for the noniterative[1], iterative[2], and double iterative[3] spectrophotometric programs which are designed to yield a value for the formation constant at each wavelength. The three step procedure, which will be discussed in detail later, is as follows:

1. The values for the formation constant (K) and the associated *maximum permitted error* (KER) at each wavelength are used to compute the true formation constant (EQ) and the *maximum permitted error* in EQ, designated EQER.

2. EQ, EQER, and the input information used to compute K and KER values are used with Program 31 (*call word* EBAAA) to compute the absorbancy index (AC) of the complex and its *maximum permitted error* (ACER) in each solution at each wavelength.

3. The output information generated by Program 31 for each wavelength is processed with Program 301 (*call word* AAAAS) or Program 505 (*call word* EEEEE) to obtain the true absorbancy index (ACT) of the complex at each wavelength and its *maximum permitted error* (ACTER).

Mathematical details of the procedures are given in Chapter XII.

The computer techniques used to obtain the true value for the formation constant (EQ), the true absorbancy indices (ACT) for the complex at each wavelength, and the associated *maximum permitted errors* (EQER and ACTER) are decribed in this chapter. In anticipation of Chapter XII the following formal definitions are adopted.

[1] Program 9 (Ch. III, Vol. I; and Ch. II, Vol. II); Program 309 (App. I, Vol. I; and Ch. II, Vol. II); Programs 25 and 325 (Ch. II, Vol. II).

[2] Programs 10–13 (Ch. IV and V, Vol. I); Programs 310–313 (App. I, Vol. I); Programs 410–413 (Ch. XI, Vol. II).

[3] Programs 14 and 15 (Ch. VI, Vol. I); Programs 314 and 315 (App. I, Vol. I); Programs 414 and 415 (Ch. XI, Vol. II).

EQ—*Mean formation constant*

ACT—*Mean absorbancy index for the complex at the designated wavelength*

EQER and ACTER—*Mean maximum permitted error in EQ and ACT respectively.*

It is essential to realize that the *maximum permitted error in a value for a parameter is the maximum possible error for the parameter and is not equivalent to the standard deviation.*

EQ and EQER are computed from the values for the formation constant (K) and the associated *maximum permitted errors* (KER) at several wavelengths by the following procedure.

METHOD A

Program 301 (*call word* AAAAS) is used with $Y(I)$ and $YER(I)$ equal to the values for K and KER calculated with data collected at the Ith wavelength. $X1ER(I)$ is set equal to zero. If λ is the number of wavelengths at which K is calculated, $X1(1) = -\lambda/2$; $X1(2) = -\lambda/2 + 1.0$; $X1(3) = -\lambda/2 + 2.0$; .....$X1(\lambda) = \lambda/2$. The subscript $(1, 2, 3, \ldots \lambda)$ denotes the wavelength at which K and KER are computed. EQ and EQER are the intercept (B) and its *maximum permitted error* (DEVB) respectively calculated with program 301. The method just described is called the *centering device* (see Chapter XII for details). To compute ACT and ACTER at each wavelength from the raw data used to solve the spectrophotometric equations for K and KER, the procedure is as follows:

Step 1. With the formation constant (EQ) the actual concentrations of A, B, and complex (C_C) in each solution at equilibrium are computed.

Step 2. With $EQ = EQ + EQER$ and the *maximum permitted deviation* for the concentration observable (A or B) there are calculated new concentrations for A, B, and the complex ($\bar{C}_C$) in each solution at equilibrium. $\bar{C}_C$ is the maximum possible value of C_C.

Step 3. The concentrations of A and B calculated in Step 1, the absorbancy indices of A and B, and the measured absorbance are used to calculate the absorbance of the complex in each solution at each wavelength.

Step 4. The concentrations of A and B calculated in Step 2, the absorbancy indices of A, and B, the measured absorbance, and its *maximum permitted deviation* are used to calculate *maximum possible absorbance* for the complex in each solution at each wavelength.

Step 5. The absorbancy index of the complex (AC) and its *maximum permitted error* (ACER) are computed for each solution at each wavelength with information obtained in Steps 3 and 4 and with complex concentrations C_C and $\bar{C}_C$, calculated in Steps 1 and 2 respectively.

Step 6. The mean absorbancy index (ACT) and its *mean maximum permitted error* (ACTER) are computed at each wavelength from values of

AC and ACER for all solutions by Method A, with $Y(I) = AC$ and $YER(I) = ACER$, or by Method B, described below.

METHOD B

The input information assembled for Program 301 (*call word* AAAAS), described for Method A with $Y(I) = AC$ and $YER(I) = ACER$, is processed with the FOR-TO-GO Program 505 (*call word* EEEEE). In this program ACT and ACTER are set equal to the average values for AC and ACER respectively. In all test calculations we have found that values for AC and ACER computed by the slow Method A are, for most practical purposes, identical with those obtained by Method B.

Program 31 (*call word* EBAAA) has been designed for calculating the input information required for Program 301 (*call word* AAAAS) or Program 505 (*call word* EEEEE) to compute the *mean absorbancy index* of the complex (ACT) and the associated *mean maximum permitted error* (ACTER) at each wavelength. With minimal additional information (see Input Format for Program 31) the input information for Programs 9–15, 25, 309–315, 325 and 410–415 is compatible with Program 31.

METHOD OF CALCULATION

In this section $QQ1 = n_1$, $QQ2 = n_2$ or $QQ3 = n_1$ and $QQ4 = n_2$.

In Program 31 (*call word* EBAAA) the actual instructions to the computer include the following.

1. Read the values for EQ, EQER, PROGN and QQ4 (if PROGN = 15, 315 or 415) or QQ1 (if PROGN = 14, 314, or 414) plus the input information for the program numbered PROGN. Details are given in the section on the Input Format for Program 31.

2. Apply the *fail–safe procedure* to all values for each of the two observables ($OAM(I)$ and $C1(I)$ or $C2(I)$). In this step all members of a set of conjugate information are set equal to zero if a value for either observable in the corresponding set of conjugate data is less than its *lowest reliable value* (WL1 or WL2) or greater than its *highest reliable value* (WU1 or WU2).

3. Calculate the concentration of complex ($C3(I)$) in each solution from the initial concentrations of the active components ($C1(I)$), or $C1(I)$ and $C2(I)$) with the *mean formation constant* (EQ). If $C3(I)$ is less than WAC2 * $C1(I)$ all members of the Ith set of conjugate information are set equal to zero.

4. Calculate the maximum possible concentration of complex ($C4(I)$) in each solution from the initial concentrations of the active components ($C1(I)$, or $C1(I)$ and $C2(I)$), the *maximum permitted deviation* for the concentration ($DEV2(I)$), and the formation constant equal to (EQ + EQER).

Note: The method used to compute the concentrations of complex (C3(I) and C4(I)) in steps 3 and 4 is determined by the values of QQ1, QQ2, QQ3, QQ4 and PROGN. For PROGN = 9, 10, 12, 25, 309, 310, 312, 325, 410 and 412, C3(I) and C4(I) are computed by direct methods. For PROGN = 11, 14, 311, 314, 411 and 414 C3(I) and C4(I) are calculated by a direct method if QQ1 = 2.0, QQ2 = 0.0 or QQ1 = 1.0 = QQ2. For all other values of QQ1 and QQ2 a search method is used (see Chapter IV, Volume I).

For PROGN = 13, 15, 313, 315, 413 and 415, C3(I) and C4(I) are computed by direct methods if QQ1 = 2.0 = QQ2 and QQ3 = 1.0 = QQ4. For all other values of QQ1, QQ2, QQ3 and QQ4 a triple search method is used (see Chapter V, Volume I).

In Programs 12, 13, 15, 312, 313, 315, 412, 413 and 415 four complex concentrations (C3(I), C4(I), C5(I) and C6(I)) are computed. C3(I) and C4(I) are still the concentrations of the complex formed between A and B. C5(I) and C6(I) refer to the complexes C_1 and C_2 in the reaction system:

$$QQ1 \cdot A \underset{\rightleftharpoons}{\overset{K_1}{\rightleftharpoons}} C_1$$
$$QQ2 \cdot B \underset{\rightleftharpoons}{\overset{K_2}{\rightleftharpoons}} C_2$$
$$QQ3 \cdot A + QQ4 \cdot B \rightleftharpoons C_3$$

Values for the two additional formation constants (K_1 and K_2) are given in the input information for the program numbered NQR.

5. Calculate the equilibrium concentrations of A and B in each solution, with values for C3(I) and C4(I) in turn. Next use the absorbancy indices, the measured absorbance (OAM(I)), and the concentrations of the complex (C3(I)), A, and B to compute the absorbancy index of the complex (AC(I)) for each solution at each wavelength. Use the *instrument reliability factor*, WAC1, as decribed in Chapters III–VI of Volume I, to reject unreliable information. Use the accepted sets of conjugate data to compute the *maximum permitted error*, ACER(I), for each AC(I) by replacing OAM(I) and C3(I) by (OAM(I) + DEV1(I)) and C4(I), respectively, and subtracting AC(I) from the answer.

6. Compute values for X1(I), corresponding to values for AC(I) and ACER(I) so that they are symmetrical about the origin. Set all X1ER(I) = 0.0.

7. Punch the input information required to compute ACT and ACTER for each wavelength with Program 301 (*call word* AAAAS) or the FOR-TO-GO Program 505 (*call word* EEEEE).

INSTRUMENT RELIABILITY FACTORS

A detailed description of all the *instrument reliability factors* associated with each program numbered PROGN will be found in the following locations:

Programs 9 and 309—Ch. III, Vol. I; Ch. II, Vol. II.
Programs 25 and 325—Ch. II, Vol. II.
Programs 10, 11, 310, 311, 410 and 411—Ch. IV, Vol. I; Ch. XI, Vol. II.
Programs 12, 13, 312, 313, 412 and 413—Ch. V, Vol. I; Ch. XI, Vol. II.
Programs 14, 15, 314, 315, 414 and 415—Ch. VI, Vol. I; Ch. XI, Vol. II.

As there are no *instrument reliability factors* associated exclusively with Program 31, the *instrument reliability factors* must be selected before the *mean formation constant* (EQ) and the associated *mean maximum permitted error* (EQER) are computed from values obtained with the spectrophotometric Programs (9–15, 25, 309–315, 325, 410–415).

FAIL-SAFE PROCEDURE

Details of the applications of the *fail–safe procedure* in Program 31 are identical to those given for the programs numbered PROGN.

INPUT COMMANDS FOR PROGRAM 31

Except for PROGN, which is the number of the program (9–15, 25, 325, 309–315, 410–415) whose input information is to be processed, there are no new commands exclusively associated with Program 31 (*call word* EBAAA). Input commands in the input formats for Programs 9–15, 25, 309–315, 325 and 410–415 are given in the chapters listed in the section "Instrument Reliability Factors".

INPUT FORMAT FOR PROGRAM 31

Each set of *input information* for the program numbered PROGN is preceded by one or two cards thus.

STATEMENT	COMMENT
READ,EQ,EQER,PROGN	Entered for all PROGN
READ,QQ1	Entered for PROGN = 14, 314 or 414
READ,QQ4	Entered for PROGN = 15, 315 or 415

DEFINITIONS

EQ—*Mean formation constant.*
EQER—*Mean maximum permitted error* in the formation constant.
QQ1—Computed with Program 14, 314 and 414.
  $QQ1.A + QQ2.B \rightleftharpoons C.$
QQ4—Computed with Program 15, 315 and 415.
  $QQ1.A \rightleftharpoons C_1.$
  $QQ2.B \rightleftharpoons C_2.$
  $QQ3.A + QQ4.B \rightleftharpoons C_3.$

OUTPUT FORMAT FOR PROGRAM 31

Information generated by Program 31 can be processed directly with Program 301 (*call word* AAAAS) or the FOR-TO-GO Program 505 (*call word* EEEEE). The information listed below is generated for each wavelength. Symbols not specifically defined here are not used in the calculation of the *mean absorbancy index* (ACT) and its associated *mean maximum permitted error* (ACTER).

STATEMENT	COMMENT
PUNCH,AAAAS,FEEDP	AAAAS = 301.0;FEEDP = 31.0.
PUNCH,KA,KB,KC,KD	*Reject–restore commands.*
PUNCH,J	J = 3. J is the number of *self-judgment cycles* to be completed in Program 301 before the *error analysis*.
PUNCH,K,L,M	*Input-commands.*
PUNCH,DEVF1,RLM1,WL1,WU1	*Instrument reliability factors.*
PUNCH,DEVF2,RLM2,WL2,WU2	
PUNCH,AC(I),AC(I+1),AC(I+2),AC(I+3)	
PUNCH,ACER(I),ACER(I+1),ACER(I+2),ACER(I+3)	
PUNCH,X1(I),X1(I+1),X1(I+2),X1(I+3)	
PUNCH,X1ER(I),X1ER(I+1),X1ER(I+2),X1ER(I+3)	

DEFINITIONS

AC(I)—the absorbancy index of the complex in the Ith solution at the wavelength indicated (see WAVEL).

ACER(I)—the *maximum permitted error* in AC(I).

X1(I)—values are symmetrical about the origin as described in the section on *method of calculation*.

X1ER(I) = 0.0.

PUNCH,G	The number of absorbancy indices calculated.
PUNCH,OPER,INSTR	Indentification. WAVEL is the number of the wavelength for which data are processed.
PUNCH,RUN,TEMP,WAVEL	

FORTRAN FOR PROGRAM NUMBER 31

CALL WORD EBAAA

```
DIMENSION C1(20),C2(20),C3(20),C4(20),C5(20),C6(20),C7(20),C8(20)
DIMENSION OAM(20),X1(20),X1ER(20),DEV1(20),DEV2(20),AC(20),ACER(20)
DIMENSION C9(20),C10(20)
1 READ,EQ,EQER,PROGN
A1=0.0
A2=0.0
A3=0.0
A4=0.0
PRONN=PROGN
B1=0.0
B2=0.0
B3=0.0
B4=0.0
CA1=0.0
CA2=0.0
CA3=0.0
CA4=0.0
CB1=0.0
CB2=0.0
CB3=0.0
CB4=0.0
AIBX=0.0
AIAX=0.0
AIC1X=0.0
AIC2X=0.0
IF(PROGN-400.0)192,192,193
193 PROGN=PROGN-100.0
192 IF(PROGN-325.0)194,195,1
195 NN=8
GO TO 197
194 IF(PROGN-25.0)196,195,196
196 IF(PROGN-300.0)2,2,3
197 READ,PROGN,FEEDP
READ,KA,KB,KC,KD,KE,KF
READ,JJ
NN=1
GO TO 198
3 NN=PROGN-308.0
GO TO 4
2 NN=PROGN-8.0
4 IF(NN-6)5,98,6
6 READ,QQ4
READ,PROGN,FEEDP
GO TO 7
98 READ,QQ1
5 READ,NPROG,FEEDP
7 IF(NN-1)1,8,9
8 READ,KA,KB,KC,KD
198 READ,J
READ,M6
READ,K,L,M
GO TO 27
9 IF(NN-3)11,10,11
10 READ,QQ1,QQ2
11 IF(NN-5)13,12,13
12 READ,QQ1,QQ2,QQ3,QQ4
13 IF(NN-6)15,14,15
14 READ,QQ2
READ,QQ1L,QQ1U
```

```
READ,PPQQ
15 IF(NN-7)17,16,1
16 READ,QQ1,QQ2,QQ3
READ,QQ4L,QQ4U
READ,PPQQ
17 IF(PRONN-400.0)199,1,200
200 READ,J,WACRR
GO TO 201
199 READ,J
201 IF(NN-3)18,18,19
18 READ,EQ0
19 IF(NN-3)171,20,21
21 IF(NN-5)22,22,23
22 READ,EQ0,EQ1,EQ2
23 IF(NN-6)20,24,25
24 READ,EQ0
25 IF(NN-7)20,26,1
26 READ,EQ0,EQ1,EQ2
20 READ,PP
171READ,M6
READ,K,L,M
READ,KA,KB,KC,KD
27 M5=M6
M4=1
IF(NN-1)1,28,29
28 READ,RLM1,WL1,WU1
READ,RLM2,WL2,WU2
GO TO 31
29 IF(NN-7)30,30,40
30 READ,RLM1,WAC1,WL1,WU1
READ,RLM2,WAC2,WL2,WU2
GO TO 41
31 GO TO (32,32,33,33),K
32 READ,DEVF1
GO TO 35
33 DO 34 I=1,20,4
34 READ,DEV1(I),DEV1(I+1),DEV1(I+2),DEV1(I+3)
DEVF1=5555.5
35 GO TO (36,37,36,37),K
36 READ,DEVF2
GO TO 39
37 DO 38 I=1,20,4
38 READ,DEV2(I),DEV2(I+1),DEV2(I+2),DEV2(I+3)
DEVF2=5555.5
39 IF(NN-1)1,40,76
40 IF(NN-7)41,41,1
41 DO 42 I=1,20,4
42 READ,OAM(I),OAM(I+1),OAM(I+2),OAM(I+3)
KR=KA+2
GO TO (165,166,167,168,169),KR
166 DO 170 I=KB,KC
170 OAM(I)=0.0
GO TO 165
169 OAM(KD)=0.0
168 OAM(KC)=0.0
167 OAM(KB)=0.0
165 IF(NN-1)1,43,45
43 IF(L-5)1,1,44
44 READ,AIAX,WAC1
GO TO 65
45 RQ=L
RQ=RQ/10.0
```

```
      DO 49 I=1,20
      P=I
      IF(P-RQ)49,50,50
50    LL=I
      GO TO 51
49    CONTINUE
51    IF(NN-3)46,46,47
47    IF(NN-6)48,46,48
46    GO TO (52,52,52,52,53,53,53,53),LL
52    READ,AIAX
      GO TO 54
53    READ,AIAX,AIBX
54    GO TO (55,56,55,56,55,56,55,56),LL
56    READ,A1,A2,A3,A4
55    GO TO (57,57,57,57,57,57,58,58),LL
58    READ,B1,B2,B3,B4
57    GO TO 65
48    READ,AIAX,AIC1X,AIBX,AIC2X
      GO TO (59,59,59,59,60,60,60,60,59,59,59,59,60,60,60),LL
60    READ,A1,A2,A3,A4
59    GO TO (61,61,61,62,62,61,62,62,62,62,62,61,61,61,62),LL
62    READ,B1,B2,B3,B4
61    GO TO (63,63,64,64,64,64,63,63,64,63,64,64,64,64,63),LL
64    READ,CA1,CA2,CA3,CA4
63    GO TO (65,66,66,66,66,65,65,65,65,65,66,65,65,66,66),LL
66    READ,CB1,CB2,CB3,CB4
65    IF(M5-M6)77,67,1
67    DO 68 I=1,20,4
68    READ,C1(I),C1(I+1),C1(I+2),C1(I+3)
      IF(NN-7)69,69,1
69    GO TO (70,71,71,70,70,71,70),NN
71    IF(LL-2)72,72,70
70    DO 73 I=1,20,4
73    READ,C2(I),C2(I+1),C2(I+2),C2(I+3)
      GO TO 75
72    DO 74 I=1,20
74    C2(I)=C1(I)
75    IF(NN-1)1,76,31
76    READ,OPER,INSTR
      READ,RUN,TEMP,WAVEL
77    G=20.0
      DO 78 I=1,20
      IF(OAM(I)-WL1)79,80,80
80    IF(OAM(I)-WU1)81,81,79
79    G=G-1.0
      OAM(I)=0.0
      AC(I)=0.0
      ACER(I)=0.0
      GO TO 78
81    GO TO (82,82,78,78),K
82    DEV1(I)=OAM(I)*DEVF1
78    CONTINUE
      IF(M5-M6)151,83,83
83    DO 89 I=1,20
      IF(C2(I)-WL2)85,86,86
86    IF(C2(I)-WU2)87,87,85
85    C2(I)=0.0
      C1(I)=0.0
      GO TO 89
87    IF(C1(I))85,85,190
190   GO TO (88,89,88,89),K
88    DEV2(I)=C2(I)*DEVF2
```

```
89 CONTINUE
GO TO (90,91,91,90,90,91,90),NN
91 IF(LL-2)92,92,93
92 DO 173 I=1,20
173 C2(I)=1.0
QQ2=0.0
93 IF(NN-2)96,94,84
94 IF(LL-2)95,95,96
95 QQ1=2.0
GO TO 84
96 QQ1=1.0
QQ2=1.0
GO TO 84
90 IF(NN-4)84,97,84
97 QQ1=2.0
QQ2=2.0
QQ3=1.0
QQ4=1.0
84 CONTINUE
GO TO (99,100,100,101,101,100,101),NN
99 DO 102 I=1,20
IF(C2(I))102,102,103
103 C3(I)=EQ*C2(I)*C1(I)/(1.0+EQ*C2(I))
C4(I)=(EQ+EQER)*(C2(I)+DEV2(I))*C1(I)/(1.0+(EQ+EQER)*(C2(I)+DEV2(I)))
C5(I)=C1(I)-C4(I)
C6(I)=C2(I)-C4(I)
C1(I)=C1(I)-C3(I)
C2(I)=C2(I)-C3(I)
102 CONTINUE
GO TO 151
100 DO 104 I=1,20
IF(C1(I))191,191,105
191 OAM(I)=0.0
GO TO 104
105 RX=EQ
IF(NN-2)1,181,106
181 IF(LL-2)182,182,186
182 C3(I)=(4.0*RX*C1(I)+1.0-SQR(8.0*RX*C1(I)+1.0))/(8.0*RX)
IF(RX-EQ)1,183,184
183 C5(I)=C3(I)
RX=EQ+EQER
C1(I)=C1(I)+DEV2(I)
GO TO 181
184 C4(I)=C3(I)
C3(I)=C5(I)
GO TO 189
186 BB=-(RX*(C1(I)+C2(I))+1.0)
C3(I)=(-BB-SQR(BB*BB-4.0*RX*RX*C1(I)*C2(I)))/(2.0*RX)
IF(RX-EQ)1,187,188
187 C5(I)=C3(I)
RX=EQ+EQER
C2(I)=C2(I)+DEV2(I)
GO TO 181
188 C4(I)=C3(I)
C3(I)=C5(I)
GO TO 189
106 R=1.0
PPT=0.0
107 PP1=1.0/(2.0**R)
108 PPT=PPT+PP1
C3(I)=PPT*C1(I)
IF(C1(I)-QQ1*C3(I))109,109,175
```

```
175 IF(C2(I)-QQ2*C3(I))109,109,174
174 C4(I)=RX*((C1(I)-QQ1*C3(I))**QQ1)*((C2(I)-QQ2*C3(I))**QQ2)
IF(C3(I)-C4(I))108,110,109
110 IF(C3(I))1,109,111
109 PPT=PPT-PP1
R=R+1.0
IF(PP1-PP)111,111,107
111 IF(RX-EQ)1,112,113
112 RX=EQ+EQER
C5(I)=C3(I)
C2(I)=C2(I)+DEV2(I)
GO TO 106
113 C4(I)=C3(I)
C3(I)=C5(I)
189 C5(I)=C1(I)-QQ1*C4(I)
C6(I)=C2(I)-DEV2(I)-QQ2*C4(I)
C1(I)=C1(I)-QQ1*C3(I)
C2(I)=C2(I)-DEV2(I)-QQ2*C3(I)
IF(LL-2)114,114,104
114 C2(I)=0.0
C6(I)=0.0
104 CONTINUE
GO TO 151
101 DO 115 I=1,20
IF(C2(I))116,116,117
116 C1(I)=0.0
C2(I)=0.0
GO TO 115
117 IF(C1(I))116,116,118
118 IF(C1(I)-C2(I))119,119,120
119 PQ2=C2(I)/C1(I)
GO TO 125
120 PQ1=C1(I)/C2(I)
121 IF(PQ1-1.0)122,123,123
123 C5(I)=0.25*C1(I)
N99=1
GO TO 127
122 IF(PQ1-5.0)123,124,124
124 C4(I)=0.0
C5(I)=0.0
N99=2
GO TO 127
125 IF(PQ2-5.0)123,126,126
126 C3(I)=0.0
C5(I)=0.0
N99=3
127 RX=EQ
N4=0
128 NNN=1
129 N4=N4+1
R=1.0
PPT=0.0
131 PP1=1.0/(2.0**R)
132 PPT=PPT+PP1
GO TO (133,134,134,134),N4
133 GO TO (134,134,135),N99
134 C6(I)=PPT*C1(I)
IF(C1(I)-QQ1*C6(I)-QQ3*C3(I))109,109,176
176 C7(I)=EQ1*((C1(I)-QQ1*C6(I)-QQ3*C5(I))**QQ1)
139 IF(C7(I)-C6(I))137,136,132
136 IF(C7(I))1,137,138
137 PPT=PPT-PP1
```

```
R=R+1.0
IF(PP1-PP)138,138,131
138 GO TO (140,141,142),NNN
140 C3(I)=C7(I)
143 NNN=NNN+1
GO TO (135,144,135),N99
141 C4(I)=C7(I)
GO TO 143
142 C5(I)=C7(I)
N99=1
IF(N4-2)129,129,145
145 GO TO (146,147,147),N99
146 GO TO (129,129,129,129,147),N4
148 C8(I)=C3(I)
C9(I)=C4(I)
C10(I)=C5(I)
C2(I)=C2(I)+DEV2(I)
RX=EQ+EQER
N4=1
GO TO 128
147 IF(RX-EQ)1,148,149
149 C6(I)=C3(I)
C7(I)=C4(I)
C3(I)=C8(I)
C4(I)=C9(I)
C8(I)=C5(I)
C5(I)=C10(I)
C9(I)=(C1(I)-QQ1*C6(I)-QQ3*C8(I))
C10(I)=(C2(I)-QQ2*C7(I)-QQ4*C8(I))-DEV2(I)
C1(I)=C1(I)-QQ1*C3(I)-QQ3*C5(I)
C2(I)=C2(I)-QQ2*C4(I)-QQ4*C5(I)
GO TO 115
144 IF(N4-1)1,150,135
135 C6(I)=PPT*C2(I)
IF(C2(I)-QQ2*C6(I)-QQ4*C5(I))109,109,177
177 C7(I)=EQ2*((C2(I)-QQ2*C6(I)-QQ4*C5(I))**QQ2)
GO TO 139
150 C6(I)=PPT*C1(I)
IF(C2(I)-QQ2*C4(I)-QQ4*C6(I))109,109,179
179 IF(C1(I)-QQ1*C3(I)-QQ3*C6(I))109,109,178
178 C7(I)=RX*((C1(I)-QQ1*C3(I)-QQ3*C6(I))**QQ3)
C7(I)=C7(I)*((C2(I)-QQ2*C4(I)-QQ4*C6(I))**QQ4)
GO TO 139
115 CONTINUE
151 DO 152I=1,20
IF(OAM(I))153,153,154
153 AC(I)=0.0
ACER(I)=0.0
X1(I)=0.0
X1ER(I)=0.0
GO TO 152
154 IF(NN-1)1,155,156
156 QQ=C1(I)*C1(I)*C1(I)
XX=AIAX*C1(I)+A1*C1(I)*C1(I)+A2*QQ+A3*QQ*C1(I)+A4*QQ*C1(I)*C1(I)
QQ=C2(I)*C2(I)*C2(I)
YY=AIBX*C2(I)+B1*C2(I)*C2(I)+B2*QQ+B3*QQ*C2(I)+B4*QQ*C2(I)*C2(I)
GO TO (157,157,157,158,158,157,158),NN
157 QQ=C5(I)*C5(I)*C5(I)
XY=AIAX*C5(I)+A1*C5(I)*C5(I)+A2*QQ+A3*QQ*C5(I)+A4*QQ*C5(I)*C5(I)
QQ=C6(I)*C6(I)*C6(I)
YX=AIBX*C6(I)+B1*C6(I)*C6(I)+B2*QQ+B3*QQ*C6(I)+B4*QQ*C6(I)*C6(I)
GO TO 159
```

```
155 XX=AIAX*C1(I)
YY=AIBX*C2(I)
XY=AIAX*C5(I)
YX=AIBX*C6(I)
159 AC(I)=OAM(I)-XX-YY
ACER(I)=OAM(I)-XY-YX+DEV1(I)
IF(AC(I)-OAM(I)*WAC1)153,160,160
160 IF(C3(I)-WAC2*C1(I))153,202,202
202 AC(I)=AC(I)/C3(I)
ACER(I)=ACER(I)/C4(I)-AC(I)
GO TO 152
158 QQ=C3(I)*C3(I)*C3(I)
ZZ=AIC1X*C3(I)+CA1*C3(I)*C3(I)+CA2*QQ+CA3*QQ*C3(I)+CA4*QQ*C3(I)*C3(I)
QQ=C4(I)*C4(I)*C4(I)
WW=AIC2X*C4(I)+CB1*C4(I)*C4(I)+CB2*QQ+CB3*QQ*C4(I)+CB4*QQ*C4(I)*C4(I)
QQ=C6(I)*C6(I)*C6(I)
ZW=AIC1X*C6(I)+CA1*C6(I)*C6(I)+CA2*QQ+CA3*QQ*C6(I)+CA4*QQ*C6(I)*C6(I)
QQ=C7(I)*C7(I)*C7(I)
WZ=AIC2X*C7(I)+CB1*C7(I)*C7(I)+CB2*QQ+CB3*QQ*C7(I)+CB4*QQ*C7(I)*C7(I)
QQ=C9(I)*C9(I)*C9(I)
XY=AIAX*C9(I)+A1*C9(I)*C9(I)+A2*QQ+A3*QQ*C9(I)+A4*QQ*C9(I)*C9(I)
QQ=C10(I)*C10(I)*C10(I)
YX=AIBX*C10(I)+B1*C10(I)*C10(I)+B2*QQ+B3*C10(I)*QQ+B4*C10(I)*C10(I)*QQ
AC(I)=(OAM(I)-XX-YY-ZZ-WW)
ACER(I)=OAM(I)+DEV1(I)-XY-YX-ZW-WZ-AC(I)
QQ=WAC1*(XX-YY-ZZ-WW)
IF(AC(I)-QQ)153,161,161
161 AC(I)=AC(I)/C5(I)
ACER(I)=ACER(I)/C8(I)
152 CONTINUE
X1(1)=-(G-1.0)/20.0
DO 162 I=2,20
IF(AC(I))162,162,163
163 X1(1)=X1(1)+0.1
X1(I)=X1(1)
X1ER(I)=0.0
162 CONTINUE
X1(1)=-(G-1.0)/20.0
X1ER(1)=0.0
AAAAS=301.0
FEEDP=31.0
PUNCH,AAAAS,FEEDP
PUNCH,KA,KB,KC,KD
J=3
PUNCH,J
PUNCH,K,L,M
PUNCH,DEVF1,RLM1,WL1,WU1
PUNCH,DEVF2,RLM2,WL2,WU2
DO 164 I=1,20,4
PUNCH,AC(I),AC(I+1),AC(I+2),AC(I+3)
PUNCH,ACER(I),ACER(I+1),ACER(I+2),ACER(I+3)
PUNCH,X1(I),X1(I+1),X1(I+2),X1(I+3)
164 PUNCH,X1ER(I),X1ER(I+1),X1ER(I+2),X1ER(I+3)
PUNCH,G
WAVEL=M4
PUNCH,OPER,INSTR
PUNCH,RUN,TEMP,WAVEL
M5=M5-1
M4=M4+1
IF(M4-M6)41,41,1
END
```

ALGOL 60 FOR PROGRAM NUMBER 31

PROCEDURE (eq,eqer,progn); ARRAY c1,c2.c3,c4 c5,c6,c7,c8,c9,c10,oam,x1,
x1er,dev1,dev2,ac acer[1:20]; REAL eq,eqer; INTEGER progn; SWITCH sw1:
=x13,x13,x14,x14; SWITCH sw2:=x16,x17,x16,x17; SWITCH sw3:=x25,x21,x24,
x23,x22; SWITCH sw4:=x27,x27,x27,x27,x28,x28,x28,x28; SWITCH sw5:=x31,
x30,x31,x30,x31,x30,x31,x30; SWITCH sw6:=x42,x42,x42,x42,x42,x42,x32,x32;
SWITCH sw7:=x36,x36,x36,x36,x35,x35,x35,x35,x36,x36,x36,x36,x35,x35,x35;.
SWITCH sw8:=x38,x38,x38,x37,x37,x38,x37,x37,x37,x37,x37,x38,x38,x38,x37;
SWITCH sw9:=x40,x40,x39,x39,x39,x40,x40,x39,x40,x39,x40,x39,x39,x39,x40;
SWITCH sw10:=x42,x41,x41,x41,x41,x42,x42,x42,x42,x42,x41,x42,x42,x41,x 41;
SWITCH sw11:=x44,x43,x43,x44,x44,x43,x44; SWITCH sw12:=x49,x49,x50,x50;
SWITCH sw13:=x52,x53,x52,x53; SWITCH sw14:=x55,x54,x54,x55,x55,x54,x55;
SWITCH sw15:=x57,x58,x58,x66,x66,x58,x66; SWITCH sw16:=x75,x76,x76,x76;
SWITCH sw17:=x76,x76,x89; SWITCH sw18:=x80,x82,x83; SWITCH sw19:=x89,
x88,x89; SWITCH sw20:=x84,x86,x86; SWITCH sw21:=x72,x72,x72,x72,x86;
SWITCH sw22:=x94,x94,x94,x97,x97,x94,x97;
COMMENT: RESOLUTION OF SPECTRA;
 BEGIN INTEGER i,j,jj,k,ka,kb,kc,kd,ke,kf,kr,L,LL,m,m4,m5,m6,nn, progn,
n99,nnn,n4,feedp,oper,instr,run,g;
 REAL al,a2,a3,a4,b1,b2,b3,b4,ca1,ca2,ca3,ca4,cb1,cb2,cb3,cb4,aiax,aibx,
aic1x,aic2x,devf1,devf2,eqo,eq1,eq2,pronn,ppqq,p,pp,ppt,pp1,pq1,pq2,qq,qq1,
qq2,qq3,qq4,qq1L,qq1u,qq4L,qq4u,rLm1,rLm2,r,rq,rx,temp,ww,wz,wacrr,
wu1,wu2,wL1,wL2,wac1,wac2,waveL,xx,xy,yx,yy,zz,zw;
 a1:=a2:=a3:=a4:=0; pronn:=progn;
 b1:=b2:=b3:=b4:=ca1:=ca2:=ca3:=ca4:=cb1:=cb2:=cb3:=cb4:=aiax:=aibx:
  =aic1x:=aic2x:=0;
 IF progn>400 THEN progn:=progn−100;
 IF progn>325 THEN GO TO X99
 ELSE IF progn=325 THEN
 BEGIN
X1: nn:=8; GO TO X2END;
 1F progn=25 THEN GO TO X1;
 IF progn≤300 THEN GO TO X4 ELSE GO TO X3;
X2: READ progn,feedp;
 READ ka,kb,kc,kd,ke,kf;
 READ jj; nn:=1; GO TO X7;
X3: nn:=progn−308; GO TO X5;
X4: nn:=progn−8;
X5: IF nn>6 THEN
 BEGIN
  READ qq4; READ progn,feedp;
  GO TO X6END
 ELSE IF nn=6 THEN READ qq1;
 READ nprog,feedp;
X6: IF nn<1 THEN GO TO X99
 ELSE IF nn=1 THEN
 BEGIN
  READ ka,kb,kc,kd;
X7: READ j; READ m6;
 READ k,L,m; GO TO X11END;
 IF nn=3 THEN READ qq1,qq2;

```
      IF nn=5 THEN READ qq1,qq2,qq3,qq4;
      IF nn=6 THEN
      BEGIN
          READ qq2; READ qq1L,qq1u;
          READ ppqqEND;
      IF nn>7 THEN GO TO X99
      ELSE IF nn=7 THEN
      BEGIN
          READ qq1,qq2,qq3; READ qq4L,qq4u;
          READ ppqqEND;
      IF pronn=400 THEN GO TO X99
      ELSE IF pronn>400 THEN
      BEGIN
          READ j,wacrr; GO TO X8END;
      READ j
X8:   IF nn≤3 THEN READ eqo;
      IF nn<3 THEN GO TO X10
      ELSE IF nn=3 THEN GO TO X9;
      IF nn≤5 THEN READ eqo,eq1,eq2;
      IF nn<6 THEN GO TO X9
      ELSE IF nn=6 THEN READ eqo;
      IF nn>7 THEN GO TO X99
      ELSE IF nn=7 THEN READ eqo,eq1,eq2;
X9:   READ pp;
X10:  READ m6;
      READ k,L,m;
      READ ka,kb,kc,kd;
X11:  m5:=m6; m4:=1;
      IF nn<1 THEN GO TO X99
      ELSE IF nn=1 THEN
      BEGIN
          READ rLm1,wL1,wu1;
          READ rLm2,wL2,wu2;
          GO TO X12END;
      IF nn>7 THEN GO TO X19;
      READ rLm1,wac1,wL1,wu1;
      READ rLm2,wac2,wL2,wu2;
      GO TO X20;
X12:  GO TO sw1[k];
X13:  READ devf1; GO TO X15;
X14:  FOR i:=1 STEP 1 UNTIL 20 DO READ dev1[i];
      devf1:=5555.5;
X15:  GO TO sw2[k];
X16:  READ devf2; GO TO X18;
X17:  FOR i:=1 STEP 1 UNTIL 20 DO READ dev2[i];
      devf2:=5555.5;
X18:  IF nn<1 THEN GO TO X99
      ELSE IF nn>1 THEN GO TO X46;
X19:  IF nn>7 THEN GO TO X99;
X20:  FOR i:=1 STEP 1 UNTIL 20 DO READ oam[i];
      kr:=ka+2; GO TO sw3[kr];
X21:  FOR i:=kb STEP 1 UNTIL kc DO oam[i]:=0;
```

```
            GO TO X25;
X22:    oam[kd]:=0;
X23:    oam[kc]:=0;
X24:    oam[kb]:=0;
X25:    IF nn<1 THEN GO TO X99
            ELSE IF nn=1 THEN
            BEGIN
                IF L≤5 THEN GO TO X99;
                READ aiax,wac1;
                GO TO X42END;
            rq:=L/10;
            FOR i:=1 STEP 1 UNTIL 20 DO
            BEGIN
                p:=i;
                IF p≥rq THEN
                BEGIN
                    LL:=i; GO TO X26END
            END;
X26:    IF nn>3∨nn≠6 THEN GO TO X34;
            GO TO sw4[LL];
X27:    READ aiax; GO TO X29;
X28:    READ aiax,aibx;
X29:    GO TO sw5[LL];
X30:    READ a1,a2,a3,a4;
X31:    GO TO sw6[LL];
X32:    READ b1,b2,b3,b4;
X33:    GO TO X42;
X34:    READ aiax,aic1x,aibx,aic2x; GO TO sw7[LL];
X35:    READ a1,a2,a3,a4;
X36:    GO TO sw8[LL];
X37:    READ b1,b2,b3,b4;
X38:    GO TO sw9[LL];
X39:    READ ca1,ca2,ca3,ca4;
X40:    GO TO sw10[LL];
X41:    READ cb1,cb2,cb3,cb4;
X42:    IF m5>m6 THEN GO TO X99
            ELSE IF m5<m6 THEN GO TO X47;
            FOR i:=1 STEP 1 UNTIL 20 DO READ c1[i];
            IF nn>7 THEN GO TO X99;
            GO TO sw11[nn];
X43:    IF LL>2 THEN
            BEGIN
X44:        FOR i:=1 STEP 1 UNTIL 20 DO READ c2[i];
                GO TO X45END;
            FOR i:=1 STEP 1 UNTIL 20 DO c2[i]:=c1[i];
X45:    IF nn<1 THEN GO TO X99
            ELSE IF nn>1 THEN GO TO X12;
X46:    READ oper,instr;
            READ run,temp,waveL;
X47:    g:=20;
            FOR i:=1 STEP 1 UNTIL 20 DO
            BEGIN
```

```
           IF(oam[i]<wL1)V(oam[i]>wu1)THEN
           BEGIN
X48:          g:=g-1;
           oam[i]:=ac[i]:=acer[i]:=0;
             GO TO X50END;
           GO TO sw12[k];
X49:       dev1[i]:=oam[i]Xdevf1
X50:     END;
         IF m5<m6 THEN GO TO X92;
         FOR i:=1 STEP 1 UNTIL 20 DO
         BEGIN
           IF(c2[i]<wL2)V(c2[i]>wu2)THEN
           BEGIN
X51:          c2[i]:=c1[i]:=0; GO TO X53END;
           IF c1[i]≤0 THEN GO TO X51;
           GO TO sw13[k];
X52:       dev2[i]:=c2[i]Xdevf2
X53:     END;
         GO TO sw14[nn];
X54:     IF LL≤2 THEN
         BEGIN
           FOR i:=1 STEP 1 UNTIL 20 DO c2[i]:=0;
           qq2:=0END;
         IF nn>2 THEN GO TO X56;
         IF nn=2VLL≤2THEN
         BEGIN
           qq1:=2; GO TO X56END;
         qq1:=qq2:=1; GO TO X56;
X55:     IF nn=4 THEN
         BEGIN
           qq1:=qq2:=2; qq3:=qq4:=1END;
X56:     GO TO sw15[nn];
X57:     FOR i:=1 STEP 1 UNTIL 20 DO
         BEGIN
           IF c2[i]>0 THEN
           BEGIN
              c3[i]:=eqXc2[i]Xc1[i]/(1+eqXc2[i]);
              c4[i]:=(eq+eqer)X(c2[i]+dev2[i])Xc1[i]/(1+(eq+eqer)
              X(c2[i]+dev2[i]));
              c5[i]:=c1[i]-c4[i];
              c6[i]:=c2[i]-c4[i];
              c1[i]:=c1[i]-c3[i];
              c2[i]:=c2[i]-c3[i]END
         END;
         GO TO X92;
X58:     FOR i:=1 STEP 1 UNTIL 20 DO
         BEGIN
           IF c1[i]≤0 THEN
           BEGIN
              oam[i]:=0; GO TO X65END;
           rx:=eq;
           IF nn<2 THEN GO TO X99
```

```
          ELSE IF nn>2 THEN GO TO X60;
X59:      IF LL≤2 THEN
          BEGIN
            c3[i]:=(4XrxXc1[i]+1-sqrt(8XrxXc1[i]+1))/(8Xrx);
            IF rx<eq THEN GO TO X99
            ELSE IF rx=eq THEN
            BEGIN
              c5[i]:=c3[i]; rx:=eq+eqer;
              c1[i]:=c1[i]+dev2[i]; GO TO X59END;
            c4[i]:=c3[i]; GO TO X6XEND;
          bb:=-(rxX(c1[i]+c2[i]+1);
          c3[i]:=(-bb-sqrt(bb↑2-4Xrx↑2Xc1[i]Xc2[i]))/(2Xrx);
          IF rx<eq THEN GO TO X99
          ELSE IF rx=eq THEN
          BEGIN
            c5[i]:=c3[i]; rx:=eq+eqer;
            c2[i]:=c2[i]+dev2[i]; GO TO X59END;
          c4[i]:=c3[i]; c3[i]:=c5[i]; GO TO X6X;
X60:      r:=1; ppt:=0;
X61:      pp1:=1/2↑r;
X62:      ppt:=ppt+pp1; c3[i]:=pptXc1[i];
          IF(c1[i]≤qq1Xc3[i]V(c2[i]≤qq2Xc3[i])THEN
          GO TO X63;
          c4[i]:=rxX((c1[i]-qq1Xc3[i])↑qq1)X((c2[i]-qq2Xc3[i])↑qq2);
          IF c3[i]<c4[i]THEN GO TO X62
          ELSE IFc3[i]>c4[i] THEN GO TO X63;
          IF c3[i]<0 THEN GO TO X99
          ELSE IF c3[i]>0 THEN GO TO X64;
X63:      ppt:=ppt-pp1; r:=r+1;
          IF pp1>pp THEN GO TO X61;
X64:      IF rx<eq THEN GO TO X99
          ELSE IF rx=eq THEN
          BEGIN
            rx:=eq+eqer; c5[i]:=c3[i]
            c2[i]:=c2[i]+dev2[i]; GO TO X60END;
          c4[i]:=c3[i]; c3[i]:=c5[i]
X6X:      c5[i]:=c1[i]-qq1Xc4[i];
          c6[i]:=c2[i]-dev2[i]-qq2Xc4[i];
          c1[i]:=c1[i]-qq1Xc3[i];
          c2[i]:=c2[i]-dev2[i]-qq2Xc3[i];
          IF LL≤2 THEN c2[i]:=c6[i]:=0
X65:      END;
          GO TO X92;
X66:      FOR i:=1 STEP 1 UNTIL 20 DO
          BEGIN
            IF c2[i] ≤0 THEN
            BEGIN
X67:          c1[i]:=c2[i]:=0; GO TO X91END;
            IF c1[i]≤0 THEN GO TO X67;
            IF c1[i]≤c2[i] THEN
            BEGIN
              pq2:=c2[i]/c1[i]; GO TO X69END;
```

```
          pq1:=c1[i]/c2[i];
          IF pq1≥1 THEN
          BEGIN
X68:         c5[i]:=0.25Xc1[i]; n99:=1;
             GO TO X70END;
          IF pq1<5 THEN GO TO X68;
          c4[i]:=c5[i]:=0; n99:=2; GO TO X70;
X69:      IF pq2<5 THEN GO TO X68;
          c3[i]:=c5[i]:=0; n99:=3;
X70:      rx:=eq; n4:=0;
X71:      nnn:=1;
X72:      n4:=n4+1; r:=1; ppt:=0;
X73:      pp1:=1/2↑r;
X74:      ppt:=ppt+pp1; GO TO sw16[n4];
X75:      GO TO sw17[n99];
X76:      c6[i]:=pptXc1[i];
          IF c1[i]≤(qq1Xc6[i]+qq3Xc3[i]) THEN GO TO X63;
          c7[i]:=eq1X(c1[i]−qq1Xc6[i]−qq3Xc5[i])↑qq1;
X77:      IF c7[i]>c6[i] THEN GO TO X74
          ELSE IF c7[i]=c6[i] THEN
                  IF c7[i]<0 THEN GO TO X99
                  ELSE IF c7[i]>0 THEN GO TO X79;
X78:      ppt:=ppt−pp1; r:=r+1;
          IF pp1>pp THEN GO TO X73;
X79:      GO TO sw18[nnn];
X80:      c3[i]:=c7[i];
X81:      nnn:nnn+1;
          GO TO sw19[n99];
X82:      c4[i]:=c7[i]; GO TO X81;
X83:      c5[i]:=c7[i]; n99:=1;
          IF n4≤2 THEN GO TO X72;
          GO TO sw20[n99];
X84:      GO TO sw21[n4];
X85:      c8[i]:=c3[i]; c9[i]:=c4[i];
          c10[i]:=c5[i]; c2[i]:=c2[i]+dev2[i];
          rx:=eq+eqer; n4:=1; GO TO X71;
X86:      IF rx<eq THEN GO TO X99
          ELSE IF rx=eq THEN GO TO X85;
X87:      c6[i]:=c3[i]; c7[i]:=c4[i];
          c3[i]:=c8[i]; c4[i]:=c9[i];
          c8[i]:=c5[i]; c5[i]:=c10[i];
          c9[i]:=(c1[i]−qq1Xc6[i]−qq3Xc8[i]);
          c10[i]:=(c2[i]−qq2Xc7[i]−qq4Xc8[i])−dev2[i];
          c1[i]:=c1[i]−qq1Xc3[i]−qq3Xc5[i];
          c2[i]:=c2[i]−qq2Xc4[i]−qq4Xc5[i];
          GO TO X91;
X88:      IF n4<1 THEN GO TO X99
          ELSE IF n4>1 THEN
          BEGIN
X89:         c6[i]:=pptXc2[i];
             IF c2[i]≤(qq2Xc6[i]+qq4Xc5[i]) THEN GO TO X63;
             c7[i]:=eq2X(c2[i]−qq2Xc6[i]−qq4Xc5[i])↑qq2;
```

```
                GO TO X77END;
X90:    c6[i]:=pptXc1[i];
        IF(c2[i]≤(qq2Xc4[i]+qq4Xc6[i]))∨(c1[i]≤(qq1Xc3[i]+qq3
          Xc6[i]))THEN GO TO X63;
        c7[i]:=rxX(c1[i]−qq1Xc3[i]−qq3Xc6[i])↑qq3;
        c7[i]:=c7[i]X(c2[i]−qq2Xc4[i]−qq4Xc6[i])↑qq4;
        GO TO X77
X91:    END;
X92:    FOR i:=1 STEP 1 UNTIL 20 DO
        BEGIN
          IF oam[i]≤0 THEN
          BEGIN
X93:        ac[i]:=acer[i]:=x1[i]:=x1er[i]:=0;
            GO TO X98END;
          IF nn<1 THEN GO TO X99
          ELSE IF nn=1 THEN GO TO X95;
          qq:=c1[i]↑3;
          xx:=aiaxXc1[i]+a1Xc1[i]↑2+a2Xqq+a3XqqXc1[i]+a4XqqXc1[i]↑2;
          qq:=c2[i]↑3;
          yy:=aibxXc2[i]+b1Xc2[i]↑2+b2Xqq+b3XqqXc2[i]+b4XqqXc2[i]↑2;
          GO TO sw22[nn];
X94:      qq:=c5[i]↑3;
          xy:=aiaxXc5[i]+a1Xc5[i]↑2+a2Xqq+a3XqqXc5[i]+a4XqqXc5[i]↑2;
          qq:=c6[i]↑3;
          yx:=aibxXc6[i]+b1Xc6[i]↑2+b2Xqq+b3XqqXc6[i]+b4XqqXc6[i]↑2;
          GO TO X96;
X95:      xx:=aiaxXc1[i]; yy:=aibxXc2[i];
          xy:=aiaxXc5[i]; yx:=aibxXc6[i];
X96:      ac[i]:=oam[i]−xx−yy;
          acer[i]:=oam[i]−xy−yx+dev1[i];
          IF(ac[i]<oam[i]Xwac1)∨(c3[i]<c1[i]Xwac2) THEN GO TO X93;
          ac[i]:=ac[i]/c3[i];
          acer[i]:=acer[i]/c4[i]−ac[i]; GO TO X98;
X97:      qq:=c3[i]↑3;
          zz:=aic1xXc3[i]+ca1Xc3[i]↑2+ca2Xqq+ca3XqqXc3[i]+ca4XqqXc3[i]↑2;
          qq:=c4[i]↑3;
          ww:=aic2xXc4[i]+cb1Xc4[i]↑2+cb2Xqq+cb3XqqXc4[i]+cb4XqqXc4[i]↑2;
          qq:=c6[i]↑3;
          zw:=aic1xXc6[i]+ca1Xc6[i]↑2+ca2Xqq+ca3XqqXc6[i]+ca4XqqXc6[i]↑2;
          qq:=c7[i]↑3;
          wz:=aic2xXc7[i]+cb1Xc7[i]↑2+cb2Xqq+cb3XqqXc7[i]+cb4XqqXc7[i]↑2;
          qq:=c9[i]↑3;
          xy:=aiaxXc9[i]+a1Xc9[i]↑2+a2Xqq+a3XqqXc9[i]+a4XqqXc9[i]↑2;
          qq:=c10[i]↑3;
          yx:=aibxXc10[i]+b1Xc10[i]↑2+b2Xqq+b3XqqXc10[i]+b4XqqXc10[i]↑2;
          ac[i]:=oam[i]−xx−yy−zz−ww;
          acer[i]:=oam[i]+dev1[i]−xy−yx−zw−wz−ac[i];
          qq:=wac1X(xx−yy−zz−ww);
          IF ac[i]≤qq THEN GO TO X93;
          ac[i]:=ac[i]/c5[i]; acer[i]:=acer[i]/c8[i]
X98:    END;
```

```
        x1[1]:=-(g-1)/20;
        FOR i:=2 STEP 1 UNTIL 20 DO
        IF ac[i]>0 THEN
        BEGIN
            x1[1]:=x1[1]+0.1; x1[i]:=x1[1];
            x1er[i]:=0 END;
        x1[1]:=-(g-1)/20; x1er[1]:=0; feedp:=31;
        PUNCH feedp; PUNCH ka,kb,kc,kd;
        j:=3; PUNCH j; PUNCH k,L,m;
        PUNCH devf1,rLm1,wL1,wu1;
        PUNCH devf2,rLm2,wL2,wu2;
            FOR i:=1 STEP 1 UNTIL 20 DO PUNCH ac[i];
            FOR i:=1 STEP 1 UNTIL 20 DO PUNCH acer[i];
            FOR i:=1 STEP 1 UNTIL 20 DO PUNCH x1[i];
            FOR i:=1 STEP 1 UNTIL 20 DO PUNCH x1er[i];
            PUNCH g; waveL:=m4;
            PUNCH oper,instr;
            PUNCH run,temp,waveL;
            m5:=m5-1; m4:=m4+1;
            IF m4≤m6 THEN GO TO X20
X99:    END EBAAA;
W1:     READ eq,eqer,progn;
        EBAAA(eq,eqer,progn);
        GO TO W1;
```

CHAPTER IX

CONDUCTANCE EQUATIONS

In Chapter VII of the preceding volume there is Feeder Program 16 (*call word* PAAAA) for calculating the input information for Program 1 (*call word* AAAAA) or Program 301 (*call word* AAAAS) in order to test data compatability with seven two dimensional equations. Feeder Program 32 (*call word* FBAAA) has been designed to generate input information for either Program 26 (*call word* ZAAAA) or Program 326 (*call word* ZAAAS). With Program 32 and either Program 26 or 326, data can be tested for compatability with the seven two dimensional conductance equations in Program 16, and three Fuoss[1] conductance equations for one : one electrolytes. Constants for the Onsager conductance equation, or, if these are known, the difference between theoretically predicted and experimentally determined values of the conductance and the associated *maximum permitted errors* can also be computed with Program 32. Also, the molar, equivalent or specific conductance (μ) can be expanded against the concentration (C) thus:

$$\mu = \mu_0 + S_1 C^{1/2} + S_2 C + S_3 C^{3/2} + \ldots + S_N C^{N/2} \qquad (1)$$

The expansion of data to its functional form is especially useful for determining the limiting conductance (μ_0) or for constructing calibration tables or charts.

In Feeder Program 32 (*call word* FBAAA), the values selected for JQ and JD before compilation determine the maximum number of data points and the maximum dimensioned equation which can be processed. After compilation, the number of data points to be processed and the dimensions of the equations can be changed by means of new values for JI and JJ which appear in the input format for Program 32. The significance of JQ, JD, JI and JJ is discussed in the section on *input commands*

---

[1] R. M. Fuoss and F. Accascina, *Electrolyte Conductance*, New York: (Interscience Publishers Inc., 1959), pp. 195 and 226.

for Program 32. The values for JQ and JD determine the storage capacity required.

In Program 32 the *fail–safe procedure* is applied two (L ≠ 16) or four (L = 16) times, and values for the ordinates and their associated *maximum permitted errors* are computed from the *accepted sets of conjugate data* and the two (L ≠ 16) or four (L = 16) sets of *instrument reliability factors*. The *reject–restore* (KA, KB, KC, KD, KE, KF) and the cycle (JC) commands are not executed in Program 32, but they are generated in the correct location in the output format. They have been incorporated so that the generated information can be processed directly with Program 26 or 326. Output information obtained with Program 32 for the two-, three-, four- and five-dimension equations is compatible with the *self-judgment programs* in Chapter I of the first volume if JJ is removed and the *reject–restore* commands are replaced by the less sophisticated set (KA, KB, KC, KD).

The value for L in the input format for Program 32 (*call word* FBAAA) determines the mode of calculation (see Input Format for Program 32). Details of the output for each value of L are given in the section on Input Commands for Program 32. Here are given the equations used in the calculations.

L = 1   The *Onsager* equation:
$$\mu = \mu_0 - (A^*\mu_0 + B^*)\sqrt{C} = \mu_0 - AB\sqrt{C}$$
Here μ is the molar or equivalent conductance; C is the concentration of ionized salt in moles or equivalents per liter. μ_0, A^*, B^*, A and B are constants at a fixed temperature. This equation applies to completely ionized one : one electrolytes, or, in modified form, to electrolytes which ionize thus:

$$MX + MX \overset{K_1}{\rightleftharpoons} C_1 \overset{K_2}{\rightleftharpoons} \text{cation} + \text{anion}.$$ Here MX is an unionized salt molecule and the concentration of the intermediate, C_1, is much less than the concentration of either ion.[2]

L = 2   The *First Fuoss* equation:
$$\mu = \mu_0 - S\sqrt{C} + EC\log_{10}C + (J - F\mu_0)C$$
μ and C have been defined for L = 1. μ_0, S, E, J and F are constants if the temperature is fixed.

L = 3   The *Second Fuoss* equation:
$$\mu = \mu_0 - S\sqrt{(\gamma C)} + E(\gamma C)\log_{10}(\gamma C) + J(\gamma C) - F\mu_0 C + K_A f^2(\gamma C)$$
μ_0, S, E, J, F, K_A and f are constants at a fixed temperature for very dilute solutions. f is the mean activity coefficient for the ions γ is the fraction of salt dissociated. Here C is the total salt concentration.

[2] P. A. D. de Maine and E. Koubek, *J. Inorg. Nucl. Chem.*, **11**, (1959), 329.

L = 4   The *Third Fuoss* equation:

$$\mu = \mu_0 - S\sqrt{(\gamma C)} + E(\gamma C)\log_{10}(\gamma C) + J(\gamma C) - F\mu_0 C + K_A f^2(\gamma C) + A_{ij}C^{3/2}$$

Except for the addition of another constant, A_{ij}, the symbols are as defined for L = 3.

The three Fuoss equations are for very dilute solutions of one : one electrolytes. Detailed definitions of the various constants are found in reference 1.

L = 5   The molar or equivalent conductance (μ) is expanded in terms of the total salt concentration thus:

$$\mu = \mu_0 + S_1 C^{1/2} + S_2 C + S_3 C^{3/2} + \cdots S_N C^{N/2}$$

The dimension of the expansion is selected by the operator (see Input Commands for Program 32).

L = 6   The Onsager coefficients (AONS, BONS) are calculated from the limiting ion conductances (($\mu_0)_1$ and ($\mu_0)_2$), the number of charges on each ion (Z_1, Z_2), the absolute temperature (T), dielectric constant (D) of the solvent and viscosity coefficient (η) of the solvent.

$$q = Z_1 Z_2((\mu_0)_1 + (\mu_0)_2)/((Z_1 + Z_2)(Z_2(\mu_0)_1 + Z_1(\mu_0)_2))$$

If ($\mu_0)_2$ is entered as zero and $Z_1 = 1$, $Z_2 = 2$, then q is calculated from the limiting equivalent conductance (μ_0) thus:

$$q = 2\mu_0/(3(\mu_0 + (\mu_0)_1))$$

This equation is due to Davies.[3]

Next the Onsager constants are calculated.

$$\text{AONS} = 2{,}801{,}000 Z_1 Z_2 q/((DT)^{3/2}(1 + q^{1/2}))$$
$$\text{BONS} = 41.25(Z_1 + Z_2)/(\eta(DT)^{1/2}).$$

L = 7   The difference between the theoretical conductance, $\mu_T = \mu_0 - (\text{AONS} \cdot \mu_0 + \text{BONS})\sqrt{C}$, and the experimental value is computed from the experimental data, the limiting conductance (μ_0), and the two Onsager coefficients (AONS, BONS).

L = 8   The limiting conductance of either the cation ($\mu_0)_1$ or anion ($\mu_0)_2$ is computed from values for q, Z_1, Z_2 and either ($\mu_0)_2$ or ($\mu_0)_1$ thus:

$$(\mu_0)_1(Z_2 \cdot R - 1) = (\mu_0)_2(1 - Z_1 \cdot R)$$

where $R = q(Z_1 + Z_2)/Z_1 Z_2$.

L = 9   The limiting equivalent conductance of a doubly charged ion ($\mu_0)_1$ from a uni-bivalent electrolyte is calculated from the limiting equivalent conductance of the salt (μ_0) and q by the Davies[3] equation thus:

$$(\mu_0)_1 = 2\mu_0/3q - \mu_0.$$

L = 10   Data compatibility is tested with the equation:

$$\mu = A + BC^n$$

Here, μ is molar or equivalent conductance; C is the total salt concentration; and n is any specified positive or negative non-zero real number.

[3] C. W. Davies, *Ion Association* (Washington, D.C.: Butterworths, 1962), pp. 9–10.

L = 11   The molar equivalent conductance (μ) and the total salt concentration (C) are to be fitted to the equation:
$$\log_{10}\mu = A + B\log_{10}C$$
Here A and B are constants for each solvent and temperature.

L = 12   A relation[4] between the specific conductance of the salt (K) and the total salt concentration (C) is tested.
$$K = A + BC$$
A and B are defined for L = 11.

L = 13   Data compatibility is to be tested with the equation:
$$K = A + BC^n$$
n is any specified non-zero real number. Other symbols are defined under L = 12.

L = 14   The specific conductance (K) is to be expanded in terms of the total salt concentration thus:
$$K = K_0 + S_1C^{1/2} + S_2C + S_3C^{3/2} + \cdots + S_NC^{N/2}$$
Instructions for selecting the dimension of the expansion are given in the section on input commands for Program 32.

L = 15   The specific conductance (K) and the total salt concentration (C) are to be fitted to the equation:
$$\log_{10}K = A + B\log_{10}C.$$

L = 16   The *conductance ratio* equation[5]
$$R = A + BC$$
Here $R = $ (Molar conductance at $T2°C$)/(molar conductance at $T1°C$). $T2 > T1$. C is the salt concentration at $T1°C$. A and B are constants for each system studied.

The equations given for L = 1–5 and 10–16 have the common mathematical form (expressed in FORTRAN)

$$Y(I,1) = SL(1) * Y(I,2) + SL(2) * Y(I,3) + \cdots + SL(N)$$

which can be solved for the slopes ($SL(1)$, $SL(2)$, $\cdots$) and intercept ($SL(N)$) with the *variable dimension self-judgment programs* (26 and 326), or, with the appropriate *self-judgment programs* (1–4, 301–304) if N is not larger than five. Output information generated by Program 32 (*call word* FBAAA) is used.

The values for K, L and M determine the *input format*, the mode of calculation and the *output format* generated by Program 32. This output information for L = 1, 2, 5, 7 and 10–16 can be processed with *Auto-plotter Program 501* (*call word* AEEEE) if JI ≤ 20 and the autoplots inspected for gross errors in individual sets of conjugate information. One card with a single item of information (JI) must be added before use as *input information* for Program 26 or 326.

[4] P. A. D. de Maine, M. M. de Maine and G. E. McAlonie, *J. Inorg. Nucl. Chem.*, **14** (1960), 268.

[5] P. A. D. de Maine and G. E. McAlonie, *J. Inorg. Nucl. Chem.*, **18** (1961), 286.

SECONDARY CORRECTION FACTORS

If the salt concentrations are calculated with Program 5, 6 or 7 (Chapter II, Volume I), errors arising from the neglect of temperature–volume changes and non-ideal behavior are eliminated. Activity coefficients can be introduced as special weighting functions in the *self-judgment program* (1–4, 301–304, 26 and 326) as described under *statistical bias*. In Program 32 the specific conductance of the solvent is automatically subtracted from the specific conductance of the solution.

INSTRUMENT RELIABILITY FACTORS

In Program 32 either two ($L \neq 16$) or four ($L = 16$) sets of *instrument reliability factors* must be entered. The first non-variable subscript denotes the observable while the second denotes the temperature. Thus DEVF1 (or DEV11(I)), RLM11, WAC11 and WU11 are associated exclusively with the specific conductance of the solution at the lower temperature, (SC1(I)). DEVF3 (or DEV12(I)), RLM12, WAC12 and WU12 are associated with the specific conductance at the higher temperature, (SC2(I)). The sets: DEVF2 (or DEV21(I)), RLM21, WL21, WU21; and DEVF4 (or DEV22(I)), RLM22, WL22, WU22 refer to the salt concentrations, C1(I) and C2(I) respectively.

DEVF is the *maximum permitted deviation* expressed as a fraction of the designated observable. DEV21(I) is the *maximum permitted deviation* in the salt concentration of the Ith solution at the lower temperature. For $L = 16$ it is assumed that the *maximum permitted deviations* for both observables of the same type (i.e. SC1(I) and SC2(I)) will be expressed in the same form (i.e. DEVF or DEV___(I)).

If the specific conductance of the solution (SC1(I)) is less than WAC11 times the specific conductance of the solvent (SSC1), the entire set of conjugate data is rejected and all members of the corresponding set of conjugate information are set equal to zero.

WL and WU are the lowest and the highest reliable values for the designated observable.

RLM is the *measured limit of reliability*. The value for RLM indicates the operator's estimate of the reliability of his raw data. It is not used in the calculations.

FAIL–SAFE PROCEDURE

If the specific conductance (SC1(I)) is less than WAC11 * SSC1 or is greater than WU11, or if the corresponding salt concentration (C1(I)) is less than WL21 or greater than WU21, all elements of the corresponding *set of conjugate information* are set equal to zero. If the equation for $L = 16$ is being tested, an additional two sets of *instrument reliability factors* which refer to the three observables ($SC2(I)$, $C2(I)$ and $SSC2$) at the higher temperature are also used to select the accepted sets of conjugate data.

For $L = 6$, 8 and 9 no *instrument reliability factors* are used in the calculation of the limiting ion conductances ($(\mu_0)_1$, $(\mu_0)_2$) and the two Onsager coefficients (AONS, BONS). However, related experimental information not actually used in the calculations, must be entered (see Input Format for Program 32). The two sets of *instrument reliability factors* for $L = 7$ are used to select reliable experimental information and calculate the *maximum permitted error* in the difference between the theoretical and experimental values of the equivalent conductance for one : one electrolytes.

STATISTICAL BIAS

Devices for reducing statistical bias which have been incorporated into Programs 26 and 326, will be used when the output for Program 32 is processed with the *variable dimension self-judgment program* (Chapter III). No additional devices have been incorporated into the *feeder program* (32).

Activity coefficients can be introduced by modifications in Program 32, or by replacing the *special weighting function* statements in the *self-judgment programs*. However, it must be remembered that in Programs 26 and 326 the input data for the ordinates are rearranged before multiplication by the *special weighting functions*. If the mean activity coefficients are to be introduced for the *second* and *third Fuoss* conductance equations, statement 999 in the *self-judgment program* (26 and 326) must be replaced by the following statements.

```
999 IF(J-5)7777,7778,7777
7778 FUNY(J) = Specified function
GO TO 7779
7777 FUNY(J) = 1.0
7779 CONTINUE.
```

INPUT COMMANDS FOR PROGRAM 32

JQ—The maximum number of *sets of conjugate data* which can be processed with program. JQ should be an integral multiple of four.

JD—The maximum dimensioned equation which can be processed with this program.

With the IBM 1620–60K machine at the University of Mississippi we have set JQ = 40 and JD = 10. Values for JQ and JD should be the same as in Programs 26 and 326.

JI—The value for JI in the input format for Program 32 is the actual number of *sets of conjugate data* to be processed. JI *must* be a multiple of four. Thus if only ten *sets of conjugate data* are to be processed, twelve sets (with all elements in two sets equal to zero) must be entered. The two zero sets will not be used in Program 32 or in any *self-judgment programs* (1–4, 301–304, 26, 326).

K, L and M values designate the *input format*, the mode of calculation, and the *output format* respectively. The value for K defines the form in which the *maximum permitted deviations* are to be entered while the value of M indicates the concentration units.

COMMAND	L VALUE	COMMENT
K = 1	1 to 15	DEVF1; DEVF2
	16	DEVF1; DEVF2; DEVF3; DEVF4
K = 2	1 to 15	DEVF1; DEV21(I)
	16	DEVF1; DEV21(I); DEVF3; DEV22(I)
K = 3	1 to 15	DEV11(I); DEVF2
	16	DEV11(I); DEVF2; DEV12(I); DEVF4
K = 4	1 to 15	DEV11(I); DEV21(I)
	16	DEV11(I); DEV21(I); DEV12(I); DEV22(I)
M = 0		Concentrations are in equivalents per liter.
M = 1		Concentrations are in moles per liter.

Here are given the calculated quantities found in the output format for each L value. YER(I,J) is the *maximum permitted error* in the Ith value for the Jth ordinate. All ordinates are given in FORTRAN.

COMMAND	COMMENT
L = 1	The ordinates and the associated *maximum permitted errors* are calculated for the Onsager and de Maine–Koubek[2] equations from the measured specific conductances of the solution (SC1(I)) and of the solvent (SSC1). C1(I) is the salt concentration. $Y(I,1) = 1000.0 * (SC1(I) - SSC1)/C1(I)$; $Y(I,2) = SQR(C1(I))$.
L = 2	The ordinates for the *First Fuoss* equation are computed from the data given for L = 1. $Y(I,1) = 1000.0 * (SC1(I) - SSC1)/C1(I)$; $Y(I,2) = SQR(C1(I))$ $Y(I,3) = C1(I) * (LOG(C1(I)))/2.30259$; $Y(I,4) = C1(I)$. *Note:* This is a four-dimensional equation. The output information, after minor changes, can be processed with Program 3 or 303.

COMMAND	COMMENT

L = 3 — The ordinates for the *Second Fuoss* equation are calculated from the specific conductance of the solution (SC1(I)) and of the solvent (SSC1), the salt concentration (C1(I)) and the dissociation constant (DC(I)) thus:

$Y(I,1) = 1000.0 * (SC1(I) - SSC1)/C1(I);$

$Y(I,2) = SQR(DC(I) * C1(I))$

$Y(I,3) = (DC(I) * C1(I)) * (LOG(DC(I) * C1(I))/2.30259)$

$Y(I,4) = DC(I) * C1(I); \quad Y(I,5) = C1(I); \quad Y(I,6) = DC(I) * C1(I).$

Note: This six dimensional equation can be solved with Program 26 (*call word* ZAAAA) or Program 326 (*call word* ZAAAS). The fourth ($Y(I,4)$) and the sixth ($Y(I,6)$) ordinates appear equal here but activity coefficients, introduced as described in the section on *statistical bias*, effect differences in these ordinates.

L = 4 — The ordinates for the *Third Fuoss* equation are calculated with the information used for L = 3. The first six ordinates in the seven dimensional equation are identical with those given for L = 3. The seventh ordinate is computed thus:

$$Y(I,7) = SQR((C1(I)) ** 3.0)$$

Note: This seven dimensional equation can be solved for the Fuoss parameters with Program 26 (*call word* ZAAAA) or Program 326 (*call word* ZAAAS). The mean activity coefficients (f) can be introduced into the *variable dimensioned self-judgment* program by replacement of the statement numbered 999 with the desired function according to instructions in the section on *statistical bias*.

L = 5 — The molar or equivalent conductance ($Y(I,1)$) is expanded against the salt concentration (C1(I)). Ordinates are calculated from the data given for L = 1. The dimension of the expansion is determined by the value entered for QQ1($= JJ$).

$Y(I,1) = 1000.0 * (SC1(I) - SSC1)/C1(I); \quad Y(I,2) = SQR(C1(I))$

$Y(I,3) = C1(I); \quad Y(I,4) = SQR((C1(I)) ** 3.0); \cdots;$

$Y(I,JJ) = SQR((C1(I)) ** QQ1).$

Note: If a large computer is available there is no limit on the number of dimensions that can be solved by Programs 26 and 326.

L = 6 — The two Onsager coefficients (AONS and BONS) and η are computed from the limiting conductance (CONO), the limiting ion conductances (CON1 and CON2), the valence of the two ions (Z_1 and Z_2), the viscosity coefficient (VIS) and dielectric constant (DE) of the pure solvent, and the absolute temperature (TABS). If Z1 = 2.0, Z2 = 1.0 and CON2 = 0.0, η, AONS and BONS will be calculated from CONO, CON1, DE, VIS and TABS by the Davies[3] equation. While the input information for L = 1 must be entered, it is not used in the calculations.

Output information obtained for L = 6 is: AONS, BONS, QQ, Z1, Z2. QQ equals η in the Onsager equation. This information is not processed with the *self-judgment programs*.

COMMAND	COMMENT

L = 7   The difference between the predicted and measured values for the equivalent conductance of one : one electrolytes is computed using the Onsager equation, information given for L = 1, and the two Onsager coefficients (AONS and BONS), the limiting equivalent conductance (CONO), and its *maximum permitted error* (DCONO). CONO and DCONO can be computed with Programs 32 and 26 or 326 with L = 1–5. The ordinates calculated are:

$$Y(I,1) = CONO - (AONS * CONO + BONS) * (SQR(C1(I))) - X$$

with X equal to $1000.0 * (SC1(I) - SSC1)/C1(I)$. $YER(I,1) = maximum$ *permitted error* in $Y(I,1)$ calculated with the *instrument reliability factors* and DCONO. $Y(I,2) = SQR(C1(I))$. The information generated by Program 32 is in two dimension form, and can be processed with the *self-judgment programs* (1, 301, 26 or 326) for analysis of the deviations.

L = 8   The limiting ion conductance of the cation or anion for a Z1 : Z2 electrolyte is calculated from the Onsager η factor (QQ), the limiting conductance of one ion (CON1 or CON2), and the valence values for both ions (Z1 and Z2). In Program 32 the limiting ion conductance must be entered as zero. Information generated includes the limiting ion conductances (CON1 and CON2) for both ions and the values entered for Z1, Z2 and QQ.

L = 9   The limiting ion conductance of the cation (CON1) is calculated from the limiting conductance (CONO) and the q factor (QQ) for a 2 : 1 electrolyte from Davies'[3] equation. Information generated includes CONO, CON1 and QQ.

L = 10   The ordinates calculated from information for L = 1 and the association constant (QQ1) are:
$Y(I,1) = 1000.0 * (SC1(I) - SSC1)/C1(I)$
$Y(I,2) = (C1(I)) * QQ1$
The output information generated by Program 32 can be processed directly with either Program 26 or 326, or, after minor changes, with either Program 1 or 301.

L = 11   Input information given for L = 1 is used to calculate the ordinates:
$Y(I,1) = (LOG(1000.0 * (SC1(I) - SSC1)/C1(I)))/2.30259$
$Y(I,2) = (LOG(C1(I)))/2.30259$
The constants which describe the two-dimension equation being tested can be computed directly with either Program 26 or 326.

L = 12   The ordinates for the first specific conductance equation are calculated from information given for L = 1.
$Y(I,1) = SC1(I) - SSC1; Y(I, 2) = C1(I)$

COMMAND	COMMENT
L = 13	From information for L = 10, Y(I,1) and Y(I,2) are calculated. Y(I,1) = SC1(I) − SSC1; Y(I,2) = (C1(I)) ** QQ1
L = 14	The specific conductance (SC1(I)) is expanded against the total salt concentration (C1(I)). The dimension of the expansion (JJ = QQ1) is determined by the value for QQ1. Y(I,1) = SC1(I) − SSC1; Y(I,2) = SQR(C1(I)); Y(I,JJ) = SQR(C1(I) ** QQ1) The slopes and intercept (the specific conductance of the salt at infinite dilution) for the expansion can be computed from the output information generated by Program 32 directly with either Program 26 or 326.
L = 15	With information for L = 1 the ordinates, Y(I,1) = (LOG(SC1(I) − SSC1))/2.30259 and Y(I,2) = (LOG(C1(I)))/2.30259, are calculated.
L = 16	The *conductance ratio equation*[5] is tested for data-compatibility by use of a two dimension *self-judgment program* (1 or 301) or a *variable dimension self-judgment program* (26 or 326). The input information required by Program 32 (*call word* FBAAA) includes the following. 1. The specific conductance of the solution (SC1(I)) and of the pure solvent (SSC1) at the lower temperature T1°C. 2. The specific conductance of the same solution (SC2(I)) and solvent (SSC2) at a higher temperature (T2°C). 3. The salt concentrations (C1(I) and C2(I)) at T1°C and T2°C respectively. The ordinates calculated are as follows. Y(I,1) = (1000.0 * (SC2(I) − SSC2) * C1(I))/(1000.0 * (SC1(I) − SSC1) * C2(I)) Y(I,2) = C1(I).

If the output information generated by Program 32 (*call word* FBAAA) with L = 1–5, 7, 10–16 is to be processed with either Program 26 (*call word* ZAAAA) or Program 326 (*call word* ZAAAS), only one card with a single item of information (JI) is added before the *first* set of information (generated by Program 32).

INPUT FORMAT FOR PROGRAM 32

(L = 16) means the information is entered only if L equal 16.

STATEMENT	COMMENT
READ,JI	The actual number of *sets of conjugate data* to be processed. JI must be a multiple of 4.
READ,FBAAA,FEEDP	FBAAA = 32.0; FEEDP — source of information.
READ,K,L,M	Input commands.
READ,QQ1 (L = 5,10,13,14)	For L = 5 or 14 QQ1 is the dimension of the expansion. For L = 10 or 13 QQ1 is the association constant.
READ,RLM11,WAC11,WU11	*Instrument reliability factors* for the specific conductance (SC1(I)) at T1°C.
READ,RLM21,WL21,WU21	*Instrument reliability factors* for C1(I).
READ,SC1(I),SC1(I+1),SC1(I+2),SC1(I+3)	Specific conductance of the solution at the lower temperature (T1°C).
READ,C1(I),C1(I+1),C1(I+2),C1(I+3)	Salt concentration at T1°C.
READ,SSC1	Specific conductance of the solvent at T1°C.
READ,RLM12,WAC12,WU12 READ,RLM22,WL22,WU22 READ,SC2(I),SC2(I+1),SC2(I+2),SC2(I+3) READ,C2(I),C2(I+1),C2(I+2),C2(I+3) READ,SSC2	(L = 16) This information is for temperature, T2°C.
READ,DC(I),DC(I+1),DC(I+2),DC(I+3)	(L = 3 or 4) DC(I) is the faction of salt ionized.

READ,DEVF1
  or
READ,DEV11(I),DEV11(I+1),DEV11(I+2),DEV11(I+3)
READ,DEVF2
  or
READ,DEV21(I),DEV21(I+1),DEV21(I+2),DEV21(I+3)
	Maximum permitted deviations for the specific conductance and salt concentration at T1°C.

READ,DEVF3
  or
READ,DEV12(I),DEV12(I+1),DEV12(I+2),DEV12(I+3)
READ,DEVF4
  or
READ,DEV22(I),DEV22(I+1),DEV22(I+2),DEV22(I+3)
	(L = 16) *Maximum permitted deviations* for the specific conductance and salt concentration at T2°C.

READ,OPER,INSTR READ,RUN,TEMP,WAVEL	Identification.
READ,KA,KB,KC,KD,KE,KF	*Reject–restore commands* for *self-judgment program.*
READ,JC	The number of cycles to be completed in the *self-judgment program* before the *error analysis.*
READ,AONS,BONS,CONO,DCONO (L = 7) READ,CONO,CON1,CON2,Z1,Z2,VIS,DE,TABS (L = 6) READ,CON1,CON2,Z1,Z2,QQ (L = 8) READ,CONO (L = 9)	

DEFINITIONS

Details of the values to be entered for the symbols in the last four READ statements are given in the section on "input commands for Program 32" (see values for L). The quantities are:

AONS,BONS—Onsager coefficients.
QQ—Onsager q term.
Z1,Z2—Valence of the cation and anion.
CONO—Limiting equivalent conductance.
DCONO—Maximum permitted error in CONO.
CON1,CON2—Limiting conductances of the cation and anion.
DE—Dielectric constant of the pure solvent.
VIS—Viscosity coefficient of the solvent.
TABS—Absolute temperature.

OUTPUT FORMAT FOR PROGRAM 32

Symbols not defined in this section have been defined for each L value in the section on Input Commands for Program 32. In the following (L = 6) and (L $\neq$ 6, 8 and 9) mean that the information will only be generated if L equals 6, and if L does not equal 6, 8 and 9, respectively. Statements without such qualifying values are executed for all L values. Data generated with Program 32 (*call word* FBAAA) require the addition of one card with a value for JI, before they can be processed with Program 26 (*call word* ZAAAA) or Program 326 (*call word* ZAAAS). If the data are to be processed with one of the *self-judgment programs* in Chapter I in Volume I, JJ must be removed and the *reject–restore commands* (KA, KB, KC, KD, KE, KF) replaced by the less sophisticated version (KA, KB, KC, KD).

STATEMENT	COMMENT
PUNCH,ZAAAS,FEEDP	ZAAAS = 326.0, FEEDP = 32.0. ZAAAS need not be charged if Program 26 is used to process the data.
PUNCH,KA,KB,KC,KD,KE,KF	*Reject–restore* commands
PUNCH,JJ	Dimension of equation to be tested. JJ = 2 for L = 6, 8 or 9.
PUNCH,JC	*Cycle command.*
PUNCH,K,L,M	*Input commands.*
PUNCH,DEVF1,RLM11,WAC11,WU11	
PUNCH,DEVF2,RLM21,WL21,WU21	Repeated JJ−1 times.
⋮ ⋮ ⋮ ⋮ ⋮	

STATEMENT	COMMENT
PUNCH,Y(I,J),Y(I+1,J),Y(I+2,J),Y(I+3,J) PUNCH YER(I,J),YER(I+1,J),YER(I+2,J),YER(I+3,J) ⋮ ⋮ ⋮ ⋮ ⋮	Executed for J = 1, 2, ⋯ JJ and I = 1, 5, ⋯ JI–3, if L = 1–5, 7, 10–16. YER(I,J) is the *maximum permitted error* in Y(I,J). Y(I,J) is defined for L commands.
PUNCH,AONS,BONS,QQ,Z1,Z2 (L = 6) PUNCH,CON1,CON2,Z1,Z2,QQ (L = 8) PUNCH,CONO,CON1,QQ (L = 9)	

DEFINITIONS

AONS,BONS—The Onsager coefficients calculated for a Z1 : Z2 electrolyte.

QQ—The Onsager q term used to calculate AONS and BONS.

CONO—Limiting equivalent conductance of the salt.

CON1—Limiting equivalent conductance of the cation with valence Z1.

CON2—Limiting equivalent conductance of the anion with valence Z2.

PUNCH,G	The number of accepted sets of conjugate information.
PUNCH,OPER,INSTR PUNCH,RUN,TEMP,WAVEL	Identification.

RELIABILITY LIMITS FOR PROGRAM 32

The devices incorporated in the *self-judgment programs* to reduce *statistical bias* have not been included in Program 32. *Round-off error* occurs in this program if the maximum word-size in the distributor is exceeded or if *under-flow errors* occur. These factors are significant only when the *instrument reliability factors* are chosen without regard to the physical facts. Thus a *lower reliability limit* value of zero implies that the observable can be measured accurately if it is zero, and such a value can lead to infinities in the calculations.

FORTRAN FOR PROGRAM NUMBER 32

CALL WORD FBAAA

```
DIMENSION SC1(JQ),SC2(JQ),C1(JQ),C2(JQ),DEV11(JQ),DEV21(JQ),DEV12(JQ)
DIMENSION DEV22(JQ),Y(JQ,JD),YER(JQ,JD),DC(JQ)
1 READ,JI
READ,FBAAA,FEEDP
READ,K,L,M
GO TO (2,2,2,2,3,2,2,2,2,3,2,2,3,3,2,2,3,3,3,3),L
3 READ,QQ1
2 READ,RLM11,WAC11,WU11
READ,RLM21,WL21,WU21
DO 4 I=1,JI,4
4 READ,SC1(I),SC1(I+1),SC1(I+2),SC1(I+3)
DO 5 I=1,JI,4
5 READ,C1(I),C1(I+1),C1(I+2),C1(I+3)
READ,SSC1
IF(L-16)7,6,7
6 READ,RLM12,WAC12,WU12
READ,RLM22,WL22,WU22
DO 8 I=1,JI,4
8 READ,SC2(I),SC2(I+1),SC2(I+2),SC2(I+3)
DO 9 I=1,JI,4
9 READ,C2(I),C2(I+1),C2(I+2),C2(I+3)
READ,SSC2
GO TO 10
7 DO 11 I=1,JI
SC2(I)=0.0
11 C2(I)=0.0
DEVF3=0.0
DEVF4=0.0
10 IF(L-3)91,92,93
93 IF(L-4)92,92,91
92 DO 94 I=1,JI,4
94 READ,DC(I),DC(I+1),DC(I+2),DC(I+3)
91 IF(K-1)1,12,15
12 READ,DEVF1
READ,DEVF2
IF(L-16)13,14,13
14 READ,DEVF3
READ,DEVF4
15 IF(K-2)13,16,20
16 READ,DEVF1
DO 17 I=1,JI,4
17 READ,DEV21(I),DEV21(I+1),DEV21(I+2),DEV21(I+3)
DEVF2=5555.0
IF(L-16)13,18,13
18 READ,DEVF3
DO 19 I=1,JI,4
19 READ,DEV22(I),DEV22(I+1),DEV22(I+2),DEV22(I+3)
DEVF4=5555.0
20 IF(K-3)13,21,25
21 DO 22 I=2,JI,4
22 READ,DEV11(I),DEV11(I+1),DEV11(I+2),DEV11(I+3)
DEVF1=5555.0
READ,DEVF2
IF(L-16)13,23,13
23 DO 24 I=1,JI,4
24 READ,DEV12(I),DEV12(I+1),DEV12(I+2),DEV12(I+3)
DEVF3=5555.0
READ,DEVF4
25 IF(K-4)13,26,1
```

```
26 DO 27 I=1,JI,4
27 READ,DEV11(I),DEV11(I+1),DEV11(I+2),DEV11(I+3)
DEVF1=5555.0
DO 28 I=1,JI,4
28 READ,DEV21(I),DEV21(I+1),DEV21(I+2),DEV21(I+3)
DEVF2=5555.0
IF(L-16)13,29,13
29 DO 30 I=1,JI,4
30 READ,DEV12(I),DEV12(I+1),DEV12(I+2),DEV12(I+3)
DEVF3=5555.0
DO 31 I=1,JI,4
31 READ,DEV22(I),DEV22(I+1),DEV22(I+2),DEV22(I+3)
DEVF4=5555.0
13 DO 32 I=1,JI
IF(K-2)33,33,34
33 DEV11(I)=DEVF1*SC1(I)
DEV12(I)=DEVF3*SC2(I)
34 GO TO (35,32,35,32),K
35 DEV21(I)=DEVF2*C1(I)
DEV22(I)=DEVF4*C2(I)
32 CONTINUE
G=0.0
JJ=0
GO TO (40,39,38,37,36,40,40,40,40,40,40,40,40,36,40,40,36,36,36),L
36 JJ=QQ1
GO TO41
37 JJ=JJ+1
38 JJ=JJ+2
39 JJ=JJ+2
40 JJ=JJ+2
41 DO 42 I=1,JI
Y(I,1)=SC1(I)-WAC11*SSC1
IF(Y(I,1))43,44,44
44 IF(SC1(I)-WU11)45,45,43
45 IF(C1(I)-WL21)43,46,46
46 IF(C1(I)-WU21)47,47,43
47 IF(L-16)53,48,53
48 Y(I,1)=SC2(I)-WAC12*SSC2
IF(Y(I,1))43,50,50
50 IF(Y(I,1)-WU12)51,51,43
51 IF(C2(I)-WL22)43,52,52
52 IF(C2(I)-WU22)53,53,43
43 DO 90 J=1,JJ
Y(I,J)=0.0
90 YER(I,J)=0.0
GO TO 42
53 IF(L-11)54,54,49
54 Y(I,1)=1000.0*(SC1(I)-SSC1)/C1(I)
YER(I,1)=1000.0*(SC1(I)+DEV11(I)-SSC1)/(C1(I)-DEV21(I))
G=G+1.0
IF(L-11)55,56,1
55 YER(I,1)=YER(I,1)-Y(I,1)
GO TO 57
56 Y(I,1)=LOG(Y(I,1))/2.30259
YER(I,1)=LOG(YER(I,1))/2.30259-Y(I,1)
57 GO TO (58,59,60,61,62,42,42,42,42,64,71),L
61 Y(I,7)=(C1(I))**(1.5)
YER(I,7)=(C1(I)+DEV21(I))**(1.5)-Y(I,7)
60 Y(I,6)=DC(I)*C1(I)
YER(I,6)=DC(I)*DEV21(I)
Y(I,5)=C1(I)
YER(I,5)=DEV21(I)
```

```
Y(I,4)=DC(I)*C1(I)
YER(I,4)=DC(I)*DEV21(I)
Y(I,3)=(DC(I)*C1(I))*(LOG(DC(I)*C1(I)))/2.30259
YER(I,3)=DC(I)*(C1(I)+DEV21(I))
YER(I,3)=YER(I,3)*(LOG(YER(I,3)))/2.30259-Y(I,3)
Y(I,2)=SQR(DC(I)*C1(I))
YER(I,2)=SQR(DC(I)*(C1(I)+DEV21(I)))-Y(I,2)
GO TO 42
59 Y(I,4)=C1(I)
YER(I,4)=DEV21(I)
Y(I,3)=C1(I)*LOG(C1(I))
YER(I,3)=(C1(I)+DEV21(I))*LOG(C1(I)+DEV21(I))-Y(I,3)
Y(I,3)=Y(I,3)/2.30259
YER(I,3)=YER(I,3)/2.30259
58 Y(I,2)=SQR(C1(I))
YER(I,2)=SQR(C1(I)+DEV21(I))-Y(I,2)
GO TO 42
62 DO 63 J=2,JJ
P=J-1
P=P*0.5
Y(I,J)=C1(I)**P
63 YER(I,J)=(C1(I)+DEV21(I))**P-Y(I,J)
GO TO 42
64 Y(I,2)=C1(I)**QQ1
YER(I,2)=(C1(I)+DEV21(I))**QQ1-Y(I,2)
GO TO 42
49 IF(L-16)65,66,42
65 Y(I,1)=SC1(I)-SSC1
YER(I,1)=SC1(I)+DEV11(I)-SSC1
IF(L-15)67,68,1
67 YER(I,1)=YER(I,1)-Y(I,1)
GO TO 69
68 Y(I,1)=LOG(Y(I,1))/2.30259
YER(I,1)=LOG(YER(I,1))/2.30259-Y(I,1)
GO TO 69
66 Y(I,1)=((SC2(I)-SSC2)*C1(I))/((SC1(I)-SSC1)*C2(I))
YER(I,1)=((SC2(I)+DEV12(I)-SSC2)*(C1(I)+DEV21(I)))
YER(I,1)=YER(I,1)/((SC1(I)-DEV11(I)-SSC1)*(C2(I)-DEV22(I)))-Y(I,1)
69 LL=L-11
G=G+1.0
GO TO (70,64,62,71,70,42,42,42),LL
70 Y(I,2)=C1(I)
YER(I,2)=DEV21(I)
GO TO 42
71 Y(I,2)=(LOG(C1(I)))/2.30259
YER(I,2)=(LOG(C1(I)+DEV21(I)))/2.30259-Y(I,2)
42 CONTINUE
READ,OPER,INSTR
READ,RUN,TEMP,WAVEL
ZAAAS=326.0
READ,KA,KB,KC,KD,KE,KF
READ,JC
FEEDP=32.0
PUNCH,ZAAAS,FEEDP
PUNCH,KA,KB,KC,KD,KE,KF
PUNCH,JJ
PUNCH,JC
PUNCH,K,L,M
PUNCH,DEVF1,RLM11,WAC11,WU11
DO 72 J=2,JJ
72 PUNCH,DEVF2,RLM21,WL21,WU21
IF(L-7)73,74,73
```

```
74 READ,AONS,BONS,CONO,DCONO
DO 75 I=1,JI
AA=Y(I,1)
Y(I,1)=CONO-(AONS*CONO+BONS)*(SQR(C1(I)))-Y(I,1)
AAAA=CONO+DCONO-(AONS*(CONO+DCONO)+BONS)*(SQR(C1(I)+DEV21(I)))
AAAA=AAAA-YER(I,1)
YER(I,1)=AAAA-AA-Y(I,1)
Y(I,2)=SQR(C1(I))
YER(I,2)=SQR(C1(I)+DEV21(I))-Y(I,2)
75 CONTINUE
GO TO 76
73 IF(L-6)76,77,78
78 IF(L-8)76,85,79
79 IF(L-9)89,89,76
76 DO 80 I=1,JI,4
DO 80 J=1,JJ
PUNCH,Y(I,J),Y(I+1,J),Y(I+2,J),Y(I+3,J)
80 PUNCH,YER(I,J),YER(I+1,J),YER(I+2,J),YER(I+3,J)
81 PUNCH,G
PUNCH,OPER,INSTR
PUNCH,RUN,TEMP,WAVEL
GO TO 1
77 READ,CONO,CON1,CON2,Z1,Z2,VIS,DE,TABS
IF(CON2)1,82,83
82 QQ=2.0*CONO/(3.0*(CON1+CONO))
GO TO 84
83 QQ=Z1*Z2*(CON1+CON2)/((Z1+Z2)*(Z2*CON1+Z1*CON2))
84 AONS=2.801*(10.0**6.0)*Z1*Z2*QQ/(SQR((DE*TABS)**3.0)*(1.0+SQR(QQ)))
BONS=41.25*(Z1+Z2)/(VIS*SQR(DE*TABS))
PUNCH,AONS,BONS,QQ,Z1,Z2
GO TO 81
85 READ,CON1,CON2,Z1,Z2,QQ
RR=QQ*(Z1+Z2)/(Z1*Z2)
IF(CON1)1,86,87
86 CON1=CON2*(1.0-RR*Z1)/(Z2*RR-1.0)
GO TO 88
87 CON2=CON1*(Z2*RR-1.0)/(1.0-RR*Z1)
88 PUNCH,CON1,CON2,Z1,Z2,QQ
GO TO 81
89 READ,CONO,QQ
CON1=(2.0*CONO)/(QQ*3.0)-CONO
PUNCH,CONO,CON1,QQ
GO TO 81
END
```

ALGOL 60 FOR PROGRAM NUMBER 32

```
PROCEDURE FBAAA(ji,feedp,k,L,m);  ARRAY sc1,sc2,c1,c2,dev11,dev21,dev12,
dev22,dc[1:jq],y,yer[1:jq,1:jd];  INTEGER ji,feedp,k,L,m;  SWITCH sw1:=x2,x2,x2,
x2,x1,x2,x2,x2,x2,x1,x2,x2,x1,x1,x2,x2,x1,x1,x1;  SWITCH sw2:=x8,x9,x8,x9;
SWITCH sw3:=x14,x13,x12,x11,x10,x14,x14,x14,x14,x14,x14,x14,x14,x10,x14,x14,
x10,x10,x10;  SWITCH sw4:=x22,x21,x20,x19,x23,x29,x29,x29,x29,x24,x28;
SWITCH sw5:=x27,x24,x23,x28,x27,x29,x29,x29;
COMMENT: CONDUCTANCE EQUATIONS;
    BEGIN INTEGER i,j,jj,jc,ka,kb,kc,kd,ke,kf,LL,oper,instr,run,g;  REAL aa,
    aaaa,aons,bons,con1,con2,cono,dcono,devf1,devf2,devf3,devf4,de,p,qq,qq1,rr,
    rLm11,rLm12,rLm21,rLm22,ssc1,ssc2,tabs,temp,vis,waveL,wac11,wac12,
    wL21,wL22,wu11,wu12,wu21,wu22,z1,z2;
        GO TO sw1[L];
X1:     READ qq1;
X2:     READ rLm11,wac11,wu11;
        READ rLm21,wL21,wu21
        FOR i:=1 STEP 1 UNTIL ji DO READ sc1[i];
        FOR i:=1 STEP 1 UNTIL ji DO READ c1[i];
        READ ssc1;
        IF L=16 THEN
        BEGIN
            READ rLm12,wac12,wu12;
            READ rLm22,wL22,wu22;
            FOR i:=1 STEP 1 UNTIL ji DO READ sc2[i];
            FOR i:=1 STEP 1 UNTIL ji DO READ c2[i];
            READ ssc2;  GO TO X4END;
X3:     FOR i:=1 STEP 1 UNTIL ji DO sc2[i]:=c2[i]:=0;
        devf3:=devf4:=0;
X4:     IF L=3∨L=4 THEN
        FOR i:=1 STEP 1 UNTIL ji DO READ dc[i];
        IF k<1 THEN GO TO X37
        ELSE IF k=1 THEN
        BEGIN
            READ devf1;  READ devf2;
            IF L≠16 THEN GO TO X7;
            READ devf3;  READ devf4END;
        IF k<2 THEN GO TO X7
        ELSE IF k>2 THEN GO TO X5;
        READ devf1;
        FOR i:=1 STEP 1 UNTIL ji DO READ dev21[i];
        devf2:=5555;
        IF L≠16 THEN GO TO X7;
        READ devf3;
        FOR i:=1 STEP 1 UNTIL ji DO READ dev22[i];
        devf4:=5555;
X5:     IF k<3 THEN GO TO X7
        ELSE IF k>3 THEN GO TO X6;
        FOR i:=2 STEP 1 UNTIL ji DO READ dev11[i];
        devf1:=5555;  READ devf2;
        IF L≠16 THEN GO TO X7;
        FOR i:=1 STEP 1 UNTIL ji DO READ dev12[i];
        devf3:=5555;  READ devf4;
X6:     IF k> 4 THEN GO TO X37
```

```
        ELSE IF k<4 THEN GO TO X7;
        FOR i:=1 STEP 1 UNTIL ji DO READ dev11[i];
        devf1:=devf2:=5555;
        FOR i:=1 STEP 1 UNTIL ji DO READ dev21[i];
        devf2:=5555;
        IF L≠16 THEN GO TO X7;
        FOR i:=1 STEP 1 UNTIL ji DO READ dev12[i];
        devf3:=devf4:=5555;
        FOR i:=1 STEP 1 UNTIL ji DO READ dev22[i];
X7:     FOR i:=1 STEP 1 UNTIL ji DO
        BEGIN
            IF k≤2 THEN
            BEGIN
                dev11[i]:=devf1Xsc1[i];
                dev12[i]:=devf3Xsc2[i]END;
            GO TO sw2[k];
X8:     dev21[i]:=devf2Xc1[i];
        dev22[i]:=devf4Xc2[i]
X9:     END;
        g:=jj:=0;
        GO TO sw3[L];
X10:    jj:=qq1;  GO TO X15;
X11:    jj:=jj+1;
X12:    jj:=jj+2;
X13:    jj:=jj+2;
X14:    jj:=jj+2;
X15:    FOR i:=1 STEP 1 UNTIL ji DO
        BEGIN
            y[i,1]:=sc1[i]−wac11Xssc1;
            IF(y[i,1]>wu11)∨(c1[i]<wL21)∨(c1[i]>wu21)THEN GO TO X16;
            IF L≠16 THEN GO TO X17;
            y[i,1]:=sc2[i]−wac12Xssc2;
            IF(y[i,1]>wu12)∨(c2[i]<wL22)∨(c2[i]>wu22)THEN
            BEGIN
X16:            FOR j:=1 STEP 1 UNTIL jj DO y[i,j]:=yer[i,j]:=0;
                GO TO X29END;
X17:        IF L>11 THEN GO TO X25;
            y[i,1]:=1000X(sc1[i]−ssc1)/c1[i];
            yer[i,1]:=1000X(sc1[i]+dev11[i]−ssc1)/(c1[i]−dev21[i]);
            g:=g+1;
            IF L>11 THEN GO TO X37
            ELSE IF L<11 THEN
            BEGIN
                yer[i,1]:=yer[i,1]−y[i,1];  GO TO X18END;
            y[i,1]:=Ln(y[i,1])/2.30259;
            yer[i,1]:=Ln(yer[i,1])/2.30259−y[i,1];
X18:        GO TO sw4[L];
X19:        y[i,7]:=c1[i]↑1.5;
            yer[i,7]:=(c1[i]+dev21[i])↑1.5−y[i,7];
X20:        y[i,6]:=dc[i]Xc1[i];  yer[i,6]:=dc[i]Xdev21[i];
            y[i,5]:=c1[i];  yer[i,5]:=dev21[i];
            y[i,4]:=dc[i]Xc1[i];  yer[i,4]:=dc[i]Xdev21[i];
            y[i,3]:=dc[i]Xc1[i]XLn(dc[i]Xc1[i])/2.30259;
```

```
             yer[i,3]:=dc[i]X(c1[i]+dev21[i]);
             yer[i,3[:=yer[i,3]XLn(yer[i,3[)/2.30259−y[i,3];
             y[i,2]:=sqrt(dc[i]Xc1[i]);
             yer[i,2[:=sqrt(dc[i]X(c1[i]+dev21[i]))−y[i,2];
             GO TO X29;
X21:         y[i,4]:=c1[i];  yer[i,4]:=dev21[i];
             y[i,3]:=c1[i]XLn[c1[i]];
             yer[i,3]:=(c1[i]+dev21[i])XLn(c1[i]+dev21[i])−y[i,3];
             y[i,3]:=y[i,3]/2.30259;  yer[i,3]:=yer[i,3]/2.30259;
X22:         y[i,2]:=sqrt(c1[i]);
             yer[i,2]:=sqrt(c1[i]+dev21[i])−y[i,2];
             GO TO X29;
X23:         FOR j:=2 STEP 1 UNTIL jj DO
             BEGIN
                p:=(j−1)X0.5;  y[i,j]:=c1[i]↑p;
                yer[i,j]:=(c1[i]+dev21[i])↑p−y[i,j]
             END;
             GO TO X29;
X24:         y[i,2]:=c1[i]↑qq1;
             yer[i,2]:=(c1[i]+dev21[i])↑qq1−y[i,2];
             GO TO X29;
X25:         IF L>16 THEN GO TO X29;
             ELSE IF L<16 THEN
             BEGIN
                y[i,1]:=sc1[i]−ssc1;
                yer[i,1]:=sc1[i]+dev11[i]−ssc1;
                IF L>15 THEN GO TO X37
                ELSE IF L<15 THEN
                BEGIN
                   yer[i,1]:=yer[i,1]−y[i,1];  GO TO X26END;
                y[i,1]:=Ln(y[i,1])/2.30259;
                yer[i,1]:=Ln(yer[i,1])/2.30259−y[i,1];
                GO TO X26END;
             y[i,1]:=(sc2[i]−ssc2)Xc1[i]/(sc1[i]−ssc1)Xc2[i];
             yer[i,1]:=(sc2[i]+dev12[i]−ssc2)X(c1[i]+dev21[i]);
             yer[i,1]:=yer[i,1]/((sc1[i]−dev11[i]−ssc1)X(c2[i]−dev22[i]))−y[i,1];
X26:         LL:=L−11;  g:=g+1;
             GO TO sw5[LL];
X27:         y[i,2]:=c1[i];  yer[i,2]:=dev21[i];  GO TO X29;
X28:         y[i,2]:=Ln(c1[i])/2.30259;
             yer[i,2]:=(Ln(c1[i]+dev21[i])/2.30259−y[i,2]
X29:         END;
             READ oper,instr;
             READ run,temp,waveL;
             READ ka,kb,kc,kd,ke,kf;
             READ jc;  feedp:=32;
             PUNCH feedp;
             PUNCH ka,kb,kc,kd,ke,kf;
             PUNCH jj;  PUNCH jc;  PUNCH k,L,m;
             PUNCH devf1,rLm11,wac11,wu11;
             FOR j:=2 STEP 1 UNTIL jj DO PUNCH devf2,rLm21,wL21,wu21;
             IF L=7 THEN
             BEGIN
```

```
        READ aons,bons,cono,dcono;
        FOR i:=1 STEP 1 UNTIL ji DO
        BEGIN
          aa:=y[i,1];
          y[i,1]:=cono-(aonsXcono+bons)Xsqrt(c1[i])-y[i,1];
          aaaa:=cono+dcono-(aonsX(cono+dcono)+bonsX(sqrt(c1[i]+dev21[i])));
          aaaa:=aaaa-yer[i,1]; yer[i,1]:=aaaa-aa-y[i,1];
          y[i,2]:=sqrt(c1[i]);
          yer[i,2]:=sqrt(c1[i]+dev21[i])-y[i,2]
        END;
        GO TO X30END;
      IF L=6 THEN GO TO X32;
      IF L=8 THEN GO TO X34;
      IF L≤9 THEN GO TO X36;
X30:  FOR i:=1 STEP 1 UNTIL ji DO
      FOR j:=1 STEP 1 UNTIL jj DO
      BEGIN
        PUNCH y[i,j];  PUNCH yer[i,j]
      END;
X31:  PUNCH g;  PUNCH oper,instr;
      PUNCH run,temp,waveL;  GO TO X37;
X32;  READ cono,con1,con2,z1,z2,vis,de,tabs;
      IF con2<0 THEN GO TO X37
      ELSE IF con2=0 THEN
      BEGIN
        qq:=2Xcono/(3X(con1+cono));
        GO TO X33END;
      qq:=z1Xz2X(con1+con2)/((z1+z2)X(z2Xcon1+z1Xcon2));
X33:  aons:=2.801X(₁₀6)Xz1Xz2Xqq/(sqrt((deXtabs)↑3)X(1+sqrt(qq)));
      bons:=41.25X(z1+z2)/(visXsqrt(deXtabs));
      PUNCH aons,bons,qq,z1,z2;  GO TO X31;
X34:  READ con1,con2,z1,z2,qq;
      rr:=qqX(z1+z2)/(z1Xz2);
      IF con1<0 THEN GO TO X37
      ELSE IF con1=0 THEN
      BEGIN
        con1:=con2X(1-rrXz1)/(z2Xrr-1);
        GO TO X35END;
      con2;=con1X(z2Xrr-1)/(1-rrXz1);
X35:  PUNCH con1,con2,z1,z2,qq;  GO TO X31;
X36:  READ cono,qq;  con1:=2Xcono/(qqX3)-cono;
      PUNCH cono,con1,qq;  GO TO X31
X37:END FBAAA;
X38:READ ji;  READ feedp;  READ k,L,m;
    FBAA(ji,feedp,k,L,m);
    GO TO X38;
```

CHAPTER X

KINETIC EQUATIONS

In this chapter a method is presented for processing kinetic data by means of which individual rate constants for almost any combination of heterogeneous or homogeneous opposed, side consecutive, chain, catalyzed, autocatalyzed, photochemical, pyrolytic or free radical reactions can be computed from concentration values of all species as a function of time.

High precision gas chromatographs and other analytical devices allow the determination of precise concentrations for many components in most heterogeneous and homogeneous systems. Frequently the unknown concentrations can be calculated from the known values in the reaction mechanism postulated.

Program 33 (*call word* GBAAA) is designed to compute the input information required for the *variable dimension expansion programs* (Chapter II) and the *variable dimension self-judgment programs* (Chapter III) from the raw data. The basic procedure, which will be described in detail later, is as follows:

Step 1. Program 33 is used to compute the input information for the *expansion program* from the raw data.

Step 2. The input information generated in Step 1 is processed with the *expansion program*.

Step 3. Information obtained from the *expansion program* is combined with the raw data and is processed by Program 33 to obtain the input information for the *self-judgment program*.

Step 4. Information from Step 3 is processed with the *self-judgment program* to obtain values for each of the rate constants in the reaction mechanism.

This method can be illustrated with the general reaction

$$i_1A + j_1B + l_1C + m_1D \underset{k_2}{\overset{k_1}{\rightleftharpoons}} i_2E + j_2F + l_2G + m_2H \quad \text{(with } k_1 > k_2\text{)} \quad (1)$$

One possible rate equation is:

$$- da_t/dt = k_1 a_t^{i_1} \cdot b_t^{j_1} \cdot c_t^{l_1} \cdot d_t^{m_1} - k_2 \cdot e_t^{i_2} \cdot f_t^{j_2} \cdot g_t^{l_2} \cdot h_t^{m_2} \qquad (2)$$
$$= k_1 Y_1 - k_2 X_1 \qquad (3)$$

Here the lower case letters subscripted with t denote the concentrations at time t of the components designated with the respective upper case letters.

The concentration expressions associated with each rate constant can be expanded heterogeneously in terms of known functions of the time $\gamma(t)$ and $\bar{\gamma}(t)$, thus:

$$Y_1 = \alpha_0 + \alpha_1 \gamma(t) + \alpha_2 (\gamma(t))^2 + \cdots \qquad (4)$$

and

$$X_1 = \beta_0 + \beta_1 \cdot \bar{\gamma}(t) + \beta_2 (\bar{\gamma}(t))^2 + \cdots \qquad (5)$$

The expansion coefficients ($\alpha_0, \alpha_1, \alpha_2, \cdots ; \beta_0, \beta_1, \beta_2$) in equations (4) and (5) can be computed for preselected limits of error in the concentrations and time by the use of one of the *variable dimension expansion programs* described in Chapter II. If equations (4) and (5) are substituted in equation (3), integration yields:

$$- a_t = k_1(\Gamma(t) - \Gamma(t_0)) - k_2(\bar{\Gamma}(t) - \bar{\Gamma}(t_0)) - a_0 \qquad (6)$$

with a_0 the concentration of A at $t = t_0$ and

$$\Gamma(t) - \Gamma(t_0) = \int_{t_0}^{t} Y_1 dt; \qquad \bar{\Gamma}(t) - \bar{\Gamma}(t_0) = \int_{t_0}^{t} X_1 dt.$$

Equation (6) is a three dimension equation which can be solved for the two slopes ($k_1, -k_2$) with the *variable dimension self-judgment programs* in Chapter III. The required input information is obtained by Program 33 from the raw data plus the expansion coefficients for equations (4) and (5). The *self-judgment program* yields the slopes ($k_1, -k_2$) and their *maximum permitted errors* with equation (6). Thus the limits of reliability for each value of each rate constant are precisely defined in terms of the pre-selected limits of error for each value of each observable. In the next section there are given the rules which must be applied to any system of reactions which is studied by this method.

RULES FOR APPLYING THE METHOD

For systems in which heterogeneous or photochemical reactions occur some of the concentration expressions such as Y_1 and X_1 in equation (3) may include surface parameters or quantum yields. Here such quantities will be considered "concentrations" as their mathematical treatment is similar to that of any other concentration term.

Rule 1. Write down the reaction mechanism to be tested. Except for a few simple reactions, the concentrations of *all species appearing in the reaction mechanism* at each time noted must be known.

Rule 2. Write down the minimum number of independent rate equations which together contain all the unknown rate constants.

Rule 3. Expand the concentration expressions associated with each rate constant, or with each group of rate constants, in terms of selected functions of the time. In Program 33 there are 25 functions and provisions are made for including an additional 20.

Rule 4. Substitute the *Functional forms* of the concentration expressions in each of the rate equations and integrate between appropriate limits.

Rule 5. Solve each of the integrated rate equations for the slopes which are the rate constants or groups of rate constants.

By this procedure the operator can select one or two functions of the time (Rule 3) which best suit his data.

APPLICATIONS OF THE NEW METHOD

To illustrate the power of the method there is outlined in this section the solution to two hypothetical problems which cannot be solved by the classical methods. It is assumed that concentrations of all species are known at each time noted. The symbols have already been defined.

PROBLEM 1

$$j_1 A + l_1 B \underset{k_2}{\overset{k_1}{\rightleftharpoons}} j_2 C + l_2 D \underset{k_4}{\overset{k_3}{\rightleftharpoons}} j_3 E + l_3 F$$

Two independent rate equations which together contain k_1, k_2, k_3 and k_4 are:

$$dc_t/dt = k_1 a_t^{j_1} b_t^{l_1} - k_2 c_t^{j_2} d_t^{l_2} + k_4 c_t^{j_3} f_t^{l_3} - k_3 c_t^{j_2} d_t^{l_2}$$
$$= k_1 a_t^{j_1} b_t^{l_1} - (k_2 + k_3) c_t^{j_2} d_t^{l_2} + k_4 e_t^{j_3} f_t^{l_3} \qquad (7)$$

and

$$da_t/dt = k_2 c_t^{j_2} d_t^{l_2} - k_1 a_t^{j_1} b_t^{l_1} \qquad (8)$$

Equations (7) and (8) must be solved for k_1, k_2, k_3 and k_4. The next step is to expand the three different concentration expressions thus:

$$X_1 = a_t^{j_1} b_t^{l_1} = \alpha_0 + \alpha_1 \gamma(t) + \alpha_2 (\gamma(t))^2 + \cdots \qquad (9)$$
$$Y_1 = c_t^{j_2} d_t^{l_2} = \beta_0 + \beta_1 \bar{\gamma}(t) + \beta_2 (\bar{\gamma}(t))^2 + \cdots \qquad (10)$$
$$Z_1 = e_t^{j_3} f_t^{l_3} = \delta_0 + \delta_1 \bar{\gamma}(t) + \delta_2 (\bar{\bar{\gamma}}(t))^2 + \cdots \qquad (11)$$

Substituting these expansions in equations (7) and (8) and integrating we obtain:

$$- c_t = k_1(\Gamma(t) - \Gamma(t_0)) - (k_2 + k_3)(\overline{\Gamma}(t) - \overline{\Gamma}(t_0)) + k_4(\overline{\overline{\Gamma}}(t) - \overline{\overline{\Gamma}}(t_0)) - c_0 \tag{12}$$

and

$$- a_t = k_2(\overline{\Gamma}(t) - \overline{\Gamma}(t_0)) - k_1(\Gamma(t) - \Gamma(t_0)) - a_0 \tag{13}$$

These two independent equations can be solved with the *variable dimension self-judgment program* for the slopes which yield k_1, k_2, k_3 and k_4.

The duplicate values for k_2 provide a sensitive test of the validity of the mechanism.

PROBLEM 2

The reaction:

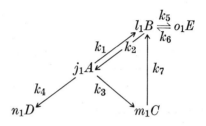

C acts as an autocatalyst for the reaction $j_1A \longrightarrow n_1D$. Here we will assume that the autocatalyst's role is accurately given by the expression:

$dd_t/dt = k_4F(c_t) \cdot a_t^{j_1}$, where $F(c_t)$ is a known function.

Two independent rate equations which contain all the rate constants are:

$$db_t/dt = k_1a_t^{j_1} - k_2b_t^{l_1} + k_7c_t^{m_1} - k_5b_t^{l_1} + k_6e_t^{o_1} \tag{14}$$

and

$$da_t/dt = - k_1a_t^{j_1} + k_2b_t^{l_1} - k_3c_t^{m_1} - k_4F(c_t)a_t^{j_1} \tag{15}$$

The solution of equations (14) and (15) requires five *expansions* as follows:

$$Y_1 = a_t^{j_1} = \alpha_0 + \alpha_1(\gamma(t)) + \alpha_2(\gamma(t))^2 + \cdots \tag{16}$$

$$Y_2 = b_t^{l_1} = \beta_0 + \beta_1(\overline{\gamma}(t)) + \beta_2(\overline{\gamma}(t))^2 + \cdots \tag{17}$$

$$Y_3 = c_t^{m_1} = \delta_0 + \delta_1(\overline{\overline{\gamma}}(t)) + \delta_2(\overline{\overline{\gamma}}(t))^2 + \cdots \tag{18}$$

$$Y_4 = e_t^{o_1} = \tilde{\alpha}_0 + \tilde{\alpha}_1(\gamma'(t)) + \tilde{\alpha}_2(\gamma'(t))^2 + \cdots \tag{19}$$

$$Y_5 = F(c_t)a_t^{j_1} = \tilde{\beta}_0 + \tilde{\beta}_1\gamma''(t) + \tilde{\beta}_2(\gamma''(t))^2 + \cdots \tag{20}$$

Substitution of these expressions in equations (14) and (15), and integration yield:

$$- b_t = k_1((\Gamma(t) - \Gamma(t_0)) - k_2(\overline{\Gamma}(t) - \overline{\Gamma}(t_0)) + k_7(\overline{\overline{\Gamma}}(t) - \overline{\overline{\Gamma}}(t_0))$$
$$- k_5(\overline{\Gamma}(t) - \overline{\Gamma}(t_0)) + k_6(\Gamma'(t) - \Gamma'(t_0)) - b_0 \tag{21}$$

and

$$- a_t = - k_1(\Gamma(t) - \Gamma(t_0)) + k_2(\bar{\Gamma}(t) - \bar{\Gamma}(t_0)) - k_3(\bar{\bar{\Gamma}}(t)$$
$$- \bar{\bar{\Gamma}}(t_0))$$
$$- k_4(\Gamma''(t) - \Gamma''(t_0)) - a_0 \qquad\qquad (22)$$

Equations (21) and (22) can be solved for their slopes and the associated *maximum permitted errors* with the *variable dimension self-judgment program* as described in Chapter III. The duplicate values for k_1, k_2 and k_4 provide a sensitive test of the hypothesis.

SECONDARY CORRECTION FACTORS

Errors in the concentrations of reactants and products arising from non-ideality or from the neglect of density–temperature–volume changes can be eliminated by using Program 5 (*call word* EAAAA, Volume I) to compute correct concentrations from raw data.

INSTRUMENT RELIABILITY FACTORS

In Program 33 RLMT,WLT,WUT and DEVFT (or DEVT(I)) are associated exclusively with the time (T(I)). RLMC(J),WLC(J),WUC(J), and DEVFC(J) (or DEVC(I,J)) are associated with the Jth concentration (C(I,J)). RLM denotes the *measured limit of reliability* for the designated observable.

WL and WU are the *lowest* and *highest reliable values* for the designated observable.

The form in which the *maximum permitted deviations* (DEVFT or DEVI(I); DEVFC(J) or DEVC(I,J)) are entered is determined by the value of K (see Input Commands for Programs 33). DEVF is the fractional part of each value of the designated observable. DEVC(I,J) is the *maximum permitted deviation* in C(I,J), the Ith value of the Jth concentration.

FAIL–SAFE PROCEDURE

In Program 33 (*call word* GBAAA) the *fail–safe procedure* is applied in turn to the time (T(I)) and to each of the concentrations (C(I,J)) in order to discard unreliable sets of conjugate data. If there is one item of unreliable data in a set, all items in the set are equated to zero.

STATISTICAL BIAS

As the *self-judgment principle* is not applied to the Feeder Program 33 (*call word* GBAAA) there are no special devices incorporated to reduce bias. Input information generated by Program 33 is processed with Programs 25, 325, 26, and 326. These programs contain the three-step normalization procedure described in Chapter III.

The *lowest reliable values* for all observables, designated by WLT and WLC(J) must not be set equal to zero.

INPUT COMMANDS FOR PROGRAM 33 (*Call Word* GBAAA)

The input commands for Program 33 (*call word* GBAAA) are conveniently classified into several classes.

1. Dimension Commands

The storage capacity required for Program 33 is determined by the values selected *before compilation* for JQ,JR,JE,JN,JT and JP.

JR—The maximum number of "concentrations" in each set of conjugate data. For the mechanism $A \to B \to C$, three "concentrations" (A, B, and C) will be entered in each set. The value of JR cannot be less than that for NC (see section 2).

JQ—The maximum number of sets of conjugate data that can be processed with the program. JQ must be a multiple of four and it must not be less than JI (see below).

JE—The maximum number of expansions to be performed. JE cannot be less than NEX (see section 3).

JP—The maximum dimension of the rate equations for which ordinates are to be computed. (*Note:* JP = JE + 1).

JN—The maximum number of independent rate equations for which ordinates are to be computed.

JT—The maximum dimension of the functional form of the "concentration" terms. JT cannot be less than the maximum value of JJ(I) (see section 3).

JI—The number of sets of conjugate data which are to be entered in the input format. JI is entered *after compilation* and it must be a multiple of four. If nine sets of conjugate data are to be processed JI is set equal to 12 and three zero-sets are entered.

2. Input Format Commands

The values entered for K, NC and JI (defined above) together determine the format in which the raw data are to be entered. The value of K defines the form in which the *maximum permitted deviations* are to be entered (see "Instrument Reliability Factors").

K=1 DEVFT; DEVFC(J)	K=3 DEVT(I); DEVFC(J)
K=2 DEVFT; DEVC(I,J)	K=4 DEVT(I); DEVC(I,J)

NC—is the number of "concentrations" entered in each set of conjugate data. For example if the reaction $A + B \overset{k_1}{\rightleftharpoons} C \rightarrow D$ with C autocatalyzing the first forward reaction is being studied, NC = 5 to denote the concentrations of A, B, C and D plus the function which describes the autocatalytic action of C.

3. Expansion Commands

PROGN, NEX, LEX1(I), LL(I), QI(I), JJ(I) and LEX2(J,I) together determine the number of *expansions*, the composition of the "concentration term" for each expansion, the kind of *expansion* and the dimensions.

PROGN—The number of the *variable dimension expansion program* to be used in processing output information from Program 33. If PROGN = 25 or 325, the output information generated by Program 33 can be processed directly with either program.

NEX—The number of *expansions* to be made. NEX cannot be greater than the dimension command, JE.

LEX1(I)—The number of "concentrations per *set of conjugate data*" to be used in the computation of the Ith "concentration term" whose functional form is to be computed in the Ith *expansion*. Note that LEX1(I) cannot be greater than NC which is defined in section 2.

LL(I) and QI(I)—define the type of expansion to be performed with Program 26 or 326 for the Ith concentration term, (Y = C(J,I))

For

LL(I) = 1   X = T(J) * QI(I)

LL(I) = 2   X = EXP(T(J) − QI(I))

LL(I) = 3   Function of time (T(J)) and QI(I) can be inserted by re-
LL(I) = 4   placing statements 47, 48 and 49. Statements 67, 68 and 69
LL(I) = 5   should be replaced by the integrated forms of the selected functions. DEVX and FB must also be replaced (see Computer Method of Solution).

With Programs 25 and 325 the equation solved is: $Y = b + S_1 X + S_2 X^2 + \cdots$

(TJ) and C(J,I) are the times and "concentration expression" associated with the Jth *set of conjugate data.*

JJ(I)—The dimension of the Ith expansion. JJ(I) cannot exceed the dimension command, JT.

LEX2(J,I)—denotes the concentrations to be used in computing the Ith "concentration expression." For the reaction $A + B \rightleftharpoons C$ there are two concentration expressions ([A] [B] and [C]). If the three concentrations are entered in the order, [A], [B], [C], the expansion commands would be:

PROGN = 325.0 or 25.0
NEX = 2
LEX1(1) = 2; LL(1) = 1 or 2; QI(1) = selected index; JJ(1) = dimension
LEX2(1,1) = 1
LEX2(2,1) = 2
LEX1(2) = 1; LL(2) = 1 or 2; QI(2) = selected index; JJ(2) = dimension
LEX2(1,2) = 1.

4. Rate Equation Commands

PROGN, NEQ, LEQ1(I) and LEQ2(J,I) together define the number of independent rate equations and their composition.

PROGN—the number of the *variable dimension self-judgment program* (26 or 326) used in solving the integrated rate equations for the specific rate constants.

NEQ—the number of independent rate equations to be solved with output information generated by Program 33 (*call word* GBAAA) and the *variable dimension self-judgment program*.

LEQ1(I)—the dimension of the Ith independent rate equation.

LEQ2(J,I)—denotes the "concentration expression" to be used in solving the Ith independent rate equation. For instance, if the reaction is:

$$A + B \underset{k_2}{\overset{k_1}{\rightleftharpoons}} C \overset{k_3}{\underset{}{\rightarrow}} D$$

there are four concentrations (A, B, C and D) to be entered and three concentration expressions ($[A][B]$, $[C]$ and $[D]$) to be expanded in terms of time. The independent rate equations are:

$$-d[A]/dt = k_1[A][B] - k_2[C] - k_4[D] \qquad (1)$$

$$-d[C]/dt = (k_3 + k_2)[C] - k_1[A][B] \qquad (2)$$

If the concentrations are entered in the order A, B, C, D the *expansion commands* are:

PROGN = 325.0 or 25.0
NEX = 4
LEX1(1) = 2; LL(1) = 1 or 2; QI(1) = selected index; JJ(1) = dimension
LEX2(1,1) = 1
LEX2(2,1) = 2
LEX1(2) = 1; LL(2) = 1 or 2; QI(2) = selected index; JJ(2) = dimension
LEX2(1,2) = 3
LEX1(3) = 1; LL(3) = 1 or 2; QI(3) = selected index; JJ(3) = dimension
LEX2(1,3) = 4

The rate equation commands are:

PROGN = 326.0 or 26.0
NEQ = 2
LEQ1(1) = 4
LEQ2(1,1) = 1
LEQ2(2,1) = 1
LEQ2(3,1) = 2
LEQ2(4,1) = 3   *Note:* The labels LEQ2(1,1) and LEQ2(1,2) refer to the
LEQ1(2) = 3   designated *concentrations.*
LEQ2(1,2) = 3
LEQ2(2,2) = 2
LEQ2(3,2) = 3

5. Reject–Restore Commands

The values entered for KA,KB,KC,KD,KE and KF together determine which sets of conjugate data are to be killed or ignored. Killed sets are eliminated from the memory and their status cannot be reviewed in the restore parts of the *self-judgment principle* in either the *expansion* or *self-judgment programs. Ignored sets* are not used during the first cycle, but in the application of the *self-judgment principle* they are reviewed in the two restore parts. As the *reject–restore commands* are not executed in Program 33 they can be changed in the output format. Here the following abbreviations are used:

Kill(KB,KC)—the KBth and KCth sets are to be killed.
Ignore(KB–KC; KD–KE)—the KBth to KCth and the KDth to KEth sets are to be ignored.

KA	Comment	KA	Comment
− 1	No sets are ignored or killed	11	Kill(KB,KC,KD)
0	Ignore(KB–KC)	12	Kill(KB,KC,KD,KE)
1	Ignore(KB)	13	Kill(KB,KC,KD,KE,KF)
2	Ignore(KB,KC)	14	Kill(KB–KC;KD–KE)
3	Ignore(KB,KC,KD)	15	No sets are ignored or killed
4	Ignore(KB,KC,KD,KE)	16	Kill(KB–KC)
5	Ignore(KB,KC,KD,KE,KF)	17	Kill(KB)
6	Ignore(KB–KC;KD–KE)	18	Kill(KB);Ignore(KC)
7	No sets are ignored or killed	19	Kill(KB,KD);Ignore(KC)
8	Kill(KB–KC)	20	Kill(KB,KD);Ignore(KC,KE)
9	Kill(KB)	21	Kill(KB,KD,KF);Ignore(KC,KE)
10	Kill(KB,KC)	22	Kill(KB–KC);Ignore(KD–KE)

6. Other Commands

Some input commands for the *expansion* (25 or 325) and *self-judgment* (26 or 326) programs are not entered in the input information for Program

33, but they appear in the output information. L, M, JC and M6 are set equal to 3, 0, 3 and 1 respectively. With Program 25 or 325 the concentrations are expanded heterogeneously against the selected function of the time (see Expansion Commands).

COMPUTER PROCEDURE OF SOLUTION

Here no attempt will be made to describe the commands executed by the computer in Program 33 (*call word* GBAAA). Instead the procedure for solving a hypothetical problem will be discussed. *Problem:* Compute all the specific rate constants for the following reaction:

$$aA + bB \xrightarrow{k_1} cC \underset{k_6}{\overset{k_2}{\rightleftharpoons}} \begin{array}{c} eE + S \xrightarrow{k_3} fF \\ \\ dD \xrightarrow{k_5} gG \xrightarrow{k_4} hH \end{array}$$

Here S denotes a surface parameter. A, B, C, D, E, F, G and H are gaseous or liquid materials. The reaction $D \rightarrow G$ is catalyzed by F and its role is described by the equation:

$$-dD_t/dt = k_5 G_t^g \log_{10} E_t - k_6 C_t^c$$

Here D_t denotes the concentration of D at time t.

The experimental information required to obtain the specific rate constants consists of only the concentrations (A_t, B_t, C_t, D_t, E_t, F_t, G_t and H_t) and the surface parameter (S_t) at each time (t) noted. The results of applying the five rules mentioned earlier are:

Rule 1. The above reaction mechanism is proposed as a possible answer.

Rule 2. Four independent rate equations which contain all the specific rate constants are:

$$- dC_t/dt = (k_2 + k_6)C_t^c - k_1 A_t^a B_t^b - k_7 G_t^g \tag{1}$$

$$- dG_t/dt = (k_4 + k_7) G_t^g - k_5 D_t^d \log_{10} E_t \tag{2}$$

$$dF_t/dt = k_3 E_t^e S_t + k_8 H_t^h \tag{3}$$

$$- dD_t/dt = k_5 G_t^g \log_{10} E_t - k_6 C_t^c \tag{4}$$

The "concentrations" in each set of conjugate data are A_t, B_t, C_t, D_t, E_t, F_t, G_t, H_t, S_t and $\log_{10} E_t$. Thus NC = 10 and NEQ = 4. There are six "concentration terms" to be expanded (NEX = 6). These are C_t^c, $A_t^a B_t^b$, G_t^g, $D_t^d \log_{10} E_t$, $E_t^e S_t$ and H_t^h. The "concentrations" and "concentration terms" are numbered in the order they are written. Expansion and rate equation commands are selected. Here it is arbitrarily assumed that all expansions will be of the first type with index (QI(I)) equal to one, and that JJ(I), the dimension of each expansion, is four.

Expansion Commands

NEX = 6

$\left.\begin{array}{l} \text{LEX1(1)} = 1;\ \text{LL(1)} = 1;\ \text{QI(1)} = 1.0;\ \text{JJ(1)} = 4 \\ \text{LEX2(1,1)} = 3 \end{array}\right\}$ First expansion

$\left.\begin{array}{l} \text{LEX1(2)} = 2;\ \text{LL(2)} = 1;\ \text{QI(2)} = 1.0;\ \text{JJ(2)} = 4 \\ \text{LEX2(1,2)} = 1 \\ \text{LEX2(2,2)} = 2 \end{array}\right\}$ Second expansion

$\left.\begin{array}{l} \text{LEX1(3)} = 1;\ \text{LL(3)} = 1;\ \text{QI(3)} = 1.0;\ \text{JJ(3)} = 4 \\ \text{LEX2(1,3)} = 7 \end{array}\right\}$ Third expansion

$\left.\begin{array}{l} \text{LEX1(4)} = 2;\ \text{LL(4)} = 1;\ \text{QI(4)} = 1.0;\ \text{JJ(4)} = 4 \\ \text{LEX2(1,4)} = 4 \\ \text{LEX2(2,4)} = 10 \end{array}\right\}$ Fourth expansion

$\left.\begin{array}{l} \text{LEX1(5)} = 2;\ \text{LL(5)} = 1;\ \text{QI(5)} = 1.0;\ \text{JJ(5)} = 4 \\ \text{LEX2(1,5)} = 5 \\ \text{LEX2(2,5)} = 9 \end{array}\right\}$ Fifth expansion

$\left.\begin{array}{l} \text{LEX1(6)} = 1;\ \text{LL(6)} = 1;\ \text{QI(6)} = 1.0;\ \text{JJ(6)} = 4 \\ \text{LEX2(1,6)} = 8 \end{array}\right\}$ Sixth expansion

Rate Equation Commands

LEQ1(I) is the dimension of the Ith independent rate equation. LEQ2(1,I) denotes the concentration on the left side of the Ith rate equation.

NEQ = 4

$\left.\begin{array}{ll} \text{LEQ1(1)} = 4 & \text{(Dimension)} \\ \text{LEQ2(1,1)} = 3 & \text{(3rd concentration)} \\ \text{LEQ2(2,1)} = 1 & \text{(1st concentration expression)} \\ \text{LEQ2(3,1)} = 2 & \text{(2nd concentration expression)} \\ \text{LEQ2(4,1)} = 3 & \text{(3rd concentration expression)} \end{array}\right\}$ First rate equation

$\left.\begin{array}{ll} \text{LEQ1(2)} = 3 & \text{(Dimension)} \\ \text{LEQ2(1,2)} = 7 & \text{(7th concentration)} \\ \text{LEQ2(2,2)} = 3 & \text{(3rd concentration expression)} \\ \text{LEQ2(3,2)} = 4 & \text{(4th concentration expression)} \end{array}\right\}$ Second rate equation

$\left.\begin{array}{ll} \text{LEQ1(3)} = 3 & \text{(Dimension)} \\ \text{LEQ2(1,3)} = 6 & \text{(6th concentration)} \\ \text{LEQ2(2,3)} = 5 & \text{(5th concentration expression)} \\ \text{LEQ2(3,3)} = 6 & \text{(6th concentration expression)} \end{array}\right\}$ Third rate equation

$\left.\begin{array}{ll} \text{LEQ1(4)} = 3 & \text{(Dimension)} \\ \text{LEQ2(1,4)} = 4 & \text{(4th concentration)} \\ \text{LEQ2(2,4)} = 4 & \text{(4th concentration expression)} \\ \text{LEQ3(3,4)} = 1 & \text{(1st concentration expression)} \end{array}\right\}$ Fourth rate equation

The input deck is then assembled (see input format for Program 33).

Rule 3. With PROGN = 325.0 or 25.0 the input information, which includes the expansion and rate equation commands (see above), is processed with Program 33 (*call word* GBAAA). The input information for the *expansion program* (25 or 325) is generated for each of the six expansions. WAVEL in the output of Program 33 designates the number of the expansion (Step 3) or the number of the rate equation (Step 5). The expansion coefficients (SL(J),J = 1, 2, 3, 4) and their *maximum permitted errors* (DEVSL(J), J = 1, 2, 3, 4) are obtained with Program 25 or 325 (see Chapter II) for each of the six expansions.

Rule 4. The expansion coefficients (SL(J)) and their *maximum permitted errors* (DEVSL(J)) for each expansion are added to the input information for Program 33 and PROGN is changed to 26.0 or 326.0. Then the input information for the *self-judgment program* (26 or 326) is generated for each rate equation. WAVEL (see Input Format for Programs 26 and 326—Chapter III) denotes the integrated rate equation.

Rule 5. The output information generated by Program 33 (Rule 4) is processed with the *self-judgment program*. The parameters (SL(J)) and the associated *maximum permitted errors* (DEVSL(J)) are related to the specific rate constants (k_1, k_2, k_3, k_4, k_5, k_6, k_7 and k_8) and their *maximum permitted errors* (denoted Δk_1, etc.) as follows:

First Rate Equation
$$k_1 = SL(2); \quad \Delta k_1 = DEVSL(2); \quad k_7 = SL(3); \quad \Delta k_7 = DEVSL(3)$$
$$k_2 + k_6 = -SL(1); \quad \Delta k_2 + \Delta k_6 = -DEVSL(1)$$

SL(4) = arbitrary integration constant.

Second Rate Equation
$$k_5 = SL(2); \quad \Delta k_5 = DEVSL(2); \quad k_4 + k_7 = -SL(1);$$
$$\Delta k_4 + \Delta k_7 = -DEVSL(1)$$

SL(3) is an arbitrary integration constant.

Third Rate Equation
$$k_3 = SL(1); \quad \Delta k_3 = DEVSL(1); \quad k_8 = SL(2); \quad \Delta k_8 = DEVSL(2)$$

SL(3) is an arbitrary integration constant.

Fourth Rate Equation
$$k_5 = -SL(1); \quad \Delta k_5 = -DEVSL(1); \quad k_6 = SL(2); \quad \Delta k_6 = DEVSL(2)$$

SL(3) is an arbitrary integration constant.

k_4 and Δk_4 are calculated from the information for the first and second rate equations. k_2 and Δk_2 are calculated from information for the first and fourth rate equations. The duplicate values for k_5 (second and fourth rate equations) provide a consistency test for the postulated mechanism.

In computing the input information with Program 33 for the *expansion* (25 or 325) and *self-judgment* (26 or 326) programs the *instrument reliability factors* are used in the calculation of *maximum permitted deviations* for each value of each ordinate. (*Note:* Input for Program 25 or 325 has $K = 4$ inserted in Program 33). Thus the *maximum permitted errors* in the specific rate constants are determined by the *instrument reliability factors* for the raw data and the accepted sets of conjugate information which remain after processing with Program 26 or 326 has been completed.

In Program 33 (*call word* GBAAA) there are provisions for incorporating three additional functions of the time (T(I)) and the expansion index (QI(J)). A careful study of the two existing functions (T(I) ** QI(J) and EXP(T(I)–QI(J))) should be made before introduction of the new functions. A general outline of the procedure is as follows:

Step 1. One of the three statements numbered 47, 48 and 49 is replaced by the selected function of T(I) and QI(J), denoted by X(I). In the expansion program equation (A) is solved for the expansion coefficients (SL(JP), JP = 1, 2, ⋯ N4)

$$Y = SL(N4) + SL(1) * X(I) + SL(2) * (X(I) ** 2.0)) + \ldots \qquad (A)$$

Y is the concentration term being expanded. Next the companion statement (DEVX(I) = 0.0) is replaced by the appropriate function of X(I), T(I), QI(J) and DEVT(I). The *maximum permitted deviation* in T(I) is DEVT(I).

Step 2. The corresponding statement numbered 67, 68 or 69 and the companion statement (FB = 1.0) are replaced by the appropriate functions of SL(JP), T(I), DEVT(I), QI(J) and DEVSL(JP). JP must not equal N4. The statements between statements 65 and 63 should be examined carefully before any changes are made. In this section of the program the left side of equation (A) is being integrated with respect to T(I).

INPUT FORMAT FOR PROGRAM 33

Here no attempt will be made to define the *expansion* and *rate equation commands* (see Input Commands for Program 33 and Computer Procedure of Solution).

STATEMENT	COMMENT
READ,PROGN,FEEDP	PROGN = 25.0 or 325.0 (*expansion*) and 26.0 or 326.0 (*self-judgment*).
READ,JI	Number of *sets of conjugate data* being processed. JI must be a multiple of four (see Dimension Command).

STATEMENT	COMMENT
READ,K,NC,NEX,NEQ	K—Input format command (*Maximum permitted deviations*). NC—Number of concentrations per *set of conjugate data*. NEX—Number of expansions. NEQ—Number of independent rate equations.
READ,DEVFT OR READ,DEVT(I),DEVT(I+1),DEVT(I+2),DEVT(I+3) (I = 1, 5, · · · JI − 3)	*Maximum permitted deviation in the time (T(I)).*
READ,DEVFC(J) (for J = 1, 2, · · · NC) OR READ,DEVC(I,J),DEVC(I+1,J),DEVC(I+2,J),DEVC(I+3,J) (I = 1, 5, · · · JI–3 for each J = 1, 2, · · · NC in turn)	*Maximum permitted deviations for "concentrations".*
READ,RLMT,WLT,WUT	*Instrument reliability factors for T(I).*
READ,T(I),T(I+1),T(I+2),T(I+3) (for I = 1, 5, · · · JI–3)	Times.
READ,RLMC(J),WLC(J),WUC(J)	*Instrument reliability factors for C(I,J).*
READ,QQ(J)	For $2C(I,J) \overset{K}{\to} D$, QQ(J) = 2.0.
READ,C(I,J),C(I+1,J),C(I+2,J),C(I+3,J) (I = 1, 5, · · · JI–3)	Jth "concentration".

> *Note:* These three statements are executed in turn for J = 1, 2, · · · NC.

READ,LEX1(I),LL(I),QI(I),JJ(I) READ,LEX2(J,I)	Expansion commands.

> These statements are executed for J = 1, 2, · · · LEX1(I) for each I = 1, 2, · · · NEX in turn.

READ,LEQ1(I) READ,LEQ2(J,I)	Rate equation commands.

> These statements are executed for J = 1, 2, · · · LEQ1(I) for each I = 1, 2, · · · NEQ in turn.

READ,OPER,INSTR READ,RUN,TEMP,WAVEL READ,KA,KB,KC,KD,KE,KF (Entered NEX times)	Identification. *Reject–restore commands.*

STATEMENT	COMMENT
READ,SL(JP),DEVSL(J)	{ Expansion coefficients (SL(JP)) and *maximum permitted errors* (DEVSL(JP)).

Entered for JP = 1, 2, · · · LEQ1(I) for each I = 1, 2, · · · NEQ in turn only if PROGN = 26.0 or 326.0

| READ,KA,KB,KC,KD,KE,KF
(Entered NEQ times) | *Reject–restore commands.* |

OUTPUT FORMATS FOR PROGRAM 33

The output information generated by Program 33 with PROGN = 25.0 or 325.0 is compatible with the *variable dimension expansion* program discussed in Chapter II. Y(I,JJ), C1(I) and C2(I) which appear in the input formats for Programs 25 and 325 (see Chapter II) have the following meanings.

Y(I,JJ)—is the Ith value for the "concentration expression" designated by WAVEL.

C1(I)—equals unity for all I as L = 3 (*heterogeneous expansion*)

C2(I)—the Ith value for the arbitrary function of T(I) and QI(J) against which the Y(I,JJ) are to be expanded (see Computer Procedure of Solution).

Output obtained from Program 33 with PROGN equal to 26.0 or 326.0 is compatible with the *variable dimension self-judgment* programs described in Chapter III. Y(I,J) and YER(I,J) are the Ith values for the Jth ordinate and its related *maximum permitted error* for the integrated rate equation designated by WAVEL.

RELIABILITY LIMITS FOR PROGRAM 33

As Program 33 is a feeder program, no special devices have been incorporated to reduce round-off error. Unless the specified maximum word size for the computer is exceeded, normal round-off error cannot occur.

FORTRAN FOR PROGRAM NUMBER 33
CALL WORD GBAAA

```
DIMENSION DEVT(JQ),DEVFC(JR),DEVC(JQ,JR),T(JQ),RLMC(JR)
DIMENSION WLC(JR),WUC(JR),QQ(JR),C(JQ,JR),LEX1(JE),LL(JE)
DIMENSION QI(JE),JJ(JE),LEX2(JR,JE),LEQ1(JN)
DIMENSION LEQ2(JP,JN),CE(JQ,JP),CER(JQ,JP),DEVX(JQ)
DIMENSION SL(JT),Y(JQ,JP),YER(JQ,JP),X(JQ),DEVSL(JT)
1 READ,PROGN,FEEDP
NQR=PROGN
IF(NQR-300)2,1,3
3 NQR=NQR-300
2 NQR=NQR-24
READ,JI
ZAP=99.99
M6=1
JC=3
M=0
L=3
READ,K,NC,NEX,NEQ
IF(K-2)83,83,5
83 READ,DEVFT
GO TO 6
5 DO 4 I=1,JI,4
4 READ,DEVT(I),DEVT(I+1),DEVT(I+2),DEVT(I+3)
6 GO TO (7,8,7,8),K
7 DO 9 J=1,NC
9 READ,DEVFC(J)
GO TO 11
8 DO 10 J=1,NC
DO 10 I=1,JI,4
10 READ,DEVC(I,J),DEVC(I+1,J),DEVC(I+2,J),DEVC(I+3,J)
11 READ,RLMT,WLT,WUT
DO 12 I=1,JI,4
12 READ,T(I),T(I+1),T(I+2),T(I+3)
DO 13 J=1,NC
READ,RLMC(J),WLC(J),WUC(J)
READ,QQ(J)
DO 13 I=1,JI,4
13 READ,C(I,J),C(I+1,J),C(I+2,J),C(I+3,J)
DO 14 I=1,JI
IF(T(I)-WLT)15,16,16
16 IF(T(I)-WUT)17,17,15
15 T(I)=0.0
DO 18 J=1,NC
18 C(I,J)=0.0
GO TO 14
17 DO19 J=1,NC
IF(C(I,J)-WLC(J))15,20,20
20 IF(C(I,J)-WUC(J))21,21,15
21 GO TO (22,19,22,19),K
22 DEVC(I,J)=DEVFC(J)*C(I,J)
19 CONTINUE
IF(K-2)23,23,14
23 DEVT(I)=DEVFT*T(I)
14 CONTINUE
DO 24 I=1,NEX
READ,LEX1(I),LL(I),QI(I),JJ(I)
N=LEX1(I)
DO 24 J=1,N
24 READ,LEX2(J,I)
DO 25 I=1,NEQ
```

```
READ,LEQ1(I)
N=LEQ1(I)
DO 25 J=1,N
25 READ,LEQ2(J,I)
READ,OPER,INSTR
READ,RUN,TEMP,WAVEL
DO 28 I=1,JI
DO 28 J=1,NEX
IF(T(I))29,29,30
29 CE(I,J)=0.0
CER(I,J)=0.0
GO TO 28
30 CE(I,J)=1.0
CER(I,J)=1.0
28 CONTINUE
DO 32 I=1,JI
IF(T(I))32,32,33
33 DO 32 J=1,NEX
N=LEX1(J)
DO 35 JP=1,NC
DO 35 JPP=1,N
IF(JP-LEX2(JPP,J))35,34,35
34 CE(I,J)=CE(I,J)*(C(I,JP)**QQ(JP))
CER(I,J)=CER(I,J)*((C(I,JP)+DEVC(I,JP))**QQ(JP))
35 CONTINUE
CER(I,J)=CER(I,J)-CE(I,J)
32 CONTINUE
WL1=1000000.0
WU1=-1000000.0
DO 36 I=1,JI
IF(T(I))36,36,37
37 DO 36 J=1,NEX
IF(WL1-CE(I,J))38,38,39
39 WL1=CE(I,J)
38 IF(WU1-CE(I,J))40,36,36
40 WU1=CE(I,J)
36 CONTINUE
K=4
DO 41 J=1,NEX
DO 42 I=1,JI
X(I)=0.0
DEVX(I)=0.0
IF(T(I))42,42,43
43 N=LL(J)
GO TO (45,46,47,48,49),N
45 X(I)=T(I)**QI(J)
DEVX(I)=(T(I)+DEVT(I))**QI(J)-X(I)
GO TO 42
46 X(I)=EXP(T(I)-QI(J))
DEVX(I)=EXP(T(I)+DEVT(I)-QI(J))-X(I)
GO TO 42
47 X(I)=0.0
DEVX(I)=0.0
GO TO 42
48 X(I)=0.0
DEVX(I)=0.0
GO TO 42
49 X(I)=0.0
DEVX(I)=0.0
42 CONTINUE
WL2=1000000.0
WU2=-1000000.0
```

```
     DO 53 I=1,JI
     IF(T(I))53,53,86
  86 IF(WL2-X(I))50,50,51
  51 WL2=X(I)
  50 IF(WU2-X(I))52,53,53
  52 WU2=X(I)
  53 CONTINUE
     READ,KA,KB,KC,KD,KE,KF
     GO TO (54,41),NQR
  54 IF(J-1)1,84,85
  84 PUNCH,JI
  85 PUNCH,PROGN,FEEDP
     PUNCH,KA,KB,KC,KD,KE,KF
     PUNCH,JJ(J)
     PUNCH,JC
     PUNCH,M6
     PUNCH,K,L,M
     PUNCH,RLMT,WL1,WU1
     PUNCH,RLMT,WL2,WU2
     DO 55 I=1,JI,4
  55 PUNCH,CER(I,J),CER(I+1,J),CER(I+2,J),CER(I+3,J)
     DO 56 I=1,JI,4
  56 PUNCH,DEVX(I),DEVX(I+1),DEVX(I+2),DEVX(I+3)
     DO 57 I=1,JI,4
  57 PUNCH,CE(I,J),CE(I+1,J),CE(I+2,J),CE(I+3,J)
     WW=1.0
     DO 58 I=1,JI,4
  58 PUNCH,WW,WW,WW,WW
     DO 59 I=1,JI,4
  59 PUNCH,X(I),X(I+1),X(I+2),X(I+3)
     WAVEL=J
     PUNCH,OPER,INSTR
     PUNCH,RUN,TEMP,WAVEL
  41 CONTINUE
     GO TO (1,60),NQR
  60 DO 63 J=1,NEX
     N4=JJ(J)
     N=N4-1
     AA=0.0
     BB=0.0
     DO 62 JP=1,N4
  62 READ,SL(JP),DEVSL(JP)
     NN=LL(J)
     DO 63 I=1,JI
     CE(I,J)=0.0
     CER(I,J)=0.0
     IF(T(I))63,63,64
  64 DO 70 JP=1,N
     PP=JP
     GO TO (65,66,67,68,69),NN
  65 PP=PP*QI(J)+1.0
     AA=AA+(SL(JP)*(T(I)**PP))/PP
     BB=((SL(JP)+DEVSL(JP))*((T(I)+DEVT(I))**PP))/PP
     GO TO 70
  66 AA=AA+(SL(JP)*EXP((T(I)-QI(J))*PP))/PP
     BB=BB+((SL(JP)+DEVSL(JP))*EXP(((T(I)+DEVT(I))-QI(J))*PP))/PP
     GO TO 70
  67 FA=1.0
     FB=1.0
     AA=AA+FA
     BB=BB+FB
     GO TO 70
```

```
68 FA=1.0
FB=1.0
AA=AA+FA
BB=BB+FB
GO TO 70
69 FA=1.0
FB=1.0
AA=AA+FA
BB=BB+FB
70 CONTINUE
CE(I,J)=AA+SL(N4)*T(I)
CER(I,J)=BB+(SL(N4)+DEVSL(N4))*(T(I)+DEVT(I))
63 CONTINUE
G=0.0
DO 75 I=1,JI
IF(T(I))75,75,76
76 G=G+1.0
75 CONTINUE
DO 61 J=1,NEQ
READ,KA,KB,KC,KD,KE,KF
N=LEQ1(J)
DO 71 JP=1,N
N4=LEQ2(JP,J)
DO 71 I=1,JI
IF(T(I))73,73,74
74 IF(JP-1)1,77,78
77 Y(I,1)=C(I,N4)
YER(I,1)=DEVC(I,N4)
GO TO 71
78 Y(I,JP)=CE(I,N4)
YER(I,JP)=CER(I,N4)-CE(I,N4)
GO TO 71
73 Y(I,JP)=0.0
YER(I,JP)=0.0
71 CONTINUE
IF(J-1)1,79,80
79 PUNCH,JI
80 PUNCH,PROGN,FEEDP
PUNCH,KA,KB,KC,KD,KE,KF
PUNCH,N
PUNCH,JC
PUNCH,K,L,M
DO 81 JP=1,N
81 PUNCH,ZAP,ZAP,ZAP,ZAP
DO 82 I=1,JI,4
DO 82 JP=1,N
PUNCH,Y(I,JP),Y(I+1,JP),Y(I+2,JP),Y(I+3,JP)
82 PUNCH,YER(I,JP),YER(I+1,JP),YER(I+2,JP),YER(I+3,JP)
PUNCH,G
PUNCH,OPER,INSTR
WAVEL=J
PUNCH,RUN,TEMP,WAVEL
61 CONTINUE
GO TO 1
END
```

ALGOL 60 FOR PROGRAM NUMBER 33

```
PROCEDURE GBAAA (progn,feedp);  ARRAY devt,t,devx,x[1:jq],devfc,rLmc,wLc,
wuc,qq[1:jr],Lex1,LL,qi,jj[1:je],Leq1[1:jn],sL,devsL[1:jt],devc,c[1:jq,1:jr],
Lex2[1:jr,1:je],Leq2[1:jp,1:jn],ce,cer,y,yer[1:jq,1:jp];  INTEGER progn,feedp;
SWITCH sw1:=x2,x3,x2,x3;  SWITCH sw2:=x6,x7,x6,x7;  SWITCH sw3:=x10,x11,
x12,x13,x14;  SWITCH sw4:=x17,x18;  SWITCH sw5:=x27,x19;  SWITCH sw6:=x20,
x21,x22,x23,x24;
COMMENT: KINETIC EQUATIONS;
      BEGIN INTEGER i,j,jc,ji,jp,k,ka,kb,kc,kd,ke,kf,L,m,m6,n,nn,nc,nqr,nex,
      neq,n4,g,oper,instr,run;
      REAL aa,bb,devft,fa,fb,pp,rLmt,temp,ww,wLt,wut,waveL,wL1,wu1,wL2,
      wu2,zap;
        nqr:=progn;
        IF nqr=300 THEN GO TO X28
        ELSE IF nqr>300 THEN nqr:=nqr-300;
        nqr:=nqr-24;  READ ji;
        zap:=99.99;  m6:=1;  jc:=L:=3;  m:=0;
        READ k,nc,nex,neq;
        IF k≤2 THEN
        BEGIN
          READ devft;  GO TO X1END;
        FOR i:=1 STEP 1 UNTIL ji DO READ devt[i];
X1:     GO TO sw1[k];
X2:     FOR j:=1 STEP 1 UNTIL nc DO READ devfc[j];
        GO TO X4;
X3:     FOR j:=1 STEP 1 UNTIL nc DO
        FOR i:=1 STEP 1 UNTIL ji DO READ devc[i,j];
X4:     READ rLmt,wLt,wut;
        FOR i:=1 STEP 1 UNTIL ji DO READ t[i];
        FOR j:=1 STEP 1 UNTIL nc DO
        BEGIN
          READ rLmc[j],wLc[j],wuc[j];
          READ qq[j];
          FOR i:=1 STEP 1 UNTIL ji DO READ c[i,j]
        END;
        FOR i:=1 STEP 1 UNTIL ji DO
        BEGIN
          IF(t[i]<wLt)∨(t[i]>wut)THEN
          BEGIN
X5:         t[i]:=0;
            FOR j:=1 STEP 1 UNTIL nc DO c[i,j]:=0;
            GO TO X8END;
          FOR j:=1 STEP 1 UNTIL nc DO
          BEGIN
            IF(c[i,j]<wLc[j])∨(c[i,j]>wuc[j])THEN GO TO X5;
            GO TO sw2[k];
X6:         devc[i,j]:=devfc[j]Xc[i,j]
X7:       END;
          IF k≤2 THEN devt[i]:=devftXt[i]
X8:     END;
        FOR i:=1 STEP 1 UNTIL nex DO
        BEGIN
```

```
        READ Lex1[i],LL[i],qi[i],jj[i];
        n:=Lex1[i];
        FOR j:=1 STEP 1 UNTIL n DO READ Lex2[j,i]
     END;
     FOR i:=1 STEP 1 UNTIL neq DO
     BEGIN
        READ Leq1[i]; n:=Leq1[i];
        FOR j:=1 STEP 1 UNTIL n DO READ Leq2[j,i]
     END;
     READ oper,instr;
     READ run,temp,waveL;
     FOR i:=1 STEP 1 UNTIL ji DO
     FOR j:=1 STEP 1 UNTIL nex DO
     BEGIN
        IF t[i]≤0 THEN
        BEGIN
          ce[i,j]:=cer[i,j]:=0;
          GO TO X9END;
        ce[i,j]:=cer[i,j]:=1
X9:  END;
     FOR i:=1 STEP 1 UNTIL ji DO
     IF t[i]>0 THEN
     FOR j:=1 STEP 1 UNTIL nex DO
     BEGIN
        n:=Lex1[j];
        FOR jp:=1 STEP 1 UNTIL nc DO
        FOR jpp:=1 STEP 1 UNTIL n DO
        BEGIN
          IF jp=Lex2[jpp,j]THEN
          BEGIN
            ce[i,j]:=ce[i,j]X(c[i,jp]↑qq[jp]);
            cer[i,j]:=cer[i,j]X((c[i,jp]+devc[i,jp])↑qq[jp])END
        END;
        cer[i,j]:=cer[i,j]−ce[i,j]
     END;
     wL1:=1000000.0;  wu1:=−1000000.0;
     FOR i:=1 STEP 1 UNTIL ji DO
     IF t[i]>0 THEN
     FOR j:=1 STEP 1 UNTIL nex DO
     BEGIN
        IF wL1>ce[i,j]THEN wL1:=ce[i,j];
        IF wu1<ce[i,j]THEN wu1:=ce[i,j]
     END;
     k:=4;
     FOR j:=1 STEP 1 UNTIL nex DO
     BEGIN
        FOR i:=1 STEP 1 UNTIL ji DO
        BEGIN
          x[i]:=devx[i]:=0;
          IF t[i]≤0 THEN GO TO X15;
          n:=LL[j];  GO TO sw3[n];
X10:      x[i]:=t[i]↑qi[j];
          devx[i]:=(t[i]+devt[i])↑qi[j]−x[i];
```

```
            GO TO X15;
X11:        x[i]:=exp(t[i]−qi[j]);
            devx[i]:=exp(t[i]+devt[i]−qi[j])−x[i];
            GO TO X15;
X12:        x[i]:=devx[i]:=0;  GO TO X15;
X13:        x[i]:=devx[i]:=0;  GO TO X15;
X14:        x[i]:=devx[i]:=0
X15:        END;
            wL2:=1000000.0;  wu2:=−1000000.0;
            FOR i:=1 STEP 1 UNTIL ji DO
            IF t[i]>0 THEN
            BEGIN
                IF wL2>x[i] THEN wL2:=x[i];
                IF wu2<x[i] THEN wu2:=x[i]
X16:        END;
            READ ka,kb,kc,kd,ke,kf;
            GO TO sw4[nqr];
X17:        IF j<1 THEN GO TO X28
            ELSE IF j=1 THEN PUNCH ji;
            PUNCH progn,feedp;
            PUNCH ka,kb,kc,kd,ke,kf;
            PUNCH jj[j];  PUNCH m6;  PUNCH k,L,m;
            PUNCH rLmt,wL1,wu1;
            PUNCH rLmt,wL2,wu2;
            FOR i:=1 STEP 1 UNTIL ji DO PUNCH cer[i,j];
            FOR i:=1 STEP 1 UNTIL ji DO PUNCH devx[i,j];
            FOR i:=1 STEP 1 UNTIL ji DO PUNCH ce[i,j];
            ww:=1;
            FOR i:=1 STEP 1 UNTIL ji DO PUNCH ww,ww,ww,ww;
            FOR i:=1 STEP 1 UNTIL ji DO PUNCH x[i];
            waveL:=j;
            PUNCH oper,instr;
            PUNCH run, temp,waveL
X18:        END;
            GO TO sw5[nqr];
X19:        FOR j:=1 STEP 1 UNTIL nex DO
            BEGIN
                n4:=jj[j];  n:=n4−1;  aa:=bb:=0;
                FOR jp:=1 STEP 1 UNTIL n4 DO READ sL[jp],devsL[jp];
                nn:=LL[j];
                FOR i:=1 STEP 1 UNTIL ji DO
                BEGIN
                    ce[i,j]:=cer[i,j]:=0;
                    IF t[i]≤0 THEN GO TO X26;
                    FOR jp:=1 STEP 1 UNTIL n DO
                    BEGIN
                        pp:=jp;  GO TO sw6[nn];
X20:                    pp:=ppXqi[j]+1;
                        aa:=sL[jp]Xt[i]↑pp/pp
                        bb:=(sL[jp]+devsL[jp])X(t[i]+devt[i]↑pp)/pp;
                        GO TO X25;
X21:                    aa:=aa+sL[jp]Xexp((t[i]−qi[j])Xpp);
                        bb:=bb+(sL[jp]+devsL[jp])Xexp((t[i]+devt[i]−qi[j])Xpp)/pp;
```

```
              GO TO X25;
X22:          fa:=fb:=1; aa:=aa+fa; bb:=bb+fb;
              GO TO X25;
X23:          fa:=fb:=1; aa:=aa+fa; bb:=bb+fb;
              GO TO X25;
X24:          fa:=fb:=1; aa:=aa+fa; bb:=bb+fb
X25:       END;
           ce[i,j]:=aa+sL[n4]Xt[i];
           cer[i,j]:=bb+(sL[n4]+devsL[n4])X(t[i]+devt[i])
         END
X26:  END;
        g:=0;
        FOR i:=1 STEP 1 UNTIL ji DO
        IF t[i]>0 THEN g:=g+1;
        FOR j:=1 STEP 1 UNTIL neq DO
        BEGIN
           READ ka,kb,kc,kd,ke,kf;
           n:=Leq1[j];
           FOR jp:=1 STEP 1 UNTIL n DO
           BEGIN
             n4:=Leq2[jp,j];
              FOR i:=1 STEP 1 UNTIL ji DO
              BEGIN
                IF t[i]>0 THEN
                BEGIN
                   IF jp<1 THEN GO TO X28
                   ELSE IF jp=1 THEN
                   BEGIN
                     y[i,1]:=c[i,n4]; yer[i,1]:=devc[i,n4];
                      GO TO X27END;
                   y[i,jp]:=ce[i,n4];
                   yer[i,jp]:=cer[i,n4]−ce[i,n4];
                   GO TO X27END;
                  y[i,jp]:=yer[i,jp]:=0
              END
X27:       END;
           IF j<1 THEN GO TO X28
           ELSE IF j=1 THEN PUNCH ji;
           PUNCH progn,feedp;
           PUNCH ka,kb,kc,kd,ke,kf;
           PUNCH n; PUNCH jc; PUNCH k,L,m;
           FOR jp:=1 STEP 1 UNTIL n DO PUNCH zap,zap,zap,zap;
           FOR i:=1 STEP 1 UNTIL ji DO
           BEGIN
             FOR jp:=1 STEP 1 UNTIL n DO PUNCH y[i,jp];
             FOR jp:=1 STEP 1 UNTIL n DO PUNCH yer[i,jp]
           END;
           PUNCH g; PUNCH oper,instr;
           waveL:=j; PUNCH run,temp,waveL
        END
X28:END GBAAA;
X29:READ progn,feedp;
    GBAAA(progn,feedp);
    GO TO X29;
```

CHAPTER XI

SPECIAL ITERATIVE PROGRAMS

Discussed in this chapter are programs numbered 410 to 415 which are almost completely automatic special versions of the six programs given in Chapters IV to VI and modified in Appendix I of Volume I. Here the related programs are listed.

Original Program		Modified Programs		Special Program	
Number	Call Word	Number	Call Word	Number	Call Word
10	JAAAA	310	JAAAS	410	JAASS
11	KAAAA	311	KAAAS	411	KAASS
12	LAAAA	312	LAAAS	412	LAASS
13	MAAAA	313	MAAAS	413	MAASS
14	NAAAA	314	NAAAS	414	NAASS
15	OAAAA	315	OAAAS	415	OAASS

The *modified programs* (310 to 315) are discussed in Appendix I of Volume I. In both the *special* and the *modified programs* the *self-judgment principle* is applied only to values of Y(I). Input information for the *original program* is compatible with its *modified* version and, with one additional item (see Input Formats for Programs 410 to 415), this input information can be processed with the *special* version. Here it is assumed that the reader is familiar with the information given for the original programs in Volume I.

In Programs 10 to 15 and 310 to 315 the basic iterative procedure used to compute the formation constant with data at each wavelength is as follows.

Step 1. An arbitrarily selected value for the formation constant (EQO) is used in computing the concentration of complex in each solution.

Step 2. The absorbance of the complex in each solution is computed with the information obtained in Step 1.

Step 3. With the information from Steps 1 and 2 a new value for the formation constant (EQ(2)) is calculated.

Step 4. EQO is replaced by EQ(2) and Steps 1, 2 and 3 are repeated. This procedure is repeated for the programmed number of cycles, J.

Step 5. The self-judgment principle is applied to the (J + 1) cycle and a new value for the formation constant (EQ(J + 1)) is computed from the accepted sets of conjugate information.

Step 6. In the (J + 2) cycle the self-judgment principle is applied again and the formation constant is recalculated. This EQ(J + 2) is used to compute the final value of the absorbancy index of the complex, AC(J + 2).

Step 7. The maximum permitted errors for EQ(J + 2) and AC (J + 2) are calculated in the (J + 3) cycle.

If some sets of conjugate information used during the first J cycles (Steps 1–4) are wrong, the formation constant may converge to an erroneous value. When wrong sets of conjugate information are rejected during the first application of the *self-judgment principle* (Step 5), the final cycle (Step 6) may be insufficient to ensure satisfactory convergence of the formation constant. In such a situation the final value for the formation constant (EQ(J + 2)) would be wrong. Normally the analyses would have to be repeated after selection of the appropriate *reject–restore* commands to ensure that "wrong" sets of conjugate information are not used in Steps 1 to 4.

In Appendix G of Volume I, convergence of iterative procedures is discussed. With the rapidly converging methods used throughout Volumes I and II, we have found satisfactory convergence when the ratio, (EQ(J) − EQ(J + 1))/EQ(J + 1) = R, is numerically less than the *maximum permitted deviation*, expressed in the form DEVF1, for the first observable. The true value of the formation constant (EQT) is defined by the inequality:

$$EQ(J + 1) - |R| \leq EQT \leq EQ(J + 1) + |R|, \text{ if } |R| \leq DEVF1$$

In Programs 410 to 415 the preselected value for WACRR is defined as the highest absolute value of R, designated $|R|$, that will be tolerated. If WACRR < $|R|$, the convergence is unsatisfactory. If WACRR ≥ $|R|$, the formation constant is said to have converged satisfactorily. These criteria constitute the WACRR *test of convergence*. The basic iterative procedure used to calculate the formation constant with data taken at each of several wavelengths is as follows.

Step A. With data taken at the first wavelength Steps 1 to 4 are executed. At the end of the second cycle and in subsequent cycles the WACRR *test of convergence* is applied. As soon as the formation constant converges satisfactorily the computer proceeds to Step 5. Step 6 is omitted.

If convergence is unsatisfactory the next iteration is made in the normal way.

Step B. After the *self-judgment principle* is applied the WACRR, *test of convergence* is made. If the formation constant has converged satisfactorily the *error analysis* (Step 7) is performed. For calculations at the next wavelength, EQO is set equal to the final value of the formation constant (EQ(J + 1)). If the convergence is unsatisfactory EQ(2) is set equal to EQ(J + 1) and J, the cycle number, is set equal to two and the calculations noted in Step A are repeated, beginning with the second iteration. It should be noted that sets of conjugate information rejected during the application of the *self-judgment principle* are removed from memory. Thus in subsequent applications of the *self-judgment principle* the rejected sets of conjugate information will not be considered.

In our laboratories we have found that with the special Programs 410 to 415 the computer time is reduced substantially. For complexes with low values of the product, formation constant times absorbancy index, the formation constants can be calculated realistically only with these special programs because it is virtually impossible to detect some kinds of "wrong" sets of conjugate information even when the data are processed with the *autoplotter programs* (see Chapter I). *However, the reader is warned that with poor data the value for the formation constant may oscillate between two values and satisfactory convergence will never occur. When this happens the computer will repeat the calculations in steps A and B indefinitely unless switch 4 is "On".* The options provided with switch 4 are given in the section "Optional External Commands for Programs 410–415."

At the end of this chapter there are given in FORTRAN the changes which must be made to the *modified programs* (310–315) to obtain the corresponding *special programs* (410–415).

INPUT COMMANDS FOR PROGRAMS 410–415

The input commands for the corresponding *original* (10–15), *modified* (310–315) and *special* (410–415), programs are identical. They are listed for Programs 10 to 15 in the first volume.

INPUT FORMATS FOR PROGRAMS 410–415

In only one card is there a difference between the input formats for the *special* (410–415) and *original* (10–15) or *modified* (310–315) programs. The read statements associated with this card are:

READ,J   (*Original* and *modified program*)
READ,J,WACRR   (*Special program*).

WACRR, defined in the introduction to this chapter, is conveniently set equal to DEVF1, the *maximum permitted deviation* for the measured absorbance (OAM(I)). If the *maximum permitted deviation* is entered in the form DEV1(I), WACRR is set equal to the smallest value for the ratio, DEV1(I)/OAM(I), which refers to the Ith solution. For the *original* or *modified programs*, J is the number of cycles or iterations to be completed before the *self-judgment principle* is applied for the first time. For the *special programs* J is the maximum number of cycles that can be completed before the *self-judgment principle* is applied for the first time.

OPTIONAL EXTERNAL COMMANDS FOR PROGRAMS 410–415

The optional external commands provided by means of switches 1, 2 and 3 in the *original* (10–15) and *modified* (310–315) *programs* are also executed in the *special programs* (410–415). Additional options for the *special programs* are as follows.

If switch 4 in "On" after the *self-judgment principle* has been applied and the convergence is unsatisfactory, the calculation is terminated and calculations with data for the next wavelength are initiated.

If switch 4 is "Off" after the *self-judgment principle* has been applied and the convergence is unsatisfactory, the recycling procedure described in Step B is executed.

If calculations are terminated, CODE = 99999999.0 is printed and punched.

OUTPUT FORMATS FOR PROGRAMS 410–415

The output formats for programs 410–415 are almost identical with those for the corresponding *original* (10–15) and *modified* (310–315) *programs* described in the first volume. Execution of the rejecting procedure described in Step B will be apparent from the cycle (J) and wavelength (M4) numbers punched at the end of each cycle or iteration. The cycle in which the *self-judgment principle* is applied is always labeled the (J + 1) cycle. One minor difference in the output formats for the *special programs* occurs when a calculation is terminated. Instead of the CODE being printed and punched as is done in the *original program*, the following commands are executed.

```
PRINT,CODE,M4,RUN
PUNCH,CODE,M4
PUNCH,OPER,INSTR
PUNCH,RUN,TEMP,WAVEL
```

M4 denotes the wavelength. RUN, OPER, INSTR, TEMP and WAVEL identify the source of the data.

CONVERSION OF PROGRAM 310 TO PROGRAM 410

ORIGINAL STATEMENT	REPLACEMENT STATEMENT

```
1 READ,JAAAS,FEEDP              1 READ,JAASS,FEEDP
READ,J                          READ,J,WACRR
NUM=310                         NUM=410
PUNCH,JAAAS,NUM,FEEDP           PUNCH,JAASS,NUM,FEEDP
                          ------------
IF(OAC(I)-WAC1*OAM(I))91,92,92  OAC(I)=SQR(OAC(I)*OAC(I))
                                IF(OAC(I)-WAC1*OAM(I))91,92,92
                          ------------
93 G1=G1+1.0                    93 G1=G1+1.0
                                OAC(I)=X1(I)
                          ------------
111 PRINT,CODE                  111 PRINT,CODE,M4,RUN
PUNCH,CODE                      PUNCH,CODE,M4
                                PUNCH,OPER,INSTR
                                PUNCH,RUN,TEMP,WAVEL
                          ------------
IF(N+3-J)635,635,151            IF(N+2-J)635,635,151
                          ------------
IF(SENSE SWITCH 1)120,68        IF(SENSE SWITCH 1)120,635
                          ------------
GO TO 68                        GO TO 635
                          ------------
IF(N+2-J)635,136,139            IF(N+1-J)635,136,139
139 IF(SENSE SWITCH 2)136,68    139 IF(SENSE SWITCH 2)136,635
                          ------------
IF(SENSE SWITCH 3)138,638       IF(SENSE SWITCH 3)138,635
638 IF(N+2-J)635,635,68
                          ------------
635 IF(N+2-J)146,141,68         635 IF(N+1-J)146,641,641
141 DO 143 I=1,20               641 IF(J-1)1,68,642
                                642 B99=SQR(EQ(J)*EQ(J))
                                JRQ=J+1
                                JKQ=J-1
                                JP=JKQ
                                A9=SQR((EQ(J)-EQ(JP))*(EQ(J)-EQ(JP
                                IF(EQ(J))652,110,652
                                652 IF(SENSE SWITCH 4)110,651
                                651 A9=A9/B99
                                IF(A9-WACRR)643,643,646
                                643 IF(N+1-J)146,141,644
                                644 DO 645 I=JRQ,N
                                SQRMX(I)=SQRMX(J)
                                SQRMY(I)=SQRMY(J)
                                AIC(I)=AIC(J)
                                645 EQ(I)=EQ(J)
                                J=N
                                GO TO 68
                                646 IF(N+1-J)146,647,68
                                647 EQ(2)=EQ(J)
                                DO 649 I=1,20
                                IF(Y(I))649,650,649
                                650 OAM(I)=0.0
                                OAC(I)=0.0
                                649 CONTINUE
                                J=2
                                GO TO 68
                                141 EQO=EQ(J)
```

```
                        DO 143 I=1,20
           ---------------
           ---------------
       CONVERSION OF PROGRAM 311 TO PROGRAM 411
           ---------------
        ORIGINAL STATEMENT              REPLACEMENT STATEMENT
           ---------------
1 READ,KAAAS,FEEDP               1READ,KAASS,FEEDP
READ,J                           READ,J,WACRR
NUM=311                          NUM=411
PUNCH,KAAAS,NUM,FEEDP            PUNCH,KAASS,NUM,FEEDP
           ---------------
IF(OAC(I)-WAC1*OAM(I))91,92,92    OAC(I)=SQR(OAC(I)*OAC(I))
                                 IF(OAC(I)-WAC1*OAM(I))91,92,92
           ---------------
93 G1=G1+1.0                     93 G1=G1+1.0
                                 OAC(I)=X1(I)
           ---------------
111 PRINT,CODE                   111 PRINT,CODE,M4,RUN
PUNCH,CODE                       PUNCH,CODE,M4
                                 PUNCH,OPER,INSTR
                                 PUNCH,RUN,TEMP,WAVEL
           ---------------
IF(N+3-J)635,635,151              IF(N+2-J)635,635,151
           ---------------
IF(SENSE SWITCH 1)120,68          IF(SENSE SWITCH 1)120,635
           ---------------
GO TO 68                          GO TO 635
           ---------------
IF(N+2-J)635,136,139              IF(N+1-J)635,136,139
139 IF(SENSE SWITCH2)136,68       139 IF(SENSE SWITCH 2)136,635
           ---------------
IF(SENSE SWITCH 3)138,638         IF(SENSE SWITCH 3)138,635
638 IF(N+2-J)635,635,68
           ---------------
635 IF(N+2-J)146,141,68           635 IF(N+1-J)146,641,641
141 DO 143 I=1,20                 641 IF(J-1)1,68,642
                                  642 B99=SQR(EQ(J)*EQ(J))
                                  JRQ=J+1
                                  JKQ=J-1
                                  JP=JKQ
                                  A9=SQR((EQ(J)-EQ(JP))*(EQ(J)-EQ(JP)))
                                  IF(EQ(J))652,110,652
                                  652 IF(SENSE SWITCH 4)110,651
                                  651 A9=A9/B99
                                  IF(A9-WACRR)643,643,646
                                  643 IF(N+1-J)146,141,644
                                  644 DO 645 I=JRQ,N
                                  SQRMX(I)=SQRMX(J)
                                  SQRMY(I)=SQRMY(J)
                                  AIC(I)=AIC(J)
                                  645 EQ(I)=EQ(J)
                                  J=N
                                  GO TO 68
                                  646 IF(N+1-J)146,647,68
                                  647 EQ(2)=EQ(J)
                                  DO 649 I=1,20
                                  IF(Y(I))649,650,649
                                  650 OAM(I)=0.0
                                  OAC(I)=0.0
                                  649 CONTINUE
                                  J=2
```

```
                                       GO TO 68
                                       141 EQO=EQ(J)
                                       DO 143 I=1,20
```


CONVERSION OF PROGRAM 312 TO PROGRAM 412

ORIGINAL STATEMENT   REPLACEMENT STATEMENT

```
1 READ,LAAAS,FEEDP                     1 READ,LAASS,FEEDP
READ,J                                 READ,J,WACRR
NUM=312                                NUM=412
PUNCH,LAAAS,NUM,FEEDP                  PUNCH,LAASS,NUM,FEEDP
```

```
IF(OAC(I)-WAC1*OAM(I))135,136,136      XYZ=OAC(I)
                                       OAC(I)=SQR(XYZ*XYZ)
                                       IF(OAC(I)-WAC1*OAM(I))135,136,136
```

```
137 G1=G1+1.0                          137 G1=G1+1.0
                                       OAC(I)=XYZ
```

```
174 PRIMT,CODE                         174 PRINT,CODE,M4,RUN
PUNCH,CODE                             PUNCH,CODE,M4
                                       PUNCH,OPER,INSTR
                                       PUNCH,RUN,TEMP,WAVEL
```

```
IF(N+3-J)635,635,178                   IF(N+2-J)635,635,178
```

```
IF(SENSE SWITCH 1)184,75              IF(SENSE SWITCH 1)184,635
```

```
GO TO 75                               GO TO 635
```

```
IF(N+2-J)635,196,195                   IF(N+1-J)635,196,195
195 IF(SENSE SWITCH 2)196,75          195 IF(SENSE SWITCH 2)196,635
```

```
IF(SENSE SWITCH 3)198,638             IF(SENSE SWITCH 3)198,635
638 IF(N+2-J)635,635,75
```

```
635 IF(N+2-J)205,200,75                635 IF(N+1-J)205,641,641
200 DO 201 I=1,20                      641 IF(J-1)1,75,642
                                       642 B99=SQR(EQ(J)*EQ(J))
                                       JRQ=J+1
                                       JKQ=J-1
                                       JP=JKQ
                                       A9=SQR((EQ(J)-EQ(JP))*(EQ(J)-EQ(JP
                                       IF(EQ(J))652,209,652
                                       652 IF(SENSE SWITCH 4)209,651
                                       651 A9=A9/B99
                                       IF(A9-WACRR)643,643,646
                                       643 IF(N+1-J)205,200,641
                                       644 DO 645 I=JRQ,N
                                       SQRMX(I)=SQRMX(J)
                                       SQRMY(I)=SQRMY(J)
                                       AIC(I)=AIC(J)
                                       645 EQ(I)=EQ(J)
                                       J=N
                                       GO TO 75
                                       646 IF(N+1-J)205,647,75
                                       647 EQ(JKQ)=EQ(J)
                                       DO 649 I=1,20
                                       IF(Y(I))649,650,649
                                       650 OAM(I)=0.0
```

```
                              OAC(I)=0.0
                              649 CONTINUE
                              J=2
                              GO TO 75
                              200 EQO=EQ(J)
                              DO 201 I=1,20
```

```
                    -------------
                    -------------
        CONVERSION OF PROGRAM 313 TO PROGRAM 413
                    -------------
```

ORIGINAL STATEMENT	REPLACEMENT STATEMENT

```
1 READ,MAAAS,FEEDP              1 READ,MAASS,FEEDP
READ,J                          READ,J,WACRR
NUM=313                         NUM=413
PUNCH,MAAAS,NUM,FEEDP           PUNCH,MAASS,NUM,FEEDP
```

```
IF(OAC(I)-WAC1*OAM(I))135,136,136   XYZ=OAC(I)
                                    OAC(I)=SQR(XYZ*XYZ)
                                    IF(OAC(I)-WAC1*OAM(I))135,136,136
```

```
137 G1=G1+1.0                   137 G1=G1+1.0
                                OAC(I)=XYZ
```

```
174 PRIMT,CODE                  174 PRINT,CODE,M4,RUN
PUNCH,CODE                      PUNCH,CODE,M4
                                PUNCH,OPER,INSTR
                                PUNCH,RUN,TEMP,WAVEL
```

```
IF(N+3-J)635,635,178            IF(N+2-J)635,635,178
```

```
IF(SENSE SWITCH 1)184,75        IF(SENSE SWITCH 1)184,635
```

```
GO TO 75                        GO TO 635
```

```
IF(N+2-J)635,196,195            IF(N+1-J)635,196,195
195 IF(SENSE SWITCH 2)196,75    195 IF(SENSE SWITCH 2)196,635
```

```
IF(SENSE SWITCH3)198,638        IF(SENSE SWITCH 3)198,635
638 IF(N+2-J)635,635,75
```

```
635 IF(N+2-J)205,200,75         635 IF(N+1-J)205,641,641
200 DO 201 I=1,20               641 IF(J-1)1,75,642
                                642 B99=SQR(EQ(J)*EQ(J))
                                JRQ=J+1
                                JKQ=J-1
                                JP=JKQ
                                A9=SQR((EQ(J)-EQ(JP))*(EQ(J)-EQ(JP)))
                                IF(EQ(J))652,209,652
                                652 IF(SENSE SWITCH 4)209,651
                                651 A9=A9/B99
                                IF(A9-WACRR)643,643,646
                                643 IF(N+1-J)205,200,641
                                644 DO 645 I=JRQ,N
                                SQRMX(I)=SQRMX(J)
                                SQRMY(I)=SQRMY(J)
                                AIC(I)=AIC(J)
                                645 EQ(I)=EQ(J)
                                J=N
                                GO TO 75
                                646 IF(N+1-J)205,647,75
                                647 EQ(JKQ)=EQ(J)
```

```
          DO 649 I=1,20
          IF(Y(I))649,650,649
          650 OAM(I)=0.0
          OAC(I)=0.0
          649 CONTINUE
          J=2
          GO TO 75
          200 EQ0=EQ(J)
          DO 201 I=1,20
```

CONVERSION OF PROGRAM 314 TO PROGRAM 414

ORIGINAL STATEMENT	REPLACEMENT STATEMENT

```
1 READ,NAAAS,FEEDP            1 READ,NAASS,FEEDP
READ,J                        READ,J,WACRR
NUM=314                       NUM=414
PUNCH,NAAAS,NUM,FEEDP         PUNCH,NAASS,NUM,FEEDP
```

```
IF(OAC(I)-WAC1*OAM(I))91,92,92    OAC(I)=SQR(OAC(I)*OAC(I))
                                  IF(OAC(I)-WAC1*OAM(I))91,92,92
```

```
93 G1=G1+1.0                   93 G1=G1+1.0
                               OAC(I)=X1(I)
```

```
111 PRINT,CODE                 111 PRINT,CODE,M4,RUN
PUNCH,CODE                     PUNCH,CODE,M4
                               PUNCH,OPER,INSTR
                               PUNCH,RUN,TEMP,WAVEL
```

```
IF(N+3-J)635,635,151           IF(N+2-J)635,635,151
```

```
IF(SENSE SWITCH 1)120,68       IF(SENSE SWITCH 1)120,635
```

```
GO TO 68                       GO TO 635
```

```
IF(N+2-J)635,136,139           IF(N+1-J)635,136,139
139 IF(SENSE SWITCH 2)136,68   139 IF(SENSE SWITCH 2)136,635
```

```
IF(SENSE SWITCH 3)138,638      IF(SENSE SWITCH 3)138,635
638 IF(N+2-J)635,635,68
```

```
635 IF(N+2-J)146,141,68        635 IF(N+1-J)146,641,641
141 DO 143 I=1,20              641 IF(J-1)1,68,642
                               642 B99=SQR(EQ(J)*EQ(J))
                               JRQ=J+1
                               JKQ=J-1
                               JP=JKQ
                               A9=SQR((EQ(J)-EQ(JP))*(EQ(J)-EQ(JP
                               IF(EQ(J))652,110,652
                               652 IF(SENSE SWITCH 4)110,651
                               651 A9=A9/B99
                               IF(A9-WACRR)643,643,646
                               643 IF(N+1-J)146,141,644
                               644 DO 645 I=JRQ,N
                               SQRMX(I)=SQRMX(J)
                               SQRMY(I)=SQRMY(J)
                               AIC(I)=AIC(J)
                               645 EQ(I)=EQ(J)
                               J=N
                               GO TO 68
```

```
646 IF(N+1-J)146,647,68
    647 EQ(2)=EQ(J)
    DO 649 I=1,20
    IF(Y(I))649,650,649
    650 OAM(I)=0.0
    OAC(I)=0.0
    649 CONTINUE
    J=2
    GO TO 68
      141 EQO=EQ(J)
      DO 143 I=1,20
```

CONVERSION OF PROGRAM 315 TO PROGRAM 415

ORIGINAL STATEMENT	REPLACEMENT STATEMENT

```
1 READ,OAAAS,FEEDP            1 READ,OAASS,FEEDP
READ,J                        READ,J,WACRR
NUM=315                       NUM=415
PUNCH,OAAAS,NUM,FEEDP         PUNCH,OAASS,NUM,FEEDP
```

```
IF(OAC(I)-WAC1*OAM(I))135,136,136   XYZ=OAC(I)
                                    OAC(I)=SQR(XYZ*XYZ)
                                    IF(OAC(I)-WAC1*OAM(I))135,136,136
```

```
137 G1=G1+1.0                 137 G1=G1+1.0
                              OAC(I)=XYZ
```

```
174 PRIMT,CODE                174 PRINT,CODE,M4,RUN
PUNCH,CODE                    PUNCH,CODE,M4
                              PUNCH,OPER,INSTR
                              PUNCH,RUN,TEMP,WAVEL
```

```
IF(N+3-J)635,635,178          IF(N+2-J)635,635,178
```

```
IF(SENSE SWITCH 1)184,75      IF(SENSE SWITCH 1)184,635
```

```
GO TO 75                      GO TO 635
```

```
IF(N+2-J)635,196,195          IF(N+1-J)635,196,195
195 IF(SENSE SWITCH 2)196,75  195 IF(SENSE SWITCH 2)196,635
```

```
IF(SENSE SWITCH 3)198,638     IF(SENSE SWITCH 3)198,635
638 IF(N+2-J)635,635,75
635 IF(N+2-J)205,200,75         635 IF(N+1-J)205,641,641
200 DO 201 I=1,20               641 IF(J-1)1,75,642
                                642 B99=SQR(EQ(J)*EQ(J))
                              JRQ=J+1
                              JKQ=J-1
                              JP=JKQ
                              A9=SQR((EQ(J)-EQ(JP))*(EQ(J)-EQ(JP)))
                              IF(EQ(J))652,209,652
                                652 IF(SENSE SWITCH 4)209,651
                                651 A9=A9/B99
                              IF(A9-WACRR)643,643,646
                                643 IF(N+1-J)205,200,641
                                644 DO 645 I=JRQ,N
                              SQRMX(I)=SQRMX(J)
                              SQRMY(I)=SQRMY(J)
                              AIC(I)=AIC(J)
                                645 EQ(I)=EQ(J)
```

```
      J=N
      GO TO 75
  646 IF(N+1-J)205,647,75
  647 EQ(JKQ)=EQ(J)
      DO 649 I=1,20
      IF(Y(I))649,650,649
  650 OAM(I)=0.0
      OAC(I)=0.0
  649 CONTINUE
      J=2
      GO TO 75
  200 EQO=EQ(J)
      DO 201 I=1,20
```

CHAPTER XII

SPECIAL TECHNIQUES

Part I.   The Mean and the Mean Maximum Permitted Error

Researchers are frequently confronted with the problem of reporting a median value ($\bar{P}$) for a parameter, P, whose values are calculated from independent sets of experimental data. If the arithmetic mean and the standard deviation are used, the reader cannot formulate precisely the limitations which must be imposed on his techniques and instruments if he is to confirm or contradict the reported result.

If the *new method* is used to process several sets of data, each value of P will have an associated *maximum permitted error* (*PER*). As the magnitude of each *PER* value is determined only by the preselected *instrument reliability factors* and the number of sets of conjugate data used in its calculation, values of P obtained by different workers or calculated from different sets of data of the same type can be compared directly. However, if several values for P and the associated *PER* are computed from different kinds of experimental information, there remains unsolved the problem of determining the median value for the parameter and the associated *mean maximum permitted error* ($\overline{PER}$), such that the value for $\overline{PER}$ clearly defines the absolute limits for the value of $\bar{P}$. Here two new concepts will be introduced and the procedure for computing $\bar{P}$ and $\overline{PER}$ will be discussed. The two new concepts are:

THE MEAN VALUE OF A PARAMETER ($\bar{P}$)

If $P_1, P_2, \cdots P_r, \cdots$ are values for the parameter calculated from independent sets of data, $\bar{P}$ is computed by solving the equation:

$$P_r = \bar{P} + \text{SL} \cdot X_r \tag{A}$$

for all P_r. In equation (A) the values of X_r, which correspond to values of

413

P_r, are chosen on a relative scale as symmetrically as possible about the origin of the X_r axis. Thus if there are five values of P, the corresponding X_r are -2.5, -1.5, $-.5$, $.5$, 1.5 (Note a zero value for X_r cannot be used here). SL, the slope in equation (A), is considered in subsequent paragraphs.

The procedure described above is called the *centering device*. It is important to note that $\bar{P}$ is not necessarily equal to the arithmetic mean.

THE MEAN MAXIMUM PERMITTED ERROR ($\overline{PER}$)

If P_1ER, P_2ER, $\cdots$ are the *maximum permitted errors* associated with P_1, P_2, $\cdots$ respectively, $\overline{PER}$ is computed by solving equation (B) for all P_rER and centered values for X_r.

$$P_rER = \overline{PER} + \Delta SL \cdot X_r \tag{B}$$

Only if all P_rER values are identical will $\overline{PER}$ equal their mean value.

The solution of equations (A) and (B) for $\bar{P}$ and $\overline{PER}$ is accomplished with Program 301 (*call word* AAAAS), or, in special cases, with FOR-TO-GO Program 505 (*call word* EEEEE). In Chapter VIII the use of these programs in conjunction with Program 31 (*call word* EBAAA) is described.

With Program 301 individual values of P and the associated PER are entered as Y(I) and YER(I) respectively. The values entered for X1(I) and X1ER(I) are X_r and zero respectively. As Program 301 contains the *self-judgment principle* some values of P may be rejected. The mean value of P, designated $\bar{P}$, and the associated *mean maximum permitted error* ($\overline{PER}$) are calculated from the accepted values of P and PER during the J and the (J + 1) cycles in the normal way (see Chapter I, Volume I). There are two advantages in using this procedure. First, values of P are deemed incorrect by the computer in terms of the original *instrument reliability factors*, which determine the associated PER value. In conventional statistical methods the operator chooses the values he wishes to ignore. Secondly any trend in the values of P can be detected immediately. The accepted values of P are constant only if the slope (SL) of equation (A) and its *maximum permitted error* (ΔSL) are such that their absolute values meet the requirement: $|SL| - |\Delta SL| \le 0 \le |SL| + |\Delta SL|$. Since SL and ΔSL are calculated together with $\bar{P}$ and $\overline{PER}$ in Program 301, any regularity in the values of P is detected immediately.

With the FOR-TO-GO Program 505 (*call word* EEEEE) the arithmetic mean for P and the mean for the associated PER values are computed from the input information for FORTRAN Program 301 (*call word* AAAAS) as described in the preceding paragraph. The *self-judgment principle* and the *normalization* and *transposition mechanism* are not incorporated into Program 505. However the reject–restore commands are executed. Thus the operator can select the values of P and PER which are to be ignored. While Program 505 is approximately twenty times faster than Program 301, its use is justified only if there is no trend in the values for P and if there is complete certainty as to the values of P and PER which are to be ignored. In our laboratories Program 505 is used only to compute the average molar absorbancy indices for complexes at several wavelengths from data originally used to compute the formation constant at each wavelength. The *mean formation constant* and its *mean maximum permitted error* are first computed with Program 301. These values and Program 31 (*call word* EBAAA) are then used to compute the molar absorbancy index for the complex in each solution at each wavelength. Next the molar absorbancy indices at each wavelength for several solutions are processed with Program 505. Details of the procedure are given in Chapter VIII. In our calculations we have found that the *mean molar absorbancy indices* and the associated *mean maximum permitted errors* obtained with Programs 301 and 505 are virtually identical.

The relationships between the mean value of a parameter or its *mean maximum permitted error* and the arithmetic mean or the standard deviation are illustrated in the following table. Here spectrophotometric data for binary (naphthalene or iodine–CCl_4) and ternary (naphthalene–iodine–CCl_4) systems, taken at twenty wavelengths at a fixed temperature, were used to compute the formation constant (K) and its *maximum permitted error* (KER) at each wavelength for the 1 : 1 reversible reaction: I_2 + naphthalene $\overset{K}{\rightleftarrows}$ complex. One of the programs in Chapters III and IV of the preceding volume, or in Chapters II and XI of this volume is used to obtain values for K and KER. Each KER is determined by the values of the *instrument reliability factors* used with the spectrophotometric program.

The *mean formation constant* ($\overline{K}$) and the *mean maximum permitted error* in $\overline{K}$ ($\overline{KER}$) given in the Table were computed with Program 301 (*call word* AAAAS). The underlined values of K and KER were rejected in the normal application of the *self-judgment principle*. The arithmetic mean and the standard deviation were calculated from the accepted values for K and KER. To complete this problem the researcher would use the values of $\overline{K}$ and $\overline{KER}$ with Program 31 (*call word* EBAAA) to compute the *molar absorbancy indices* of the complex (AC) and the associated *maximum permitted errors* (ACER) from the original data for each ternary solution (naphthalene–iodine–CCl_4) at each wavelength. Next Program 505 would be used to compute the *mean molar absorbancy index* ($\overline{AC}$) and the *mean maximum permitted error* ($\overline{ACER}$) at each of the twenty wavelengths.

Table 9

Formation constants (K) and the Associated *Maximum Permitted Error* (KER) at the Indicated Wavelength (λ) for the 1 : 1 Iodine–Naphthalene Complex in Carbon Tetrachloride at T2°C

λ in A	K	KER	λ in A	K	KER
4000	2.250	0.060	3500	2.060	0.100
3950	2.200	0.040	3450	2.250	0.040
3900	2.180	0.060	3400	2.410	0.070
3850	2.200	0.060	3350	2.210	0.050
3800	2.300	0.100	3300	2.210	0.060
3750	2.220	0.040	3250	2.270	0.040
3700	2.000	0.060	3200	2.180	0.020
3650	2.200	0.060	3150	2.300	0.040
3600	2.270	0.040	3100	2.290	0.060
3550	2.180	0.060	3000	2.600	0.050
			Arithmetic mean	2.239	0.0442*
			Mean formation constant	2.2386	0.0532†

* Standard deviation (K at 3200 is included).   † Mean *maximum permitted error.*

INPUT COMMANDS AND FORMAT FOR PROGRAM 505

FOR-TO-GO Program 505 (*call word* EEEEE) is designed specifically for processing the output information generated by Program 31 (*call word* EBAAA). There are no input commands associated exclusively with Program 505. The *reject–restore* commands which are executed in Program 505 are selected before use of the spectrophotometric program to compute the formation constant and its *maximum permitted error* at each wavelength. The locations of the *reject–restore* commands are given in Chapter VIII.

OUTPUT FORMAT FOR PROGRAM 505

For each set of input information, computed by means of Program 31 from data at a single wavelength, there is generated by Program 505 one card with five items of information.

STATEMENT	COMMENT
PUNCH,11,R,B,G,RUN,WAVEL	R—Mean formation constant. B—Mean *maximum permitted error.* G—Number values averaged. RUN— Identification WAVEL— WAVEL designates the wavelength for which data are processed.

FOR-TO-GO PROGRAM NUMBER 505

CALL WORD EEEEE

```
C  C  FORGO OR FOR-TO-GO 3-62 PROGRAM NUMBER 505(CALL WORD EEEEE)
11    FORMAT(F7.3,F7.3,F5.1,F7.1,F8.1)
      DIMENSION Y(20),X1(20),X1ER(20),YER(20)
1     READ,AAAAS,FEEDP
      READ,KA,KB,KC,KD
      READ,J
      READ,K,L,M
      READ,DEVF1,RLM1,WL1,WU1
      READ,DEVF2,RLM2,WL2,WU2
      DO 2 I=1,20,4
      READ,Y(I),Y(I+1),Y(I+2),Y(I+3)
      READ,YER(I),YER(I+1),YER(I+2),YER(I+3)
      READ,X1(I),X1(I+1),X1(I+2),X1(I+3)
2     READ,X1ER(I),X1ER(I+1),X1ER(I+2),X1ER(I+3)
      READ,G
      READ,OPER,INSTR
      READ,RUN,TEMP,WAVEL
      G=0.0
      KE=KA+2
      GO TO (3,4,5,6,7),KE
7     Y(KD)=0.0
6     Y(KC)=0.0
5     Y(KB)=0.0
      GO TO 3
4     DO 8 I=KB,KC
8     Y(I)=0.0
3     B=0.0
      R=0.0
      DO 9 I=1,20
      IF(Y(I))10,9,10
10    B=B+YER(I)
      G=G+1.0
      R=R+Y(I)
9     CONTINUE
      IF(G)1,1,12
12    B=B/G
      R=R/G
      PUNCH 11,R,B,G,RUN,WAVEL
      GO TO 1
      END
```

ALGOL 60 FOR PROGRAM NUMBER 505

```
PROCEDURE EEEEE(feedp,ka,kb,kc,kd,j,k,L,m,devf1,rLm1,wL1,wu1,devf2,
rLm2,wL2,wu2,y,yer,x1,x1er,g,oper,instr,run,temp,waveL); ARRAY y,yer,x1,
x1er,[1:20]; INTEGER feedp,ka,kb,kc,kd,j,k,L,m,g,oper,instr,run; REAL devf1,
rLm1,wL1,wu1,devf2,rLm2,wL2,wu2,temp,waveL; SWITCH sw1:=x5,x4,x3,x2,x1;
COMMENTS: SPECIAL TECHNIQUES;
        BEGIN INTEGER i,ke; REAL b,r;
          g:=0; ke:=ka+2;
          GO TO sw1[ke];
X1:     y[kd]:=0;
X2:     y[kc]:=0;
X3:     y[kb]:=0; GO TO X5;
X4:     FOR i:=kb STEP 1 UNTIL kc DO y [i]:=0;
X5:     b:=r:=0;
        FOR i:=1 STEP 1 UNTIL 20 DO
        BEGIN
          IF y[i]=0 THEN GO TO Y5;
          b:=b+yer[i]; g:=g+1; r:=r+y[i]
Y5:     END;
        IF g>0 THEN
        BEGIN
          b:=b/g; r:=b/g;
          PUNCH r,bb,g,run,waveL END
X6: END EEEEE;
X7: READ feedp;
    READ ka,kb,kc,kd;  READ j;
    READ k,L,m;
    READ devf1,rLm1,wL1,wu1;
    READ devf2,rLm2,wL2,wu2;
    FOR i:=1 STEP 1 UNTIL 20 DO READ y[i];
    FOR i:=1 STEP 1 UNTIL 20 DO READ yer[i];
    FOR i:=1 STEP 1 UNTIL 20 DO READ x1[i];
    FOR  i:=1 STEP 1 UNTIL 20 DO READ x1er[i];
    READ g; READ oper,instr;
    READ run,temp,waveL;
    EEEEE(feedp,ka,kb,kc,kd,j,k,L,m,devf1,rLm1,wL1,wu1,devf2,rLm2,wL2,
    wu2,y[i],yer[i],x1er[i],oper,instr,run,temp,waveL);
    GO TO X7;
```

Part II. Data Transposition

In some spectrophotometric studies of complex formation in systems containing two active components (X and Y) and an inert solvent (S), with the concentration of X much less than that of Y, data are collected at several wavelengths for solutions with the concentration of X varied and the concentrations of Y fixed. A set of information is represented in matrix forms thus:

$$\left\| \begin{array}{l} A(1,1,k) \quad\; A(1,2,k)\ldots\ldots\ldots\ldots A(1,J,k) \\[1em] A(2,1,k) \quad\; A(2,2,k)\ldots\ldots\ldots\ldots A(2,J,k) \\ \quad\vdots \qquad\qquad\qquad\qquad\qquad\quad \vdots \\ A(i,1,k)\ldots\ldots\ldots\ldots A(i,j,k)\ldots A(i,J,k) \\ \quad\vdots \qquad\qquad\qquad\qquad\qquad\quad \vdots \\ A(I,1,k)\ldots\ldots\ldots\ldots A(I,j,k)\ldots A(I,J,k) \end{array} \right\| \equiv \|A(I,J,k)\|$$

Here $A\,(i,j,k)$ is the absorbance measured at the ith wavelength for the solution with the jth and kth concentrations of X and Y respectively. $\|A(I, J, k)\|$ denotes the matrix for solutions with the kth concentration of Y and J concentrations of X measured at I wavelengths.

Often it is necessary to process blocks of data which have concentrations of X varied and of Y constant, then to rearrange the data and process new blocks with X concentration constant and Y concentration varied. Here is the program for rearranging such data. The block of rearranged data for K solutions (Y concentration varied) with the jth concentration of X, measured at I wavelengths is denoted as $\|A(I,j, K)\|$.

INPUT COMMANDS FOR PROGRAM 34

Program 34 (*call word* HBAAA) has been designed to rearrange up to twenty blocks of information. Each of the M6 blocks will contain data collected at M4 wavelengths for each of 20 solutions. The input commands are as follows:

M4—The number of wavelengths per block. M4 cannot be greater than 12 in the program given here for an IBM 1620 60K.

M6—The number of blocks, each with M4 wavelengths. M6 cannot exceed 20.

With computers of storage capacity larger than that of the IBM 1620 60K, M4 can exceed 12.

INPUT FORMAT FOR PROGRAM 34

STATEMENT	COMMENT
READ,BLOCK,TEMP,M6,M4	BLOCK and TEMP are identification. M6 and M4 are *input commands*.
READ,OAM(J,I),OAM(J,I+1),OAM(J,I+2),OAM(J,I+3)	

> OAM(J,I) is the absorbance measured at the Jth wavelength of the Ith solution, with the concentration of Y fixed. The blocks of information are read in thus:
> $\quad$ ||A(I,20,1)||
> $\quad$ ||A(I,20,2)|| $\quad\}$ X varied.
> (M6 blocks each with M4 wavelengths.)

READ,C1(I),C1(I+1),C1(I+2),C1(I+3)	20 concentrations of X.
READ,C2(I),C2(I+1),C2(I+2),C2(I+3)	20 concentrations of Y.

OUTPUT FORMAT FOR PROGRAM 34

STATEMENT	COMMENT
PUNCH,BLOCK,TEMP,M6,M4	See *input format*.
PUNCH,OAM(J2,I),OAM(J3,I),OAM(J4,I),OAM(J5,I)	

> The rearranged blocks, each with Y varied and X fixed, are generated as follows.
> $\quad$ ||A(I,1,20)||
> $\quad$ ||A(I,2,20)|| $\quad\}$ Y varied.
> (The number of blocks generated will equal the number of non-zero concentrations of X).

PUNCH,C2(I),C2(I+1),C2(I+2),C2(I+3)	20 concentrations of Y.

FORTRAN FOR PROGRAM NUMBER 34

CALL WORD HBAAA

```
DIMENSION OAM(240,20),C1(20),C2(20),J1(20)
1 READ,BLOCK,TEMP,M6,M4
M=M6*M4
DO 2 J=1,M
DO 3 I=1,20,4
3 READ,OAM(J,I),OAM(J,I+1),OAM(J,I+2),OAM(J,I+3)
2 CONTINUE
M=M+1
IF(M-240)12,13,1
12 DO 4 J=M,240
DO 5 I=1,20
5 OAM(J,I)=0.0
4 CONTINUE
13 DO 6 I=1,20,4
6 READ,C1(I),C1(I+1),C1(I+2),C1(I+3)
DO 7 I=1,20,4
7 READ,C2(I),C2(I+1),C2(I+2),C2(I+3)
PUNCH,BLOCK,TEMP,M6,M4
DO 8 I=1,20
IF(C1(I))8,8,15
15 DO 9 J=1,M4
DO 10 K=1,20
10 J1(K)=(K-1)*M4+J
DO 11 K=1,20,4
J2=J1(K)
J3=J1(K+1)
J4=J1(K+2)
J5=J1(K+3)
11 PUNCH,OAM(J2,I),OAM(J3,I),OAM(J4,I),OAM(J5,I)
9 CONTINUE
8 CONTINUE
DO 14 I=1,20,4
14 PUNCH,C2(I),C2(I+1),C2(I+2),C2(I+3)
GO TO 1
END
```

ALGOL 60 FOR PROGRAM NUMBER 34

```
PROCEDURE HBAAA(block,temp,m6,m4);  ARRAY oam[1:240,1:20],c1,c2,
j1[1:20];  INTEGER m6,m4;  REAL block,temp;
COMMENT: DATA TRANSPOSITION PROGRAM;
     BEGIN INTEGER m,i,j,k,j2,j3,j4,j5;
        m:=m6Xm4;
        FOR j:=1 STEP 1 UNTIL m DO
        FOR i:=1 STEP 1 UNTIL 20 DO READ oam[j,i];
        m:=m+1;
        IF m>240 THEN GO TO X3
        ELSE IF m<240 THEN
        FOR j:=m STEP 1 UNTIL 240 DO
        FOR i:=1 STEP 1 UNTIL 20 DO oam[j,i]:=0;
X1:     FOR i:=1 STEP 1 UNTIL 20 DO READ c1[i];
        FOR i:=1 STEP 1 UNTIL 20 DO READ c2[i];
        PUNCH block,temp,m6,m4;
        FOR i:=1 STEP 1 UNTIL 20 DO
        BEGIN
           IF c1[i]≤0 THEN GO TO X2;
           FOR j:=1 STEP 1 UNTIL m4 DO
           BEGIN
              FOR k:=1 STEP 1 UNTIL 20 DO j1[k]:=(k−1)Xm4+j;
              FOR k:=1 STEP 1 UNTIL 20 DO
              BEGIN
                 j2:=j1[k];  j3:=j1[k+1];
                 j4:=j1[k+2];  j5:=j1[k+3];
                 PUNCH oam[j2,i],oam[j3,i],oam[j4,i],oam[j5,i]
              END
           END
X2:     END;
        FOR i:=1 STEP 1 UNTIL 20 DO PUNCH c2[i]
X3:  END HBAAA;
X4:  READ block,temp,m6,m4;
     HBAAA(block,temp,m6,m4);
     GO TO X4;
```

Part III. Absorption Band Ratio Method

In their paper on the temperature broadening of the 5200A iodine absorption band de Maine, de Maine and Jurinski[1] used the absorbance ratio, (OAM(I) at T2°C/OAM(I) at T1°C), as a sensitive indication of solvent impurity or unsuspected complexes. Here the ratio R(I, J) equals AB(I, J, T2)/AB(I, J, T1) where AB(I, J, T2) and AB(I, J, T1) are the apparent molar absorbancy indices of the solute in the Ith solution at the Jth wavelength at T2 and T1°C respectively. T2 is higher than T1 and there is a single solute.

R(I, J) values indicate the following.

1. R(I, J) can be independent of I (i.e., the ratio is independent of solute concentration) only if the solute (S) obeys Beer's Law or if one or both of the following reactions occur.

$$S \rightleftarrows S* \qquad (1)$$

$$S + S_0 \rightleftarrows C \qquad (2)$$

$S*$, S_0 and C are an unsuspected isomer of the solute, the solvent, and a complex between one molecule of S and the solvent, respectively. For reaction (2) the solute concentration is very much smaller than the concentration of the solvent.

2. If R(I,J) is constant and less than one at the absorption maximum for all I's, the occurrence of reaction (1) and/or (2) is indicated.

3. If R(I,J) is independent of I and greater than one at the absorption maximum, reaction (1) with $S*$ an exothermic form of S is indicated.

4. If R(I,J) equals one at all wavelengths, the solute obeys Beer's Law.

R(I,J) plotted as a function of the wavelength (J) will be above one, then decrease to one at the absorption maximum and then increase again if normal collision band broadening occurs. The presence of an unsuspected solute species will be indicated by abnormal plots of R(I,J) versus J. This subject is considered in some detail in reference (1).

With Program 35 (*call word* IBAAA) as many as twenty values for R(I,J) at each wavelength can be computed with input information at T1°C and T2°C for Programs 9 (*call word* IAAAA) or 309 (*call word* IAAAS). The *output information* is compatible with Programs 1 (AAAAA), 301 (AAAAS) and 505 (EEEEE) and it may be processed with *Autoplotter* Program 502 (*call word* BEEEE).

METHOD OF CALCULATION

A "set of input information" for Program 9 or 309 contains data collected at all wavelengths. The instructions to the computer include the following.

[1] M. M. de Maine, P. A. D. de Maine and N. B. Jurinski, *J. Miss. Acad. Sci.*, 8 (1962), 267.

(a) Read the set of input information with data for M6 wavelengths and the lower temperature (T1°C).

(b) Read the set of input information with data for M6 wavelengths and the higher temperature (T2°C).

(c) Apply the *fail–safe procedure* to both sets of information.

(d) Execute the *reject–restore commands* given in each of the two sets of input information.

(e) Calculate the ratio R(I,J) for each of the solutions at each wavelength.

(f) Use the *instrument reliability factors* given in each of the two sets of input information to compute the *maximum permitted error* for each R(I,J).

(g) Use the *centering device* to distribute the values of R(I,J) at each wavelength evenly about the origin of the $X1$ axis. This device is described in Part I of this chapter.

(h) Punch the input information required for Program 301 (*call word* AAAAS) or Program 505 (*call word* EEEEE). The use of these two programs is described in Part I of this chapter. Here $Y(I) = R(I,J)$, $YER(I,J) = maximum\ permitted\ error$ in R(I,J) and $X1ER(I) = 0.0$. One deck of information is obtained for each of the M6 wavelengths.

INPUT COMMANDS AND FORMAT FOR PROGRAM 35

There are no input commands associated exclusively with Program 35. The input commands which appear in the two sets of input information (see Method of Calculation) have been given in Chapter II for Programs 9 and 309.

The input information for Program 35 consists of the two sets of input information in Program 9 or 309 for a single system (solute plus solvent) measured at two temperatures. The set of input information collected at the lower temperature is read in first, followed by the set collected at the higher temperature.

OUTPUT FORMAT FOR PROGRAM 35

The output information generated by Program 35 for each of the M6 wavelengths is compatible with Program 301 (*call word* AAAAS) or Program 505 (*call word* EEEEE). Here is the output format for Program 35.

STATEMENT	COMMENT
PUNCH,AAAAS,FEEDP	AAAAS = 301.0, FEEDP = 35.0.
PUNCH,KA1,KB1,KC1,KD1	*Reject–restore* commands for the lower temperature (T1°C).
PUNCH,JJ	*Cycle command.*
PUNCH,K,L,M	*Input commands* for program 9 or 309.
PUNCH,DEVF22,D,WL11,WU11	⎧ *Instrument reliability*
PUNCH,DEVF21,D,WL21,WU21	⎨ *factors* at T1°C. ⎩ D = RLM1.
PUNCH,Y(I,M4),Y(I+1,M4),Y(I+2,M4),Y(I+3,M4)	Y(I,M4) = R(I,J).
PUNCH,YER(I,M4),YER(I+1,M4),YER(I+2,M4),YER(I+3,M4)	⎧ YER(I,M4) is the *maximum permitted error* in R(I,J).
PUNCH,X1(I,M4),X1(I+1,M4),X1(I+2,M4),X1(I+3,M4)	X1(I,M4) etc. are chosen so that the corresponding Y(I,M4) etc. are arranged symmetrically about the origin of the XI axis.
PUNCH,A,A,A,A	A, the *maximum permitted error* in X1(I,M4), is zero.
PUNCH,G	The number of ratios for the M4th wavelength.
PUNCH,OPER,INSTR	⎱ Identification.
PUNCH,RUN,TEMP,WAVEL	⎰ WAVEL = M4.

This format is repeated M6 times.

FORTRAN FOR PROGRAM NUMBER 35

CALL WORD IBAAA

```
DIMENSION Y(20,50),YER(20,50),C(20,2),X(20,50),DEV1(20,2),DEV2(20,2)
1 READ,IAAAS,FEEDP
READ,KA1,KB1,KC1,KD1
READ,JJ
READ,M61
READ,K,L,M
READ,D,WL11,WU11
READ,D,WL21,WU21
IF(K-2)10,10,11
10 READ,DEF11
GO TO 12
11 DO 13 I=1,20,4
13 READ,DEV1(I,1),DEV1(I+1,1),DEV1(I+2,1),DEV1(I+3,1)
DEF11=5555.0
12 GO TO (14,15,14,15),K
14 READ,DEF21
GO TO 16
15 DO 17 I=1,20,4
17 READ,DEV2(I,1),DEV2(I+1,1),DEV2(I+2,1),DEV2(I+3,1)
DEF21=5555.0
16 DO 3 I=1,20,4
3 READ,Y(I,1),Y(I+1,1),Y(I+2,1),Y(I+3,1)
DO 4 I=1,20,4
4 READ,C(I,1),C(I+1,1),C(I+2,1),C(I+3,1)
READ,OPER,INSTR
READ,RUN,TEMP,WAVEL
DO 2 J=2,M61
DO 5 I=1,20,4
5 READ,Y(I,J),Y(I+1,J),Y(I+2,J),Y(I+3,J)
2 CONTINUE
READ,IAAAS,FEEDP
READ,KA2,KB2,KC2,KD2
READ,J
READ,M62
READ,K,L,M
READ,D,WL12,WU12
READ,D,WL22,WU22
IF(K-2)18,18,19
18 READ,DEF12
GO TO 20
19 DO 21 I=1,20,4
21 READ,DEV1(I,2),DEV1(I+1,2),DEV1(I+2,2),DEV1(I+3,2)
20 GO TO (22,23,22,23),K
22 READ,DEF22
GO TO 24
23 DO 25 I=1,20,4
25 READ,DEV2(I,2),DEV2(I+1,2),DEV2(I+2,2),DEV2(I+3,2)
24 DO 6 I=1,20,4
6 READ,X(I,1),X(I+1,1),X(I+2,1),X(I+3,1)
DO 7 I=1,20,4
7 READ,C(I,2),C(I+1,2),C(I+2,2),C(I+3,2)
READ,OPER,INSTR
READ,RUN,TEMP,WAVEL
DO 8 J=2,M62
DO 9 I=1,20,4
9 READ,X(I,J),X(I+1,J),X(I+2,J),X(I+3,J)
8 CONTINUE
KE=KA1+2
GO TO (26,27,28,29,30),KE
```

```
30 C(KD1,1)=0.0
29 C(KC1,1)=0.0
28 C(KB1,1)=0.0
26 GO TO 32
27 DO 31 I=KB1,KC1
31 C(I,1)=0.0
32 KE=KA2+2
GO TO (33,34,35,36,37),KE
37 C(KD2,2)=0.0
36 C(KC2,2)=0.0
35 C(KB2,2)=0.0
33 GO TO 38
34 DO 39 I=KB2,KC2
39 C(I,2)=0.0
38 DO 40 J=1,M61
DO 41 I=1,20
IF(C(I,1)-WL21)42,43,43
43 IF(C(I,1)-WU21)45,45,42
45 IF(Y(I,J)-WL11)42,46,46
46 IF(Y(I,J)-WU11)47,47,42
47 IF(X(I,J)-WL12)42,48,48
48 IF(X(I,J)-WU12)49,49,42
49 IF(C(I,2)-WL22)42,50,50
50 IF(C(I,2)-WU22)51,51,42
42 Y(I,J)=0.0
X(I,J)=0.0
YER(I,J)=0.0
GO TO 41
51 IF(DEF11-5555.0)52,53,53
52 DEV1(I,1)=DEF11*Y(I,J)
53 IF(DEF12 -5555.0)54,55,55
54 DEV1(I,2)=DEF12*X(I,J)
55 IF(DEF21 -5555.0)56,57,57
56 DEV2(I,1)=DEF21*C(I,1)
57 IF(DEF22-5555.0)58,59,59
58 DEV2(I,2)=DEF22*C(I,2)
59 YER(I,J)=((Y(I,J)-DEV1(I,1))/(C(I,1)+DEV2(I,1)))
YER(I,J)=((X(I,J)+DEV1(I,2))/(C(I,2)-DEV2(I,2)))/YER(I,J)
Y(I,J)=(X(I,J)/C(I,2))/(Y(I,J)/C(I,1))
YER(I,J)=YER(I,J)-Y(I,J)
41 CONTINUE
40 CONTINUE
AAAAS=301.0
FEEDP=35.0
M4=0
60 M4=M4+1
PUNCH,AAAAS,FEEDP
PUNCH,KA1,KB1,KC1,KD1
PUNCH,JJ
PUNCH,K,L,M
PUNCH,DEF22,D,WL11,WU11
PUNCH,DEF21,D,WL21,WU21
G=0.0
DO 61 I=1,20
IF(Y(I,M4))62,61,62
62 G=G+1.0
61 CONTINUE
DD=-0.1
XMN=-G/20.0
DO 63 I=1,20
IF(Y(I,M4))64,63,64
64 DD=DD+0.1
```

```
X(I,M4)=XMN+DD
63 CONTINUE
A=0.0
DO 65 I=1,20,4
PUNCH,Y(I,M4),Y(I+1,M4),Y(I+2,M4),Y(I+3,M4)
PUNCH,YER(I,M4),YER(I+1,M4),YER(I+2,M4),YER(I+3,M4)
PUNCH,X(I,M4),X(I+1,M4),X(I+2,M4),X(I+3,M4)
65 PUNCH,A,A,A,A
PUNCH,G
PUNCH,OPER,INSTR
WAVEL=M4
PUNCH,RUN,TEMP,WAVEL
IF(M61-M4)1,1,60
END
```

ALGOL 60 FOR PROGRAM NUMBER 35

PROCEDURE IBAAA(feedp,ka1,kb1,kc1,kd1,jj,m61,k,L,m,d,wL11,wu11,wL21, wu21); ARRAY y,yer,x [1:20,1:50],c,dev1,dev2[1:20,1:2]; INTEGER feedp,ka1, kb1,kc1,kd1,jj,m61,k,L,m; REAL d,wL11,wu11,wL21,wu21; SWITCH sw1:=x2, x3,x2,x3; SWITCH sw2:=x6,x7,x6,x7; SWITCH sw3:=x13,x12,x11,x10,x9; SWITCH sw4:=x18,x17,x16,x15,x14;
COMMENT: ABSORPTION BAND RATIO METHOD;
    BEGIN INTEGER oper,instr,run,j,m62,i,ka2,kb2,kc2,kd2,ke,m4,g;
    REAL def11,def21,def12,def22,waveL,temp,dd,xmn,a;
      IF k≤2 THEN
      BEGIN
         READ def11; GO TO X1END;
         FOR i:=1 STEP 1 UNTIL 20 DO READ dev1[i,1];
         def11:=5555;
X1:   GO TO sw1[k];
X2:   READ def21; GO TO X4;
X3:   FOR 1:=1 STEP 1 UNTIL 20 DO READ dev2[i,1];
         def21:=5555;
X4:   FOR i:=1 STEP 1 UNTIL 20 DO READ y[i,1];
         FOR i:=1 STEP 1 UNTIL 20 DO READ c[i,1];
         READ oper,instr;
         READ run,temp,waveL;
         FOR j:=2 STEP 1 UNTIL m61 DO
         FOR i:=1 STEP 1 UNTIL 20 DO READ y[i,j];
         READ feedp;
         READ ka2,kb2,kc2,kd2;
         READ j; READ m62; READ k,L,m;
         READ d,wL12,wu12;
         READ d,wL22,wu22;
         IF k≤2 THEN
         BEGIN
            READ def12; GO TO X5END;
            FOR i:=1 STEP 1 UNTIL 20 DO READ dev1[i,2];
X5:   GO TO sw2[k];
X6:   READ def22; GO TO X8;
X7:   FOR i:=1 STEP 1 UNTIL 20 DO READ dev2[i,2];
X8:   FOR i:=1 STEP 1 UNTIL 20 DO READ x[i,1];
         FOR i:=1 STEP 1 UNTIL 20 DO READ c[i,2];
         READ oper,instr;
         READ run,temp,waveL;
         FOR j:=2 STEP 1 UNTIL m62 DO
         FOR i:=1 STEP 1 UNTIL 20 DO READ x[i,j];
         ke:=ka1+2;
         GO TO sw2[ke];
X9:   c[kd1,1]:=0;
X10:   c[kc1,1]:=0;
X11:   c[kb1,1]:=0;
X12:   FOR i:=kb1 STEP 1 UNTIL kc1 DO c[i,1]:=0;
X13:   ke:=ka2+2;
         GO TO sw4[ke];
X14:   c[kd2,2]:=0;
X15:   c[kc2,2]:=0;

```
X16:   c[kb2,2]:=0;
X17:   FOR i:=kb2 STEP 1 UNTIL kc2 DO c[i,2]:=0;
X18:   FOR j:=1 STEP 1 UNTIL m61 DO
       BEGIN
          FOR i:=1 STEP 1 UNTIL 20 DO
          BEGIN
             IF(c[i,1]<wL21)∨(c[i,1]>wu21)∨(y[i,j]<wL11)∨(y[i,j]>wu11)
               ∨(x[i,j]<wL12)∨(x[i,j]>wu12)∨(c[i,2]<wL22)∨(c[i,2]>wu22)THEN
             BEGIN
X19:            y[i,j]:=x[i,j]:=yer[i,j]:=0;
                GO TO X20END;
             IF def11<5555 THEN dev1[i,1]:=def11Xy[i,j];
             IF def12<5555 THEN dev1[i,2]:=def12Xx[i,j];
             IF def21<5555 THEN dev2[i,1]:=def21Xc[i,1];
             IF def22<5555 THEN dev2[i,2]:=def22Xc[i,2];
             yer[i,j]:=((y[i,j]−dev1[i,1])/(c[i,1]+dev2[i,1]));
             yer[i,j]:=((x[i,j]+dev1[i,2])/(c[i,2]−dev2[i,2]))/yer[i,j];
             y[i,j]:=(x[i,j]/c[i,2])/(y[i,j]/c[i,1]);
             yer[i,j]:=yer[i,j]−y[i,j]
X20:      END
X21:   END;
       feedp:=35;  m4:=0;
X22:   m4:=m4+1;
       PUNCH feedp;
       PUNCH ka1,kb1,kc1,kd1;
       PUNCH jj;  PUNCH k,L,m;
   −   PUNCH def22,d,wL11,wu11;
       PUNCH def21;d,wL21,wu21;
       g:=0;
       FOR i:=1 STEP 1 UNTIL 20 DO
       IF y[i,m4]≠0 THEN g:=g+1;
       dd:=−0.1;  xmn:=−g/20;
       FOR i:=1 STEP 1 UNTIL 20 DO
       IF y[i,m4]≠0 THEN
       BEGIN
          dd:=dd+0.1;  x[i,m4]:=xmn+ddEND;
       a:=0;
       FOR i:=1 STEP 1 UNTIL 20 DO PUNCH y[i,m4];
       FOR i:=1 STEP 1 UNTIL 20 DO PUNCH yer[i,m4];
       FOR i:=1 STEP 1 UNTIL 20 DO PUNCH x[i,x];
       FOR i:=1 STEP 1 UNTIL 20 DO PUNCH a,a,a,a;
       PUNCH g;  PUNCH oper,instr;
       waveL:=m4;  PUNCH run,temp,waveL;
       IF m61>m4 THEN GO TO X22
X23:END IBAAA;
X24:READ feedp;
    READ ka1,kb1,kc1,kd1;
    READ jj;  READ m61;
    READ k,L,m;
    READ d,wL11,wu11;
    READ d,wL21,wu21;
    IBAAA(feedp,ka1,kb1,kc1,kd1,jj,m61,k,L,m,d,wL11,wu11,wL21,wu21);
    GO TO X24;
```

Part IV. Jurinski's Equations

Jurinski[2] has shown that each of the two sets of equations:

$$A + B \underset{K_2}{\overset{K_1}{\rightleftarrows}} C_1 \atop C_1 + A \underset{}{\overset{}{\rightleftarrows}} C_2 \Big\} (I) \qquad\qquad A + B \underset{K_2}{\overset{K_1}{\rightleftarrows}} C_1 \atop 2A + B \underset{}{\overset{}{\rightleftarrows}} C_2 \Big\} (II)$$

can be solved for K_1, K_2 and the absorbancy indices (A_{C_1} and A_{C_2}) of the two complexes (C_1 and C_2) with spectral data taken at a single wavelength for solutions containing both A and B. Each of the equation sets yields a four dimension equation

$$y = m_1 x_1 + m_2 x_2 + m_3 x_3 + B \tag{A}$$

if it is assumed that the concentration of A is much greater than the concentration of B, and if all four species (A, B, C_1 and C_2) obey Beer's Law. For both equation sets, the ordinates in equation (A) are related to the raw data thus:

$$y = C_A/a_Q; \; x_3 = C_A^2/a_Q; \; x_2 = C_A^2 \text{ and } x_1 = C_A \tag{B}$$

with $a_Q = A_M - a_A C_A - a_B C_B$. C_A and C_B are the concentrations of A and B before equilibrium. A_M is the measured absorbance. a_A and a_B are the absorbancy indices of A and B determined from data for the separate systems.

m_1 and B in equation (A) are identical for equation sets (I) and (II). The unknown parameters (K_1, K_2, a_{C_1} and a_{C_2}) are related to the slopes (m_1, m_2, m_3) and intercept (B) of equation (A) thus:

FOR EQUATION SET (I)

$$K_1 = m_1/B; \; K_2 = m_2/m_1; \; a_{C_1} = 1/m_1 + a_A + a_B;$$
$$a_{C_2} = -m_3/m_2 + 2a_A + a_B$$

FOR EQUATION SET (II)

$$K_1 = m_1/B; \; K_2 = m_2/B; \; a_{C_1} = 1/m_1 + a_A + a_B;$$
$$a_{C_2} = -m_3/m_2 + 2a_A + a_B$$

The linear equation (A) can be solved for its slopes (m_1, m_2 and m_3) and intercept (B) with Program 3, Program 303, or one of the variable dimension *self-judgment programs* (26 and 326). Program 36 can be used to calculate the input information required for Program 303 from input information originally intended for use with Program 10 or Program 310. The *input format* for Programs 10 and 310 is identical and it is described in Chapter IV of Volume I.

[2] N. B. Jurinski, *J. Miss. Acad. Sci.*, **10** (1964), 74.

METHOD OF CALCULATION

The phrase "one set of input information" means all information normally required to solve by Program 10 or 310 the equation, $A + B \overset{K}{\rightleftharpoons} C$, for K and the absorbancy index of the complex with data taken at a single wavelength. The absorbancy indices of A and B, designated a_A and a_B, can be expressed in *functional form* thus:

$$a_A = {}_A a_0 + A_1 \cdot C_A + A_2 \cdot C_A^2 + A_3 \cdot C_A^3 + A_4 \cdot C_A^4$$

Here ${}_A a_0$ is the concentration independent part of a_A. C_A is the concentration of A.

The instructions to the computer include the following:

(a) Read the first set of input information; then execute the *fail–safe procedure* and the *reject–restore* command in the normal way.

(b) Compute the values for the ordinates of equation (A) as defined in equation (B). In computing a_Q the *functional forms* of a_A and a_B are used.

(c) Compute the *maximum permitted errors* for each value of each ordinate with the *maximum permitted deviations* for the measured absorbancies and the corresponding concentrations of B, given in the set of input information for Program 10 or 310.

(d) Punch the input information required by Program 303 to solve equation (A) for m_1, m_2, m_3, and B with data at a single wavelength.

These calculations are made for each of the M6 wavelengths for which information is available in the input for Program 10 or 310.

INPUT COMMANDS AND FORMAT FOR PROGRAM 36

There are no special input commands associated exclusively with Program 36. Input commands which appear in the input format for Program 10 or 310 and which are executed in Program 36, have been given in Chapter IV of Volume I.

The input formats for Programs 10, 310 and 36 are identical, and they are described for Program 10 in Chapter IV of Volume I.

OUTPUT FORMAT FOR PROGRAM 36

The output information generated by Program 36 for each wavelength is compatible with Program 303 by use of which the slopes, intercept, and their *maximum permitted errors* can be calculated.

STATEMENT	COMMENT
PUNCH,CAAAS,FEEDP	$\begin{cases} \text{CAAAS} = 303.0; \\ \text{FEEDP} = 36.0. \end{cases}$
PUNCH,KA,KB,KC,KD	*Reject–restore commands.*
PUNCH,J	*Cycle commands.*
PUNCH,K,L,M	*Input commands.*
PUNCH,DEVF1,RLM1,WL1,WU1 PUNCH,DEVF2,RLM2,WL2,WU2 PUNCH,DEVF3,RLM3,WL3,WU3 PUNCH,DEVF4,RLM4,WL4,WU4	$\begin{cases} \textit{Instrument reliability factors.} \\ \text{DEVF3} = \text{DEVF4} = \text{DEVF2}; \\ \text{RLM3} = \text{RLM4} = \text{RLM2}; \\ \text{WL3} = \text{WL4} = \text{WL2}; \\ \text{WU3} = \text{WU4} = \text{WU2}. \end{cases}$
PUNCH,Y(I),Y(I+1),Y(I+2),Y(I+3) PUNCH,YER(I),YER(I+1),YER(I+2),YER(I+3) PUNCH,X1(I),X1(I+1),X1(I+2),X1(I+3) PUNCH,X1ER(I),X1ER(I+1),X1ER(I+2),X1ER(I+3) PUNCH,X2(I),X2(I+1),X2(I+2),X2(I+3) PUNCH,X2ER(I),X2ER(I+1),X2ER(I+2),X2ER(I+3) PUNCH,X3(I),X3(I+1),X3(I+2),X3(I+3) PUNCH,X3ER(I),X3ER(I+1),X3ER(I+2),X3ER(I+3)	$\begin{cases} \text{Here } Y(I) = C_A/a_Q; \ X1(I) = \\ C_A^2/a_Q; \quad X2(I) = C_A^2 \text{ and} \\ X3(I) = C_A. \ \text{YER(I), X1ER} \\ \text{(I), X2ER(I) and X3ER(I)} \\ \text{are the associated } \textit{Maximum} \\ \textit{permitted errors.} \end{cases}$
PUNCH,G	$\begin{cases} \text{The number of values for} \\ Y(I) \text{ at this wavelength.} \end{cases}$
PUNCH,OPER,INSTR PUNCH,RUN,TEMP,WAVEL	Identification.

This format is repeated M6–1 times.

FORTRAN FOR PROGRAM NUMBER 36

CALL WORD JBAAA

```
DIMENSION C1(20),C2(20),FM1(20),FM2(20),OAM(20),DEV1(20),DEV2(20),Y(
DIMENSION YER(20),X1(20),X1ER(20),Z1(20),Z2(20)
DIMENSION X2(20),X2ER(20),X3(20),X3ER(20)
1 READ,JAAAS,FEEDP
FEEDP=JAAAS
READ,J
N=J
READ,EQO
READ,M6
READ,K,L,M
READ,KA,KB,KC,KD
READ,RLM1,WAC1,WL1,WU1
READ,RLM2,WAC2,WL2,WU2
M5=M6
M4=0
A1=0.0
A2=0.0
A3=0.0
A4=0.0
B1=0.0
B2=0.0
B3=0.0
B4=0.0
AIBX=0.0
AIAX=0.0
DO 100 I=1,20
X1ER(I)=0.0
X2ER(I)=0.0
100 X3ER(I)=0.0
2 IF(M6-M5)1,3,3
3 DO 4 I=1,20,4
4 READ,OAM(I),OAM(I+1),OAM(I+2),OAM(I+3)
G=20.0
IF(L-40)5,5,6
5 READ,AIAX
6 IF(L-40)9,9,8
8 READ,AIAX,AIBX
9 IF(M6-M5)1,10,10
10 IF(L-10)20,20,11
11 IF(L-20)12,12,13
12 READ,A1,A2,A3,A4
GO TO 20
13 IF(L-30)20,20,14
14 IF(L-40)12,12,15
15 IF(L-50)20,20,16
16 IF(L-60)12,12,17
17 IF(L-70)19,19,18
18 READ,A1,A2,A3,A4
19 READ,B1,B2,B3,B4
20 IF(M6-M5)1,301,43
301 IF(M-2)21,21,23
21 DO 22 I=1,20,4
22 READ,C1(I),C1(I+1),C1(I+2),C1(I+3)
GO TO 25
23 DO 24 I=1,20,4
24 READ,FM1(I),FM1(I+1),FM1(I+2),FM1(I+3)
25 DO 670 I=1,20
C2(I)=0.0
670 FM2(I)=0.0
```

```
    IF(L-20)31,31,26
26  IF(M-1)1,27,174
174 IF(M-3)28,27,28
27  DO 29 I=1,20,4
29  READ,C2(I),C2(I+1),C2(I+2),C2(I+3)
    GO TO 31
28  DO 30 I=1,20,4
30  READ,FM2(I),FM2(I+1),FM2(I+2),FM2(I+3)
31  IF(K-1)1,32,33
32  READ,DEVF1
    READ,DEVF2
33  IF(K-2)43,34,36
34  READ,DEVF1
    DO 35 I=1,20,4
35  READ,DEV2(I),DEV2(I+1),DEV2(I+2),DEV2(I+3)
    DEVF2=5555.0
36  IF(K-3)43,37,39
37  DO 38 I=1,20,4
38  READ,DEV1(I),DEV1(I+1),DEV1(I+2),DEV1(I+3)
    DEVF1=5555.0
    READ,DEVF2
39  IF(K-4)43,40,1
40  DO 41 I=1,20,4
41  READ,DEV1(I),DEV1(I+1),DEV1(I+2),DEV1(I+3)
    DO 42 I=1,20,4
42  READ,DEV2(I),DEV2(I+1),DEV2(I+2),DEV2(I+3)
    DEVF1=5555.0
    DEVF2=5555.0
43  DO 67 I=1,20
    KE=KA+2
    GO TO (90,91,92,93,94),KE
91  DO 95 J=KB,KC
95  C1(J)=0.0
    GO TO 90
94  C1(KD)=0.0
93  C1(KC)=0.0
92  C1(KB)=0.0
90  IF(M-1)1,45,46
45  Z1(I)=C1(I)
    Z2(I)=C2(I)
46  IF(M-2)44,47,48
47  Z1(I)=C1(I)
    Z2(I)=FM2(I)
48  IF(M-3)44,49,50
49  Z1(I)=FM1(I)
    Z2(I)=C2(I)
50  IF(M-4)44,51,1
51  Z1(I)=FM1(I)
    Z2(I)=FM2(I)
44  IF(K-2)52,52,53
52  DEV1(I)=DEVF1*OAM(I)
53  IF(K-1)1,54,55
55  IF(K-3)58,54,58
54  IF(L-20)56,56,57
56  DEV2(I)=DEVF2*Z1(I)
    GO TO 58
57  DEV2(I)=DEVF2*Z2(I)
58  IF(OAM(I)-WL1)66,59,59
59  IF(OAM(I)-WU1)60,60,66
60  IF(L-20)61,61,64
61  IF(Z1(I)-WL2)66,62,62
62  IF(Z1(I)-WU2)67,67,66
```

```
 64  IF(Z2(I)-WL2)66,65,65
 65  IF(Z2(I)-WU2)67,67,66
 66  Z1(I)=0.0
     Z2(I)=0.0
     DEV1(I)=0.0
     DEV2(I)=0.0
     Y(I)=0.0
     YER(I)=0.0
     OAM(I)=0.0
     X1(I)=0.0
     X1ER(I)=0.0
     X2ER(I)=0.0
     X2(I)=0.0
     X3ER(I)=0.0
     X3(I)=0.0
     G=G-1.0
 67  CONTINUE
     IF(M6-M5)1,505,506
506  J=N
     GO TO 625
505  READ,OPER,INSTR
     READ,RUN,TEMP,WAVEL
625  M5=M5-1
     M4=M4+1
     CAAAS=303.0
     DO 96 I=1,20
     IF(OAM(I))97,97,98
 97  Y(I)=0.0
     YER(I)=0.0
     X1(I)=0.0
     X1ER(I)=0.0
     X2(I)=0.0
     X2ER(I)=0.0
     X3(I)=0.0
     X3ER(I)=0.0
     GO TO96
 98  IF(Z1(I))97,97,99
 99  QQ=Z1(I)*Z1(I)*Z1(I)
     AA=AIAX+A1*Z1(I)+A2*Z1(I)*Z1(I)+A3*QQ+A4*Z1(I)*QQ
     QQ=Z2(I)*Z2(I)*Z2(I)
     BB=AIBX+B1*Z2(I)+B2*Z2(I)*Z2(I)+B3*QQ+B4*QQ*Z2(I)
     AR=AA*Z1(I)+BB*Z2(I)
     AQ=OAM(I)-AR
     IF(AQ-WAC1*OAM(I))97,101,101
101  YER(I)=(Z1(I)*(Z2(I)+DEV2(I)))/(AQ-DEV1(I))
     Y(I)=(Z1(I)*Z2(I))/AQ
     YER(I)=YER(I)-Y(I)
     X1(I)=Z2(I)
     X2(I)=Z2(I)*Z2(I)
     X3(I)=(Z1(I)*Z2(I)*Z2(I))/AQ
 96  CONTINUE
     RLM3=RLM2
     RLM4=RLM2
     WL3=WL2
     WL4=WL2
     WU3=WU2
     WU4=WU2
     DEVF3=DEVF2
     DEVF4=DEVF2
     PUNCH,CAAAS,FEEDP
     PUNCH,KA,KB,KC,KD
     PUNCH,J
```

```
PUNCH,K,L,M
PUNCH,DEVF1,RLM1,WL1,WU1
PUNCH,DEVF2,RLM2,WL2,WU2
PUNCH,DEVF3,RLM3,WL3,WU3
PUNCH,DEVF4,RLM4,WL4,WU4
DO 103 I=1,20,4
PUNCH,Y(I),Y(I+1),Y(I+2),Y(I+3)
PUNCH,YER(I),YER(I+1),YER(I+2),YER(I+3)
PUNCH,X1(I),X1(I+1),X1(I+2),X1(I+3)
PUNCH,X1ER(I),X1ER(I+1),X1ER(I+2),X1ER(I+3)
PUNCH,X2(I),X2(I+1),X2(I+2),X2(I+3)
PUNCH,X2ER(I),X2ER(I+1),X2ER(I+2),X2ER(I+3)
PUNCH,X3(I),X3(I+1),X3(I+2),X3(I+3)
103 PUNCH,X3ER(I),X3ER(I+1),X3ER(I+2),X3ER(I+3)
PUNCH,G
PUNCH,OPER,INSTR
PUNCH,RUN,TEMP,WAVEL
IF(M5)1,1,2
END
```

ALGOL 60 FOR PROGRAM NUMBER 36

PROCEDURE JBAAA(feedp,j,eqo,m6,k,L,m,ka,kb,kc,kd,rLm1,wac1,wL1,n,wu1, rLm2,wac2,wL2,wu2); ARRAY c1,c2,fm1,fm2,oam,dev1,dev2,y,yer,x1,x1er,x2, x2er,x3,x3er,z1,z2[1:20]; INTEGER feedp,j,eqo,n,m6,k,L,m,ka,kb,kc,kd; REAL rLm1,wac1,wL1,wu1,rLm2,wac2,wL2,wu2; SWITCH sw1:=x11,x7,x10,x9,x8; COMMENT: JURINSKI'S EQUATION;

      BEGIN INTEGER i,ke,m4,m5,n,g,oper,instr,run; REAL aa,aq,ar,a1,a2,a3,a4, aiax,aibx,bb,b1,b2,b3,b4,devf1,devf2,devf3,devf4,qq,rLm3,rLm4,temp,waveL, wL3,wL4,wu3,wu4;

      m5:=m6;

      m4:=a1:=a2:=a3:=a4:=b1:=b2:=b3:=b4:=aibx:=aiax:=0;

      FOR i:=1 STEP 1 UNTIL 20 DO x1er[i]:=x2er[i]:=x3er[i]:=0;

X1:   IF m6<m5 THEN GO TO X19;

      FOR i:=1 STEP 1 UNTIL 20 DO READ oam[i];

      g:=20;

      IF L≤40 THEN READ aiax;

      ELSE IF L>40 THEN READ aiax,aibx;

      IF m6<m5 THEN GO TO X19;

      IF L≤10 THEN GO TO X3

      ELSE IF L≤20 THEN

      BEGIN

X2:   READ a1,a2,a3,a4; GO TO X3END;

      IF(L≤40∧L>30)∨(L≤60∧L>50)THEN GO TO X2

      ELSE IF (L≤30)∨(L≤50∧L>40)THEN GO TO X3

      ELSE IF L>70 THEN READ a1,a2,a3,a4;

      READ b1,b2,b3,b4;

X3:   IF m6<m5 THEN GO TO X19

      ELSE IF m6>m5 THEN GO TO X6;

      IF m≤2 THEN

      BEGIN

        FOR i:=1 STEP 1 UNTIL 20 DO READ c1[i];

        GO TO X4END;

      FOR i:=1 STEP 1 UNTIL 20 DO READ fm1[i];

X4:   FOR i:=1 STEP 1 UNTIL 20 DO c2[i]:=fm2[i]:=0;

      IF L>20 THEN

      BEGIN

        IF m<1 THEN GO TO X19

        ELSE IF m=1∨m=3 THEN

        BEGIN

          FOR i:=1 STEP 1 UNTIL 20 DO READ c2[i];

          GO TO X5END;

        FOR i:=1 STEP 1 UNTIL 20 DO READ fm2[i]END;

X5:   IF k<1 THEN GO TO X19

      ELSE IF k=1 THEN

      BEGIN

      READ devf1; READ devf2END;

      IF k<2 THEN GO TO X6

      ELSE IF k=2 THEN

      BEGIN

      READ devf1;

      FOR i:=1 STEP 1 UNTIL 20 DO READ dev2[i];

      devf2:=5555END;

```
        IF k<3 THEN GO TO X6
        ELSE IF k=3 THEN
        BEGIN
            FOR i:=1 STEP 1 UNTIL 20 DO READ dev1[i];
            devf1:=5555;  READ devf2END;
        IF k>4 THEN GO TO X19
        ELSE IF k=4 THEN
        BEGIN
            FOR i:=1 STEP 1 UNTIL 20 DO READ dev1[i];
            FOR i:=1 STEP 1 UNTIL 20 DO READ dev2[i];
            devf1:=devf2:=5555END;
X6:     FOR i:=1 STEP 1 UNTIL 20 DO
        BEGIN
            ke:=ka+2;  GO TO sw1[ke];
X7:     FOR j:=kb STEP 1 UNTIL kc DO c1[j]:=0;
        GO TO X11;
X8:     c1[kd]:=0;
X9:     c1[kc]:=0;
X10:    c1[kb]:=0;
X11:    IF m<1 THEN GO TO X19
        ELSE IF m=1 THEN
        BEGIN
            z1[i]:=c1[i];  z2[i]:=c2[i]END;
        IF m<2 THEN GO TO X12
        ELSE IF m=2 THEN
        BEGIN
            z1[i]:=c1[i];  z2[i]:=fm2[i]END;
        IF m<3 THEN GO TO X12
        ELSE IF m=3 THEN
        BEGIN
            z1[i]:=fm1[i];  z2[i]:=c2[i]END;
        IF m>4 THEN GO TO X19
        ELSE IF m=4 THEN
        BEGIN
            z1[i]:=fm1[i];  z2[i]:=fm2[i]END;
X12:    IF k≤2 THEN dev1[i]:=devf1Xoam[i];
        IF k=1Vk=3 THEN
        BEGIN
            IF L≤20 THEN
            BEGIN
                dev2[i]:=devf2Xz1[i];
                GO TO X13END;
            dev2[i]:=devf2Xz2[i]END;
X13:    IF(oam[i]<wL1)Voam[i]>wu1 THEN GO TO X14;
        IF(L≤20)∧((z1[i]<wL2)V(z1[i]>wu2))THEN GO TO X14;
        IF(z2[i]≥wL2)∧(z2[i]≤wu2)THEN GO TO X15;
X14:    z1[i]:=z2[i]:=dev1[i]:=dev2[i]:=y[i]:=yer[i]:=oam[i]:=x1[i]:=x1er[i]:=x2er[i]
            :=x2[i]:=x3er[i]:=x3[i]:=0;  g:=g-1
X15:    END;
        IF m6<m5 THEN GO TO X19
        ELSE IF m6>m5 THEN
        BEGIN
            j:=n;  GO TO X16END;
```

```
          READ oper,instr;
          READ run,temp,waveL;
X16:      m5:=m5-1;  m4:=m4+1;
          FOR i:=1 STEP 1 UNTIL 20 DO
          BEGIN
             IF oam[i]≤0 THEN
             BEGIN
X17:         y[i]:=yer[i]:=x1[i]:=x1er[i]:=x2[i]:=x2er[i]:=x3[i]:=x3er[i]:=0;  GO TO
                X18END;
             IF z1[i]≤0 THEN GO TO X17;
             qq:=z1[i]↑3;
             aa:=aiax+a1Xz1[i]+a2Xz1[i]↑2+a3Xqq+a4Xz1[i]Xqq;
             qq:=z2[i]↑3;
             bb:=aibx+b1Xz2[i]+b2Xz2[i]↑2+b3Xqq+b4Xz2[i]Xqq;
             ar:=aaXz1[i]+bbXz2[i];  aq:=oam[i]−ar;
             IF aq<wac1Xoam[i]THEN GO TO X17;
             yer[i]:=(z1[i]X(z2[i]+dev2[i]))/(aq−dev1[i]);
             y[i]:=z1[i]Xz2[i]/aq;  yer[i]:=yer[i]−y[i]:
             x1[i]:=z2[i];  x2[i]:=z2[i]Xz2[i];
             x3[i]:=(z1[i]Xz2[i]↑2)/aq
X18:      END;
          rLm3:=rLm4:=rLm2;
          wL3:=wL4:=wL2;
          wu3:=wu4:=wu2;
          devf3:=devf4:=devf2;
          PUNCH feedp;
          PUNCH ka,kb,kc,kd;
          PUNCH j;  PUNCH k,L,m;
          PUNCH devf1,rLm1,wL1,wu1;
          PUNCH devf2,rLm2,wL2,wu2;
          PUNCH devf3,rLm3,wL3,wu3;
          PUNCH devf4,rLm4,wL4,wu4;
          FOR i:=1 STEP 1 UNTIL 20 DO PUNCH y[i];
          FOR i:=1 STEP 1 UNTIL 20 DO PUNCH yer[i];
          FOR i:=1 STEP 1 UNTIL 20 DO PUNCH x1[i];
          FOR i:=1 STEP 1 UNTIL 20 DO PUNCH x1er[i];
          FOR i:=1 STEP 1 UNTIL 20 DO PUNCH x2[i];
          FOR i:=1 STEP 1 UNTIL 20 DO PUNCH x2er[i];
          FOR i:=1 STEP 1 UNTIL 20 DO PUNCH x3[i];
          FOR i:=1 STEP 1 UNTIL 20 DO PUNCH x3er[i];
          PUNCH g;
          PUNCH oper,instr;
          PUNCH run,temp,waveL;
          IF m5>0 THEN GO TO X1
X19:END JBAAA;
X20:READ feedp;  READ j; n:=j;
     READ eqo;  READ m6;  READ k,L,m;
     READ ka,kb,kc,kd;
     READ rLm1,wac1,wL1,wu1;
     READ rLm2,wac2,wL2,wu2;
     JBAAA(feedp,j,eqo,m6,k,L,m,ka,kb,kc,kd,rLm1,wac1,wL1,wu1,n,rLm2,
     wac2,wL2,wu2);
     GO TO X20;
```

APPENDIX A

TEST PROGRAMS

The FOR-TO-GO and FORTRAN programs in Chapters I–V, VIII, and XI were tested with information generated by the *test programs* (101–107) discussed in Appendices A and B of Volume I and in this appendix. Programs 29 and 329 were partially tested, as described in Chapter VI. All other programs were tested with actual data from experimental work. Most programs have been used extensively by the group at the University of Mississippi to process their spectral[1–10], viscosity[3,4], conductance[3,4,11–13], cryoscopic[9,14], and dielectric constant[15] data.

The input commands for the program to be tested must be considered in order that use of the *test programs* be satisfactory. In Table 10 are listed the test programs and the corresponding FORTRAN (and FOR-TO-GO) programs.

The test procedures for Programs 1–4, 10–15, 301–304 and 310–315 have been described in Appendix A of Volume I. In this appendix test procedures for Programs 9, 22–28, 31, 309, 322–328, 410–415 and 501–504 are described. It is assumed that the reader is familiar with the *input*

[1] C. C. Thompson, Jr. Ph.D. Thesis, University of Mississippi, 1964.
[2] C. C. Thompson, Jr. and P. A. D. de Maine, *J. Am. Chem. Soc.*, **85** (1963), 3096.
[3] D. O. Johnston, Ph.D. Thesis, University of Mississippi, 1963.
[4] D. O. Johnston and P. A. D. de Maine, *J. Chem. Eng. Data.*, **8** (1963), 586.
[5] J. T. Bell, Ph.D. Thesis, University of Mississippi, 1963.
[6] N. B. Jurinski, Ph.D. Thesis, University of Mississippi, 1963.
[7] M. S. Smith, Jr. Ph.D. Thesis, University of Mississippi, 1963.
[8] M. S. Smith, Jr., P. A. D. de Maine and M. M. de Maine, *J. Miss. Acad. Sci.*, **8** (1962), 244.
[9] R. D. Srivastava and P. A. D. de Maine, *J. Miss. Acad. Sci.*, **10** (1964), 51.
[10] V. Ramakrishnan and P. A. D. de Maine, *J. Miss. Acad. Sci.*, **10**, (1964), 82.
[11] W. R. Carper, Ph.D. Thesis, University of Mississippi, 1963.
[12] W. R. Carper, and P. A. D. de Maine, *J. Chem. Eng. Data*, **9** (1964), 316.
[13] W. R. Carper, and P. A. D. de Maine, *J. Chem. Eng. Data* (submitted).
[14] P. A. D. de Maine and R. D. Srivastava, *J. Miss. Acad. Sci.*, **10** (1964), 67.
[15] J. S. Menendez, M. S. Thesis, University of Mississippi (in preparation).

Table 10

FOR-TO-GO and FORTRAN programs used by each test program. Programs 1–4, 9–15, 101–105, 301–304, and 309–315 are discussed in Volume I. Programs 22–28, 31, 106, 107, 322–328, and 410–415 are given in this volume

Test Program		FOR-TO-GO *or* FORTRAN *Program*
		Number
Number	*Call-word*	
101	ABBBB	1,26,301,326,501
102	BBBBB	2,26,302,326,501
103	CBBBB	3,26,303,326,501
104	DBBBB	4,26,304,326,501
105	EBBBB	10–15,310–315,410–415,503,504
106	FBBBB	9,22–25,27,309,322–325,327,502
107	GBBBB	9–15,31,309–315,410–415,502–503

commands for the program to be tested. Only the two new *Test Programs* 106 and 107 will be given here.

INSTRUMENT RELIABILITY FACTORS

In Programs 106 (*call word* FBBBB) and 107 (*call word* GBBBB) the *instrument reliability factors*, which appear in both the *input* and *output* *formats*, are not used in the calculations. These factors can be changed in the output, before the FOR-TO-GO or FORTRAN program is tested. *Instrument reliability factors* have been defined for the FORTRAN programs which are to be tested. *It should be noted that for Programs 28 and 328, RLM(2) and WAC(2) are input commands. RLM(2) defines the curvature. WAC(2) is the dimension of the expansion.*

INPUT COMMANDS FOR PROGRAMS 106 AND 107

There are no special commands associated exclusively with Programs 106 and 107. The cycle (J) and *reject–restore* (KA,KB,KC,KD,KE and KF) commands are not executed in the *test programs*.

The number of the program being tested (PROGN) determines the input format for the *test program* and the output information generated.

METHOD OF CALCULATION IN PROGRAMS 106 AND 107

In Programs 106 and 107 the simplest methods are used in computing the desired test information. For example with the following three equilibrium reactions, solved in Programs 12, 312 and 412, the measured absorbance (OAM(I)) and the two initial concentrations (C1(I) and C2(I)) are computed from the equilibrium concentrations of C_1 and B, and the formation constants, K_1 and K_2.

$$2A \underset{}{\overset{K_1}{\rightleftharpoons}} C_1$$

$$2B \underset{}{\overset{K_2}{\rightleftharpoons}} C_2$$

$$A + B \underset{}{\overset{K_3}{\rightleftharpoons}} C_3$$

If M6 (the number of wavelengths) is greater than one, the absorbancy indices for each successive wavelength are incremented by the selected amount, as described in the *input formats* for Programs 106 and 107.

Tests for Programs 9, 22–25, 27, 309, 322–325, 327 and 502

Test Program 106 (*call word* FBBBB) generates information which can be processed directly with Programs 9, 22–25, 309 or 322–325. If the *self-judgment principle* incorporated in these programs is being tested, the errors in the two (OAM(I) and C1(I)) or three (OAM(I),C1(I) and C2(I)) observables must be introduced in the output generated by Program 106. For Programs 9 and 309, L must equal 6 or 7.

Autoplotter Program 502 (*call word* BEEEE) can be tested with the input information obtained from Program 106 for the other programs listed above. If Program 502 is being tested with data for Programs 25, 27, 325 and 327, JI, the number of sets of conjugate data, must equal 20.

For Programs 27 and 327 the value of L determines the method used to compute OAM(I), and in the input format L has the same meaning as it does in Programs 25 and 325. (See *input commands* for Programs 25 and 325 in Chapter II.) The L value also determines whether the expansion indices (QQ1 and QQ2) are to be entered. Complete tests of all functional expansions in Programs 27 and 327 can be made only with actual experimental data.

Tests for Programs 26, 326 and 501

Output information generated by the four *test programs* in Appendix A of Volume I can be used to test *Autoplotter Program* 501 (*call word* AEEEE) and the two *variable dimension self-judgment programs* (26 and 326).

If Programs 26 and 326 are to be tested the following changes in the output information obtained from the *test programs* must be made.

STATEMENT EXECUTED IN TEST PROGRAM	REPLACEMENT INFORMATION
PUNCH,PROGN,PEEDP	$\begin{cases} \text{JI}(=20 \\ \text{PROGN}(26.0 \text{ or } 326.0); \text{ FEEDP} \end{cases}$
PUNCH,KA,KB,KC,KD	$\begin{cases} \text{KA,KB,KC,KD,KE,KF,} \\ \text{JJ} \end{cases}$

The new *reject–restore* commands (KA, KB, KC, KD, KE, and KF) are described in Chapter III. JJ is the dimension of the equation which will be 2, 3, 4 or 5 for 101, 102, 103 or 104 respectively.

Tests for Programs 309, 410, 411, 414 and 503

If the first card (Programs 309, 410 and 411) (or first two cards (Program 414)) is removed from the output information obtained from *Test Program* 107, then the information is compatible with Programs 309, 410, 411 and 414. *Autoplotter Program* 503 (*call word* CEEEE) can be tested with input information for Programs 10, 11, 14, 310, 311, 314, 410, 411 and 414 as described in Chapter I. Test information for Programs 10, 11, 14, 310, 311 and 314 can be computed with Test Program 105 (see Appendix B, Volume I) or 107.

Tests for Programs 412, 413, 415 and 504

Output information generated by Test Program 107 is compatible with Programs 12, 13, 15, 312, 313, 315, 412, 413 and 415 after removal of the first card (Programs 12, 13, 312, 313, 412 and 413) or the first two cards (Programs 15, 315 and 415). *Input information* for these nine FOR-TRAN programs can be processed with *Autoplotter Program* 504 (*call word* DEEEE) as described in Chapter I.

Tests for Programs 28, 31 and 328

Output information generated by *Test Program* 107 (*call word* GBBBB) can be processed directly with Programs 28, 31 and 328. JI, the number of sets of conjugate information, has been set equal to twenty.

INPUT FORMAT FOR PROGRAM 106

Here "READ, KA, KB, KC, KD, (NQR $\neq$ 25, 27, 325 and 327)" means that the four items of information are to be entered at the designated location if NQR = 9, 22–24, 309 or 322–324. Before the input information for Program 106 is assembled, the *input commands* and *formats* for the FORTRAN program to be tested should be carefully studied. K, L, M, QQ1, QQ2, JI, KA, KB, KC, KD, KE, KF, J, M6 and QQ1 (for L = 5) are defined in the *input commands* and *formats* for the first FORTRAN program to be tested. The two sets of *instrument reliability factors*, DEVF1 or DEV1(I), RLM1, WL1, WU1 and DEVF2 or DEV2(I), RLM2, WL2, WU2, refer to the measured absorbance (OAM(I)) and first concentration, if L = 1, 2, 4 or 5, or to the second concentration if L = 3, 6 or 7 in the output generated by Program 106.

STATEMENT		COMMENT
READ,NQR,TEST		NQR—Number of program being tested
		TEST—Number of test
READ,K,L,M		*Input Commands*
READ,QQ1,QQ2	(NQR = 27 or 327 and L ≥ 5)	Expansion Indices
READ,JI	(NQR = 25, 27, 325 or 327)	Number of sets of conjugate data being processed. JI must be a multiple of four
READ,EQ,AIC,AI1		WAC is an *Instrument Reliability*
READ,EQI,AICI,AII1,WAC		*Factor* used if L ≥ 5

DEFINITIONS

For L = 6 or 7 EQ is the formation constant. For L = 1 − 5 EQ * AIC is the first slope (S_1) in the equation $Y = AI1 * C1(I) + S_1 * X^2 + S_2 * X^3 + \cdots$
$S_1 = EQ * AIC$, $S_2 = (EQ + EQI) * AIC$; $S_3 = (EQ + 2.0 * EQI) * AIC$, etc.
$Y = OAM(I)$; $X =$ a function of C1(I) and C2(I) defined by the value of L.
AIC and AI1 are the absorbancy indices of the complex and the "uncomplexed" molecules at the first wavelength.
AICI and AII1 are the increments for AIC and AI1 defined thus:
Second Wavelength: AIC and AI1 are replaced by (AIC + AICI) and (AI1 + AII1) respectively.
Third Wavelength: AIC and AI1 are replaced by (AIC + 2 * AICI) and (AI1 + 2.0 * AII1) respectively.
Increments are added to AIC and AI1 at all programmed wavelengths.

READ,KA,KB,KC,KD,KE,KF		*Reject–restore* commands
	(NQR = 25, 27, 325 or 327)	
READ,JJ		Dimension of expansion
READ,KA,KB,KC,KD	(NQR = 9, 22–24, 309 or 322–324)	*Reject–restore* Commands
READ,J		*Cycle command*
READ,M6		Number of wavelengths
READ,QQ1	(L = 5)	i.e. QQ1·A $\rightleftharpoons$ A$_{QQ1}$
READ,RLM1,WL1,WU1		*Instrument reliability*
READ,RLM2,WL2,WU2		*factors*

STATEMENT	COMMENT
READ,DEVF1 OR READ,DEV1(I),DEV1(I+1),DEV1(I+2),DEV1(I+3) READ,DEVF2 OR READ,DEV2(I),DEV2(I+1),DEV2(I+2),DEV2(I+3) READ,C1(I),C1(I+1),C1(I+2),C1(I+3) READ,C2(I),C2(I+1),C2(I+2),C2(I+3) (L = 3, 6 or 7)	*Maximum permitted deviations* whose format is determined by the value entered for K

> *Note:* C1(I) and C2(I) are the concentrations of the uncomplexed
> components at equilibrium

READ,OPER,INSTR READ,RUN,TEMP,WAVEL	Identification

OUTPUT FORMATS FOR PROGRAM 106

The output information generated by Program 106 can be processed
directly with the FORTRAN program to be tested. Alternately, the
information described in Chapter I can be added before processing with
Autoplotter Program 502 (*call word* BEEEE).

INPUT FORMAT FOR PROGRAM 107

Test Program 107 (*call word* GBBBB) yields information that can be
processed directly with Program 31 (*call word* EBAAA), if NPR equals
9–15, 309–315, or 410–415, and Program 28 (*call word* BBAAA) or 328
(*call word* BBAAS), if NPR equals 28 or 328. If NPR equals 9 or 309, L
must equal 6 (Scott equation) or 7 (Ketelaar equation). (*Note:* in Program
107 if L ≤ 5, the computer sets L = 6.) No attempt should be made to
assemble the input information for Program 107 until the input commands
for the program to be tested (28, 31 and 328) and the spectrophotometric
program (9, 309–315, 410–415), if Program 31 is being tested, are carefully
considered. If the first card (for NPR = 9–13, 309–313 or 410–413)
or the first two cards (for NPR = 14, 15, 314, 315, 414 or 415) are removed, output information generated by *Test Program* 107 can be processed directly with the spectrophotometric program numbered NPR.
Symbols that are not exclusively associated with Test Program 107 have
been defined elsewhere. Twenty sets of conjugate data are computed with
Program 107.

STATEMENT	COMMENT
READ,NPR,TEST	NPR—Number of spectrophotometric program whose input is to be computed TEST—Number of test
READ,PP	Concentration increment, defined in Chapter IV, Volume I. Conveniently chosen equal to 0.0001
READ,WACRR (NPR = 410–415)	Defined in Ch. XI, Vol. II
READ,K,L,M	*Input commands*
READ,QQ1L,QQ1U READ,PPQQ	(NPR = 14,314, or 414) (see Ch. VI, Vol. I)
READ,QQ1	NPR = 11,14,311,314,411 or 414 if L ≤ 20 (see Ch. IV, VI, Vol. I)

READ,QQ1,QQ2	NPR = 11,14,28,311,314,328,411 or
	   414 if L > 20 {see Ch. IV, VI, Vol. I
	   Ch. V, Vol. II

READ,QQ4L,QQ4U READ,PPQQ	(NPR = 15,315 or 415) (see Ch. VI, Vol. I)
READ,QQ1,QQ2,QQ3,QQ4	(NPR = 13,15,313,315,413 or 415) (see Ch. V, VI, Vol. I)
READ,EQ1,AIC1,AIAX READ,AIC1I,AIAXI	NPR = 9 or 309. NPR = 10,11,14,28,310,311,314, 328,410,411 or 414 if L ≤ 40
READ,EQ1,AIC1,AIAX,AIBX READ,AIC1I,AIAXI,AIBXI	NPR = 10,11,14,28,310,311,314,328,410, 411 or 414 if L > 40
READ,EQ1,EQ2 READ,AIC1,AIC2,AIC3,AIAX,AIBX READ,AIC1I,AIC2I,AIC3I,AIAXI,AIBXI	NPR = 12,13,15,312,313,315, 412,413, or 415

DEFINITIONS

For NPR = 11,14,28,311,314,328,411 and 414 QQ1 and QQ2 are defined thus:

$$QQ1.A \, + \, QQ2.B \underset{}{\overset{K_1}{\rightleftharpoons}} C_1 \tag{1}$$

If L ≤ 20 QQ2 = 0 (Not entered)
For NPR = 13,15,313,315,413 or 415 the reactions are:

$$QQ1 \, . \, A \overset{K_1}{\rightleftharpoons} C_1 \tag{2}$$

$$QQ2 \, . \, B \overset{K_2}{\rightleftharpoons} C_2 \tag{3}$$

$$QQ3 \, . \, A + QQ4 \, . \, B \overset{K_3}{\rightleftharpoons} C_3 \tag{4}$$

(For NPR = 12,312 or 412, QQ1 = QQ2 = 2.0,QQ3 = QQ4 = 1.0)
If NPR = 9 or 309 or if NPR = 10, 310 or 410 and L > 40, QQ1 = QQ2 = 1.0 in equation (1). For L ≤ 20 and NPR = 10, 310 or 410, QQ1 = 2.0
EQ1 is the value of K_1 in equations (1) or (2).
EQ2 is the value of K_2 in equation (3).
AIC1,AIC2,AIC3,AIAX and AIBX are the concentration independent parts of the absorbancy indices for C_1,C_2,C_3, A and B respectively.
AIC1I,AIC2I,AIC3I,AIAXI and AIBXI are the increments for AIC1,AIC2, AIC3,AIAX and AIBX, respectively, which are to be added to the designated absorbancy indices at each of the 2, 3, 4 ⋯ M6 wavelengths for which information is to be computed.
Note: K_3 in equation (3) is computed from the concentrations (see below) entered for Program 107. Specified values of QQ1,QQ2,QQ3 and QQ4 are not entered.

STATEMENT	COMMENT
READ,WAC1 (NPR = 9 or 309) OR READ,WAC1,WAC2 (NPR ≠ 9 or 309)	$\left\{\begin{array}{l}\textit{Instrument reliability factors.}\\ \text{For NPR} = 28 \text{ or } 328 \text{ WAC2 is the}\\ \text{dimension of expansion.}\end{array}\right.$
READ,A1,A2,A3,A4 READ,B1,B2,B3,B4 READ,CA1,CA2,CA3,CA4 READ,CB1,CB2,CB3,CB4	$\left(\begin{array}{l}\text{Coefficients which define temperature dependent}\\ \text{part of the absorbancy indices for } A, B, C_1(\text{CA})\\ \text{and } C_2(\text{CB}) \text{ respectively. } C_1 \text{ and } C_2 \text{ are the com-}\\ \text{plexes in equations (2) and (3) (see box above).}\end{array}\right.$
READ,C1(I),C1(I + 1),C1(I + 2),C1(I + 3)	$\left\{\begin{array}{l}\text{Concentration of complex } C_1 \text{ in equations}\\ \text{(1) or (2).}\end{array}\right.$
READ,C2(I),C2(I + 1),C2(I + 2),C2(I + 3)	$\left\{\begin{array}{l}\text{Concentration of } B \text{ at equilibrium (equations}\\ \text{(1), (3) and (4))}\end{array}\right.$
$\left\{\begin{array}{l}\text{Not entered if } L \leq 20 \text{ for NPR} = 10,11,14,28,310,311,314,328,\\ 410,411 \text{ or } 414.\end{array}\right\}$	
READ,C3(I),C3(I + 1),C3(I + 2),C3(I + 3)	$\left\{\begin{array}{l}\text{The concentration of } C_3 \text{ in equation (4)}\\ \text{(see box)}\end{array}\right.$
Only entered for NPR = 12,13,15,312,313,315,412,413 or 415.	
READ,RLM1,WL1,WU1 $\left.\right\}$ READ,RLM2,WL2,WU2 $\left.\right\}$	$\textit{Instrument reliability factors.}$ For NPR = 28 or 328 RLM2 defines the curvature (see Chapter V, Volume II)
READ,KA,KB,KC,KD,KE,KF (NPR = 28 or 328) OR READ,KA,KB,KC,KD (NPR ≠ 28 or 328)	$\left.\right\}\textit{Reject--restore}$ commands
READ,J	$\textit{Cycle command}$
READ,M6	Number of wavelengths
READ,OPER,INSTR READ,RUN,TEMP,WAVEL	$\left.\right\}$Identification
READ,DEVF1 OR READ,DEV1(I),DEV1(I + 1),DEV1(I + 2),DEV1(I + 3) READ,DEVF2 OR READ,DEV2(I),DEV2(I + 1),DEV2(I + 2),DEV2(I + 3)	$\left(\begin{array}{l}\textit{Maximum permitted deviation} \text{ in}\\ \text{the measured absorbance}\\ (\text{OAM(I)}) \text{ and one concentration}\\ \text{which appear in the output}\\ \text{generated by Program 107.}\end{array}\right.$

OUTPUT FORMAT FOR PROGRAM 107

The output information generated by Program 107 can be processed directly with Programs 28 or 328, if NPR = 28 or 328, or Program 31 if NPR ≠ 28 or 328. For NPR = 9–15, 309–315 or 410–415 the output information can be used to test the spectrophotometric program numbered NPR, or to test *Autoplotter Programs* 502, 503 and 504, as described earlier. The *reject–restore* commands, J, and the *instrument reliability factors* can be changed after the information has been processed with Program 107.

FORTRAN FOR PROGRAM NUMBER 106

CALL WORD FBBBB

```
DIMENSION OAM(20),C1(20),C2(20),DEV1(20),DEV2(20)
1 READ,NPR,TEST
JI=20
READ,K,L,M
JJ=0
NPP=0
NQR=NPR
IF(NPR-300)11,1,12
12 NQR=NPR-300
11 NQR=NQR-8
IF(NQR-1)1,13,14
13 PUNCH,NPR,TEST
GO TO 17
14 QNR=NPR
NQR=NQR-12
IF(NQR-5)15,16,71
71 NQR=5
NPP=1
IF(L-5)16,72,72
72 READ,QQ1,QQ2
16 READ,JI
PUNCH,JI
15 PUNCH,QNR,TEST
17 READ,EQ,AIC,AI1
READ,EQI,AICI,AI1I,WAC
IF(NQR-5)18,19,1
19 READ,KA,KB,KC,KD,KE,KF
READ,JJ
PUNCH,KA,KB,KC,KD,KE,KF
IF(L-6)66,65,65
65 JJ=2
66 PUNCH,JJ
GO TO 20
18 READ,KA,KB,KC,KD
PUNCH,KA,KB,KC,KD
20 READ,J
READ,M6
IF(L-5)2,3,2
3 READ,QQ1
2 READ,RLM1,WL1,WU1
READ,RLM2,WL2,WU2
GO TO (4,4,5,5),K
4 READ,DEVF1
GO TO 7
5 DO 6 I=1,JI,4
6 READ,DEV1(I),DEV1(I+1),DEV1(I+2),DEV1(I+3)
7 GO TO (8,9,8,9),K
8 READ,DEVF2
GO TO 21
9 DO 10 I=1,JI,4
10 READ,DEV2(I),DEV2(I+1),DEV2(I+2),DEV2(I+3)
21 DO 24 I=1,JI,4
24 READ,C1(I),C1(I+1),C1(I+2),C1(I+3)
GO TO (25,25,26,25,25,26,26),L
26 DO 27 I=1,JI,4
27 READ,C2(I),C2(I+1),C2(I+2),C2(I+3)
25 READ,OPER,INSTR
READ,RUN,TEMP,WAVEL
PUNCH,J
```

```
      PUNCH,M6
      PUNCH,K,L,M
      PUNCH,RLM1,WL1,WU1
      PUNCH,RLM2,WL2,WU2
      GO TO (28,28,29,29),K
   28 PUNCH,DEVF1
      GO TO 32
   29 DO 31 I=1,JI,4
   31 PUNCH,DEV1(I),DEV1(I+1),DEV1(I+2),DEV1(I+3)
   32 GO TO (33,34,33,34),K
   33 PUNCH,DEVF2
      GO TO 36
   34 DO 35 I=1,JI,4
   35 PUNCH,DEV2(I),DEV2(I+1),DEV2(I+2),DEV2(I+3)
   36 M4=0
   37 IF(M6-M4)1,1,38
   38 IF(M4)1,39,40
   40 AIC=AIC+AICI
      AI1=AI1+AI1I
   39 M4=M4+1
      IF(M4)1,78,58
   78 CONTINUE
      GO TO (54,55,56,57,58),NQR
   57 JJ=JJ+1
   56 JJ=JJ+1
   55 JJ=JJ+1
   54 JJ=JJ+2
   58 DO 41 I=1,JI
      R=EQ
      RR=0.0
      GO TO (42,42,43,42,44,45,45),L
   42 OAM(I)=EQ*AIC*C1(I)*C1(I)+AI1*C1(I)
      IF(JJ-2)41,41,59
   59 DO 60 JP=3,JJ
      R=R+EQI
   60 RR=RR+R*AIC*(C1(I)**JP)
      OAM(I)=OAM(I)+RR
      GO TO 41
   43 OAM(I)=EQ*AIC*C2(I)*C1(I)+AI1*C1(I)
      IF(JJ-2)41,41,61
   61 DO 62 JP=3,JJ
      R=R+EQI
   62 RR=RR+R*AIC*C1(I)*(C2(I)**(JP-1))
      OAM(I)=OAM(I)+RR
      GO TO 41
   44 OAM(I)=EQ*(C1(I)**QQ1)*AIC+AI1*C1(I)
      IF(JJ-2)41,41,64
   64 DO 63 JP=3,JJ
      JPP=QQ1
      QQ2=JPP+JP-2
      R=R+EQI
   63 RR=RR+R*(C1(I)**QQ2)*AIC
      OAM(I)=OAM(I)+RR
      GO TO 41
   45 X=(EQ*C2(I)*C1(I))/(1.0+EQ*C2(I))
      OAM(I)=AIC*X+AI1*(C1(I)-X)
      JJ=2
   41 CONTINUE
      DO 46 I=1,JI,4
   46 PUNCH,OAM(I),OAM(I+1),OAM(I+2),OAM(I+3)
      IF(NPP)1,75,74
   74 IF(L-5)75,76,76
```

```
76 PUNCH,QQ1,QQ2
75 CONTINUE
GO TO (47,47,47,47,48,48,48),L
48 PUNCH,AI1,WAC
47 IF(M4-1)1,49,37
49 DO 50 I=1,JI,4
50 PUNCH,C1(I),C1(I+1),C1(I+2),C1(I+3)
IF(NPP)1,77,51
77 CONTINUE
GO TO (51,51,52,51,51,52,52),L
52 DO 53 I=1,JI,4
53 PUNCH,C2(I),C2(I+1),C2(I+2),C2(I+3)
51 PUNCH,OPER,INSTR
PUNCH,RUN,TEMP,WAVEL
GO TO 37
END
```

ALGOL 60 FOR PROGRAM NUMBER 106

PROCEDURE FBBBB(npr,test,ji,k,L,m); ARRAY oam,c1,c2,dev1,dev2[1:20];
INTEGER npr,ji,k,L,m; REAL test; SWITCH sw1:=x5,x5,x6,x6; SWITCH sw2:
=x8,x9,x8,x9; SWITCH sw3:=x12,x12,x11,x12,x12,x11,x11; SWITCH sw4:=x13,
x13,x14,x14; SWITCH sw5:=x16,x17,x16,x17; SWITCH sw6:=x24,x23,x22,x21,x25;
SWITCH sw7:=x26,x26,x27,x26,x28,x29,x29; SWITCH sw8:=x33,x33,x33,x33,x32,
x32,x32; SWITCH sw9:=x36,x36,x35,x36,x36,x35,x35;
COMMENT: TEST PROGRAMS;
    BEGIN INTEGER oper,instr,run,jj,npp,nqr,ka,kb,kc,kd,ke,kf,m6,jp,j,m4,
    jpp,i; REAL aic,ai1,aici,ai1i,devf1,devf2,eq,eqi,qq1,qq2,r,rr,rLm1,rLm2,
    temp,wac,wL1,wL2,wu1,wu2,waveL,x;
      jj:=npp:=0; nqr:=npr;
      IF npr=300 THEN GO TO X37
      ELSE IF npr>300 THEN nqr:=npr−300;
      nqr:=nqr−8;
      IF nqr<1 THEN GO TO X37
      ELSE IF nqr=1 THEN
      BEGIN
        PUNCH npr,test; GO TO X2END;
      qnr:=nqr; nqr:=nqr−12;
      IF nqr<5 THEN GO TO X1
      ELSE IF nqr>5 THEN
      BEGIN
        nqr:=5; npp:=1;
        IF L≥5 THEN READ qq1,qq2END;
      READ ji; PUNCH ji;

X1:   PUNCH qnr,test;
X2:   READ eq,aic,ai1;
      READ eqi,aici,ai1i,wac;
      IF nqr>5 THEN GO TO X37
      ELSE IF nqr=5 THEN
      BEGIN
        READ ka,kb,kc,kd,ke,kf;
        READ jj;
        READ ka,kb,kc,kd,ke,kf;
        IF L≥6 THEN jj:=2;
        PUNCH jj; GO TO X4END;
X3:   READ ka,kb,kc,kd;
      PUNCH ka,kb,kc,kd;
X4:   READ j; READ m6;
      IF L=5 THEN READ qq1;
      READ rLm1,wL1,wu1;
      READ rLm2,wL2,wu2;
      GO TO sw1[k];
X5:   READ devf1; GO TO X7;
X6:   FOR i:=1 STEP 1 UNTIL ji DO READ dev1[i];
X7:   GO TO sw2[k];
X8:   READ devf2; GO TO X10;
X9:   FOR i:=1 STEP 1 UNTIL ji DO READ dev2[i];
X10:   FOR i:=1 STEP 1 UNTIL ji DO READ c1[i];
      GO TO sw3[L];
X11:   FOR i:=1 STEP 1 UNTIL ji DO READ c2[i];

```
X12:    READ oper,instr;
        READ run,temp,waveL;
        PUNCH j; PUNCH m6; PUNCH k,L,m;
        PUNCH rLm1,wL1,wu1;
        PUNCH rLm2,wL2,wu2;
        GO TO sw4[k];
X13:    PUNCH devf1; GO TO X15;
X14:    FOR i:=1 STEP 1 UNTIL ji DO PUNCH dev1[i];
X15:    GO TO sw5[k];
X16:    PUNCH devf2; GO TO X18;
X17:    FOR i:=1 STEP 1 UNTIL ji DO PUNCH dev2[i];
X18:    m4:=0;
X19:    IF(m6≤m4)∨(m4<0)THEN GO TO X37
        ELSE IF m4>0 THEN
        BEGIN
            aic:=aic+aici; ai1:=ai1+ai1iEND;
        m4:=m4+1;
        IF m4<0 THEN GO TO X37
        ELSE IF m4=0 THEN
        BEGIN
X20:        GO TO sw6[nqr];
X21:        jj:=jj+1;
X22:        jj:=jj+1;
X23:        jj:=jj+1;
X24:        jj:=jj+2END;
X25:    FOR i:=1 STEP 1 UNTIL ji DO
        BEGIN
            r:=eq; rr:=0; GO TO sw7[L];
X26:        oam[i]:=eqXaicXc1[i]↑2+ai1Xc1[i];
            IF jj≤2 THEN GO TO X30;
            FOR jp:=3 STEP 1 UNTIL jj DO
            BEGIN
                r:=r+eqi; rr:=rr+rXaicXc1[i]↑jp
            END;
            oam[i]:=oam[i]+rr; GO TO X30;
X27:        oam[i]:=eqXaicXc2[i]Xc1[i]+ai1Xc1[i];
            IF jj≤2 THEN GO TO X30;
            FOR jp:=3 STEP 1 UNTIL jj DO
            BEGIN
                r:=r+eqi; rr:=rr+rXaicXc1[i]Xc2[i]↑(jp−1)
            END;
            oam[i]:=oam[i]+rr; GO TO X30;
X28:        oam[i]:=eqXc1[i]↑qq1Xaic+ai1Xc1[i];
            IF jj≤2 THEN GO TO X30;
            FOR jp:=3 STEP 1 UNTIL jj DO
            BEGIN
                jpp:=qq1; qq2:=jpp+jp−2;
                r:=r+eqi; rr:=rr+rXc1[i]↑qq2Xaic
            END;
            oam[i]:=oam[i]+rr; GO TO X30;
X29:        x:=eqXc2[i]Xc1[i]/(1+eqXc2[i]);
            oam[i]:=aicXx+ai1X(c1[i]−x);
            jj:=2
```

```
X30:   END;
       FOR i:=1 STEP 1 UNTIL ji DO PUNCH oam[i];
       IF npp<0 THEN GO TO X37
       ELSE IF npp>0∧L≥5 THEN PUNCH qq1,qq2;
X31:   GO TO sw8[L];
X32:   PUNCH ai1,wac;
X33:   IF m4<1 THEN GO TO X37
       ELSE IF m4>1 THEN GO TO X19;
       FOR i:=1 STEP 1 UNTIL ji DO PUNCH c1[i];
       IF npp<0 THEN GO TO X37
       ELSE IF npp=0 THEN
       BEGIN
X34:      GO TO sw9[L];
X35:      FOR i:=1 STEP 1 UNTIL ji DO PUNCH c2[i]END;
X36:   PUNCH oper,instr;
       PUNCH run,temp,waveL; GO TO X19
X37:END FBBBB;
X38:READ npr,test; ji:=20; READ k,L,m;
     FBBBB(npr,test,ji,k,L,m);
     GO TO X38;
```

FORTRAN FOR PROGRAM NUMBER 107

CALL WORD GBBBB

```
DIMENSION OAM(20),C1(20),C2(20),C3(20),DEV1(20),DEV2(20),C4(20),C5(20)
1 READ,NPR,TEST
NQR=NPR
READ,PP
IF(NQR-300)2,1,3
3 NPR=NQR-300
2 NPR=NPR-8
IF(NPR-100)144,1,140
140 NPR=NPR-100
READ,WACRR
144 READ,K,L,M
NPP=NPR
IF(NPP-7)150,150,151
151 NPR=3
150 IF(NPR-1)1,4,7
4 IF(L-6)5,6,6
5 L=6
6 LL=3
GO TO10
7 Q=L
Q=Q/10.0
DO 8 I=1,20
P=I
IF(Q-P)9,9,8
9 LL=I
GO TO 10
8 CONTINUE
10 GO TO (11,13,19,23,25,22,26),NPR
11 QQ1=1.0
QQ2=1.0
15 AIBX=0.0
AIBXI=0.0
READ,EQ1,AIC1,AIAX
EQ=EQ1
READ,AIC1I,AIAXI
GO TO 27
13 IF(LL-2)14,14,16
14 QQ1=2.0
QQ2=0.0
GO TO 15
16 IF(LL-4)11,11,17
17 QQ1=1.0
QQ2=1.0
18 READ,EQ1,AIC1,AIAX,AIBX
EQ=EQ1
READ,AIC1I,AIAXI,AIBXI
GO TO 27
19 IF(LL-2)20,20,21
20 READ,QQ1
QQ2=0.0
GO TO 15
21 READ,QQ1,QQ2
IF(LL-4)15,15,18
22 READ,QQ1L,QQ1U
READ,PPQQ
IF(LL-2)20,20,21
23 QQ1=2.0
QQ2=2.0
QQ3=1.0
```

```
QQ4=1.0
24 READ,EQ1,EQ2
READ,AIC1,AIC2,AIC3,AIAX,AIBX
READ,AIC11,AIC21,AIC31,AIAXI,AIBXI
GO TO 27
25 READ,QQ1,QQ2,QQ3,QQ4
GO TO 24
26 READ,QQ4L,QQ4U
READ,PPQQ
GO TO 25
27 IF(NPR-1)1,28,29
28 READ,WAC1
GO TO 30
29 READ,WAC1,WAC2
30 A1=0.0
A2=0.0
A3=0.0
A4=0.0
B1=0.0
B2=0.0
B3=0.0
B4=0.0
CA1=0.0
CA2=0.0
CA3=0.0
CA4=0.0
CB1=0.0
CB2=0.0
CB3=0.0
CB4=0.0
GO TO (31,31,31,32,32,31,32),NPR
31 GO TO (33,34,33,34,33,34,33,34),LL
34 READ,A1,A2,A3,A4
33 IF(LL-6)42,42,35
35 READ,B1,B2,B3,B4
GO TO 42
32 GO TO (36,36,36,36,37,37,37,37,36,36,36,36,37,37,37),LL
37 READ,A1,A2,A3,A4
36 GO TO (38,38,38,39,39,38,39,39,39,39,39,38,38,38,39),LL
39 READ,B1,B2,B3,B4
38 GO TO (40,40,41,41,41,40,40,41,40,41,40,41,41,41,40),LL
41 READ,CA1,CA2,CA3,CA4
40 GO TO (42,43,43,43,43,42,42,42,42,43,42,42,43,43),LL
43 READ,CB1,CB2,CB3,CB4
42 DO 44 I=1,20,4
44 READ,C1(I),C1(I+1),C1(I+2),C1(I+3)
DO 45 I=1,20
45 C2(I)=0.0
GO TO (48,47,47,46,46,47,46),NPR
47 IF(LL-2)51,51,48
48 DO 49 I=1,20,4
49 READ,C2(I),C2(I+1),C2(I+2),C2(I+3)
GO TO 51
46 DO 50 I=1,20,4
50 READ,C3(I),C3(I+1),C3(I+2),C3(I+3)
GO TO 48
51 READ,RLM1,WL1,WU1
READ,RLM2,WL2,WU2
IF(NPP-7)155,155,156
156 READ,KA,KB,KC,KD,KE,KF
GO TO 157
155 READ,KA,KB,KC,KD
```

```
157 READ,J
READ,M6
M5=M6
M4=0
READ,OPER,INSTR
READ,RUN,TEMP,WAVEL
GO TO (52,52,53,53),K
52 READ,DEVF1
GO TO 55
53 DO 54 I=1,20,4
54 READ,DEV1(I),DEV1(I+1),DEV1(I+2),DEV1(I+3)
55 GO TO (56,57,56,57),K
56 READ,DEVF2
GO TO 59
57 DO 58 I=1,20,4
58 READ,DEV2(I),DEV2(I+1),DEV2(I+2),DEV2(I+3)
59 IF(M5)1,1,60
60 M4=M4+1
M5=M5-1
IF(M4-1)1,61,62
62 GO TO (63,63,63,64,64,63,64),NPR
63 AIC1=AIC1+AIC11
AIAX=AIAX+AIAXI
AIBX=AIBX+AIBXI
GO TO 61
64 AIC2=AIC2+AIC21
AIC3=AIC3+AIC31
GO TO 63
61 DO 69 I=1,20
AA=0.0
AC1=0.0
AC2=0.0
AB=0.0
GO TO (68,66,66,67,67,66,67),NPR
66 IF(LL-2)12,12,68
12 C3(I)=C1(I)
C2(I)=0.0
C1(I)=(C3(I)/EQ1)**(1.0/QQ1)
GO TO 70
68 C3(I)=C1(I)
C1(I)=(C3(I)/(EQ1*(C2(I)**QQ2)))**(1.0/QQ1)
GO TO 70
67 C5(I)=C3(I)
C3(I)=C1(I)
C1(I)=(C3(I)/EQ1)**(1.0/QQ1)
C4(I)=EQ2*(C2(I)**QQ2)
EQ3=C5(I)/((C1(I)**QQ3)*(C2(I)**QQ4))
QQ=C3(I)*C3(I)
AC1=CA1*C3(I)+CA2*QQ+CA3*QQ*C3(I)+CA4*QQ*QQ
QQ=C4(I)*C4(I)
AC2=CB1*C4(I)+CB2*QQ+CB3*QQ*C4(I)+CB4*QQ*QQ
EQ1=EQ3
70 QQ=C1(I)*C1(I)
AA=A1*C1(I)+A2*QQ+A3*QQ*C1(I)+A4*QQ*QQ
QQ=C2(I)*C2(I)
AB=B1*C2(I)+B2*QQ+B3*QQ*C2(I)+B4*QQ*QQ
EQ=EQ1
EQ0=EQ1+2.0
GO TO (73,73,73,74,74,73,74),NPR
73 AA=AA+AIAX
AB=AB+AIBX
OAM(I)=AIC1*C3(I)+AA*C1(I)+AB*C2(I)
```

```
      IF(LL-2)75,75,76
   76 C2(I)=C2(I)+QQ2*C3(I)
   75 C1(I)=C1(I)+QQ1*C3(I)
      AA=AA-AIAX
      AB=AB-AIBX
      GO TO 69
   74 AC1=AC1+AIC1
      AC2=AC2+AIC2
      AA=AA+AIAX
      AB=AB+AIBX
      OAM(I)=AIC3*C5(I)+AC1*C3(I)+AC2*C4(I)+AA*C1(I)+AB*C2(I)
      C1(I)=C1(I)+QQ1*C3(I)+QQ3*C5(I)
      C2(I)=C2(I)+QQ2*C4(I)+QQ4*C5(I)
      AC1=AC1-AIC1
      AC2=AC2-AIC2
      AA=AA-AIAX
      AB=AB-AIBX
   69 CONTINUE
      IF(M4-1)1,77,105
   77 IF(NPP-7)152,152,158
  158 PROGN=NQR
      JI=20
      PUNCH,JI
      PUNCH,PROGN,TEST
  153 PUNCH,J
      PUNCH,M6
      PUNCH,K,L,M
      PUNCH,KA,KB,KC,KD,KE,KF
      GO TO 154
  152 EQER=0.05*EQ
      PROGN=NQR
      PUNCH,EQ,EQER,PROGN
      IF(NPR-6)78,79,80
   79 PUNCH,QQ1
   78 PUNCH,NQR,TEST
      GO TO 81
   80 PUNCH,QQ4
      PUNCH,PROGN,TEST
   81 IF(NPR-1)1,82,84
   82 PUNCH,KA,KB,KC,KD
      PUNCH,J
      PUNCH,M6
      PUNCH,K,L,M
      GO TO 83
   84 IF(NPR-3)85,86,85
   86 PUNCH,QQ1,QQ2
   85 IF(NPR-5)87,88,87
   88 PUNCH,QQ1,QQ2,QQ3,QQ4
   87 IF(NPR-6)93,90,91
   90 PUNCH,QQ2
      PUNCH,QQ1L,QQ1U
   92 PUNCH,PPQQ
      GO TO 93
   91 PUNCH,QQ1,QQ2,QQ3
      PUNCH,QQ4L,QQ4U
      GO TO 92
   93 IF(NQR-400)141,1,142
  142 PUNCH,J,WACRR
      GO TO 143
  141 PUNCH,J
  143 CONTINUE
      GO TO (83,95,95,94,94,95,94),NPR
```

```
95 PUNCH,EQO
GO TO 96
94 PUNCH,EQO,EQ1,EQ2
96 IF(NPR-2)146,146,145
145 PUNCH,PP
146 PUNCH,M6
PUNCH,K,L,M
PUNCH,KA,KB,KC,KD
154 PUNCH,RLM1,WAC1,WL1,WU1
PUNCH,RLM2,WAC2,WL2,WU2
GO TO 105
83 PUNCH,RLM1,WL1,WU1
PUNCH,RLM2,WL2,WU2
139 GO TO (97,97,98,98),K
97 PUNCH,DEVF1
GO TO 100
98 DO 991=1,20,4
99 PUNCH,DEV1(I),DEV1(I+1),DEV1(I+2),DEV1(I+3)
100 GO TO (101,102,101,102),K
101 PUNCH,DEVF2
GO TO 103
102 DO 104 I=1,20,4
104 PUNCH,DEV2(I),DEV2(I+1),DEV2(I+2),DEV2(I+3)
103 IF(NPR-1)1,105,132
105 DO 106 I=1,20,4
106 PUNCH,OAM(I),OAM(I+1),OAM(I+2),OAM(I+3)
IF(NPR-1)138,138,109
138 IF(L-5)107,107,108
108 PUNCH,AIAX,WAC1
107 GO TO 124
109 GO TO (96,110,110,111,111,110,111),NPR
110 IF(LL-4)112,112,113
112 PUNCH,AIAX
GO TO 114
113 PUNCH,AIAX,AIBX
114 GO TO (115,116,115,116,115,116,115,116),LL
116 PUNCH,A1,A2,A3,A4
115 IF(LL-6)124,124,117
117 PUNCH,B1,B2,B3,B4
GO TO 124
111 PUNCH,AIAX,AIC1,AIBX,AIC2
GO TO (118,118,118,118,119,119,119,119,118,118,118,118,119,119,119),LL
119 PUNCH,A1,A2,A3,A4
118 CONTINUE
GO TO (120,120,120,121,121,120,121,121,121,121,121,120,120,120,121),LL
121 PUNCH,B1,B2,B3,B4
120 CONTINUE
GO TO (122,122,123,123,123,122,122,123,122,123,122,123,123,123,122),LL
123 PUNCH,CA1,CA2,CA3,CA4
122 CONTINUE
GO TO (124,125,125,125,125,124,124,124,124,124,125,124,124,125,125),LL
125 PUNCH,CB1,CB2,CB3,CB4
124 IF(M4-1)1,126,133
126 DO 127 I=1,20,4
127 PUNCH,C1(I),C1(I+1),C1(I+2),C1(I+3)
GO TO (128,129,129,128,128,129,128),NPR
129 IF(LL-2)130,130,128
128 DO 131 I=1,20,4
131 PUNCH,C2(I),C2(I+1),C2(I+2),C2(I+3)
130 IF(NPR-1)1,132,139
132 PUNCH,OPER,INSTR
PUNCH,RUN,TEMP,WAVEL
```

```
133 DO 136 I=1,20
GO TO (134,134,134,135,135,134,135),NPR
134 C2(I)=C2(I)-QQ2*C3(I)
C1(I)=C3(I)
GO TO 136
135 C1(I)=C1(I)-QQ1*C3(I)-QQ3*C5(I)
C2(I)=C2(I)-QQ2*C4(I)-QQ4*C5(I)
C1(I)=C3(I)
C3(I)=C5(I)
136 CONTINUE
IF(M6-M4)1,1,60
END
```

ALGOL 60 FOR PROGRAM NUMBER 107

PROCEDURE GBBBB(npr,test,nqr,pp); ARRAY oam,c1,cq,c3,dev1,dev2,c4,
c5[1:20]; INTEGER npr,nqr; REAL test,pp; SWITCH sw1:=x3,x5,x7,x11,x13,x10,
x14; SWITCH sw2:=x17,x17,x17,x20,x20,x17,x20; SWITCH sw3:=x19,x18,x19,x18,
x19,x18,x19,x18; SWITCH sw4:=x22,x22,x22,x22,x21,x21,x21,x21,x22,x22,x22,x22,
x21,x21,x21; SWITCH sw5:=x24,x24,x24,x23,x23,x24,x23,x23,x23,x23,x23,x24,x24,x24,
x23; SWITCH sw6:=x26,x26,x25,x25,x25,x26,x26,x25,x26,x25,x26,x25,x25;x25,x26;
SWITCH sw7:=x28,x27,x27,x27,x27,x28,x28,x28,x28,x28,x27,x28,x28,x27,x27;
SWITCH sw8:=x30,x29,x29,x31,x31,x29,x31; SWITCH sw9:=x34,x34,x35,x35;
SWITCH sw10:=x37,x38,x37,x38; SWITCH sw11:=x41,x41,x41,x42,x42,x41,x42;
SWITCH sw12:=x45,x44,x44,x46,x46,x44,x46; SWITCH sw13:=x48,x48,x48,x49,x49,
x48,x49; SWITCH sw14:=x60,x56,x56,x57,x57,x56,x57; SWITCH sw15:=x61,x61,
x62,x62; SWITCH sw16:=x64,x65,x64,x65; SWITCH sw17:=x58,x69,x69,x73,x73,
x69,x73; SWITCH sw18:=x72,x71,x72,x71,x72,x71,x72,x71; SWITCH sw19:=x75,
x75,x75,x75,x74,x74,x74,x74,x75,x75,x75,x75,x74,x74,x74; SWITCH sw20:=x77,
x77,x77,x76,x76,x77,x76,x76,x76,x76,x76,x77,x77,x77,x76; SWITCH sw21:=x79,
x79,x78,x78,x78,x79,x79,x78,x79,x78,x79,x78,x78,x78,x79; SWITCH sw22:=x81,
x80,x80,x80,x80,x81,x81,x81,x81,x81,x80,x81,x81,x80,x80; SWITCH sw23:=x8x,
x82,x82,x8x,x8x,x82,x8x; SWITCH sw24:=x85,x85,x85,x86,x86,x85,x86;
COMMENT: TEST PROGRAMS;
    BEGIN INTEGER i,j,ji,ka,kb,kc,kd,ke,kf,k,L,LL,m,m4,m5,m6,npp,oper,
    instr,run,progn; REAL aa,ab,ac1,ac2,aic1,aic2,aic3,aic1i,aic2i,aic3i,aiax,
    aibx,aiaxi,aibxi,devf1,devf2,eq,eqo,eq1,eq2,eqer,p,ppqq,qq1,qq2,qq3,qq4,qq,
    q,qq1L,qq1u,qq4L,qq4u,rLm1,rLm2,temp,wac1,wac2,wacrr,wL1,wL2,wu1,
    wu2,waveL;
        IF nqr=300 THEN GO TO X87
        ELSE IF nqr>300 THEN npr:=nqr−300;
        npr:=npr−8;
        IF npr=100 THEN GO TO X87
        ELSE IF npr>100 THEN
        BEGIN
            npr:=npr−100; READ wacrr END;
        READ k,L,m; npp:=npr;
        IF npp>7 THEN npr:=3;
        IF npr<1 THEN GO TO X87
        ELSE IF npr>1 THEN GO TO X1;
        IF L<6 THEN L:=6;
        LL:=3; GO TO X2;
X1:   q:=L/10;
        FOR i:=1 STEP 1 UNTIL 20 DO
        BEGIN
            p:=i;
            IF q≤p THEN
            BEGIN
                LL:=i; GO TO X2END
        END;
X2:   GO TO sw1[npr];
X3:   qq1:=qq2:=1;
X4:   aibx:=aibxi:=0;
        READ eq1,aic1,aiax; eq:=eq1;
        READ aic1i,aiaxi; GO TO X15;
X5:   IF LL≤2 THEN

```
           BEGIN
               qq1:=2;  qq2:=0;  GO TO X4END;
           IF LL≤4 THEN GO TO X3;
           qq1:=qq2:=1;
X6:        READ eq1,aic1,aiax,aibx;  eq:=eq1;
           READ aic1i,aiaxi,aibxi;  GO TO X15;
X7:        IF LL≤2 THEN
           BEGIN
X8:            READ qq1;  qq2:=0;  GO TO X4END;
X9:        READ qq1,qq2;
           IF LL≤4 THEN GO TO X4ELSE GO TO X6;
X10:       READ qq1L,qq1u;  READ ppqq;
           IF LL≤ 2 THEN GO TO X8 ELSE GO TO X9;
X11:       qq1:=qq2:=2;  qq3:=qq4:=1;
X12:       READ eq1;eq2;
           READ aic1,aic2,aic3,aiax,aibx;
           READ aic1i,aic2i,aic3i,aiaxi,aibxi;
           GO TO X15;
X13:       READ qq1,qq2,qq3,qq4;  GO TO X12;
X14:       READ qq4L,qq4u;  READ ppqq;  GO TO X13;
X15:       IF npr<1 THEN GO TO X87
           ELSE IF npr=1 THEN
           BEGIN
               READ wac1;  GO TO X16 END;
           READ wac1,wac2;
X16:       a1:=a2:=a3:=a4:=b1:=b2:=b3:=b4:=ca1:=ca2:=ca3:=ca4:=cb1:=cb2:=cb3:=cb4
           :=0;
           GO TO sw2[npr];
X17:       GO TO sw3[LL];
X18:       READ a1,a2,a3,a4;
X19:       IF LL≤6 THEN GO TO X28;
           READ b1,b2,b3,b4;  GO TO X28;
X20:       GO TO sw4[LL];
X21:       READ a1,a2,a3,a4;
X22:       GO TO sw5[LL];
X23:       READ b1,b2,b3,b4;
X24:       GO TO sw6[LL];
X25:       READ ca1,ca2,ca3,ca4;
X26:       GO TO sw7[LL];
X27:       READ cb1,cb2,cb3,cb4;
X28:       FOR i:=1 STEP 1 UNTIL 20 DO READ c1[i];
           FOR i:=1 STEP 1 UNTIL 20 DO READ c2[i]:=0;
           GO TO sw8[npr];
X29:       IF LL>2 THEN
           BEGIN
X30:           FOR i:=1 STEP 1 UNTIL 20 DO READ c2[i];
               GO TO X32;
X31:           FOR i:=1 STEP 1 UNTIL 20 DO READ c3[i];
               GO TO X30END;
X32:       READ rLm1,wL1,wu1;
           READ rLm2,wL2,wu2;
           IF npp>7 THEN
           BEGIN
```

```
        READ ka,kb,kc,kd,ke,kf;
        GO TO X33END;
        READ ka,kb,kc,kd;
X33:    READ j;  READ m6;  m5:=m6;  m4:=0;
        READ oper,instr;
        READ run,temp,waveL;
        GO TO sw9[k];
X34:    READ devf1;  GO TO X36;
X35:    FOR i:=1 STEP 1 UNTIL 20 DO READ dev1[i];
X36:    GO TO sw10[k];
X37:    READ devf2;  GO TO X39;
X38:    FOR i:=1 STEP 1 UNTIL 20 DO READ dev2[i];
X39:    IF m5≤0 THEN GO TO X87;
X40:    m4:=m4+1;  m5:=m5−1;
        IF m4<1 THEN GO TO X87
        ELSE IF m4=1 THEN GO TO X43;
        GO TO sw11[npr];
X41:    aic1:=aic1+aic1i;  aiax:=aiax+aiaxi;
        aibx:=aibx+aibxi;  GO TO X43;
X42:    aic2:=aic2+aic2i;  aic3:=aic3+aic3i;
        GO TO X41;
X43:    FOR i:=1 STEP 1 UNTIL 20 DO
        BEGIN
          aa:=ac1:=ac2:=ab:=0;
          GO TO sw12[npr];
X44:    IF LL≤2 THEN
        BEGIN
          c3[i]:=c1[i];  c2[i]:=0;
          c1[i]:=(c3[i]/eq1)↑(1/qq1);  GO TO X47END;
X45:    c3[i]:=c1[i];
        c1[i]:=(c3[i]/(eq1Xc2[i]↑qq2)))↑(1/qq1);
        GO TO X47;
X46:    c5[i]:=c3[i];  c3[i]:=c1[i];
        c1[i]:=(c3[i]/eq1)↑(1/qq1);
        c4[i]:=eq2Xc2[i]↑qq2;
        eq3:=c5[i]/(c1[i]↑qq3Xc2[i]↑qq4);
        qq:=c3[i]↑2;
        ac1:=ca1Xc3[i]+ca2Xqq+ca3XqqXc3[i]+ca4Xqq↑2;
        qq:=c4[i]↑2;
        ac2:=cb1Xc4[i]+cb2Xqq+c3XqqXc4[i]+cbbXqq↑2;
        eq1:=eq3;
X47:    qq:=c1[i]↑2;
        aa:=a1Xc1[i]+a2Xqq+a3XqqXc1[i]+a4Xqq↑2;
        qq:=c2[i]↑2;
        ab:=b1Xc2[i]+b2Xqq+b3XqqXc2[i]+b4Xqq↑2;
        eq:=eq1;  eqo:=eq1÷2;  GO TO sw13[npr];
X48:    aa:=aa+aiax;  ab:=ab+aibx;
        oam[i]:=aic1Xc3[i]+aaXc1[i]+abXc2[i];
        IF LL>2 THEN c2[i]:=c2[i]+qq2Xc3[i];
        c1[i]:=c1[i]+qq1Xc3[i];
        aa:=aa−aiax;  ab:=ab−aibx;  GO TO X50;
X49:    ac1:=ac1+aic1;  ac2:=ac2+aic2;
        aa:=aa+aiax;  ab:=ab+aibx;
```

```
          oam[i]:=aic3Xc5[i]+ac1Xc3[i]+ac2Xc4[i]+aaXc1[i]+abXc2[i];
          c1[i]:=c1[i]+qq1Xc3[i]+qq3Xc5[i];
          c2[i]:=c2[i]+qq2Xc4[i]+qq4Xc5[i];
          ac1:=ac1-aic1; ac2:=ac2-aic2;
          aa:=aa-aiax; ab:=ab-aibx
X50:    END:
        IF m4<1 THEN GO TO X87
        ELSE IF m4>1 THEN GO TO X67;
        IF npp>7 THEN
        BEGIN
          progn:=nqr; ji:=20; PUNCH ji;
           PUNCH progn,test; PUNCH j; PUNCH m6;
           PUNCH k,L,m;  PUNCH ka,kb,kc,kd,ke,kf;
           GO TO X59END;
        eqer:=0.05Xeq; progn:=nqr;
        PUNCH eq,eqer,progn;
        IF npr=6 THEN PUNCH qq1
        ELSE IF npr>6 THEN GO TO X51;
        PUNCH nqr,test;  GO TO X52;
X51:    PUNCH qq4;  PUNCH progn,test;
X52:    IF npr<1 THEN GO TO X87
        ELSE IF npr=1 THEN
        BEGIN
           PUNCH ka,kb,kc,kd;  PUNCH j;
           PUNCH m6;  PUNCH k,L,m;  GO TO X60END;
        IF npr=3 THEN PUNCH qq1,qq2;
        IF npr=5 THEN PUNCH qq1,qq2,qq3,qq4;
        IF npr=6 THEN
        BEGIN
           PUNCH qq2;  PUNCH qq1L,qq1u;
X53:       PUNCH ppqq;  GO TO X54END
        ELSE IF npr>6 THEN
        BEGIN
           PUNCH qq1,qq2,qq3;
           PUNCH qq4L,qq4u;  GO TO X53END;
X54:    IF nqr=400 THEN GO TO X87
        ELSE IF nqr>400 THEN
        BEGIN
           PUNCH j,wacrr;  GO TO X55END;
        PUNCH j;
X55:    GO TO sw14[npr];
X56:    PUNCH eqo;  GO TO X58;
X57:    PUNCH eqo,eq1,eq2;
X58:    IF npr>2 THEN PUNCH pp;
        PUNCH m6;  PUNCH k,L,m;
        PUNCH ka,kb,kc,kd;
X59:    PUNCH rLm1,wac1,wL1,wu1;
        PUNCH rLm2,wac2,wL2,wu2;  GO TO X67;
X60:    PUNCH rLm1,wL1,wu1;
X6X:    PUNCH rLm2,wL2,wu2;  GO TO sw15[k];
X61:    PUNCH devf1;  GO TO X63;
X62:    FOR i:=1 STEP 1 UNTIL 20 DO PUNCH dev1[i];
X63:    GO TO sw16[k];
```

```
X64;    PUNCH devf2;  GO TO X66;
X65;    FOR i:=1 STEP 1 UNTIL 20 DO PUNCH dev2[i];
X66:    IF npr<1 THEN GO TO X87
        ELSE IF npr>1 THEN GO TO X83;
X67:    FOR i:=1 STEP 1 UNTIL 20 DO PUNCH oam[i];
        IF(npr≤1)∧(L≤5)THEN GO TO X81
        ELSE IF(npr≤1)∧(L>5)THEN
        BEGIN
            PUNCH aiax,wac1;  GO TO X81END;
X68:    GO TO sw17[npr];
X69:    IF LL≤4 THEN
        BEGIN
            PUNCH aiax;  GO TO X70END;
        PUNCH aiax,aibx;
X70:    GO TO sw18[LL];
X71:    PUNCH a1,a2,a3,a4;
X72:    IF LL≤6 THEN GO TO X81;
        PUNCH b1,b2,b3,b4;  GO TO X81;
X73:    PUNCH aiax,aic1,aibx,aic2;  GO TO sw19[LL];
X74:    PUNCH a1,a2,a3,a4;
X75:    GO TO sw20[LL];
X76:    PUNCH b1,b2,b3,b4;
X77:    GO TO sw21[LL];
X78:    PUNCH ca1,ca2,ca3,ca4;
X79:    GO TO sw22[LL];
X80:    PUNCH cb1,cb2,cb3,cb4;
X81:    IF m4<1 THEN GO TO X87
        ELSE IF m4=1 THEN
        BEGIN
            FOR i:=1 STEP 1 UNTIL 20 DO PUNCH c1[i];
            GO TO sw23[npr];
X82:        IF LL>2 THEN
X8X:        FOR i:=1 STEP 1 UNTIL 20 DO PUNCH c2[i];
        IF npr<1 THEN GO TO X87
        ELSE IF npr>1 THEN GO TO X6X;
X83:    PUNCH oper,instr;
        PUNCH run,temp,waveLEND;
X84:    FOR i:=1 STEP 1 UNTIL 20 DO
        BEGIN
            GO TO sw24[npr];
X85:        c2[i]:=c2[i]−qq2Xc3[i];
            c1[i]:=c3[i];  GO TO X89;
X86:        c1[i]:=c1[i]−qq1Xc3[i]−qq3Xc5[i];
            c2[i]:=c[i]−qq2Xc4[i]−qq4Xc5[i];
            c1[i]:=c3[i];  c3[i]:=c5[i]
X89:    END;
        IF m6>m4 THEN GO TO X40
X87:END GBBBB;
X88:READ npr,test;  nqr:=npr;  READ pp;
    GBBBB(npr,test,nqr,pp);
    GO TO X88;
```

ALGOL 60

The ALGOL 60 appearing in this work was neither written nor designed with a particular computer in mind. In this case the use of the language is essentially to facilitate and assist an understanding of the FORTRAN procedures involved. In the event the ALGOL 60 is to be used for calculation on a particular computer, one may find minor technical modifications necessary in the programs.

APPENDIX C

BASIC NOTES ON COMPUTER LANGUAGES AND DATA-PROCESSING

Many excellent books on computer languages and computer logic have been published in recent years. References cited in this appendix[1-6] indicate only those books used by the authors in their own study. A new student is advised to select some textbook that deals specifically with his computer. The best method of learning a computer language is to work many small problems and to consult frequently with an experienced program writer.

This appendix is written primarily for the chemist who may wish to process his own data but who has no computer experience.

COMPUTER LANGUAGES

Computer programs are similar to games of chess in that the fundamental rules are exceedingly simple whereas the actual game (or program) may be exceptionally complicated. We can carry this illustration one stage further. Two individuals who cannot converse with each other may play

[1] E. I. Organick, *A Primer for Programming with the FORTRAN Language* (University of Houston: Computing and Data Processing Center, 1961).

[2] J. W. Hamblen, *The IBM 650 and Some of Its Programming Languages* (University of Kentucky: Computer Center).

[3] *IBM 1620 FORTRAN: PRELIMINARY SPECIFICATIONS* (International Business Machines Corp., Publication No. J26–4200–2, © 1959, 1960).

[4] D. D. McCracken, *A Guide to ALGOL Programming* (New York: John Wiley and Sons, Inc., 1962).

[5] H. Bottenbruch, "Structure and Use of ALGOL, 60," *Journal of the Association for Computing Machinery*, **9** (1962), 161–221.

[6] P. Naur (ed.), "Report on the Algorithmic Language ALGOL 60," *Comm. Association for Computing Machinery*, **3** (1960), 299–314; and *Numer. Math.*, **2** (1960), 106–136.

the game so long as they obey the same rules. This means that each individual must have learned the game in a language that can be directly translated into the correct moves. All digital computers do their actual calculations in a machine language based on the binary number system. While programs can be written in the machine language itself, thus effecting an economy in memory storage, this is often unfeasible because of the cumbersome nature of the machine language. It is then feasible to write the program in a less cumbersome language (ABC, FORTRAN, ALGOL 60, MAD, GAT, etc.) and to use a compiler with which the computer translates the program into machine language.

Each digital computer manufacturer has devised a computer language, and a specific compiler is used for each language. Unfortunately there is no useful universal computer language. The theoretical language, ALGOL 60, is universally used to report new programs, and manufacturers are attempting to devise compilers that will achieve a direct machine translation of ALGOL 60 to machine language. Thus it is reasonable to anticipate the universal use of ALGOL 60 and to suppose that our European colleagues who are unfamiliar with FORTRAN will find it easier to translate from ALGOL 60. For this reason we have translated literally from the FORTRAN into ALGOL 60. Suitable entry and exit ALGOL 60 commands have been devised.

It is claimed that more than 80 percent of the world's computers can translate into their machine language one of the many forms of IBM FORTRAN. If storage capacity is no limitation, minor changes in these forms make them compatible. In this book, only IBM FORTRAN 4–1–61 (used with the IBM 1620 computer with card *input* and *output*) is presented.

Here is a schematic representation of interrelations between languages.

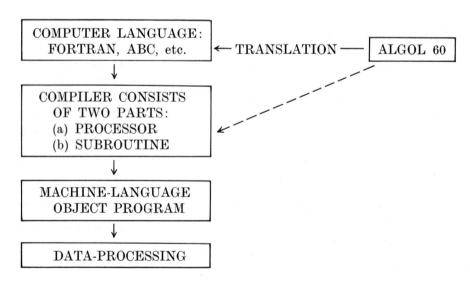

Here is a brief survey of some of the rules and terms of IBM FOR-TRAN 4–1–61.

Fixed- and Floating-Point Numbers

All numbers are designated by an alphabetic character alone or followed by up to four characters which may be either numerical or alphabetic. Words beginning with I, J, K, L, M, or N designate fixed-point or integer (i.e., no decimal point) numbers. All other words designate floating-point numbers (i.e., with decimal). Fixed-point numbers cannot have more than five numerals and floating-point numbers cannot have more than eight numerals unless exponentiated. Thus I, IX, IXX, IXXX, or IXXXX can have any value between $+$ 99999 and $-$ 99999; and A, AX, AXX, AXXX, or AXXXX can have any value between $+$99999999.0 and $-$99999999.0 (without exponent) or any positive or negative number in the range 1.0000000E-50 to 99999999.0E $+$ 49 (with exponent.)

Exponents

Floating-point numbers may be entered in one of the following forms:
0.00005251, 5.25E-5, 5.251E-05, 5251E-8, 5251E-08.
Numbers like $12345678.0 \times 10^{20}$ can be entered only in exponential form, thus:
12345678.0E20, 1.2345678E27, etc.

Subscripted Variables

Words designating either fixed-point or floating-point numbers are called variables. Fixed- or floating-point variables can be subscripted only with fixed-point variables, thus: I(J), IX(J), IXX(J), IXXX(J), or IXXXX(J) means the Jth value for the designated fixed-point variable. Thus by using subscripted variables, it is possible to enter 2, 10, 20, 100, or more different values for the variable call-name.

Variables can also be subscripted thus: A(J, K), meaning the value of an element in the Jth row and Kth column of an array called A.

Dimension of a Subscripted Variable

The number of values to be entered for each subscripted variable is given in the *dimension* statement found at the beginning of each program. Thus the statements: DIMENSION Y(20), X1(20), X1ER(20), DEV1(20), DEV2(20), YC(20), YER(20) and DIMENSION A(3), P(3), XX1(20), YY(20), which appear at the beginning of Program 1 (*call word* AAAAA), indicate that either twenty or three different values will be used for the variables.

The statement DIMENSION Y(50, 10) means that 500 values in an array will be used.

Arithmetic Operations

The binary operations involving two operands are: $+$, $-$, $*$, $/$, $**$. Examples are:

Operation	Meaning
A + B	A plus B
A − B	A minus B
A * Q	A multiplied by Q
C/D	C divided by D
Y ** X	Y raised to the power X
A ** 2	A squared

The following rules apply to arithmetic operations.

(a) Mixed mode (i.e., A + I) operands may not be used.

(b) A + −B has no meaning. One must enter either A + (−B), or A − B.

(c) If several operations occur in the statement or equation, their order of precedence is: exponentiation, negation, multiplication and division, addition and subtraction. Thus $G = P + Q * R ** V - B/D$ means $G = P + Q \times R^V - B/D$ and $G = A/B * C - E * F ** Q$ means $G = (A/B) \times C - E \times F^Q$.

(d) Parentheses are used to define operations. Thus $G = (A ** B) ** C - (B + A)/(E * F - D)$ means $G = A^{BC} - (B + A)/[(E \times F) - D]$ and $G = A ** (B ** C * (D + E))$ means $G = A^{[BC \times (D+E)]} = A^{D \times BC} + A^{E \times BC}$.

(e) Fixed-point variables cannot be divided into each other with decimal-point accuracy. Thus, $3/6 = 0$, $6/4 = 1$, and $6/6 = 1$.

Subroutines

Functions that are programmed into the computer with IBM FOR-TRAN 4–1–61 are:

FUNCTION	IBM 1620 COMMAND
Sine	SIN or SINF
Cosine	COS or COSF
Arctangent	ATN or ATNF
Square Root	SQR or SQRF
Natural Logarithm	LOG or LOGF
Exponential	EXP or EXPF

Arguments are always enclosed in parentheses thus: SIN(X) or SINF(X), LOG(A + B/C − E), etc.

The arguments for the sine and cosine functions are given in radians.

Computer Commands

The commands executed by the computer may be divided into three classes thus

(a) INPUT COMMANDS

READ,A,B,C,D means that A, B, C, and D are read from a punched card. ACCEPT,X,Y,Z means that X, Y, and Z are accepted when they are entered on the typewriter.

(b) OUTPUT COMMANDS

PUNCH,A,B,C,D means A, B, C, and D are to be punched on a card. PRINT,X,Y,Z means X, Y, and Z are to be printed by the typewriter.

(c) OPERATIONAL COMMANDS

1. *Mixed Modes.* Although mixed-mode expressions such as A + I are not permissible, the following statements are permitted.

A = I means the fixed-point number I is to be changed into a floating-point number and stored in A.

I = A means the floating-point number A is to be truncated to the nearest integer and stored in I.

2. *Equality.* A = B + C ** D − E means $B + C^D − E$ is to be calculated and then stored in A. NN = NN + 1 is not an algebraic equality. It means "add one to NN and store results in NN."

3. *"GO TO" Statement. GO TO* 10 means go to the statement numbered 10. GO TO (1,9,10,13,1,6 ⋯), J means go to the Jth statement number inside the parentheses. Thus J = 3 denotes reference to statement 10. The maximum value permitted for J is 24.

4. *"IF" Statement.* The statement IF(A − B)11,1,40 means if A > B go to statement 40, if A = B go to statement 1, and if A < B go to statement 11. Note that if A and B are arithmetic expressions, the IF statement is still permitted.

5. *"DO" Loop.* The statements

$$\left. \begin{array}{l} \text{DO 10 I = J,K} \\ \text{10 A(I) = B(I)*C} \end{array} \right\} \quad \text{or} \quad \left\{ \begin{array}{l} \text{DO 10 I = J,K} \\ \text{A(I) = B(I)*C} \\ \text{10 CONTINUE} \end{array} \right.$$

mean calculate A(I) for I = J,J + 1, ⋯ K, then continue to the next command.

The statements

$$\left. \begin{array}{l} \text{DO 10 I = J,K,M} \\ \text{10 A (I) = B(I)*C} \end{array} \right\} \quad \text{or} \quad \left\{ \begin{array}{l} \text{DO 10 I = J,K,M} \\ \text{A(I) = B(I)*C} \\ \text{10 CONTINUE} \end{array} \right.$$

mean calculate A(I) for I = J, J + M, J + 2M ⋯, then continue to the next command when I > K.

DATA-PROCESSING PROCEDURE

The FORTRAN program is processed with the *compiler* to obtain the *machine-language object program*, which is read into the computer. The data to be processed are then read in and the calculations are made.

Discussed in this section are the procedures for the transfer of the experimental data to IBM cards and for the processing of information. As an illustration, we shall suppose that data at four wavelengths and 25°C for 10 samples of A dissolved in CCl_4 are to be tested for compatibility with the Beer's Law equation by the use of Program 9 (*call word* IAAAA). We shall assume that the concentrations of all samples have been calculated correctly by conventional methods or with Program 5 (*call word* EAAAA), Program 6 (*call word* FAAAA), or Program 7 (*call word* GAAAA). The "manufactured" *raw data* to be processed are given in the following table.

Table 11

Concentrations and Absorbancies at the Indicated Wavelengths for A dissolved in Carbon Tetrachloride at 25°C

Sample No.	1	2	3	4	5	6	7	8	9	10
Conc. in moles/liter	0.01	0.02	0.03	0.04	0.05	0.06	0.07	0.08	0.09	0.10

Wavelength (Å)	*Measured Absorbancies*									
4000	0.020	0.041	0.060	0.080	0.101	0.119	0.140	0.161	0.180	0.202
4200	0.036	0.070	0.100	0.130	0.161	0.192	0.221	0.250	0.280	0.311
4400	0.050	0.100	0.150	0.200	0.250	—	0.350	0.400	—	0.500
4600	0.025	0.045	0.066	0.086	0.107	0.126	0.147	0.167	—	0.207

STEPS TAKEN IN PROCESSING "RAW DATA"

Choice of Program

If Beer's Law is obeyed exactly, the ordinate $Y(I) =$ (Absorbance/ concentration of A) will be independent of the concentration of A, and the data will be described by a one-dimensional equation. With Program 9 (*call word* IAAAA), the calculation will be terminated at the end of the first cycle for each wavelength, and CODE $= 88888888.0$ will be printed and punched. As all information is required, Switch 1 should be *off*.

It is probable that the actual data will deviate slightly from Beer's Law. With Program 9, slight *actual errors* in Y(I) will give very large *actual errors* in X1(I) (= concentration of *A*). Unless the *maximum permitted deviation* in the concentration of *A* (DEVF2 or DEV2(I)) is made very large, the calculation will be terminated at the end of the first cycle for each wavelength and either 88888888.0 or 99999999.0 will be printed and punched. If DEVF2 or DEV2(I) is large, the *maximum permitted errors* in the slope and intercept will be large. Thus it would be advisable to use Special Program 309 (*call word* IAAAS), in which the *self-judgment principle* is not applied to X1(I) (see Appendix I). In our example, Switch 1 was left *on*, but in situations of uncertainty, Switch 1 should be *off* to yield maximum information.

Choice of Instrument Reliability Factors and Input Commands

Having selected the modification of Program 9 (Special Program 309, *call word* IAAAS) to process the data, refer next to page 101. Set K = 1 (for a fixed *maximum permitted deviation* of one percent in both observables), L = 1, M = 0, and M6 = 4. In the experiments it was decided that all values of the measured absorbance below 0.060 and above 1.200 are unreliable, and that the reliable range of concentration values for *A* is 0.001 to 1.00. Thus the *instrument reliability factors* are:

For Absorbance	*For [A]* (*concn. of A*)
RLM1 = 0.01	RLM2 = 0.01
DEVF1 = 0.01	DEVF2 = 0.01
WL1 = 0.060	WL2 = 0.001
WU1 = 1.200	WU2 = 1.000

To select a value for J (number of cycles), one would normally process the data at one wavelength with J = 2, 3, etc., and then select the minimum "safe" value for J. In our laboratory, J = 3 is normally considered sufficient.

Input Format

The required information is punched onto IBM cards and these are assembled. The *input format* for Special Program 309 (*call word* IAAAS) is now given. Numbers on each line correspond to the numbers on a single card.

ACTUAL FORMAT	COMMENT
309 0.0	IAAAS,FEEDP
−1 0 0 0	KA, KB, KC, KD
3	J (No. of cycles/wavelength)
4	M6 (No. of wavelengths)
1 1 0	
0.01 0.060 1.200	
0.01 0.001 1.00	*Instrument reliability factors*
0.01	
0.01	
0.020 0.041 0.060 0.080	
0.101 0.119 0.140 0.161	Measured absorbance at the
0.180 0.202 0.0 0.0	first wavelength
0.0 0.0 0.0 0.0	
0.0 0.0 0.0 0.0	
0.01 0.02 0.03 0.04	
0.05 0.06 0.07 0.08	
0.09 0.10 0.0 0.0	Concentrations (moles/liter) of A
0.0 0.0 0.0 0.0	
0.0 0.0 0.0 0.0	
00000000.0 0	OPER,INST,
1.0 25.0 4000.0	RUN,TEMP,WAVEL

0.036 0.070 0.100 0.130	
0.161 0.192 0.221 0.250	
0.280 0.311 0.0 0.0	Absorbance at second wavelength
0.0 0.0 0.0 0.0	
0.0 0.0 0.0 0.0	
0.050 0.100 0.150 0.200	
0.250 0.0 0.350 0.400	
0.0 0.500 0.0 0.0	Absorbance at third wavelength
0.0 0.0 0.0 0.0	
0.0 0.0 0.0 0.0	
0.025 0.045 0.066 0.086	
0.107 0.126 0.147 0.167	
0.0 0.207 0.0 0.0	Absorbance at fourth wavelength
0.0 0.0 0.0 0.0	
0.0 0.0 0.0 0.0	

Output Format

The entire *output format* for the sample calculation with Switch 1 *on* is given below. No attempt is made to define the numbers. The reader can identify the various items from the *output format* outline on page 103. Underlined are the items of information included in the table in the following section (describing the publication format).

OUTPUT FROM PROGRAM NUMBER 309

CALL WORD IAAAS

```
            9              309        .00000000
            3                1
            4
           -1               0           0           0
            1               1           0
   1.0000000E-02  1.0000000E-02  6.0000000E-02  1.2000000
    .00000000
   1.0000000E-02  1.0000000E-02  1.0000000E-03  1.0000000
    .15972226     1.9940973      8.0000000      8.0000000
            1               1
   1.0990820E-02  5.2089453E-02
    .00000000      .00000000     -1.1111000E-03  4.8610000E-04
    .00000000      .00000000      6.9560240E-03 -3.0439780E-03
  -1.7916700E-02  2.0347400E-02   5.2778000E-03 -5.6249000E-03
    .11217339     7.3919860E-03  -3.3043981E-02  3.5216880E-02
   8.4723000E-03 -9.9305000E-03   .00000000      .00000000
  -5.3043984E-02  6.2173390E-02   .00000000      .00000000
    .00000000      .00000000      .00000000      .00000000
    .00000000      .00000000      .00000000      .00000000
    .00000000      .00000000      .00000000      .00000000
    .00000000      .00000000      .00000000      .00000000
    .13184931     1.9988357      7.0000000      8.0000000
            2               1
   8.3664386E-03  6.3454671E-02
    .00000000      .00000000      2.7912000E-03  4.1096000E-03
    .00000000      .00000000     -2.1169466E-02 -3.1169468E-02
  -1.4571800E-02   .00000000      8.0650000E-03 -3.1164000E-03
    .11051885      .00000000     -6.1169471E-02  2.3635730E-02
   1.0702200E-02 -7.9794000E-03   .00000000      .00000000
  -8.1169474E-02  6.0518850E-02   .00000000      .00000000
    .00000000      .00000000      .00000000      .00000000
    .00000000      .00000000      .00000000      .00000000
    .00000000      .00000000      .00000000      .00000000
    .00000000      .00000000      .00000000      .00000000
    .13184931     1.9988357      7.0000000      8.0000000
            3               1
   8.3664386E-03  6.3454671E-02
    .00000000      .00000000      2.7912000E-03  4.1096000E-03
    .00000000      .00000000     -2.1169466E-02 -3.1169468E-02
  -1.4571800E-02   .00000000      8.0650000E-03 -3.1164000E-03
    .11051885      .00000000     -6.1169471E-02  2.3635730E-02
   1.0702200E-02 -7.9794000E-03   .00000000      .00000000
  -8.1169474E-02  6.0518850E-02   .00000000      .00000000
    .00000000      .00000000      .00000000      .00000000
    .00000000      .00000000      .00000000      .00000000
    .00000000      .00000000      .00000000      .00000000
    .00000000      .00000000      .00000000      .00000000
   7.3392380E-04  1.9972365E-02   8.0000000      8.0000000
            4               1
    .00000000               0
   1.0000000      25.000000     4000.0000
            9              309        .00000000
            3                2
            4
           -1               0           0           0
            1               1           1
   1.0000000E-02  1.0000000E-02  6.0000000E-02  1.2000000
    .00000000
   1.0000000E-02  1.0000000E-02  1.0000000E-03  1.0000000
```

```
 -4.2325396         3.4769065         9.0000000         9.0000000
         1                 2
   4.9342754E-02     9.3492492E-03
   .00000000        -.10774440         1.6597100E-02     5.7605200E-02
   .00000000        -1.4543818E-02     3.9212910E-03     1.3610012E-02
   4.5279500E-02     2.2954200E-02     2.3485800E-02     1.3303300E-02
   1.0697957E-02     5.4232470E-03     5.5488940E-03     3.1431020E-03
  -1.5132900E-02    -5.6347100E-03     .00000000         .00000000
  -3.5754350E-03    -1.3312910E-02     .00000000         .00000000
   .00000000         .00000000         .00000000         .00000000
   .00000000         .00000000         .00000000         .00000000
   .00000000         .00000000         .00000000         .00000000
   .00000000         .00000000         .00000000         .00000000
 -3.6930837         3.4249931         6.0000000         9.0000000
                           2
   1.8188279E-02     4.9249484E-03
   .00000000         .00000000        -1.9132600E-02     2.7269900E-02
   .00000000         .00000000        -5.1806890E-03     7.3840060E-03
   2.0339100E-02     3.4081000E-03     9.3343000E-03     4.5465000E-03
   5.5072980E-03     9.2283100E-04     2.5275490E-03     1.2310600E-03
  -1.8495500E-02     .00000000         .00000000         .00000000
  -5.0081590E-03     .00000000         .00000000         .00000000
   .00000000         .00000000         .00000000         .00000000
   .00000000         .00000000         .00000000         .00000000
   .00000000         .00000000         .00000000         .00000000
   .00000000         .00000000         .00000000         .00000000
 -3.4982992         3.4094104         7.0000000         9.0000000
         3                 2
   1.5912306E-02     4.5485808E-03
   .00000000         .00000000        -2.8872000E-02     1.9478500E-02
   .00000000         .00000000        -8.2531190E-03     5.5679690E-03
   1.4495500E-02    -4.8770000E-04     7.3866000E-03     4.5465000E-03
   4.1435690E-03    -1.3936600E-04     2.1115020E-03     1.2996230E-03
  -1.6547400E-02     .00000000         .00000000         .00000000
  -4.7301910E-03     .00000000         .00000000         .00000000
   .00000000         .00000000         .00000000         .00000000
   .00000000         .00000000         .00000000         .00000000
   .00000000         .00000000         .00000000         .00000000
   .00000000         .00000000         .00000000         .00000000
   7.1428571E-09     3.4094104E-02     7.0000000         9.0000000
         4                 2
   .00000000         0
   1.0000000         25.000000         4000.0000
         9               309             .00000000
         3                 3
         4
        -1                 0                 0                 0
         1                 1                 1
   1.0000000E-02     1.0000000E-02     6.0000000E-02     1.2000000
   .00000000
   1.0000000E-02     1.0000000E-02     1.0000000E-03     1.0000000
   .00000000         5.0000000         7.0000000         7.0000000
         1                 3
   .00000000         .00000000
   .00000000        -.00000000        -.00000000        -.00000000
   .00000000         .00000000         .00000000         .00000000
  -.00000000         .00000000        -.00000000        -.00000000
   .00000000         .00000000         .00000000         .00000000
   .00000000        -.00000000         .00000000         .00000000
   .00000000         .00000000         .00000000         .00000000
   .00000000         .00000000         .00000000         .00000000
   .00000000         .00000000         .00000000         .00000000
```

```
 .00000000      .00000000      .00000000      .00000000
 .00000000      .00000000      .00000000      .00000000
 .00000000     5.0000000      7.0000000      7.0000000
        2              3
 .00000000      .00000000
 .00000000     -.00000000     -.00000000     -.00000000
 .00000000      .00000000      .00000000      .00000000
-.00000000      .00000000     -.00000000     -.00000000
 .00000000      .00000000      .00000000      .00000000
 .00000000     -.00000000      .00000000      .00000000
 .00000000      .00000000      .00000000      .00000000
 .00000000      .00000000      .00000000      .00000000
 .00000000     ..00000000      .00000000      .00000000
 .00000000      .00000000      .00000000      .00000000
 .00000000      .00000000      .00000000      .00000000
 .00000000     5.0000000      7.0000000      7.0000000
        3              3
 .00000000      .00000000
 .00000000     -.00000000     -.00000000     -.00000000
 .00000000      .00000000      .00000000      .00000000
-.00000000      .00000000     -.00000000     -.00000000
 .00000000      .00000000      .00000000      .00000000
 .00000000     -.00000000      .00000000      .00000000
 .00000000      .00000000      .00000000      .00000000
 .00000000      .00000000      .00000000      .00000000
 .00000000      .00000000      .00000000      .00000000
 .00000000      .00000000      .00000000      .00000000
 .00000000      .00000000      .00000000      .00000000
 .00000000     5.0000000E-02  7.0000000      7.0000000
        4              3
 .00000000      0
1.0000000      25.000000      4000.0000      .00000000
        9            309
        3              4
        4
       -1              0              0              0
        1              1              1
1.0000000E-02  1.0000000E-02  6.0000000E-02  1.2000000
 .00000000
1.0000000E-02  1.0000000E-02  1.0000000E-03  1.0000000
-1.7387295     2.2278791      7.0000000      7.0000000
        1              4
1.4688532E-02  8.4478545E-03
 .00000000      .00000000     -2.4282800E-02  8.3301000E-03
 .00000000      .00000000     -1.3965823E-02  4.7908030E-03
9.4270000E-04  2.3555300E-02  6.1679000E-03  1.2809000E-03
5.4213200E-04  1.3547439E-02  3.5474350E-03  7.3659600E-04
 .00000000    -1.5993800E-02   .00000000      .00000000
 .00000000    -9.1985800E-03   .00000000      .00000000
 .00000000      .00000000      .00000000      .00000000
 .00000000      .00000000      .00000000      .00000000
 .00000000      .00000000      .00000000      .00000000
 .00000000      .00000000      .00000000      .00000000
-1.3571428     2.1983928      6.0000000      7.0000000
        2              4
8.9682575E-03  6.6082693E-03
 .00000000      .00000000      .00000000     -5.8928000E-03
 .00000000      .00000000      .00000000     -4.3421500E-03
-9.4641000E-03  1.6964100E-02  3.3928000E-03  2.3214000E-03
-6.9737250E-03  1.2499958E-02  2.4999540E-03  1.7104880E-03
 .00000000    -7.3214000E-03   .00000000      .00000000
 .00000000    -5.3947700E-03   .00000000      .00000000
```

```
.00000000        .00000000        .00000000        .00000000
.00000000        .00000000        .00000000        .00000000
.00000000        .00000000        .00000000        .00000000
.00000000        .00000000        .00000000        .00000000
-1.3571428       2.1983928        6.0000000        7.0000000
         3                4
 8.9682575E-03   6.6082693E-03
.00000000        .00000000        .00000000       -5.8928000E-03
.00000000        .00000000        .00000000       -4.3421500E-03
-9.4641000E-03   1.6964100E-02    3.3928000E-03    2.3214000E-03
-6.9737250E-03   1.2499958E-02    2.4999540E-03    1.7104880E-03
.00000000       -7.3214000E-03    .00000000        .00000000
.00000000       -5.3947700E-03    .00000000        .00000000
.00000000        .00000000        .00000000        .00000000
.00000000        .00000000        .00000000        .00000000
.00000000        .00000000        .00000000        .00000000
.00000000        .00000000        .00000000        .00000000
-1.4491721E-04   2.1995126E-02    7.0000000        7.0000000
         4                4
.00000000        0
1.0000000        25.000000        4000.0000
```

Publication Format

The results of this experiment would appear in a single table thus.

Table 12

Results obtained for tests of data compatibility with Beer's Law at the indicated wavelengths for A dissolved in carbon tetrachloride at 25°C. Special program 309 (*call word* IAAAS). *Instrument reliability factors* used throughout were: absorbance— RLM1 = 0.01 = DEVF1, WL1 = 0.060, WU1 = 1.200; concn. of A—RLM2 = 0.01 = DEVF2, WL2 = 0.001, WU2 = 1.00. *Accepted sets of conjugate data* (ASOCD) are listed with the concentration of A in parentheses. S and ΔS refer to the slope; a_A and Δa_A are the absorbancy index of A at zero concentration and its *maximum permitted error*. SQRMY is the square-root-mean-square deviation in each value for a_A.

Wave-length (Å)	ASOCD	S	ΔS	a_A	Δa_A	SQRMY
4000	0.060(0.03),0.080(0.04),0.101(0.05),0.119(0.06) 0.140(0.07),0.161(0.08),0.180(0.09),0.202(0.10)	0.132	0.0007	2.00	0.020	0.0084
4200	0.100(0.03),0.130(0.04),0.161(0.05),0.192(0.06) 0.221(0.07),0.250(0.08),0.280(0.09)	−3.50	0.0	3.41	0.034	0.016
4400	0.100(0.02),0.150(0.03),0.200(0.04),0.250(0.05) 0.350(0.07),0.400(0.08),0.500(0.10)	0.0	0.0	5.00	0.050	0.0
4600	0.086(0.04),0.107(0.05),0.126(0.06),0.147(0.07) 0.167(0.08),0.207(0.10)	−1.36	0.0001	2.19	0.022	0.009

APPENDIX D

CRAMER'S METHOD FOR SOLVING LINEAR EQUATIONS WITH VARIABLE DIMENSIONS

Even with the special three-step normalization procedure, described on page 182, the *Crout reduction method* is extremely sensitive to deviations from the median curve. This fact is an advantage when noniterative procedures are used because if the data do not fit the selected equation there is a break-down in the analysis and the calculation is terminated. In this case the CODE = 88888888.0 is printed and punched. In iterative procedures break-downs in the analysis occur frequently for, unless the parameters being iterated are guessed very accurately, there are substantial deviations from the median curve computed at some stage in each iteration. This is particularly true in iterative procedures with two dimensional equations.

If the advantages gained by using the *Crout reduction method* (see Chapter III) are to be sacrificed for decreased sensitivity to variations in the data, Programs 25 to 29 and 325 to 329 should be replaced by Programs 1025 to 1029 and 1325 to 1329 respectively. Instructions for converting the first series to the second series of programs are given at the end of this appendix. In the 1000 series *Cramer's determinant method* is used.

The input and output commands for related programs in the two series are identical, and formats differ only in the program numbers. In the new programs CODE = 88888888.0 in the output format means that the calculation is terminated because *Cramer's* delta determinant is zero. This occurs only if one of the slopes in the equation being tested is exactly zero.

In Programs 1025 to 1029 and 1325 to 1329, the special three-step normalization procedure, described on page 182, is retained and the element with the highest numerical value is always located in the (1,1) position of each determinant. Wilkinson[1] has stated that this procedure reduces round-off errors in evaluating the determinant. All determinants are evaluated by first diagonalizing them by a series of simple operations. The actual computational method used will be illustrated here for the system of N independent N-dimensional linear equations which are obtained in applications of the method of least-squares to a N-dimensional linear equation with form:

$$m_1x_1 + m_2x_2 + m_3x_3 + \cdots + m_{N1-}x_{N-1} + c = y \tag{1}$$

The $N(N + 1)$th order matrix, with the last column designating the variable y, is:

$$\begin{Vmatrix} b_{1,1} & \cdots & b_{1,r} & \cdots & b_{1,N+1} \\ b_{i,1} & \cdots & b_{i,r} & \cdots & b_{i,N+1} \\ b_{N,1} & \cdots & b_{N,r} & \cdots & b_{N,N+1} \end{Vmatrix} = (b_{ij}) = B$$

To solve this system of equations by *Cramer's method*, $(N + 1)$ determinants must be evaluated. The first of these is the so-called delta determinant designated by: $\delta = |b_{ij}|$. The next N determinants are constructed from δ by replacing each of the columns in turn by the $(N + 1)$th column in the matrix (b_{ij}). Instructions to the computer include the following:

Step 1. After executing the several devices to reduce statistical bias the $N(N + 1)$ elements are stored in matrix B.

Step 2. The first of the $N + 1$ determinants to be evaluated, A, is constructed from matrix B.

Step 3. The element with the highest numerical value, designated a_{ij}, in determinant A is translated to the $(1, 1)$ position and the scaling factor (SUM) is set equal to $(-1)^{i+j}$.

Step 4. All elements in each row of A are divided by their elements in the Ith column and SUM is multiplied by the elements in the Ith column. For rows with the element in the Ith column equal to zero this step is omitted.

Step 5. All elements in the Ith row are subtracted from the corresponding elements in each of the other rows of determinant A.

Step 6. Steps 4 and 5 are executed for each column in the determinant A.

Step 7. Steps 2 to 6 are executed for each of the $(N + 1)$ determinants to be evaluated, and the parameters for equation (1) are computed in the normal way.

[1] J. H. Wilkinson, *J. Assoc. Computing Machinery*, **8** (1961), 281.

INSTRUCTIONS FOR CONVERSION OF PROGRAMS 25–29 AND 325–329 TO PROGRAMS 1025–1029 AND 1325–1329

The relationships between programs of the two series are shown next.

Replacement Numbers	Program Call-Word	Original Numbers	Program Call-Word
1025	YACCA	25	YAAAA
1026	ZACCA	26	ZAAAA
1027	ABCCA	27	ABAAA
1028	BBCCA	28	BBAAA
1029	CBCCA	29	CBAAA
1325	YACCS	325	YAAAS
1326	ZACCS	326	ZAAAS
1327	ABCCS	327	ABAAS
1328	BBCCS	328	BBAAS
1329	CBCCS	329	CBAAS

Two changes must be made in the parent program (25, 26, 27, 28, 29, 325, 326, 327, 328, or 329). These are:

(A) Program Identification

The program number (NUM) and call word for each program must be changed to conform with the new designations (see above table). For example, to obtain Program 1025 (*call word* YACCA) from Program 25 (*call word* YAAAA) the following changes must be made. In each program there are only three statements to be changed.

Replacement Statement	Original Statement
1 READ,YACCA,FEEDP	1 READ,YAAAA,FEEDP
NUM=1025	NUM=25
PUNCH,YACCA,NUM,FEEDP	PUNCH,YAAAA,NUM,FEEDP

Input information for the new series of programs can be processed with the Autoplotter Programs (see Chapter I) only if the number of the original program appears in the input format. Thus to use the autoplotter programs one number (program number) in the input information must be changed.

(B) Conversion of Crout to Cramer Method

(1) To each of the original programs the statement:
DIMENSION B(JR,JR)
must be added immediately after the last dimension statement.

(2) The *thirty* statements beginning with: DO 80 J = 1, JR and ending with: 81 SL(JAN) = A(JAN, JR) − SUM2 are replaced by the following forty-seven statements:

STATEMENTS 1-25

```
DO 563 I=1,JR
DO 563 J=1,JR
563 B(I,J)=A(I,J)
JK=−1
555 JK=JK+1
IF(JK)93,556,557
557 DO 558 I=1,JJ
558 A(I,JK)=B(I,JR)
556 SUM2=1.0
IF(JK−JJ)559,560,93
559 JB=JJ+1
DO 561 J=2,JJ
JB=JB−1
JA=JB−1
DO 562 I=1,JJ
562 A(I,JB)=A(I,JA)
561 CONTINUE
JB=JJ−1
SUM=(−1.0)**JB
DO 564 I=1,JJ
564 A(I,1)=B(I,JJ)
560 DO 80 JA=1,JJ
DO 81 I=1,JJ
IF(A(I,JA))82,81,82
82 SUM=SUM*A(I,JA)
```

STATEMENTS 26-47

```
AA=A(I,JA)
DO 83 J=1,JJ
83 A(I,J)=A(I,J)/AA
81 CONTINUE
DO 84 I=1,JJ
IF(I−JA)85,84,85
85 DO 86 J=1,JJ
86 A(I,J)=A(I,J)−A(JA,J)
84 CONTINUE
80 CONTINUE
DO 87 I=1,JJ
87 SUM=SUM*A(I,I)
IF(JK)88,89,88
89 SUM2=SUM
IF(SUM2)90,61,90
88 SL(JK)=SUM/SUM2
90 IF(JJ−JK)93,93,91
91 DO 94 I=1, JR
DO 94 J=1,JR
94 A(I,J)=B(I,J)
GO TO 555
93 CONTINUE
```

APPENDIX E

SUGGESTED IMPROVEMENTS

PROGRAMS 1–4, 9–15, 22–29, 301–304, 309–315, 322–329, and 410–415

In programs that have the *Self-Judgment Principle* (SJP) incorporated, the *Maximum Permitted Error* (MPE) in the parameters is computed from the *Accepted Sets of Conjugate Information* after execution of the last programmed cycle of the SJP. Thus the *Error Analysis* is done after the results of the data-compatibility tests are known.

In the *Error Analysis* the MPE in the parameters (DESL1 and DEVB in Programs 1 and 301) are obtained by solving equation (A) with *Accepted Sets of Conjugate Information* (one set is Y(I), X1(I), YER(I), and X1ER(I) and the computed value for the slope (SL1).*

$$Y'(I) = YER(I) - SL1 . X1ER(I) = DESL1 . X1(I) + DEVB \quad (A)$$

In some programs in Volumes I and II, the MPE's in the ordinates, denoted by YER(I) and X1ER(I), are positive numbers. Thus in solving equation (A) unrealistic values for the MPE's in the parameters can occur.† To always obtain realistic values for the MPE's the *Error Zones* should be divided into two approximately equal parts. For the right-hand part, $YER(I) \geq 0; X1ER(I) \leq 0$. In the left-hand part, $YER(I) \leq 0$; $X1ER(I) \geq 0$. This insures that the MPE's in the parameters will always have the maximum value and be determined by the *Instrument Reliability Factors* selected. Arguments advanced in Volumes I and II are not altered by the changes suggested.

Instructions that must be added to FORTRAN PROGRAMS 1–4, 9–15, 22–29, 301–304, 309–315, 322–329, and 410–415 are given next and the special problems associated with the iterative programs (10–15, 310–315, and 410–415) are examined at the end of this appendix.

---

* Here the Error Analysis in Programs 1 and 301 is used for illustration.
† In private communications Dr. C. C. Thompson, Jr. pointed this out to the author.

PROGRAMS 1, 9, 301, and 309

ORIGINAL STATEMENT
DO 76 I = 1,20

REPLACEMENT STATEMENT
IF(N − J)78,78,1150
1150 CONTINUE
DO 76 I = 1,20

43 DO 44 I = 1,20
IF(Y(I))45,44,45
45Y(I) = YER(I) − SLI*X1ER(I)
IF(Y(I))44,46,44
46Y(I) = 0.000001
44 CONTINUE

43 G88 = G1/2.0
G99 = 0.0
DO 44 I = 1,20
IF(Y(I))45,44,45
45 YER(I) = SQR(YER(I)*YER(I))
X1ER(I) = SQR(X1ER(I)*X1ER(I))
IF(G99 − G88)1500,1501,1501
1500 Y(I) = YER(I) + SL1*X1ER(I)
GO TO 1502
1501 Y(I) = − YER(I) − SL1*X1ER(I)
1502 G99 = G99 + 1.0
IF(Y(I))44,1503,44
1503 Y(I) = 0.000001
44 CONTINUE

PROGRAMS 2, 22, 302, and 322

ORIGINAL STATEMENT
DO 402 I = 1,20

REPLACEMENT STATEMENT
IF(N − J)405,405,1150
1150 CONTINUE
DO 402 I = 1,20

14 DO 18 I = 1,20
IF(Y(I))15,18,15
15 Y(I) = YER(I) − SL1*X1ER(I)
    − SL2*X2ER(I)
IF(Y(I))18,16,18
16 Y(I) = 0.000001
18 CONTINUE

14 G88 = G1/2.0
G99 = 0.0
DO 18 I = 1,20
IF(Y I))15,18,15
15 YER(I) = SQR(YER(I)*YER(I))
X1ER(I) = SQR(X1ER(I)*X1ER(I))
X2ER(I) = SQR(X2ER(I)*X2ER(I))
DEVB = SL1*X1ER(I) + SL2*X2ER(I}
IF(G99 − G88)1500,1501,1501
1500 Y(I) = YER(I) + DEVB
GO TO 1502
1501 Y(I) = − YER(I) − DEVB
1502 G99 = G99 + 1.0
IF(Y(I))18,1503,18
1503 Y(I) = 0.000001
18 CONTINUE

PROGRAMS 3, 23, 303, and 323

ORIGINAL STATEMENT
DO 402 I = 1,20

REPLACEMENT STATEMENT
IF(N − J)406,406,1150
1150 CONTINUE
DO 402 I = 1,20

```
14 DO 18 I = 1,20                    14 G88 = G1/2.0
IF(Y(I))15,18,15                     G99 = 0.0
15 Y(I) = YER(I) − SL1*X1ER(I)       DO 18 I = 1,20
   − X2ER(I)*SL2 − SL3*X3ER(I)       IF(Y(I))15,18,15
IF(Y(I))18,16,18                     15 YER(I) = SQR(YER(I)*YER(I))
16 Y(I) = 0.000001                   X1ER(I) = SQR(X1ER(I)*X1ER(I))
18 CONTINUE                          X2ER(I) = SQR(X2ER(I)*X2ER(I))
                                     X3ER(I) = SQR(X3ER(I)*X3ER(I))
                                     DEVB = SL1*X1ER(I) + SL2*X2ER(I)
                                         + SL3*X3ER(I)
                                     IF(G99 − G88)1500,1501,1501
                                     1500 Y(I) = YER(I) + DEVB
                                     GO TO 1502
                                     1501 Y(I) = − YER(I) − DEVB
                                     1502 G99 = G99 + 1.0
                                     IF(Y(I))18,1503,18
                                     1503 Y(I) = 0.000001
                                     18 CONTINUE
```

PROGRAMS 23 and 323

ORIGINAL STATEMENT

```
IF(P(5) − SQR(Y(I)*Y(I)))60,59,59
60 P(5) = SQR(Y(I)*Y(I))
```

REPLACEMENT STATEMENT

```
IF(P(5) − SQR(Y(I)*Y(I)))2000,59,59
2000 P(5) = SQR(Y(I)*Y(I))
```

PROGRAMS 4, 24, 304, and 324

ORIGINAL STATEMENT

```
DO 402 I = 1,20
```

REPLACEMENT STATEMENT

```
IF(N − J)908,908,1150
1150 CONTINUE
DO 902 I = 1,20
```

ORIGINAL STATEMENT

```
53 DO 56 I = 1,20
IF(Y(I))54,56,54
54 Y(I) = YER(I) − SL1*X1ER(I)
   − SL2*X2ER(I) − SL3*X3ER(I)
   − SL4*X4ER(I)
IF(Y(I))56,55,56
55 Y(I) = 0.000001
56 CONTINUE
```

REPLACEMENT STATEMENT

```
53 G88 = G1/2.0
G99 = 0.0
DO 56 I = 1,20
IF(Y(I))54,56,54
54 YER(I) = SQR(YER(I)*YER(I))
X1ER(I) = SQR(X1ER(I)*X1ER(I))
X2ER(I) = SQR(X2ER(I)*X2ER(I))
X3ER(I) = SQR(X3ER(I)*X3ER(I))
X4ER(I) = SQR(X4ER(I)*X4ER(I))
DEVB = SL1*X1ER(I) + SL2*X2ER(I)
    + SL3*X3ER(I)
DEVB = DEVB + SL4*X4ER(I)
IF(G99 − G88)1500,1501,1501
1500 Y(I) = YER(I) + DEVB
GO TO 1502
1501 Y(I) = − YER(I) − DEVB
1502 G99 = G99 + 1.0
IF(Y(I))56,1503,56
1503 Y(I) = 0.000001
56 CONTINUE
```

PROGRAMS 10, 11, 14, 310, 311, 314, 410, 411, and 414

ORIGINAL STATEMENT
141 DO 143 I = 1,20
IF(Y(I))144,143,144

REPLACEMENT STATEMENT
141 G88 = G2/2.0
G99 = 0.0
DO 143 I = 1,20
IF(Y(I))1500,143,1500
1500 YER(I) = SQR(YER(I)*YER(I))
X1ER(I) = - SQR(X1ER(I)*X1ER(I))
G99 = G99 + 1.0
IF(G99 - G88)144,1501,1501
1501 YER(I) = - YER(I)
X1ER(I) = - X1ER(I)

For 410, 411, and 414 the first original statement is DO 143 I = 1,20 and the first replacement statement is G88 = G2/2.0

PROGRAMS 12, 13, 15, 312, 313, 315, 412, 413, and 415

ORIGINAL STATEMENT
200 DO 201 I = 1,20
IF(Y(I))202,201,202

REPLACEMENT STATEMENT
200 G88 = G2/2.0
G99 = 0.0
DO 201 I = 1,20
IF(Y(I))1500,201,1500
1500 G99 = G99 + 1.0
YER(I) = SQR(YER(I)*YER(I))
X1ER(I) = - SQR(X1ER(I)*X1ER(I))
IF(G99 - G88)202,1501,1501
1501 YER(I) = - YER(I)
X1ER(I) = - X1ER(I)

For 412, 413, and 415 the first original statement is DO 201 I = 1,20 and the first replacement statement is G88 = G2/2.0

PROGRAMS 25, 27, 325, and 327

ORIGINAL STATEMENT
137 DO 134 I = 1,JI

139 Y(I,JJ) = YER(I,JJ) - Y(I,JJ)

REPLACEMENT STATEMENT
137 G88 = G2/2.0
G99 = 0.0
DO 134 I = 1,JI

139 G99 = G99 + 1.0
YER(I,JJ) = SQR(YER(I,JJ)
*YER(I,JJ))
IF(G99 - G88)1500,1501,1501
1500 Y(I,JJ) = YER(I,JJ) - Y(I,JJ))
GO TO 1502
1501 Y(I,JJ) = - YER(I,JJ) + Y(I,JJ)
1502 IF(Y(I,JJ))134,1503,134
1503 Y(I,JJ) = 0.0000001

PROGRAMS 26 and 326

ORIGINAL STATEMENT
137 DO 134 I = 1,JI

REPLACEMENT STATEMENT
137 G88 = G2/2.0
G99 = 0.0
DO 134 I = 1,JI

DO 141 JQ = 1,JK

DO 141 JQ = 1,JK
YER(I,JQ) = SQR(YER(I,JQ)
        *YER(I,JQ))

Y(I,JJ) = −SQR(Y(I,JJ)*Y(I,JJ))
Y(I,JJ) = YER(I,JJ) − Y(I,JJ)

G99 = G99 + 1.0
IF(G99 − G88)1500,1501,1501
1500 Y(I,JJ) = YER(I,JJ) + Y(I,JJ)
GO TO 1502
1501 Y(I,JJ) = − YER(I,JJ) − Y(I,JJ)
1502 IF(Y(I,JJ))134,1503,134
1503 Y(I,JJ) = 0.0000001

PROGRAMS 28 and 328

ORIGINAL STATEMENT
119 DO 134 J = 1,JJ

REPLACEMENT STATEMENT
119 G88 = G2/2.0
G99 = 0.0
DO 134 J = 1,JJ

139 Y(I,JJ) = YER(I,JJ) − Y(I,JJ)

139 G99 = G99 + 1.0
YER(I,JJ) = SQR(YER(I,JJ)
        *YER(I,JJ))
IF(G99 − G88)1500,1501,1501
1500 Y(I,JJ) = YER(I,JJ) − Y(I,JJ)
GO TO 1502
1501 Y(I,JJ) = − YER(I,JJ) + Y(I,JJ)
1502 IF(Y(I,JJ))134,1503,134
1503 Y(I,JJ) = 0.0000001

PROGRAMS 29 and 329

ORIGINAL STATEMENT
135 DO 134 J = 1,JJ

REPLACEMENT STATEMENT
135 G88 = G2/2.0
G99 = 0.0
DO 134 J = 1,JJ

139 Y(I,JJ) = YER(I,JJ) − Y(I,JJ)

139 G99 = G99 + 1.0
YER(I,JJ) = SQR(YER(I,JJ)
        *YER(I,JJ))
IF(G99 − G88)1500,1501,1501
1500 Y(I,JJ) = YER(I,JJ) − Y(I,JJ)
GO TO 1502
1501 Y(I,JJ) = − YER(I,JJ) + Y(I,JJ)
1502 IF(Y(I,JJ))134,1503,134
1503 Y(I,JJ) = 0.000001

SPECIAL PROBLEMS ASSOCIATED with PROGRAMS 10–15, 310–315 and 410–415

In Programs 10–15, 310–315, and 410–415 iterative procedures are used to compute an equilibrium constant (K) and an absorbancy index (A_C) from spectrophotometric data. In a recent examination[1] of the relationship between the *Maximum Permitted Deviations* for the raw-data and the *Maximum Permitted Errors* for the parameters KER and ACER, it has been found that KER and ACER are very sensitively dependent on the form in which the principle equation is solved. In fact there appears to be a minimum value for each KER–ACER pair for each equation form. Some workers may prefer to use this new information in the programs affected. The following changes should be made to the original programs.

Beginning with the statement 141 DO 143 I = 1,20 or DO 143 I = 1,20, sixteen statements (Programs 10, 310, and 410) or thirteen (Programs 11, 14, 311, 314, 411, and 414) statements should be replaced by the following sixty-one statements. For Programs 410, 411 and 414 the statement 141 EQO = EQ(J) must also be removed.

```
141 EQO = EQ(J)
N228 = 1
N765 = NUM − 9
DO 7700 IR = 1,10
IF(N765 − 100)7701,7702,7702
7702 N765 = N765 − 100
7700 CONTINUE
7701 QQN = 1.0
QR1 = 1.0
QR2 = 1.0
GO TO (7703,7704,7710,7705,7704,7705),N765
7703 IF(L − 20)7709,7709,7710
7709 QR1 = 4.0
QR2 = 4.0
GO TO 7710
7704 QR1 = QQ1
QQN = QQ1
GO TO 7710
7705 QR1 = QQ3
7710 G88 = G2/2.0
G99 = 0.0
DO 143 I = 1,20
IF(Y(I))150,143,1500
1500 CONTINUE
YER(I) = SQR(YER(I)*YER(I))
X1ER(I) = − SQR(X1ER(I)*X1ER(I))
```

[1] P.A.D. de MAINE (in preparation).

```
G99 = G99 + 1.0
IF(G99 − G88)144,1501,1501
1501 YER(I) = − YER(I)
X1ER(I) = − X1ER(I)
144 Y(I) = YER(I) − X1ER(I)*QR1/AIC(J)
X1(I) = (QR2/X1(I))
IF(Y(I))143,145,143
145 Y(I) = 0.000001
143 CONTINUE
J = J + 1
GO TO 107
146 J = J − 1
GO TO (9130,9131),N228
9130 N228 = N228 + 1
DEVAI = − SL1*AIC(J)*AIC(J)/QQN
G88 = G2/2.0
G99 = 0.0
DO 9132 I = 1,20
IF(Y(I))9133,9132,9133
9133 G99 = G99 + 1.0
YER(I) = SQR(YER(I)*YER(I))
X1ER(I) = SQR(X1ER(I)*X1ER(I))
YER(I) = (YER(I) − X1ER(I)*YY(I)/XX1(I))/(XX1(I) + X1ER(I))
X1ER(I) = − X1ER(I)
IF (G99 − G88) 1580,1581,1581
1581 YER(I) = − YER(I)
X1ER(I) = − X1ER(I)
1580 CONTINUE
X1ER(I) = 1.0/(XX1(I) − X1ER(I)) − 1.0/XX1(I)
Y(I) = YER(I) − X1ER(I)/(EQ)J)*AIC(J))
X1(I) = 1.0/XX1(I)
9132 CONTINUE
J = J + 1
GO TO 107
9131 DEVEQ = ( − SL1*EQ(J)*AIC(J) − DEVAI/AIC(J))*EQ(J)
```

Beginning with the statement 200 DO 201 I = 1,20 or DO 201 I = 1,20, twelve (Programs 12, 312, and 412) or thirteen (Programs 13, 15, 313, 315, 413, and 415) statements should be replaced by the same sixty-one statements given above except that 141, 143, 144, 145, 146, and 107 are replaced by 200, 201, 202, 203, 205, and 153 respectively. For Programs 412, 413, and 415 the statement 200 EQO = EQ(J) must also be removed.

INDEX

491